ELEMENTARY BUSINESS
AND
ECONOMIC STATISTICS

ELEMENTARY BUSINESS
AND
ECONOMIC STATISTICS

CECIL H. MEYERS
University of Minnesota

WADSWORTH PUBLISHING COMPANY, INC.
BELMONT, CALIFORNIA

To Corinne

L.C. Cat. Card No.: 66-14182

Printed in the United States of America

PREFACE

This volume is designed as a text for an introductory course in business and economic statistics. The aim has been to provide a basic yet thorough understanding of the use of statistics as a means of discovering quantitative information, of communicating information, and of deciding certain issues. The book does not prerequire college mathematics, although the student who has such a background should find challenging material here.

The materials in this textbook are a part of the general fund of statistical knowledge. Those who teach and practice this discipline will be familiar with the concepts and terminology used here. Because the book deals with basic concepts, I have tried to emphasize fundamentals and simplify presentation.

The book attempts to give the student a background in both descriptive and inferential statistics. The topics included in this book are those most likely to be useful to students of business and economics whose statistical education begins and ends with the elementary course. This criterion means that only the classical approach to statistics is included. To hold the book to a reasonable length and in line with the current emphasis on inferential statistics, it was necessary to omit some material traditionally included in the basic course. Thus, there is no chapter on "graphics" or on "sources of data," although some material on the latter point does appear in Chapter 1. The book also omits a number of more sophisticated topics such as multiple correlation and power curves. However, the amount of material included is more than adequate for a single-semester beginning course.

In the problems and questions, there is considerable variation in types, level of difficulty, and in time required for solution. The problems are placed to facilitate assignments; they follow the study of a particular concept or set of concepts. This arrangement allows the student an opportunity to grasp the material and to fix the concepts firmly in mind before moving on to new materials.

I wish to extend my gratitude to Professors Richard O. Sielaff, John Dettmann, and Philip Friest for encouragement and help over long but pleasant years. My thanks also to Reyburn Roulston, John Boyer, Michael Behr, and Robert Panian. Professor John Hafstrom, now of San Bernardino State College, served as my mentor on certain parts of the manuscript, and helped me avoid error. A number of other individuals served as constructive critics at various stages of writing. I wish to thank Professors Sarah Bedrosian, Cecil Bigelow, Ramona First, Mildred Massey, Henry L. Munn, William Peters, Joseph Safer, Theodore Sielaff, and Roger Walker for their generous assistance. Thanks also to James McDaniel, Robert Gormley, and the Wadsworth staff for their professional help. I would also like to thank the many students who served as a sampling universe for various ideas and teaching approaches employed in the classroom over a decade of experimentation.

I am indebted to the late Sir Ronald A. Fisher, F.R.S., Cambridge, and Messrs. Oliver and Boyd Ltd., Edinburgh, for permission to reprint Tables II and IV from *Statistical Methods for Research Workers.* I wish to thank Professor George W. Snedecor and the Iowa State University Press for permission to use the Table of *F*, Table 10.3 in *Statistical Methods.* I am also grateful to the other writers and publishers who granted permission to use copyrighted materials. To the members of my own family—Corinne, Bill, Cynthia, and Robert—I give heartfelt thanks for their patience. While all those mentioned have helped to bring the book to its present state, I alone am responsible for any possible errors and shortcomings.

CECIL H. MEYERS

CONTENTS

I

An Introduction to Statistics

2

The Frequency Distribution

3

Measures of Central Tendency

4

Measures of Dispersion

5

An Introduction to Probability

6

The Normal and Binomial Distributions

7

Introduction to Sampling and Statistical Inference

8

Some Technical Problems of Sampling

9

Statistical Inference and the Testing of Hypotheses

IO

Additional Methods of Testing Hypotheses

II

The Use and Construction of Index Numbers

I2

Time Series and Trend Fitting

13

Trend Fitting and Seasonal Indices

14

Two-Variable Linear Correlation

Appendices and Index

ELEMENTARY BUSINESS
AND
ECONOMIC STATISTICS

I AN INTRODUCTION TO STATISTICS

1.1 What Is the Study of Statistics?

It is common knowledge that statistics involves the collection and use of numerical information. Precisely how the information is collected and what disposition is made of it is not so widely understood. One of the major objectives of this book is to provide a basis for understanding how numerical information is assembled, transformed into useful types of information, and finally used in problem-solving and decision-making.

It should be noted first that statistics is not just one thing but a collection of many things. For example, as a science it is concerned with methods by which problems may be approached. As an art it is concerned with the applications of methods and results to an infinite number of possible uses.

It may be said, further, that statistics consists of a group of *methods* employed to supply numerical information about the environment in which man lives and works. In formal terms statistics may be defined as *a science of numerical information which employs the processes of measurement and collection, classification, analysis, decision-making, and communication of results in a manner understandable and verifiable by others.* Less formally, it may be said that statistics is both an *art* and a *science*, and while it may be highly theoretical at some points, it also employs many easily understood arithmetical concepts— such as an ordinary average. Statistics provides techniques for *discovering knowledge* and for *simplifying* large masses of data to ordinary numbers. Statistics provides a means for presenting information in meaningful and understandable form and is a vehicle for transmitting and storing information and for stating the results of measurement and enumeration. Statistics also is a method for solving certain kinds of problems, and it provides methods by which data may be collected and analyzed. Finally, statistics often serves as the informational segment of the decision-making process.

1

Viewing the question from another vantage point, it might be said that a *statistician* is a practitioner of the art and science of statistics. As such, the statistician must know the methods available to solve certain kinds of problems capable of numerical expression. This means he must first *understand the problem to be solved.* Secondly, he must be able to discern *what types of numerical information may throw light on the problem.* Next, he must be able to obtain the necessary information through *collection methods* such as library research or a process of sampling. Fourth, he must be able to *classify the information* in a logical manner so that tools of analysis may be brought to bear on the original problem; and, finally, he must be able to *communicate the results* to others who will use the information to decide the issue at hand. These results should be communicated in such a way that they can be verified by other knowledgeable persons. However, the statistician's task does not really end at this point, because he must keep in mind the necessity of adding new knowledge to the body of skills and methods which comprise the science of statistics.

In an elementary study of statistics, the beginning student is expected to become familiar with the methods of statistics, to learn to use the simpler but effective tools of statistics, and to come to understand the results of statistical inquiries at a somewhat sophisticated level. Since much of the business and economic environment involves the use of numerical information, the student will find many occasions to put this statistical knowledge to use in understanding the environment in which he lives and works.

Some Background Information

To provide additional information about the question: "What is the study of statistics?", some background knowledge will be helpful. The word "statistics" seems to have been derived from the Latin root for "state," and the term apparently grew out of the usage of governments as they collected numerical information concerning the populations and areas under their jurisdiction. Even at an early stage in social organization it was necessary for an administrator to have certain numerical information at his disposal. This compelling need has in no way diminished with the passage of time.

The study of statistics, particularly business and economic statistics, focuses on two general areas: *descriptive statistics* and *inferential statistics.* While these two areas are complementary, they do have their individual differences, as noted below.

Consider first the area of *descriptive statistics.* It would be well nigh impossible to describe a country, state, city, or geographical region without resorting to numerical statements about population, age groupings, land area, income, industries, exports, production, agriculture, and so on. From another point of view, the businessman who studies carefully the balance sheet of his firm is formulating a perspective for his business policies and operations largely through the use of descriptive statistical information as supplied by the accounting process. The study of economics today requires the use of large masses of numerical information on prices, wages, income, production, productivity, markets, consumer buying plans, and many other types of numerical information. These masses of information are *nearly always presented in a summary form*—for example, in the form of an arithmetic average. A summary of the data gives the reader essential information without cluttering up the presentation with the mass of numbers used in the original calculations. Statistical summarization can be an extremely efficient method of presentation because the statistics have been refined and simplified, making the information readily available in a highly usable form.

The types of information just mentioned can be considered descriptive statistics because the data (facts) are presented in summary form, and the summarization probably has utilized many of the statistics to be presented in this book. That is, descriptive statistics include several types of averages, index numbers, measures of deviation, percentages, and the like. The criterion by which a statistic can be judged "descriptive" is that no attempt is made to apply probability theory to the statistics in order to project the facts into unknown numerical areas. In other words, no educated guesses are made or inferences drawn about unknown statistics. The facts are presented as facts—no more, no less. These facts may, of course, be shown on a graph and related to other facts or to historical time periods. Frequently the information is presented in the form of statistical tables.

As an example of descriptive statistics, suppose that a historical study has been made showing the per capita use of electricity over a period of several recent years. This study will show what the past record has been. This information is interesting in its own right because it does help describe what changes have been taking place in this one variable. The information may also help reveal the manner in which the consumer and industry have been mechanizing to do new tasks, or to do old tasks by new means.

Now, while it is clear that this historical information is useful in telling us where we have been, it can also help us see where we are *tending to move* in the future. Once we begin projecting the past information into the future, we begin moving into unknown areas where it is impossible to make statements which are "certain" in the sense that they will actually come true. However, it is often possible to use probability theory to assess the "chances" that a statement about the future is a correct statement. The ability to move from known to unknown facts is a matter of the utmost importance and value. This "leap" from the known to the unknown is generally described as the *inductive method*. In this book the inductive method as applied to statistical data is described as *statistical inference* or *inferential statistics*.

Inferential statistics are based on partial information, which is then used to draw conclusions about the totality (generally known as the *population* or *universe*) in which the information originated. To illustrate: Suppose a large cardboard box is placed on a table so that you cannot see what is in it. Someone agrees to reach into the box and pull out one object, and this object turns out to be a small transparent plastic box of the type used to display hardware. On the basis of this knowledge alone, what can be inferred about the contents of the larger box? Clearly, the only inference possible is that the cardboard box contains small plastic display boxes. The conclusion just drawn may, however, be incorrect, and only further information can establish its truth or falsity. This, then, is the basic problem of inference: On the basis of a small quantity of knowledge about a statistical universe, the characteristics of that universe are to be stated. Although this approach involves the cost of occasional error, it is also a highly efficient tool for extending knowledge. From a statistical point of view the problem is also one of finding methods to reduce the possibility of error, and these methods invariably utilize some knowledge of probability theory.

To summarize: Descriptive statistics involve techniques for summarizing data and presenting those data in a usable form such as a table or a graph. These statistics tell where we have been. Stated more precisely, descriptive statistics describe the past behavior of a variable through time. On the other hand, inferential statistics take the historical data and by the use of probability theory formulate statements about the future behavior of the variable. Thus inferential statistics project from the known to the unknown. Both of these approaches are part of the materials in this book.

1.2 Use of Statistics in Measurement and in Providing Information

A good deal of what this book is about concerns measurement and information and the question of making decisions on the basis of incomplete information. It is therefore essential to acquire a basic understanding of the theory or rationale and the mechanistic techniques by which measurement is carried out and under which information originates and is put to use.

The objective of a process of measurement is the determination of dimensions—that is, size. *Dimensions or sizes are determined by comparison with a "standard" used in the measurement process.* Almost everyone possesses an intuitive understanding of measurement. For example, when it is said that something is "five yards long" everyone knows the length and the standard used in measurement. Measurement turns out to be a process of valuation—that is, valuation of one thing in terms of another, and thus valuation is also a matter of comparison and a basis for making judgments and reaching conclusions. However, the degree of precision with which something may be measured runs from exact to crude, and in some cases measurement may be a matter of rough (but useful) estimation. Statistical measurement should, of course, be as precise as possible given the tools at hand and the limitations imposed by time and cost factors.

In addition to measurement, another method of gathering numerical information is through the process of counting—that is, *enumeration*. Here numbers are employed in their cardinal (how many?) sense. For decision-making and administrative purposes it is often essential to know *how many* things are involved. For example, it would be important for a business manager to know how many salesmen were employed; how many automobiles the firm owned; how many employees were on the payroll; how many dollars of sales occurred last month; how many items were produced last month; and so on. As a matter of fact, this type of knowledge is required to a greater or lesser degree of everyone and is not the special province of statistics alone.

Taken together, *measurement and enumeration provide the basic methods of obtaining information on the size* of an object, tell us how many objects there are, and otherwise allow us to determine the dimensions of the "thing" in which we are interested. Numbers, of course, allow us to express these dimensions.

Given the need for information, and on the assumption that something is being measured or counted because there exists a need for these data, the next major question is: "How accurate should the measurements be?" In general, this question is answered by asking another: "What are the requirements of the problem?" Once the requirements are stated, it is then possible to attempt to achieve that level of accuracy. For example, one place to the right of the decimal might be required (as in index numbers) or several places (as in calculating some averages). However, when considering this question of accuracy it is easy to be attracted to one of two extremes and (a) demand more accuracy than is required and thus lose our way in a sea of endless detail and painstaking efforts, or (b) allow so much tolerance in measurement that the actual dimensions appear as if in a fog rather than in a clear and penetrating light. In this book it is suggested that you carefully consider the requirements of the problem (as stated or inferred) and that in practice neither extreme of measurement should be the master. This is not to say, of course, that measurements should not be as accurate as possible under the requirements and restrictions placed on the information.

In discussing the accuracy of the measurement and counting processes, it should be emphasized that: (1) The requirements of accuracy are set by the problem at hand, and this implies that one must understand the problem itself and determine what is essential and what is trivial about that problem and what accuracy is demanded. (2) The essentiality or triviality of a particular matter must be judged in terms of already existing knowledge possessed by whoever is responsible for the final determination of the question. Certainly, no user of statistical information or no one who determines what statistics will be gathered can adequately state the informational requirements without some *prior knowledge of the subject*. This kind of personal ability is ordinarily acquired only by patient study, careful inquiry, constant scrutiny of method and approach, and a storing of this knowledge within the limits of the mental and organizational capacity of the individual. In fine, then, the requirements of the problem determine accuracy as judged by the person responsible for the information.

1.3   Informational Uses of Statistics

It has been observed that statistics involve numerical information which results from measurements or from an enumeration. Now, how might this kind of information be used? Although it is impossible to elaborate all possible uses, some examples may be given. In business applications, knowledge of the number of persons in a market provides useful information for policy-making purposes. From an economic point of view, the measurement of a price level provides information as to the changes taking place in that particular variable. Measures of economic activity such as the Industrial Production Index allow businessmen and government officials to assess changes taking place in industrial production and to draw inferences about the economy as a whole. If an assembly process produces parts, a sample may be drawn and inspected to provide information on whether or not the process is producing at acceptable standards. *The use of statistical information depends primarily upon the requirements and opportunities of the recipient.*

The gathering of statistics to provide information is ordinarily a costly process, and it would be supposed that statistics are collected only when the informational return can be justified. This point raises a good number of questions which ought to be explored before statistics are gathered. Some of these questions refer to the use of the information, while others refer to technical matters related to the actual gathering of the data. Among the questions raised are the following:

1. *Of what possible use is the information?* There ought to be some chance that the information will be of use either in a practical matter of immediate significance or in the gaining of new knowledge as a function of pure research. Since it is frequently impossible to know if the data will be of practical significance, it may be desirable to take the chance that valuable information will be derived from the study.

2. There is a question as to whether the information *can be gathered quickly enough to be of significance.* The results of some statistical investigations are available only after considerable delay during which time the problem may have grown worse, or the value of the statistical results may have diminished because the results were received too late to be significant.

3. Technical questions arise as to *how the data can and should be gathered.* The following chapters will explore many of the avenues through which information can be collected—direct measurements, census, sample, counting, secondary sources, and so on. Questions should be raised as to whether one method or another is more appropriate to the problem at hand.

4. When the information has been gathered, *how should it be presented?* Should it be in the form of an average, a frequency distribution, a time series, an index number, a confidence interval, or should some other form of presentation be used? Frequently the very nature of the problem limits the choice as to what statistical measures should be used to convey the information.

5. There is a question as to how the information so gathered and presented should be *used in application.* For example, in a firm it might be asked: Does the information indicate some difficulty in the production process? In the supply of raw materials? In the sales efforts? Or, from another point of view, does a construction price level index suggest that costs of constructing a new building are excessive at this time? Clearly, the applications of statistical information to practical problems would seem to be almost without limit.

6. Questions may arise as to the *reliability* of the information. In other words, can we trust the numbers (as they are presented) to be quite accurate and to measure what they purport to measure? For example, estimates of the number of unemployed persons made in the early 1930's varied from approximately 7 million to about 13 million. Thus, any particular estimate was not to be characterized by a high degree of reliability. On the other hand, current population data, as furnished by the U.S. Census Bureau each decade, would be considered highly reliable information.

7. Once information has been gathered, there is a question as to how and where the information *should be stored* after its initial use. This factor of retention will not be a concern of this book, but it should be clear that means and techniques for storing the information for as long as it might be useful are most desirable.

8. Finally, there is the question of how to *extract the most usable information* from the collected data. In the chapters dealing with sampling and statistical inference, this problem will be explored at some length. Since in many cases the information collected is necessarily incomplete—that is, the information is derived from sampling processes—the incomplete information must provide all the required data. This task of making the best possible use of the data is obviously of major importance.

Use of Statistics in Administrative Decisions

In the control of an administrative unit, useful information is of paramount importance. Those who direct must know not only what is being directed but also whether the desired directions are being achieved in practice. They must also continuously question whether or not policies should be altered. Various types of information must be received before these decisions are made. Some of the information will be statistical in nature. For example, business firms require information on markets, prices, employment, wages, gross income, expenses for various items, capital structure, tax liabilities, and many other items. Some administrative units such as government will require information on population, taxes, crime rates, income, prices, natural resources, housing, industry structure, and many others. These informational requirements will be met through many sources, but a major form of expression is statistical. To say that in the modern world the quantity of numerical information has been growing rapidly is certainly not an overstatement.

Sources of Information

Information of value to business firms may be derived from *internal* or *external* sources or both. What are the internal sources of statistical data? In addition to the accounting department, there may be the sales department, engineering, production, personnel, credit, treasury, research and development, as well as other specialized departments. In general, the larger the administrative unit the more complex is the information structure and the more organized and structured are the informational requirements. In complex organizations there exists not only a large amount of information-gathering activities and reporting but also the problem of seeing to it that the information is useful and is made available on a timely basis to those who will make decisions with its assistance.

External sources of information include all the ordinary channels of communication, such as newspapers, specialized newspapers and magazines, trade association reports, publications of various bureaus of business research in colleges and universities, publications of the Federal Reserve Board of Governors and of the Federal Reserve Banks, reports from federal and state governmental agencies, reports from specialized engineering and research firms and others. The list is practically unlimited. A few of the more readily available statistical references are given at the end of this chapter.

1.4   Summary

Statistical information today is widely used and is a constant part of the business environment. The subject of statistics studies how numerical information is gathered and structured, how inferences may be drawn from data, and how decisions based on the data can be made. Statistics are also useful in defining problems ("What percentage of the parts produced by this machine are defective?") and in throwing light on problems ("Average sales are declining by $50,000 per month!"), and statistics are useful in keeping track of a variable such as the Consumer Price Index. In short, statistics have a broad range of usefulness, and it will be one of the aims of this book to provide some introductory insights into statistical techniques and uses of information.

Exercise 1.1

1. Obtain an annual report of a large corporation. What statistical information is presented in the report? Does the report communicate information quickly and readily by the use of tables and graphs? How might the management have utilized the information in managing the corporation?

2. Obtain a copy of *Business Week, U.S. News and World Report, Dun's Review, Forbes* or a similar magazine. Estimate what percentage of the total information presented is statistical in nature. (a) Do the statistics convey information in brief, readily understandable form? (b) If the information presented statistically had instead been presented in narrative form, how much additional space might be required? Would the information be as valuable in narrative as in numerical form? (c) Could the statistical information given be applied to a broad range of economic problems? Why?

3. What statistical information would be required to briefly describe your home state? (a) Look up your home state in an encyclopedia. What statistical information is given there? (b) How much of the total information given is statistical in nature?

4. How does a person judge information to be valuable? To be trivial? Suppose you were asked to provide information concerning your home state and to be reasonably brief. What information would you include? Exclude? Why?

5. From what sources does a business firm acquire information of a statistical nature? Is all of this information valuable? Why?

Bibliography

Sources of Statistical Data. The following listing is suggestive only. There are hundreds of sources and source books filled with information in statistical form. The reference shelves of any college library hold many statistical sources of information. For a good listing of statistical sources see "Bibliography of Sources" in the *Statistical Abstract of the United States (Year).*

Statistical Abstract of the United States (Year)

This book is published yearly by the United States Department of Commerce and contains some 34 separate sections of data.

Economic Almanac

This book is published biennially by the National Industrial Conference Board. It contains statistics on nearly every phase of United States industry.

Economic Report of the President (Year)

This volume is published annually in January and contains a large volume of statistical materials on United States economic conditions.

Federal Reserve Bulletin

The *Bulletin* is published monthly by the Federal Reserve Board of Governors.

Monthly Labor Review

The *Review* is published monthly by the United States Department of Labor.

Specialized News and Reporting Services. The following specialized publications are informational in character and give large amounts of data in statistical form. The list is suggestive only.

Business Week, Forbes, U.S. News and World Report, The Wall Street Journal, The Journal of Commerce, Factory Magazine, Dun's Review and Modern Industry, Foreign Commerce Weekly, Barron's

In addition to the sources mentioned, there are many publications of trade associations, but these are not always available on a library basis. For a listing of such associations, see the *Encyclopedia of American Associations* (Detroit, the Gale Research Company). See also Paul Wasserman, *Information for Administrators: A Guide to Publications and Services for Management in Business and Government* (Ithaca, N.Y.: Cornell University Press, 1957).

References Relative to Measurement and Method. On the general subject of measuring business and economic variables see:

Lewis, John P., *Business Conditions Analysis.* New York: McGraw-Hill Book Company, 1959.

Snyder, Richard M., *Measuring Business Changes.* New York: John Wiley & Sons, Inc., 1955.

On the subject of scientific method and the methods of research, the following references are especially useful:

Beveridge, W. I. B., *The Art of Scientific Investigation.* New York: The Modern Library Paperback Series, Random House, rev. ed., 1957.

Rigby, Paul H., *Conceptual Foundations of Business Research.* New York: McGraw-Hill Book Company, 1965.

Sullivan, J. W. N., *The Limitations of Science.* New York: The New American Library of World Literature, Inc., Mentor Series, 1949. The original hardcover edition of this book was published by Viking Press in 1933.

Wilson, E. B., Jr., *An Introduction to Scientific Research.* New York: McGraw-Hill Book Company, 1952.

2

THE FREQUENCY DISTRIBUTION

2.1 Introduction

One of the fundamental concepts in statistical analysis is the *frequency distribution*. This term may refer to a table or to a body of methods by which tabular information is obtained and structured. Two examples of frequency distributions are shown in Tables 2.1 and 2.2.

Table 2.1

Automobile Ownership by Income Size of Household, 1960

Households by Income-Size Groups	Number of Households (thousands)
Less than $2,000	9,983
2,000 to 3,999	9,780
4,000 to 5,999	11,547
6,000 to 7,999	9,241
8,000 to 9,999	5,330
10,000 to 14,999	4,861
15,000 to 24,999	1,537
25,000 and over	609
	52,888

SOURCE: *Survey of Current Business,* September 1963, p. 24. Data derived from census figures.

Table 2.2

Number of Employees by Age Groupings, XYZ Corporation

Age of Employee (years)	Number of Employees
20 – 29	46
30 – 39	68
40 – 49	75
50 – 59	63
60 – 69	21
	273

SOURCE: Hypothetical.

The techniques employed in constructing a frequency distribution provide a means of classifying and organizing relatively large masses of data with the objective of *simplifying the data and making further refinements possible*. The principal method of construction is to group the large number of individual data into a relatively small number of classes. For example, in Table 2.1 some 52,888,000 households have been placed in eight classes. The grouping is accomplished by applying a generally accepted set of rules to the original data. Even though the grouping results in a meaningful presentation of information, further refinements are possible; these will be shown in subsequent paragraphs and chapters.

Objectives of This Chapter

The objectives of the present chapter are (a) to indicate the nature of the problem for which the frequency distribution is useful, (b) to explain the methodology for constructing frequency distributions from original data, and (c) to provide an explanation of and insights into the technical features of a frequency distribution.

2.2   Nature of the Frequency Distribution

To indicate the type of problem which gives rise to the need for a frequency distribution, suppose the management of a large chain of retail stores wished to study the wages of part-time employees as paid during one week. The payroll department could furnish a listing of the dollar amounts paid each employee. Thus, original information is supplied in the form of a large number of individual measurements—that is, wages. These measurements constitute the *raw data* of the problem. A *variable*, part-time wages, is the specific thing to be measured. Each wage as recorded may be termed an *item*. The entire group of wages may be considered as a *set*, namely, the set of all measurements of the variable.

The form in which the raw data are supplied by the payroll department would be a set of perhaps several hundred wages. These are the raw data. At this point the raw data are simply a jumbled mass of numbers devoid of apparent order or meaning. It would be an almost impossible task to look at the raw wage data and form an accurate overall impression of the part-time wage problem. In other words, there now exists a large mass of data from which information is sought, but little can be discerned while the data remain in this jumbled form. What is required now is a technique for classifying and organizing these wage-numbers from the payroll department into a *small, usable table which clearly indicates the pattern or distribution of wages and throws light on the problem for which the data were collected.*

The first step in structuring the payroll data is to *employ an orderly process known as grouping* through which the mass of wage data may be reduced to intelligible proportions. The result of the process of grouping will be a relatively few classes containing the original wage information *in summary form.* The frequencies of the groups will show the manner in which the data are distributed from the highest to the lowest wage values and will indicate which values occur most and least frequently. When this structuring of the data by grouping has been accomplished, the primary problem of reducing a large mass of data to a small, readily understandable form is completed. As we shall see, further techniques of refinement can be applied to the frequency distribution that results from the process just described.

In approaching the problem of grouping a set of raw data into classes, the most obvious technique is to arrange the items from the lowest to the highest values of the variable.[1] In this form, the data are said to be *arrayed.* When the array has been constructed, certain features of the data become visible at a glance. For example, the highest and the lowest wage paid are easily discernible, as is any tendency for the data to bunch together at certain values. While the data in arrayed form are now arranged logically according to magnitude, there has been no compression or summarization of the data. The numbers exist in the same quantity as before, but at least they are in organized form.

In actual problems involving the construction of a frequency distribution, a number of questions emerge prior to the actual gathering of data. These questions include defining the area in which information is required and deciding whether such information can be helpful to the problem at hand. There may be technical questions as to what variable should be measured and how accurate the measurements should be. When these matters are decided, the data can be collected.

When the significant data have been gathered, the process of compressing this information into classes raises a number of questions. For example, questions arise as to *how wide* the classes should be, *how many* classes should be established, and *how the class limits should be stated.* In the automobile ownership distribution eight classes were given. These classes vary somewhat in width. Here, the term "width" refers to the difference between the two numbers which identify the class. The second class of the automobile distribution covers a range from $2,000 to $2,999

---

[1] If the data of the problem should have a large number of items, it is quite possible to skip over the array stage by establishing the classes and simply sorting the items into the appropriate groups.

inclusive while the seventh class covers a range from $15,000 to $24,999 inclusive. If the classes had been given in uniform widths of $1,000, some 25 or more classes would have been required.

The questions posed above must be decided in a manner which will carry out the objectives for which the distribution is designed. We shall examine both the questions and the possible answers in the next few pages.

General Procedure for Constructing a Frequency Distribution

The general procedure for deciding the issues of a statistical inquiry leading to the construction of a frequency distribution may be shown as follows:

1. The original problem is defined by the statistician, or by management, and informational requirements are established. In other words, the question is: "What is the problem and what kind of data will shed light on that problem?" Here we shall assume a frequency distribution is required.

2. When the frequency distribution has been decided upon, the necessary measurements are made to supply the raw data. However, before the actual process of measurement or enumeration is carried out, a specific level of accuracy must be determined. For example, will the measurements be taken to the nearest inch, tenth of an inch, or to the nearest one-hundredth of an inch? As will be observed later, the specific items to be measured will often be determined by sampling methods.

3. Once the raw data have been collected, the next step is to arrange those data in the form of an array. Under some circumstances this step may be unnecessary, but it will be assumed an array is desirable at this point.

4. The number of classes is determined along with the width of each class, and the measurements are then sorted into the proper classes. When this step is completed, the result is a table similar to the examples given at the beginning of this chapter.

5. From the distribution several kinds of information may now be derived. These will be shown in detail in later chapters; they will include measures of central tendency such as the arithmetic mean and various measures of scatter such as the standard deviation. Graphs may also be constructed for ease in visualizing the information of the distribution.

Origins of the Raw Data

The set of all items (measurements) which become part of the frequency distribution originates in "practical" or "actual" situations. Suppose that a machine produces a particular product whose length is specified as 2.5 inches ± .05 inches. As the machine operates, it produces a large quantity of parts whose lengths would, it is expected, be between 2.45 and 2.55 inches. All of the parts produced by the machine during a given period can be considered as a *universe* or *population*. The words "universe" and "population" may be thought of as including all things which conform to a particular definition.

Now, the machine cannot be allowed to operate continuously without some supervision and periodic checks on its performance. It will be necessary to measure a few of these parts from time to time to discern whether the desired degree of accuracy, i.e., ±.05 inches, is being achieved. This periodic checking is part of the process known as *industrial quality control.*

To determine the average performance of the machine in order to know what future results to expect, it may be considered desirable to measure a large number of parts in order to provide a standard by which quality can be checked from time to time. Thus, the machine will be run for a predetermined period and perhaps two or three hundred items will be selected at random for measurement. Each measurement will be recorded as an item. The set of all such measurements forms the raw data, which will then be refined into a frequency distribution.

With this background in mind, let us now observe the frequency distribution at closer range and begin to identify and describe the more technical aspects involved in constructing and using it.

2.3 Identifying the Parts

The term *frequency distribution* is here used to refer to a set of measurements or enumerations expressed in tabular or graphic form. Table 2.3 illustrates the frequency distribution and identifies its parts.

Classes

Each of the horizontal rows in the table is a *class* and is sometimes loosely referred to as a class interval. There are eight classes in Table 2.3.

Table 2.3

A Frequency Distribution of the Wages of Part-Time Employees

Stated Class Limits	Midpoint	Frequency	Class Boundaries
$23 – 27	25	5	$22.50 – 27.50
28 – 32	30	10	27.50 – 32.50
33 – 37	35	10	32.50 – 37.50
38 – 42	40	12	37.50 – 42.50
43 – 47	45	10	42.50 – 47.50
48 – 52	50	8	47.50 – 52.50
53 – 57	55	4	52.50 – 57.50
58 – 62	60	1	57.50 – 62.50

Stated Class Limits

These pairs of values provide the upper and lower limits for each interval and are the numbers as printed in the table. As printed, these numbers reflect the accuracy of measurement by the significant digits shown. If you are a little rusty on the concept of significant digits, you may want to review Appendix A.

Midpoint

Each class midpoint is the "halfway" mark—the intermediate point between each pair of stated class limits. The value of the midpoint for each class can be determined by adding the upper and lower stated limits of the class and dividing by 2.

Frequency

The frequency of each class indicates how many items are contained in each class. Alternatively one might say the frequency column reveals how many of the original measurements are included in each of the class intervals.

Class Interval

This is best illustrated by example: The first class of Table 2.3 has stated class limits of $23 to $27. In this same row observe also that the class boundaries are $22.50 to $27.50. The "class interval" is the difference between the upper and lower class boundaries and equals $5 in all classes in this particular distribution. It may be said that the *width* of the class is $5. A class boundary "splits the difference" between the end of one interval and the beginning of the next. In the case of the first and last classes of the distribution, one simply assumes that a fictitious or zero frequency class exists below or above the printed class limit, and then halves the difference between limits to determine the boundary.

Comment on Class Intervals

Sometimes the frequency distribution is constructed with open-end classes. This type of classification may be observed in Table 2.1. For example, there the first class interval is specified as "Less than $2,000." It is, therefore, impossible to determine the width of the interval. The same point can be made about the last class interval, which reads "$25,000 and over." The width of the open-end interval is indeterminate. The width of all classes other than the first and last can, however, be determined, because they are necessarily closed classes.

Functions of a Frequency Distribution

When a frequency distribution has been properly constructed, the resulting table will serve several objectives:

1. The distribution will compress a large mass of data into a relatively small, easy-to-read table.

2. The distribution can serve as the basis for additional analysis and interpretation.

3. The frequency column will indicate those values which occur most and least frequently. In this case the midpoints will be taken as representative of the items in each class. When analyzing a distribution in terms of values which occur most and least frequently, we are actually referring to the probability that any individual measurement of the variable will fall in one of the classes of the table. The relationship between frequency and probability should be kept in mind; it will be a matter of importance in later chapters.

4. The class limits of the distribution indicate the values over which the variable is ranging. The word *range* is defined as the difference between the highest and lowest values of the variable. Thus, a frequency distribution will show the approximate range of values the variable can assume *only if* the distribution has all class limits printed as shown in Tables 2.2 and 2.3. If the first and last classes are open-ended—as shown in Table 2.1—the range of the variable cannot be determined.

5. Central values such as the arithmetic average (usually known as the "mean") can be estimated by inspection.

2.4   Basic Principles of Enumeration and Measurement

Variables are said to be either *continuous* or *discontinuous*. The word *discrete* is also used to mean discontinuous. If, for example, the variable under consideration is the number of parts found in an inventory bin, the variable can take only integer values. It is therefore said to be *discontinuous* or *discrete*. On the other hand, if the variable under consideration was the length or weight of an object, then it is necessary to apply some standard of measurement, such as inches, miles, ounces, pounds, tons, to determine the value of the variable. Since this type of measurement could theoretically take any value whatsoever within the range of the variable, it is known as a *continuous variable*. How *precise* a measurement actually is depends upon how far the process of measurement is carried out—that is, to hundredths, thousandths, ten-thousandths, and so on.

How *accurate* a measurement actually is depends upon the amount of possible error in the measurement and reporting process. These points are discussed more fully below.

Discontinuous Variables

Discontinuous values are values reported in a manner which leaves "gaps" between any two succeeding values of the variable. For example, you might think of counting automobile tires, tubes of toothpaste, books, typewriters, dollars, dollars and cents, or employees. Observe that these things are only expressed as whole numbers, and therefore the reported values of the variable show arithmetic gaps between successive numbers. If the measurements are estimates or rounded numbers, the gaps will be larger than if unit counts were made. In all cases, the accuracy of the count or estimate should be indicated by the significant digits reported.

A discontinuous variable, however, need not consist of whole numbers. If the variable consisted of an enumeration of things which occurred as half-units, such as the right and left halves of a metal container for a solenoid, then the counting gaps are only $\frac{1}{2}$ of a unit wide. In this case the count would be $\frac{1}{2}, 1, 1\frac{1}{2}, 2, 2\frac{1}{2}, \ldots, k$. Obviously, other fractional units would be subject to the same principle.

Continuous Variables

The values of a continuous variable can change by infinitely small amounts through the range of the variable. Thus, if the range of the variable is between 1 and 2, the space between these two integers is occupied by a continuous series of numbers and no gaps can exist.

To illustrate the term *continuous* as used in statistics, consider first the realities of physical measurement. The instruments of measurement are themselves accurate within limits of "thousandths of an inch" or "ten-thousandths of an inch" and even more, but observe that the final measurement can never be truly exact. Secondly, such measurements taken from instruments must ultimately be "read" by a person or a machine, and thus human and mechanical factors of judgment and error are involved. As an example, you might think of an individual trying to measure accurately—and this means to the millionths or billionths and beyond—the diameter of a piece of wire. Admittedly at some point the measurement ceases, either because such accuracy is unnecessary or because the instruments have reached their limitations. In other words, continuous data are, *as a matter of necessity*, made discontinuous by the limitations of measurement. Thus, a certain amount of error, minute though it may be, creeps into the data.

Consequently, then, in the measurement of a continuous variable, such as height, weight, length, intelligence, distance, the values reported as the measurements are *necessarily rounded numbers.* Going a step further, it may be seen that the value reported as the measurement of a continuous variable *represents not a point but an interval in which the exact measurement is expected to fall.* The notion of a point (single number) is suggested by the reporting of a measurement, but that reported or recorded value actually represents an interval. One of the problems we face is to understand how to interpret and place limits on the "interval in which the true value falls" and to account for the potential error of measurements.

Suppose, for example, that a physical measurement of length is reported as 1.3 inches. The manner of stating the number tells us that the measurements were made to the nearest tenth of an inch.[2] In other words, in the judgment of the person making the measurement, the actual length of the object was closer to 1.3 inches than to 1.2 or 1.4 inches. Further, the actual measurement must have fallen somewhere between 1.25 and 1.35 inches to be reported as 1.3 inches. Thus, the interval of measurement is 1.25 to 1.35 inches.

From this discussion we reach the interesting conclusion that *measurements of a continuous variable are actually approximations.* Measurements are the reported values of the variable, and these reported values are really the midpoints of an arithmetic space marking out the boundaries within which the true value is expected to fall.

Exercise 2.1

1. Define each of the following terms:

    (a) measurement.
    (b) unit of measurement.
    (c) item.
    (d) frequency.
    (e) classes.
    (f) stated class limits.
    (g) class boundaries.
    (h) open-ended interval.

    (i) universe or population.
    (j) width of class intervals.
    (k) continuous variable.
    (l) discontinuous variable.
    (m) data.
    (n) grouping.
    (o) range.
    (p) enumeration.

2. Before data are gathered, what questions should be asked and answered?

3. Explain the procedure for constructing a frequency distribution.

---

[2] If some other type of rounding were used, such as rounding up to the next tenth of an inch or rounding down to the last tenth of an inch, this fact would have to be specified along with the reported value.

4. What are the general objectives achieved in the construction of a frequency distribution?

5. Contrast the word "measurement" to the word "enumeration."

6. Once a frequency distribution has been constructed, what kinds of information become immediately available?

7. Contrast the precision of a measurement to the accuracy of a measurement.

8. Distinguish between continuous and discontinuous measurements. What kinds of variables are clearly discontinuous?

9. What does it mean to say that "the measurement of a continuous variable represents not a point but an interval in which the exact measurement is expected to fall"?

10. In the following reported measurements of a variable in which the measurements have been rounded to the nearest unit, what is the interval in which the exact measurement is expected to fall?

(a) 7 inches.
(b) 11.5 centimeters.
(c) 23 miles.
(d) $146.
(e) $146.05.
(f) 0.005 thousandths of an inch.

2.5   Constructing a Frequency Distribution: Basic Procedure

Up to this point we have been developing the basic principles of the frequency distribution, the principles of measurement and the reporting of numerical information as these may be applied to the frequency distribution. Our task now is to develop the principles which are used in the construction of a frequency distribution. In other words, we shall begin with the raw data as gathered from an enumeration or measurement process and will then structure the data into a frequency distribution.

The steps to be followed in structuring the data are: (1) ordering the data on the basis of magnitude, thus constructing an array; (2) determining how many classes are appropriate to the data; (3) stating the class limits; (4) analyzing the frequencies by cumulating them and by conversion to percentages; (5) analyzing the distribution by means of graphs —that is, the histogram, frequency polygon and ogive.

To illustrate this sequence of steps, assume the 60 items of raw data shown in Table 2.4 represent the wages paid in a certain week to 60 part-time employees of a large supermarket (the quantity of data has been made small to avoid unnecessary detail). The sequence for structuring these frequency data is shown in Tables 2.5–2.7.

The wage data for this problem have been rounded to the nearest whole dollar. It may be observed that the raw data of Table 2.4 are a set of rather jumbled numbers. However, these numbers have been *arrayed* on the basis of magnitude in Table 2.5. Then, in Table 2.6, the frequency with which each dollar value occurs in the data is shown. For example,

Table 2.4						
		The Raw Data				
$45	55	53	40	31	50	30
42	45	47	40	33	40	25
28	28	35	35	47	30	25
38	50	25	30	49	31	38
36	26	60	40	50	45	35
40	47	40	50	49	50	35
30	30	55	45	26	45	33
35	40	50	30	45	35	43
42	55	35	50			

Table 2.5						
		The Array				
$25	30	35	40	42	47	50
25	30	35	40	43	47	53
25	30	35	40	45	49	55
26	30	35	40	45	49	55
26	31	35	40	45	50	55
28	31	35	40	45	50	60
28	33	36	40	45	50	
30	33	38	40	45	50	
30	35	38	42	47	50	

Table 2.6

The Frequency (*f*) Table

Value	f	Value	f
$25	3	$42	2
26	2	43	1
28	2	45	6
30	6	47	3
31	2	49	2
33	2	50	6
35	7	53	1
36	1	55	3
38	2	60	1
40	8		

Table 2.7

The Frequency Distribution

Weekly Wages in Dollars	Number of Persons Earning the Stated Wage
23 – 27	5
28 – 32	10
33 – 37	10
38 – 42	12
43 – 47	10
48 – 52	8
53 – 57	4
58 – 62	1

looking at the array, notice that $25 appears three times and this is shown as a frequency (*f*) of 3 in the frequency table. The other dollar values appear in the same manner. Finally, the class intervals appearing in Table 2.7 were established and the frequencies (taken either from the array or the frequency table) were grouped into the classes shown. Thus, the first class from $23 to $27 inclusive shows five items, the class from $28 to $32 inclusive shows ten items, and so on. Observe that all classes are $5 wide as determined by the difference between class boundaries. (Class boundaries and midpoints for this problem were shown in Table 2.3.)

Writing the Class Limits

There are three major methods of stating class intervals. These methods are shown below.

1. If the data have been rounded to the *nearest unit* (such as the nearest tenth, hundredth, integer, ten, hundred, etc.) the limits may be written as:

8.5 – 10.4		8.5 to 10.4
10.5 – 12.4	or	10.5 to 12.4
12.5 – 14.4		12.5 to 14.4
and so on		and so on.

2. If the data have been rounded to the *last completed unit*, the limits may be
    written as:
                        8.5 but under 10.5
                        10.5 but under 12.5
                        12.5 but under 14.5
                        and so on.

3. If the data have been rounded to the *next unit*, the limits may be written as:
                        over 8.5 and including 10.5
                        over 10.5 and including 12.5
                        over 12.5 and including 14.5
                        and so on.

Observe that in the examples shown above, the rounding occurred in
"tenths." If the measurements were made to "hundredths" the class
limits would have been written as "8.50 – 10.49," "10.50 – 12.49," where
the rounding was to the nearest hundredth. Or, if the rounding was to the
last completed hundredth, the limits would have been written as "8.50
but under 10.50," "10.50 but under 12.50," and so on. If the rounding
had been to the next hundredth, the limits would be written as "over 8.50
and including 10.50," "over 10.50 and including 12.50." Thus, the
method of stating class limits indicates the type of rounding and the
accuracy of measurement.

It might be observed that the class boundaries of Table 2.3 are shown
in the manner customary with dollar values. Thus, the stated class limits
show that the rounding was to the nearest dollar, while the class boundaries
are expressed in half dollars. If the data has involved measurements in,
say, inches—rather than dollars—the class boundaries could then have
been written as 22.5 – 27.5, 27.5 – 32.5, etc.

Determining the Number of Class Intervals

Moving from the raw data to the frequency distribution is relatively
simple as far as making the array or frequency table is concerned. However, two important questions arise as soon as grouping is attempted.
These questions are: (1) How many class intervals are appropriate to the
data? (2) How should the class limits be stated?

As a general rule-of-thumb the number of classes should not be less
than 6 nor more than 18. If the number of items in the set is small, the
number of class intervals should be close to 6 or 8. However, if the
number of items is large, there may be 10, 12, or more intervals. This is
merely a rough rule and provides only a general notion of the appropriate
manner of classes.

Greater precision can be achieved by applying a formula:

$$\text{number of classes} = 1 + (3.322 \log N),$$

where N = the number of items in the distribution. The formula is sometimes useful in an alternate form:

$$\text{width of the class interval} = \frac{\text{range of the data}}{1 + (3.322 \log N)}.$$

It would be unusual for this formula to yield an integer answer. Thus, whatever value is provided by the formula should be *rounded up to the next higher* integer. Under some circumstances it may also be necessary to add an extra class interval in order to accommodate the range of the data. Consequently, the formula should be regarded as providing assistance in determining the number of classes for a set of data. *The formula is not to be used with extreme rigidity.*

Rules and Objectives for Frequency Distribution Construction

The principles outlined below will suggest the necessary guides for constructing a frequency distribution from raw data. Since constructing a frequency distribution is more of an art than a science, the rules must be interpreted with sufficient flexibility to adapt them to specific types of problems and specific informational objectives.

1. Generally speaking, class intervals should be uniform in width if additional computations are to be undertaken. These additional computations include the determination of the mean, median, mode, and standard deviation, as explained in succeeding chapters.

2. Empty classes are not permitted. An empty class contains no items—that is, the frequency is zero. The class intervals should be selected to provide a relatively smooth gradation of the frequencies. This likewise implies there should not be classes in which the frequencies are too heavily concentrated relative to the remainder of the classes.

3. Open-end classes should be avoided if the mean and standard deviation are subsequently to be calculated. Open-end classes were shown in Table 2.1.

4. Class intervals should be stated in a manner that indicates the accuracy of measurement and type of rounding.

5. In general it is desirable (whenever possible) to write the stated class limits in convenient numbers. For example, beginning the limits with values such as 5, 10, 15, 20, and so on is a convenience to the reader.

6. Ideally, the items in each class should be evenly distributed throughout the class because the midpoint will then be a representative value for all items in the class. However, since the data must be taken as they exist, the ideal is seldom achieved in practice.

7. From an overall point of view, it is desirable to achieve a symmetry in the distribution. This would mean even class intervals, convenient expression of class limits, a smooth distribution of frequencies, and midpoints of convenient values. In actual statistical data contexts the ideal is seldom

attainable in its pure form, and it becomes necessary to compromise some objectives to gain others. This matter involves an element of judgment which the trained eye and mind should achieve.

To summarize: It may be said that the statistician must be something of an artist to achieve a frequency distribution meeting all the requirements of an ideal distribution. However, the principles of construction are generally somewhat flexible and the actual difficulties encountered in moving from the raw data to the distribution are minimal. The following exercises provide an opportunity to apply the principles and methods explained in the chapter thus far.

Exercise 2.2

1. Given the following sets of stated class limits. Indicate the type of rounding and the accuracy of measurement or enumeration for each set of limits.

Set A	Set B
10 – 12	15.0 – 19.9
13 – 15	20.0 – 24.9
etc.	etc.

Set C	Set D
Over 10.00 and including 11.00	150 but less than 200
Over 11.00 and including 12.00	200 but less than 250
etc.	etc.

2. What are the class boundaries and class widths for each of the sets of data above?

3. According to the formula for the number of class intervals, how many intervals would be appropriate for a set of data having 50 items? 300 items? 500 items? 1,000 items? 5,000 items?

4. Using the set of raw data given below, construct a frequency distribution following the rules and objectives for constructing a distribution as explained in Section 2.5. Assume the data have been gathered in an enumerative process and consist of numbers of a certain type of replacement part carried by retailers in various sections of the United States.

```
14  24  10  17  13  17  21  12  14  16  17  15  22  17  16  10  21
20  21  16  24  12  25  15  19  23  18  14  11  22  18  22  19  16
14  15  11  16  13  15  13  23  20  15  18  19  23  12  13  19
```

Instructions: (a) Construct an array of the data. (b) From the array construct a frequency distribution which appropriately fits the data. (You will probably have to try several groupings experimentally until a satisfactory distribution has been secured.)

When the distribution has been completed, answer the following questions: (a) What is the range of the data? (b) What values occur most and least frequently? Use midpoints to express your answer. (c) Which class is relatively the most important? Why? (d) Estimate the average number of items carried in the inventories (or in problem 5 below, the number of seconds). (e) How might a graph of your distribution be drawn?

(f) If you were an executive responsible for making decisions about the data, what general conclusions might you draw? Could you draw many conclusions until you knew the nature of the problem for which these data were collected?

5. Assume the following data measure the reading time (in seconds) of a group of individuals who pretested an advertisement. Rounding was to the nearest hundredth.

```
13.92  13.80  15.40  15.20  13.82  17.15  12.06  12.90  11.53  14.94
16.40  13.62  15.25  16.20  13.26  14.82  11.90  13.95  12.95  17.40
14.25  10.50  14.60  15.28  14.05  11.19  13.95  12.43  12.98  13.58
11.60  12.77  14.22  15.15  11.85  16.87  12.95  13.47  15.60  11.12
15.20  12.50  13.98  17.20  13.28  14.65  12.87  12.80  12.73  14.20
12.54  16.25  11.85  13.67  11.35  11.09  14.90  17.03  11.90  11.25
14.60  14.47  12.74  13.20  15.83  13.93  12.91  14.40  14.53  13.40
14.25  13.95  10.89  14.35  13.60  13.87  13.99  16.25  11.19  14.30
11.60  10.26  16.99  13.57  16.25  12.65  14.17  10.32  12.92  17.25
14.13  16.20  13.15  15.30  13.90  15.95  13.91  14.55  13.60  14.05
16.18  15.30  15.95  11.90  13.87  15.40  15.95  15.07  17.50  17.60
```

Instructions: same as for problem 4 above.

2.6   Cumulative and Percentage Frequencies

For some types of analysis it is desirable to observe how many items are above or below a given value. Column 3 of Table 2.8 was constructed by adding—that is, cumulating—the frequency column downward while column 4 was obtained by adding the frequency column (f) upward. From these columns certain questions may be answered. For example, "How many part-time employees received a wage less than $52.50?" Answer: 55 employees. Or, "How many employees made more than $52.50?" Answer: 5 employees. Observe that technically only the class boundaries, not the class limits, can be employed in raising the types of questions indicated above. The boundaries provide a continuous distribution of values, whereas the limits would show gaps if the type of rounding were to the nearest unit.

It is a very simple matter to convert columns 2, 3, and 4 of Table 2.8 to percentages by dividing each frequency by 60, the total number of items included in the distribution. When this is done, the percentages appear as shown in columns 5, 6, and 7. From these percentage frequencies certain types of questions could be answered. For example, "What percentage of the part-time employees made less than $37.50?" Answer: 41.7 per cent. Or, "What percentage of the employees made more than $37.50?" Answer: 58.3 per cent. The use of percentage figures often aids in making the data more easily understood by the layman. Another use suggests itself too. If the supermarket considered in this problem were one of a chain of stores, management might find it

Table 2.8

Cumulative Frequencies and Percentages

Class Boundaries (1)	f (2)	Cumulative Frequencies "Less Than" Upper Limit (3)	Cumulative Frequencies "More Than" Lower Limit (4)	Frequencies as a Percentage (5)	Cumulative Percentage "Less Than" Upper Limit (6)	Cumulative Percentage "More Than" Lower Limit (7)
22.50 – 27.50	5	5	60	8.3	8.3	100.0
27.50 – 32.50	10	15	55	16.7	25.0	91.7
32.50 – 37.50	10	25	45	16.7	41.7	75.0
37.50 – 42.50	12	37	35	20.0	61.7	58.3
42.50 – 47.50	10	47	23	16.7	78.4	38.3
47.50 – 52.50	8	55	13	13.3	91.7	21.6
52.50 – 57.50	4	59	5	6.7	98.4	8.3
57.50 – 62.50	1	60	1	1.6*	100.0	1.6
	60			100.0		

* A rounding adjustment was made on this figure to bring the total to 100.0 per cent.

desirable to make comparisons among the individual stores. Percentage figures would facilitate such comparisons, particularly if the store-unit sizes varied a good deal. Cumulative and percentage frequencies may be used with open-ended distributions as well as with distributions of varying interval widths.

2.7   The Histogram, Frequency Polygon, and Ogive

The *histogram* is a type of graph based on the data given in a frequency distribution. An example of a histogram is shown in Illustration 2.1.

Illustration 2.1   The Histogram (from Data of Table 2.8)

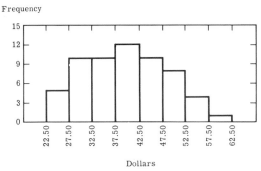

The histogram is similar in appearance to a bar chart (where importance is shown by the height of a "bar" on the graph) except that in the histogram the bars are adjoining. In the histogram the horizontal axis shows the class boundaries while the vertical axis provides the arithmetic scale for measuring frequencies. The horizontal axis is marked off in such manner as to permit the width of one class interval on either side of the end columns, while the vertical axis is scaled to accommodate the interval having the highest frequency. The size of the graph itself is generally chosen on the basis of convenience in presenting the data.

It may be noted that each bar of the histogram encloses an area reflecting the product of class width and class frequency. Thus, the relative importance of each class interval is indicated by the area of the appropriate bar. For the distribution as a whole, the total frequencies in the distribution are represented by the total area of the bars comprising the histogram. The histogram provides a visual impression of the nature and characteristics of the frequency distribution it represents. That is, it indicates the relative importance of each class, the range of the distribution, and the approximate values occurring most and least frequently. The histogram has the same general advantages all well-designed charts possess: ease of comprehension, visual perception, and ability to summarize data.

The *frequency polygon* is constructed by use of the same general principles as were applied to the histogram: class boundaries are used and the width of one class interval on either side of the end classes is left open. The frequencies of each class interval are, however, plotted on the class midpoints, and the two "end" classes (which were purposely left open) are regarded as classes of zero frequency. Thus, the curve is plotted by first placing "dots" at the proper frequency height and midpoint of each class, including the two empty classes on either end. The dots are then connected with a series of straight lines as shown in Illustration 2.2.

Illustration 2.2   The Frequency Polygon (from Data of Table 2.8)

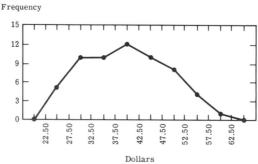

It should be observed that the more classes a frequency distribution possesses, the smoother the polygon becomes. Too, the curve itself suggests clearly the nature of the particular frequency distribution it represents. The area enclosed by the polygon reflects the total frequencies in the distribution. Although a discussion of frequency-curve types must be deferred until a later chapter, it may be noted here that the frequency polygon shown in Illustration 2.2, while not a particularly smooth curve, displays characteristics akin to the *normal curve*, which is of central importance in modern statistics. The normal curve will be considered in detail in Chapter 6 and will not be defined at this point. Suffice it to say at the moment that the frequency polygon is a first step in visualizing the characteristics of distributions which form a large part of our later statistical studies.

The *ogive* is a particular type of chart constructed from the cumulative frequency columns of the frequency distribution. To illustrate the ogive, observe the cumulative frequency columns of Table 2.8. There you will notice that the cumulative "less than" column indicates that 5 persons made less than \$27.50, 15 persons made less than \$32.50, 25 persons made less than \$37.50, and so on up to the final statement that all the part-time employees (60) made less than \$62.50. This information may be transferred to a chart in a way as to make clear the nature of the relationship between wages paid and numbers of persons. On an ogive chart these data will be known as the "less than" curve, shown in Illustration 2.3.

Illustration 2.3   The ogive (from Data of Table 2.8)

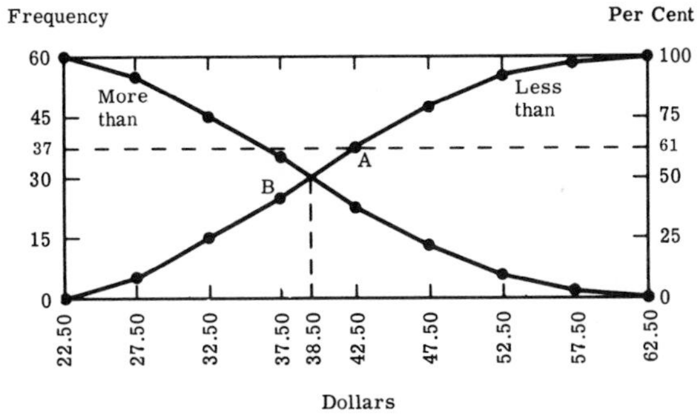

Exactly the same reasoning applies to the cumulative "more than" column. For example, there it may be observed that all part-time employees (60) made more than \$22.50, that 55 persons made more than \$27.50, and so on. This kind of information may be transferred to a chart, as illustrated by the "more than" curve in Illustration 2.3.

Before taking note of the general mechanics for constructing the ogive curves, it should be observed that presenting frequency distribution data in this form has the same set of advantages offered by any reasonable and well-constructed graph or chart. In other words, the ogive presents a visual impression of the shape of the data, provides for the interpolation of intermediate X and Y values (that is, values other than the class boundaries), and permits the interpolation of percentage values as well as the absolute frequency values. These points are shown in Illustration 2.3 and further elaborated in the list below.

Instructions for graphing the *ogive* are essentially the same as those employed for the histogram. Class boundaries are used but the X axis is scaled to allow for no more than the entire range of the class boundaries; the Y axis is designed to accommodate the total number of items in the distribution. Seen as a whole, the X or horizontal axis is used for the data, the Y or vertical axis for frequencies, and both are designed to allow the ogives to use up the entire vertical and horizontal distances. When the "less than upper limit" column is graphed, the frequency values are plotted *on the upper limit;* when the "more than lower limit" column is graphed, frequency values are plotted *on the lower limit.* The resulting dots for each ogive are then connected with straight lines. Some of the significant features of the ogive may be summarized as follows:

1. Notice that the information contained in Table 2.8 is conveniently summarized in graphic form by the ogive. The ogive therefore permits ready interpolation by those who understand its use.

2. Observe point A on the chart: this point reveals that 37 employees made less than \$42.50 and, when we read the right-hand scale, reveals that about 61 per cent of the wages were less than \$42.50. Other values can readily be interpolated.

3. Observe that the greater the slope of the line, the more rapidly the frequencies are changing. To illustrate: between points B and A the slope of the "less than" line is at its maximum gradient and indicates that this class contains the greatest number of frequencies.

4. The two ogives intersect at the 50 per cent grid. The type of construction requires that ogives intersect at this point. If a perpendicular be dropped from the intersection to the X axis (see dashed line), the value of the *median* may be interpolated. The median is defined as a value such that one-half of the items appear on either side of that value. Here the median is \$39.50.

5. If the two ogives intersect at the midpoint of the X axis, the distribution may be considered symmetric. If the ogives intersect to the left of the midpoint of the X axis, the distribution is out of symmetry—that is, it is "skewed" to the right. The word *skewness* means lack of symmetry. If the frequencies tend to "tail out" (slope more gently) towards the right of the graph, the skewness is said to be to the right, or positive. This is the situation in Illustration 2.3. Should the ogive curves intersect to the right of the X-axis midpoint, the distribution is skewed to the left or negative.

In the ogives of Illustration 2.3, the skewing effect may be seen both by observing the position of the point of intersection and by noting the fact that the two curves slope more gently (tail out) on the right-hand side of the chart. This distribution is therefore skewed moderately to the right.

The important features of the histogram, the frequency polygon, and the ogive may be summarized as follows.

1. In the histogram, the area of each bar is the product of class width and frequency. Thus, the area of the bar indicates the relative importance of the class it represents. If the class intervals of a histogram were unequal, it would be necessary to judge the importance of each class by comparing the area of that class to the total area of the histogram. However, when class intervals are equal, the relative importance of each class depends only upon the frequency because area will be proportional to frequency in all classes. Thus, in the case of equal class intervals, visual inspection clearly reveals the relative heights of the bars, and the importance of each class may be readily determined by the height of the bar alone.

2. In the frequency polygon, the total area under the envelope is equal to the total area of the histogram constructed from the same data (assuming an identical scale has been used for both illustrations).

3. The histogram may be constructed from either continuous or discrete data. The frequency polygon—which involves a smoothing process—would be incorrect for types of data involving discontinuities of great magnitude.

4. The ogive is of particular use for interpolation of values other than those appearing at the class limits. Interpolation, however, must be approached cautiously if the data involve discontinuities of great magnitude.

5. Frequency polygons, histograms, and ogives are simply graphic methods of presenting data. As such they have the advantages and disadvantages of graphic methods in general: ease of comprehension, visual perception, ability to summarize data and sometimes to oversimplify data. The ogive particularly is a somewhat complicated type of presentation for those not skilled in statistical techniques.

Exercise 2.3. The histogram, frequency polygon, and ogive. *Instructions:* For each of the following distributions, construct (1) a histogram, (2) a frequency polygon, and (3) a "more than" and a "less than" ogive curve.
Problem 1:

Class Limits	f	Cumulative Less Than Upper Limit	Cumulative More Than Lower Limit
10.0 – 10.4	3		
10.5 – 10.9	5		
11.0 – 11.4	8		
11.5 – 11.9	14		
12.0 – 12.4	20		
12.5 – 12.9	25		
13.0 – 13.4	20		
13.5 – 13.9	14		
14.0 – 14.4	8		
14.5 – 14.9	5		
15.0 – 15.4	3		
	125		

Problem 2:

Class Limits	f	Cumulative Less Than Upper Limit	Cumulative More Than Lower Limit
.05 – .09	8		
.10 – .14	14		
.15 – .19	25		
.20 – .24	40		
.25 – .29	55		
.30 – .34	60		
.35 – .39	53		
.40 – .44	38		
.45 – .49	27		
.50 – .54	13		
.55 – .59	7		
	340		

Problem 3:

Class Limits	f	Cumulative Less Than Upper Limit	Cumulative More Than Lower Limit
22 but under 25	5		
25 " " 28	10		
28 " " 31	14		
31 " " 34	22		
34 " " 37	15		
37 " " 40	12		
40 " " 43	8		
43 " " 46	4		
	90		

Problem 4:

Class Limits	f	Cumulative Less Than Upper Limit	Cumulative More Than Lower Limit
Over 7.5 and including 9.5	30		
" 9.5 " " 11.5	45		
" 11.5 " " 13.5	70		
" 13.5 " " 15.5	90		
" 15.5 " " 17.5	70		
" 17.5 " " 19.5	45		
" 19.5 " " 21.5	30		.
	380		

Questions about Problem 1

1. Should the true class limits or the stated class limits be used in graphing this distribution? Why?
2. From your histogram does this distribution appear symmetrical?
3. Does the appearance of the polygon differ appreciably from that of the histogram with respect to skewness?
4. From the ogive, determine the value of the median.
5. Do the "more than" and "less than" curves intersect at the 50 per cent level?
6. Thirty per cent of the frequencies are less than what value?
7. There are 82 items which exceed what value?
8. What is the median frequency?
9. There are 20 items which exceed what value?
10. What per cent of the frequencies are less than a value of 13.65?
11. What per cent of the frequencies have a value less than 11.55?
12. Do the curves intersect at the midpoint of the middle class interval?
13. Why is it that the two curves intersect at the 50 per cent level but do not necessarily meet at the midpoint of the midclass interval?
14. Seventy-five per cent of the frequencies are below what value? Above what value?

Questions about Problem 2

1. From the appearance of the histogram does this distribution appear symmetrical?
2. Is symmetry (or lack of symmetry) determined more readily from the histogram or from the polygon?
3. Do you feel that the histogram presents an accurate, easy-to-grasp picture of the distribution?

4. If the horizontal scale were "stretched," would the histogram present an accurate visual picture?

5. From the ogive, determine the value of the median.

6. Do the "more than" and "less than" curves intersect at the 50 per cent level?

7. Do the two curves intersect at the midpoint of the middle class interval?

8. If these curves intersect to the right of the midclass midpoint, the distribution is said to be skewed to the _____ or _____ skewed.

9. The farther to the right (or left) the curves intersect, the greater the degree of _____ in the distribution.

10. Twenty-five per cent of the frequencies are less than what value?

11. What is the median frequency?

12. There are 224 items less than what value?

13. What per cent of the frequencies are less than a value of .260?

14. What per cent of the frequencies have a value less than .475?

15. How many frequencies have a value more than .125?

16. How many of the frequencies are above the value of .395? How many frequencies are below that value? What is the sum of these two frequencies? Why?

Questions about Problem 3

1. What are the appropriate class limits to be used in plotting the histogram?

2. From the polygon does this distribution appear skewed? If so, in what direction is the skewness?

3. From the ogive determine the value of the median.

4. How many frequencies are less than a value of 39? More than 39?

5. What per cent of the frequencies have a value less than 39? More than 39?

6. Twenty-five per cent of the frequencies are less than what value?

7. What is the median frequency?

8. Eighty per cent of the frequencies are less than what value?

9. Sixty per cent of the frequencies are more than what value?

10. What per cent of the frequencies have a value of less than 40 per cent?

11. Can you discover, by observing the slope of the curves at various points, where the frequencies are the greatest? Explain.

12. As you observe the ogive, can you discover whether or not the distribution is skewed? If the distribution is skewed, is it greatly skewed? In what direction is the skewness?

Questions about Problem 4 (These questions concern only the ogive.)

1. What is the median frequency?

2. What is the value of the median?

3. Is this distribution skewed? Is it greatly skewed? In what direction?

4. Why is it that the two curves do not, in this distribution, intersect at the midpoint of the midclass interval?

5. What percentage of the items have a value of 18.9 or more?

6. How many items have a value of less than 11.1?

7. What percentage of frequencies are below a value of 12.1?

8. How many items have a value of less than 18.5? More than 18.5? What is the sum of these frequencies? Why?

9. Seventy-five per cent of the items are less than what value?

10. Twenty-five per cent of the items are more than what value?

11. There are 300 items with a value of less than what?

12. There are 120 items with a value of more than what?

2.8 Summary

The frequency distribution is an extremely useful technique for presenting, refining, and summarizing statistical information. The central principle employed is that of grouping—that is, classification. Beginning with the raw data of the problem and continuing through the array and the final distribution, a number of general organizational and arithmetic principles are employed to assure reasonably accurate and useful results. This chapter has been concerned with these principles, the reasons for their existence, and their usefulness in statistical analysis.

The frequency distribution is of considerable value to the student of business and economics, not only because it is interesting of itself, but because certain types of knowledge and understanding of the economic environment depend, in part, on information made available through this type of presentation.

It may be noted that economic statistics will frequently utilize uneven class intervals and open-end classes because of the nature of the data. Since a large portion of economic information must deal with such variables as income, assets, sales, and other data in which economic size (money value) is a central factor, distributions will rarely skew to the left; they will generally tend either to skew to the right or to be symmetric. Too, since economic size may range to millions and billions of dollars, uneven class intervals are used to accommodate the wide range of the variable. In many cases of economic measurement, an open-end class at the high values of the variable is necessary to limit the distribution to reasonable size. Thus, when economic information occurs in frequency-distribution form, it will not necessarily reflect all the ideals of construction as viewed in this chapter. However, the distributions will conform to the general principles as set forth herein, and frequency distributions must be regarded as being among the most useful techniques for handling certain types of economic information. The frequency distribution is also of immense value in describing sampling results. This is pointed out at length in later chapters.

A considerable amount of internally generated information (that is, internal to the firm itself) may be expressed in frequency-distribution form. We have, for example, referred to the measurement of length (length of parts) earlier in this chapter. Data of this type tend to yield somewhat more "ideal" distributions with even class intervals and with all classes closed. Such data tend to approximate the theoretical distributions to be studied in later chapters.

Subsequent chapters will continue to employ the concepts of a frequency distribution developed herein and will present additional uses of the frequency distribution. Perhaps it is not too much to say that the frequency distribution is a central concept in the entire study of statistics. Many concepts to be developed subsequently will depend upon a knowledge of the frequency distribution. Among these concepts are probability, the binomial and normal distributions, sampling, statistical inference, and statistical tests. All of these concepts and measures will be taken up in later chapters.

Key Terms and Concepts of This Chapter

Raw data	Midpoint
Frequency, item	Empty classes
Range of the variable	Open-ended classes
Continuous variable	Class interval
Discrete variable	Frequency polygon
Methods of rounding numbers	Histogram
(a) nearest unit	Cumulative frequencies
(b) last completed unit	Median
(c) next higher unit	Skewness
Array	Universe or population
Stated class limits	Ogive
Class boundaries	N = Number of items in the
Grouped data	distribution
Set	

Exercise 2.4.   *General questions about the frequency distribution.*

1. Which of the following are discrete variables and which are continuous variables? If under some conditions the variable could be either discrete or continuous, give an explanation.
   (a) pounds.
   (b) watts.
   (c) magazine articles.
   (d) board feet (lumber).
   (e) chairs.
   (f) windows.
   (g) temperature.
   (h) parts inspected.
   (i) postage stamps.
   (j) cost of postage.

2. What accomplishments are normally achieved by grouping data into a frequency distribution?

3. Given that a certain set of data has a range of 70, the number of items is 800. About how many class intervals should this distribution contain, and how wide should they be?

4. Criticize the following distribution:

Class Interval	f
8 – 9.0	16
9 – 10	2
11 – 12	0
12 – 13	150
13 – 14	50
14 – 17	30
18 – 22	90

5. Under what conditions are open-end intervals useful?

6. Under what conditions are unequal class intervals useful?

7. How should class limits be written when the data are in whole numbers?

8. If you are given a distribution in which you find the class intervals written as "12.30 but under 12.40," what are you to assume about the accuracy of the measurements?

9. Explain, using a diagram if desirable, why the areas under the envelope of the frequency polygon and histogram would actually be equal.

10. What is meant by the term "skewed distribution"?

11. When a distribution is skewed, how does this appear in the ogive "more than lower limit" curve?

12. Given the following distribution. Assume that this is a study of the actual time employees spend at their jobs per week—that is, the limits represent a 40-hour week minus time spent at the lunch counter, water cooler, reporting late, leaving early, and so on.

	f	"Less Than"	"More Than"	Percentage Frequencies
30 hr and under 31 hr	1	1	90	1.1
31 " " 32	4	5	89	4.4
32 " " 33	5	10	85	5.6
33 " " 34	9	19	80	10.0
34 " " 35	16	35	71	17.8
35 " " 36	30	65	55	33.3
36 " " 37	13	78	25	14.4
37 " " 38	7	85	12	7.8
38 " " 39	4	89	5	4.4
39 " " 40	1	90	1	1.1
	90			99.9*

* Total does not add to 100.0 because of rounding.

(a) What is the range of the variate?

(b) What value (if any) occurs most frequently?

(c) How many persons were at their jobs more than 38 hours per week?

(d) How many persons were at their jobs less than 30 hours per week?

(e) What percentage of persons were at their job more than 35.5 hours per week?

(f) If you were to pick any employee at random, the chances would be greatest that you would pick an employee in what interval?

(g) Does this distribution suggest the employees here are any worse or any better than employees elsewhere? Why?

(h) Someone makes the statement, after observing this distribution, that the employees are not putting forth "too much" effort. What might be said in an objective reply?

(i) If this same survey were to be made again one month later, would the results be likely to be the same? What factors might be operating in this situation?

13.   Given the following set of class limits: 0 – 2, 3 – 5, 6 – 8.

(a) What is the width of the class interval?

(b) Give the class boundaries for the first class.

(c) What is the midpoint of the third class?

Exercise 2.5.   *Constructing the frequency distribution from an array.* The following values are in the form of an array taken from a sample in which the measurements were made to the nearest hundredth of an inch. Construct a frequency distribution which, following good rigid practice, best represents the data.

.01	.16	.23	.27	.31	.35	.37	.40	.43	.45	.48	.53	.59	.68
.02	.17	.23	.29	.32	.35	.37	.40	.44	.45	.48	.53	.59	.69
.03	.17	.23	.29	.32	.35	.37	.40	.44	.45	.48	.53	.59	.69
.04	.17	.24	.29	.32	.35	.37	.40	.44	.45	.48	.53	.59	.69
.05	.17	.24	.29	.32	.35	.37	.40	.44	.45	.48	.53	.59	.71
.06	.17	.25	.29	.32	.35	.37	.40	.44	.46	.48	.53	.60	.71
.06	.18	.25	.29	.32	.35	.37	.40	.44	.46	.50	.53	.60	.72
.07	.18	.25	.29	.32	.35	.37	.40	.44	.46	.50	.53	.60	.72
.07	.19	.26	.30	.32	.36	.37	.41	.44	.46	.50	.53	.61	.73
.09	.20	.26	.30	.32	.36	.37	.41	.44	.46	.50	.56	.61	.73
.10	.20	.26	.30	.33	.36	.37	.41	.44	.46	.50	.56	.62	.75
.10	.20	.26	.30	.33	.36	.39	.41	.44	.46	.50	.56	.62	.75
.11	.20	.26	.30	.33	.36	.39	.41	.44	.46	.51	.56	.62	.76
.11	.21	.26	.30	.33	.36	.39	.41	.44	.46	.51	.56	.63	.77
.12	.21	.26	.30	.33	.36	.39	.41	.44	.46	.51	.56	.63	
.12	.21	.27	.31	.33	.36	.39	.41	.44	.47	.51	.56	.63	
.13	.21	.27	.31	.33	.36	.39	.43	.45	.47	.51	.57	.64	
.14	.21	.27	.31	.33	.36	.39	.43	.45	.47	.51	.57	.64	
.14	.22	.27	.31	.33	.36	.39	.43	.45	.47	.52	.57	.64	
.15	.22	.27	.31	.33	.36	.40	.43	.45	.47	.52	.57	.65	
.15	.22	.27	.31	.33	.37	.40	.43	.45	.47	.52	.57	.65	
.15	.22	.27	.31	.33	.37	.40	.43	.45	.47	.52	.57	.65	
.16	.22	.27	.31	.35	.37	.40	.43	.45	.47	.52	.57	.68	
.16	.23	.27	.31	.35	.37	.40	.43	.45	.48	.52	.57	.68	

Exercise 2.6. *Constructing a frequency distribution from a frequency table.* The following values are in the form of a frequency table. The measurements were taken as deviations from a "norm" in the case of a machine which was out of proper adjustment. The measurements were rounded to the next higher unit.

X	f	X	f	X	f	X	f
.674	2	.608	5	.560	4	.510	9
.670	3	.605	4	.558	7	.505	7
.660	2	.600	3	.555	8	.500	7
.665	2	.597	4	.550	3	.495	4
.650	1	.595	4	.549	7	.490	3
.649	2	.590	5	.545	7	.480	3
.645	3	.587	6	.540	8	.475	2
.640	3	.585	4	.535	8	.472	2
.632	4	.580	5	.533	10	.465	2
.628	3	.575	5	.530	9	.460	2
.620	4	.573	6	.525	11	.455	2
.613	5	.570	5	.520	7	.440	2
.610	4	.565	7	.514	8	.430	2

Bibliography

Bowen, Earl K., *Statistics, With Applications in Management and Economics*, chap. 4, Homewood, Ill.: Richard D. Irwin, Inc., 1960.

Croxton, Frederick E., and Dudley J. Cowden, *Applied General Statistics*, 2nd ed., chap. 8, Englewood Cliffs, N.J.: Prentice-Hall, Inc., 1955.

——————, *Practical Business Statistics*, 3rd ed., chap. 15. Englewood Cliffs, N.J.: Prentice-Hall, Inc., 1960.

Freund, John E., and Frank J. Williams, *Modern Business Statistics*, chap. 2. Englewood Cliffs, N.J.: Prentice-Hall, Inc., 1958.

Mills, Frederick C., *Statistical Methods*, 3rd ed., chap. 3. New York: Holt, Rinehart & Winston, Inc., 1955.

Neiswanger, William Addison, *Elementary Statistical Methods*, rev. ed., chap. 8 New York: The Macmillan Company, 1956.

Neter, John, and William Wasserman, *Fundamental Statistics for Business Economics*, chap. 6. Boston: Allyn and Bacon, Inc., 1962.

Smith, C. Frank, and D. A. Leabo, *Basic Statistics for Business Economics*, chap. 2. Homewood, Ill.: Richard D. Irwin, Inc., 1964.

Tuttle, Alva, M., *Elementary Business and Economic Statistics*, chap. 9. New York: McGraw-Hill Book Company, 1957.

3 MEASURES OF CENTRAL TENDENCY

3.1 Introduction

In Chapter 2 the frequency distribution was described as a means of classifying and summarizing large masses of data according to a specific set of rules. The resulting distribution provided a means of describing the pattern which emerged as the outcome of grouping many separate measurements of a variable according to the rules for grouping.

The present chapter will carry the process of summarization and condensation of the data closer to its logical conclusion. In short, measures of central tendency will now be developed which are of assistance in further refining the data. These measures, primarily the *mean, median*, and *mode*, will help make it possible to compare one set of data with another where, logically, such comparability exists. Measures of central tendency also make it possible to compare an actual (empirical) set of data with known standard distributions such as the normal and binomial distributions. The latter are the subjects of a subsequent chapter.

The statistics to be met in the present chapter are known as *measures of central tendency* because, as the term implies, they provide information about the middle or center of the data. Measures of central tendency are considered to be *typical* or *representative* values for the set of data as a whole. In a manner of speaking, measures of central tendency stand in place of all the individual items in the distribution. The next chapter will develop measures which provide information about the ends of the data, or more correctly, about the *dispersion* or *scatter* of the data. In essence the present chapter continues to pursue the objective of refining sets of empirical data to types of information which, in a brief but highly understandable manner, describe the important informational features of that data and make useful comparisons and other kinds of derived information possible.

Usefulness in Decision-Making

In the making of decisions or in the process of experimentation and research it is often of utmost importance to know the *average* value of a variable. For example, a sales manager may need to know the average number of calls made per day by salesmen in the field. The manager of an automobile fleet may need to know the average number of miles traveled per week or per month by the autos in the fleet in order to determine proper maintenance, insurance, and trade-in policies. A railroad official will require information regarding the average number of passengers carried per car on the various passenger runs. Likewise this official will want to know the average number of miles each passenger is carried on the various trains.

In all of these situations responsible officials will be assisted in decision-making by timely information. From this information they may wish to establish firm decision rules of general applicability. In other words, a sales manager might make it a rule to automatically call in a salesman for a personal interview whenever his weekly number of calls drops below the average for three consecutive weeks. Or, the fleet manager may decide to reallocate the automobiles among personnel whenever the actual individual automobile mileage drops below the fleet average for four consecutive weeks. In these situations, the responsible officials are enabled to keep abreast of changing developments, to watch for irregularities or for more fundamental changes which may be signaled by changes in average values, and subsequently to take appropriate action.

To illustrate certain points of particular importance in this chapter, suppose we further elaborate the fleet manager's situation. Assume he has a fleet of 100 passenger autos in use. Each week mileages are recorded and delivered to the fleet manager. Some automobiles will show zero mileage because of breakdowns and the like. At the end of a year, 5,200 mileage values will have been recorded. Suppose these values are grouped into a frequency distribution and, when drawn in polygon form, the graphic result of Illustration 3.1 is obtained. (Observe that the polygon has been smoothed.)

The fleet manager now has information as to the *range* of miles fleet autos are driven per week—that is, from 0 to 1,200 miles. He can observe from the distribution which values occur most frequently (the *modal* value) and also how the frequencies taper off on each side of the modal value. The fleet manager knows that the *average* number of miles each auto is driven per week is 575 and that only a very few autos will be driven more than 1,000 miles per week or less than 200 miles per week. He also discovers that one-half the autos are driven less than 550 miles, while one-half

Illustration 3.1   Frequency Curve for a Distribution of 5,200 Mileage Values for a Fleet of Passenger Autos Driven by a Firm's Salesmen

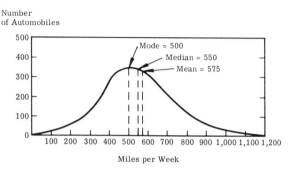

are driven more than 550 miles. The figure of 550 miles is the *median* value. In other words, given this kind of information, the fleet manager has an accurate picture of the performance of the autos, and when this information is related to other types of information—such as the area of the sales and delivery territory and the general policies of the company with respect to sales techniques—a clear picture of the position of the fleet's operation emerges. Too, higher levels of management are enabled to decide broad policies because they have accurate and timely information at hand.

3.2   Symbols Employed in This Chapter

The following symbols are used in the present chapter:

A and B = special terms used in calculating the mode. See Section 3.9.

c = a correction factor.

f = frequency. May also be used to designate the frequency column.

f_c = cumulative frequency. The meaning is further elaborated in Section 3.7.

i = the width of a class interval.

i_m = the width of the median class. See Section 3.7.

Med = median.

Mo = mode.

N = the total number of items (frequencies) in a given set of data.

Q_1 = first quartile.

Q_3 = third quartile.

P_n = percentile. The subscript indicates the particular percentile. Thus, P_{10} is the tenth percentile; P_{15} is the fifteenth percentile, and so on.

w = a weight.

X = one value of the variable or, in a general sense, the X variable.

$\bar{X}$ = the arithmetic mean of a set of X values.

$\bar{X}'$ = an assumed mean (origin).

x = an arithmetic deviation measured along the X axis, as $x = X - \bar{X}$.

x' = an arithmetic deviation measured along the X axis, but from an assumed origin, as $x' = X - \bar{X}'$.

Σ = an operational symbol meaning "take the sum of." For example, ΣX means add the X items to find their sum. Σ is the Greek capital letter *sigma*.

3.3   The Arithmetic Mean

One of the simplest and most valuable, yet most easily abused concepts in statistics is the simple arithmetic *average* or *mean*. It would seem that everyone has a notion of the term "average," but few would know much more than the general technique of calculation. Our purpose here will be to explore in depth this highly useful concept, for perhaps no single "statistic" has more applicability and is more widely used than the arithmetic mean.

The general formula for the arithmetic mean (or average) is

$$\bar{X} = \frac{\Sigma X}{N}.$$

When an average $\bar{X}$ (read X-bar) is quoted, it is stated as a number. For example, in a particular problem the mean might be 15. The mean value quoted may be used to represent all items in the set from which that average was derived. By way of example, in the set of numbers 8, 10, 13, 15, 20, and 24, the $\Sigma X = 90$, $N = 6$, and $\bar{X}$ is 15. To quote an average (or mean) value is a means of simplifying information by stating only one number, a number which is believed to be representative of all the values in the original set. The term "representative" is used to suggest that the average is so similar to the numbers in the set that it may serve as a typical example of those numbers. However, the mean value of a set of numbers will be typical only if the numbers themselves are clustered close to that central value. Thus, if the set of data is 8, 10, 13, 15, 20, 24, and 120, the $\bar{X}$ is 30. The question now raised is whether or not 30 is a representative value. In this case 30 is not particularly representative, even though it is a perfectly good arithmetic mean. Whether the mean can be considered typical or representative of a set of data is in the final analysis a matter of informed and careful judgement. In problems where the data clearly cluster around the mean, the mean is a typical value.

When the mean is stated, any variations among the original numbers in the data are ignored as are the original numbers themselves, since only the mean is quoted. Because all are submerged into one, the one value quoted must represent all those items whose identity is now lost in the averaging process.

The set of data from which the mean or average is derived must be cohesive; that is, there must be a common bond between the items of the set. For example, all items must represent wages paid to a specific group of people defined in a rigorous manner; or all items must represent miles per week per auto, and so on. To take an average of "rabbits and horses" would under ordinary conditions be meaningless.

There are other limitations to the use of the arithmetic average. It is not appropriate for all types of problems requiring a central value. The median and the mode are appropriate under particular circumstances. These matters will be further examined in later sections of this chapter.

Two major arithmetic features of the mean help make clear the concept of an average. (1) The mean is a value such that the algebraic sum of the deviations of the items from that mean value is always zero. (2) The mean of a group of items is a value such that it may be substituted for each of the items in the group without changing the sum of the items. The two examples of Illustrations 3.2 and 3.3 (purposely made extremely simple) will clarify these points.

Illustration 3.2   Computation of the Mean

X	x Deviations
6	-4
7	-3
9	-1
11	$+1$
13	$+3$
14	$+4$
60	0

$$\bar{X} = \frac{60}{6} = 10$$

or, expressed as a formula,

$$\bar{X} = \frac{\Sigma X}{N},$$

where $\bar{X}$ = the arithmetic mean,
$\quad x$ = an arithmetic deviation from the mean,
$\quad N$ = the number of items in the set,
$\quad \Sigma$ = the operational symbol *sigma*, meaning "take the sum of."

Illustration 3.3 Substitution of the Mean for Individual Items

$$X$$
$$10$$
$$10$$
$$10$$
$$10$$
$$10$$
$$10$$
$$\overline{}$$
$$60$$

or, $\qquad N\bar{X} = \Sigma\, X.$

Note that if a constant be added to (or subtracted from) each X item, the mean will be increased (or decreased) by the value of the constant. The student should try adding and subtracting 5 from each X value of Illustration 3.2 and calculating the mean. Note, too, that if each X item be multiplied by a constant, the mean will also be multiplied by that amount.

In considering the mean it should be noted that each X item bears a unique relationship to its own mean. In the set of X values, 6, 7, 9, 11, 13, and 14, the mean is calculated as $\bar{X} = 10$. If the X values be shown in relation to each other and to their mean by locating them on the X axis (the abscissa) they will appear as in Illustration 3.4. The value $X = 6$ is located -4 units from the mean; the value $X = 7$ is located -3 units from the mean, the value $X = 11$ is located $+1$ unit from the mean, and so on. The values -4, -3, -1, $+1$, $+3$, and $+4$ can be regarded as "deviations" of the X items from their mean value. Arithmetically, the deviation (x) can be defined as

$$x = X - \bar{X},$$

where $X =$ an item of the group,
$\qquad \bar{X} =$ the mean of the X items,
$\qquad x =$ arithmetic deviation.

Referring to Illustration 3.4, it can be observed that *if the deviations be considered as a whole*, their sum must necessarily be zero. This indicates

Illustration 3.4 Arithmetic Deviations of the X Values of the Data in Illustration 3.2

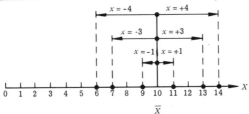

that the arithmetic mean is a value such that it divides the deviations of a set of data into two equal (negative and positive) parts. Too, the deviations represent a change of scale from the original location of X items with reference to the zero point on the abscissa to a scale for locating the X items with reference to their own mean.

The term *deviation* as used in the context of statistics is of such importance that its meaning and implication ought to be quite clear. In a very general sense deviation implies a "turning away" from the correct or proper path or course. However, the concept of an arithmetic deviation implies two essential factors: (1) an origin or reference point and (2) another point or object located some distance from the origin. Since it is customary to regard the reference point as the "origin" or "true" value, the second point or object is said to be deviating from the first. The amount of deviation is expressed as the difference—measured in units standard to the problem—between two values. For illustrative purposes we can think of an object lying on an X scale and to the left of a point of reference on that scale. The object then displays a negative deviation from the point of reference (origin). If an object is located on the X scale and to the right of a point of reference on that scale, the object is said to have a positive deviation—expressed in the measurement units of the problem. Thus, if it can be said that the average income of factory workers is $110 per week, then a wage of $90 may be expressed as an income deviation of $-$20. A wage of $120 may be expressed as an income deviation of $10. A wage of $110 would represent a deviation of zero.

Exercise 3.1. Answer the following questions as indicated.
1. The average (or mean) value is generally considered to be a "typical" or "representative" value. Why should this be the case? Under what circumstances might the mean not be typical?
2. Why is it necessary that the mean be calculated from a set of cohesive data? Is it correct to say that the mean is calculated by simply adding a group of numbers and dividing by the number of items in the group?
3. Explain why $N\bar{X} = \Sigma X$.
4. Explain why $\Sigma x = 0$.
5. Define each of the following terms: deviation, origin, reference point. What simple formula may be used with X values to determine the numerical value of a particular deviation?

3.4   Calculation of the Arithmetic Mean

Ungrouped Data

Under ordinary circumstances the technical aspects of calculating the mean are unusually simple. A listing of numbers is supplied together with instructions to "find the mean." All that is required, of course, is to sum the items and divide that sum by the number of items in the group. This requires no further comment. However, because it will be most convenient to solve certain kinds of problems by use of methods which differ somewhat from the ordinary mean calculation, it will be desirable to illustrate the use of a method which may be called the "assumed-mean method." This procedure is sometimes also known as the "assumed-origin method."

Assumed-Mean Method

It has been observed that the algebraic sum of the arithmetic deviations from the true mean is zero. Consequently, if some value—other than the true mean—were taken as the reference point for measuring deviations, the sum of the deviations would not be zero.

Example. In the set of items given in Illustration 3.5(a) (purposely made extremely simple) "assume" the mean of the items is 5 and measure deviations (x') from this assumed mean ($\bar{X}'$).

Illustration 3.5(a) Calculation of Deviations from an Assumed Mean of 5

X	x'
1	-4
4	-1
3	-2
8	$+3$
	$\overline{-4}$

In this illustration note that the algebraic sum of the deviations is -4. Since this sum is not 0, the assumed mean is not the true mean. The minus sign indicates that the assumed mean exceeds the true mean.

The assumed mean of 5 may now be corrected to the true mean by use of a "correction factor" as follows:

$$\bar{X} = \bar{X}' + c \quad \text{and} \quad c = \frac{\Sigma\, x'}{N} \quad \text{or} \quad \frac{-4}{4} = -1 = c,$$

and finally, 5 (the assumed mean) minus 1 (the correction factor) equals 4, the true mean.

It is interesting to observe that when the mean of a set of data is determined by the ordinary technique of summation and division by N, the process is actually establishing an origin of zero from which each X value is measured [see Illustration 3.5(b)] and to which $\Sigma\ X/N$ is then added

Illustration 3.5(b)   Data of Illustration 3.5(a) Shown as Deviations from an Origin of 0

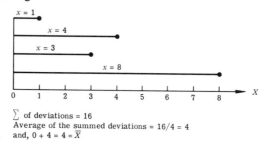

Σ of deviations = 16
Average of the summed deviations = 16/4 = 4
and, 0 + 4 = 4 = $\overline{X}$

to yield the proper mean value. In other words, one might think of the mean as ordinarily computed as representing a correction from an origin of zero.

When the assumed-mean method of calculation is used, any natural number may be selected as the origin. It is however, desirable to select an origin as close as possible to the true mean value because the $\Sigma\ x'$ will then be relatively small and the correction required to adjust the origin to the true mean will also be relatively small. Obviously, if an origin far removed from the true mean were selected, the correction would then be large. Likewise, if the origin selected were more positive than the true mean, the correction factor would be negative, and vice versa.

These points may be shown by using the data of Illustration 3.5(a) and visualizing the X items as (1) deviations from an origin of zero, as shown in Illustration 3.5(b), and (2) deviations from the arbitrary origin of $\overline{X}' = 5$, as shown in Illustration 3.6.

Illustration 3.6   Data of Illustration 3.5(a) Shown from an Arbitrary Origin of 5. Assumed-Origin Method of Mean Calculation

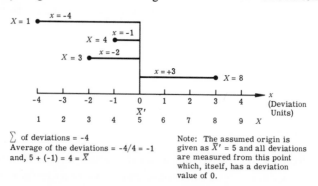

Σ of deviations = -4
Average of the deviations = -4/4 = -1
and, 5 + (-1) = 4 = $\overline{X}$

Note: The assumed origin is given as $\overline{X}' = 5$ and all deviations are measured from this point which, itself, has a deviation value of 0.

Exercise 3.2.   In the following practice problems you are to find the true mean by the "assumed-origin" method. (There is no restriction on the value you may assume. However, it is a good idea to select a mean which appears to be close to the true mean.) You should set up the problems as shown in the previous example.

1. 8	2. 16	3. 25	4. 42
7	18	31	51
6	23	37	56
3	12	22	48
4	19	35	59
9	20	26	39
2		27	43
1			38

5. 75	6. 155	7. 108.93	8. 1,156.2
63	120	115.74	1,324.2
84	156	99.17	1,429.4
65	178	105.34	1,265.3
77	132	110.62	2,018.3
92	147	98.25	2,136.4
	163	100.68	
	181	109.27	

9. Now go back to problems 1 and 2 above and draw graphs similar to Illustrations 3.5(b) and 3.6. When you have drawn the graph for the assumed-origin method of mean calculation, consider this question: How would your graph change and what would be the effect on the value of the deviations if you shifted the assumed mean to the left? To the right? Why?

10. In the usual manner of calculating the mean from ungrouped data, it may be said that zero is used as the origin. Explain.

3.5   The Weighted Average

A good many kinds of statistical information require knowledge of the concept of *weighting*. In its ordinary usage, the word "weight" refers to a sense of heaviness or to a sense of the "gravity" or importance of a particular thing or concept. From a statistical point of view the term is used to indicate the relative importance or frequency of the individual items in the data. To further illustrate these points, consider the distribution shown in Table 3.1. The classes in this distribution are of

Table 3.1

Class Limits	f
over 10 but under 11	15
over 11 but under 12	30
over 12 but under 13	40
over 13 but under 14	25
over 14 but under 15	10
	120

equal width, but the classes are clearly not of equal importance. The first class may be considered as having an importance equal to 15/120; the second class an importance of 30/120; the third class an importance of 40/120, and so on. The importance of each class is actually its "weight." In other words, in a frequency distribution of equal intervals, the frequencies of each class show the weight of that class. The role assigned to the various class frequencies is that of specifying how important each class is in the overall distribution.

Another way of looking at the concept of a "weight" can be illustrated as follows: Some of a student's college classes may be weighted at 5 credits, some at 3 credits, and some at 1 or 2 credits. In considering the relative importance of each class from the point of view of required classroom and study time, the student adjusts his schedule in accordance with the credit weight. Admittedly certain more subtle factors may enter this situation and cause him to readjust his personal evaluation of the importance or weight of classes from time to time, but the *principle of weighting* nevertheless holds.

By way of numerical illustration, suppose an extremely simple set of data is given as follows: 5, 6, and 10. If the instructions are to "find the mean," it is only necessary to sum the values and divide by three. This computation is ordinarily known as an "unweighted" average, because each item enters the calculation only once. An example is shown in Illustration 3.7. However, a more careful scrutiny of the problem reveals

Illustration 3.7   Calculation of the Mean (Equal Weights)

X	Weight w	wX
5	1	5
6	1	6
10	1	10
	3	21

$$\bar{X} = \frac{\Sigma wX}{\Sigma w} = \frac{21}{3} = 7$$

that it is not an unweighted average—each item has entered with a frequency (weight) of one. This point need not be labored because the problem is generally regarded as an unweighted average—even though technically an unweighted average is an impossibility. In an ordinary set of data (unweighted) the mean would be calculated without weights. However, Illustration 3.7 shows that weights are actually used although they are implicit in the ordinary method of summing the X values and dividing by N.

If the data employed in Illustration 3.7 were modified to include unequal weights for each of the items, the problem would then appear as in Illustration 3.8. Note that the item 5 has a weight of 4, the item 6 has a weight of 3, and the item 10 has a weight of 1. What this implies is that the original data were as follows: 5, 5, 5, 5, 6, 6, 6, 10. When the mean of this group of items is calculated, we might expect its value to differ from that of the mean in Illustration 3.7 because these are really two different problems. In Illustration 3.8 the "weighted" average is in fact

Illustration 3.8 Calculation of the Weighted Mean (Unequal Weights)

X	Weight w	wX
5	4	20
6	3	18
10	1	10
	8	48

$$\bar{X} = \frac{\Sigma wX}{\Sigma w} = \frac{48}{8} = 6$$

somewhat less than the "unweighted" average of Illustration 3.7 because of the greater emphasis placed on the smaller X values by associating them with the higher weights. Conversely, had the higher-valued items been associated with the higher weights, the mean would have shifted toward the higher values. Observe, too, that it is the *ratio of the weights* which determines the resulting mean; that is, the weights may be multiplied or divided by a constant without altering the value of the mean. This point will be illustrated in the problems of Exercise 3.3.

Assumed-Mean Method: Weighted Average

To employ the assumed-mean method of calculating the mean where the problem involves weighting, the technique shown in Table 3.2 may be utilized. The method is as follows.

Table 3.2

Computation of the Weighted Arithmetic Mean by Use of an Assumed Origin

X	w	x'	wx'
6	9	-3	-27
8	5	-1	-5
9	5	0	0
11	3	2	6
14	2	5	10
18	5	9	45
	29		29

The assumed origin is 9.
The correction factor is

$$c = \frac{\Sigma wx'}{\Sigma w} = \frac{29}{29} = 1.$$

The true mean is $\bar{X}' + c$, or $9 + 1 = 10$.

1. Select one of the X values to be the "assumed origin." It is reasonable to choose a value somewhat near one's estimate of the true mean.
2. Subtract the assumed mean from each X value and record the difference in the x' column (x' means the deviations are from an assumed mean).
3. Compute the products for wx' and find their sum. Note that in the illustration given in Table 3.2, this sum is 29.
4. Compute the correction factor as $\Sigma wx'/\Sigma w$. Thus, in the illustration, $29/29 = 1$.
5. Add the correction factor to the assumed mean to obtain the true mean. Thus in the illustration, $9 + 1 = 10 = \bar{X}$.

Observe that the mean of Table 3.2 could have been obtained by multiplying each X value by its appropriate weight, summing, and dividing by the sum of the weights. However, the purpose of the illustration is to portray a principle. While it is clear that the method utilizing an arbitrary origin would be of little value in simple problems, it can be an important time-saver in more complex situations. It is to be noted that in choosing an arbitrary origin for the mean, a new set of values measured by the x' scale (rather than an X scale) and shown in the x' column emerges, while the deviations around that arbitrary origin are then multiplied by the proper weight in order to yield the full deviation value. These deviations are then summed algebraically and divided by the sum of the weights. Since the arbitrary origin in Table 3.2 was other than the true mean, the sum of the wx' column was not zero. That is, from the arbitrary origin a positive accumulation (error) of 29 units occurs which must then be allocated among the 29 units of weight, yielding an average error of 1 unit (correction factor) which is then added to the assumed mean (9) to yield the true mean (10).

Exercise 3.3. *Instructions:* Find the weighted average in each of the following practice problems. Compare the weighted with the nonweighted averages. Calculate the means by the method shown in Illustration 3.8.

1.	X	w	2.	X	w	3.	X	w	4.	X	w
	4	1		4	9		7	2		13	9
	6	8		6	7		8	4		15	8
	8	5		8	5		12	10		18	2
	10	7		10	8		16	4		20	1
	12	9		12	1		20	2		25	0

5.	X	w	6.	X	w	7.	X	w
	30	10		30	1		12.5	1,000
	46	20		46	2		52.6	325
	51	30		51	3		61.8	565
	62	30		62	3		66.4	100
	74	20		74	2		66.6	50
	76	10		76	1			
	81	10		81	1			

8. The weights in problem 6 were derived by dividing the weights of problem 5 by a constant, 10. Since the X values were identical, although the absolute value of the weights changed, did the mean change? Why? Suppose you divided the weights of problem 7 by a constant (perhaps 5)— would the mean change? Could you divide or multiply the weights by any constant in a weighted-average problem without changing the mean?

9. Now apply the assumed-mean method as illustrated in Table 3.2 to problems 1 through 7.

10. Suppose the column heading of problems 1 through 7 were changed to read as follows: $X =$ the midpoints of the class intervals; $w =$ the frequency of each class. Would the calculation of the mean be altered in any way? Why?

3.6   Finding the Mean of a Frequency Distribution

The technique for computing the mean of a frequency distribution does not differ basically from that used with the weighted average. There are three varieties of this basic method. Method I as shown in Illustration 3.9 is a straightforward weighted-average type of computation and has the advantage that it can be used whether or not the class intervals are equal.

Illustration 3.9   Calculation of the Mean of a Frequency Distribution (Method I)

Class Intervals	Midpoint X	Frequency f	Frequency × Midpoint fx
$23 – 27	25	5	$125
28 – 32	30	10	300
33 – 37	35	10	350
38 – 42	40	12	480
43 – 47	45	10	450
48 – 52	50	8	400
53 – 57	55	4	220
58 – 62	60	1	60
		60	2,385

Calculations:

$$\bar{X} = \frac{\Sigma fx}{N} = \frac{2,385}{60} = \$39.75.$$

Note: This method may be used when class intervals are either equal or unequal.

A second method (Method II) for calculating the mean of a frequency distribution is useful when the class intervals are equal. Method II makes use of the even intervals and an assumed mean. Thus in Illustration 3.10

a zero is placed in the deviation column somewhere near the middle of the distribution. The zero indicates that the midpoint of the class is being selected as the arbitrary origin and all other midpoints are measured as deviations from that origin. Observe that the deviations are expressed as integers and are signed numbers. A minus deviation indicates a midpoint value lower than the arbitrary origin, while a plus deviation indicates a midpoint value higher than the arbitrary origin. Since an assumed origin is used, a correction factor must also be employed as indicated in the formulas given with Illustration 3.10.

Illustration 3.10 Calculation of the Mean of a Frequency Distribution (Method II)

Class Intervals	Mid-point X	Frequency f	Deviations in Class Intervals x'	fx'
$23 – 27	25	5	−2	−10
28 – 32	30	10	−1	−10
33 – 37	35	10	0	0
38 – 42	40	12	1	12
43 – 47	45	10	2	20
48 – 52	50	8	3	24
53 – 57	55	4	4	16
58 – 62	60	1	5	5
		60		57

Calculations:

$$c = \frac{\Sigma fx'}{N} i = \left(\frac{57}{60}\right)(5) = 4.75,$$

$$\bar{X} = \bar{X}' + c = \$35 + 4.75 = \$39.75$$

where c = a correction factor,
$\bar{X}'$ = an assumed origin,
x' = a deviation from an assumed origin measured in class intervals,
i = the width of a class interval, measured from boundary to boundary,
$\bar{X}$ = the true mean.

Note: This method may be used *only* when all class intervals are equal.

A third method (Method III) for calculating the mean from a frequency distribution is again identical to the weighted-average calculation, except that the frequencies are expressed in relative (decimal) terms. With this method each midpoint is multiplied by the corresponding relative frequency and all such values are then summed. The result is the mean of the distribution. This method, which may be used whether or not the intervals are equal, is shown in Illustration 3.11.

Illustration 3.11   Calculation of the Mean of a Frequency Distribution (Method III)

Class Intervals	Midpoint X	Frequency f	Relative Frequency f/N	Midpoint × Relative Frequency fx/N
$23 – 27	25	5	5/60 = .0833	2.0825
28 – 32	30	10	10/60 = .1667	5.0010
33 – 37	35	10	10/60 = .1667	5.8345
38 – 42	40	12	12/60 = .2000	8.0000
43 – 47	45	10	10/60 = .1667	7.5015
48 – 52	50	8	8/60 = .1333	6.6650
53 – 57	55	4	4/60 = .0667	3.6685
58 – 62	60	1	1/60 = .0167	1.0020
		60	60/60 = 1.0000	39.7550

The mean, as determined by the method of relative frequencies is $39.755. There is a slight error of .005 due to rounding.
Calculations:

$$\bar{X} = \Sigma \frac{fx}{N} = 39.755.$$

All terms remain as previously defined.

Note: This method may be used when class intervals are either equal or unequal.

The relative frequencies employed in the calculation of the mean in Method III are actually empirical probability values for the random variable X. The expression of relative frequencies in terms of probability will serve as the basis for statistical testing and decision-making in later applications. For the moment it is desirable to concentrate on methodology. The problems given in Exercise 3.4 will provide practice in the methods explained above.

Exercise 3.4.   *Calculating the mean of a frequency distribution.*   Sixteen problems are given below along with instructions as to the method to be used in calculating the mean. Assume that the X values refer to pounds of weight and are the midpoints of class intervals. The $f_1, \ldots, f_4$ columns are the frequencies associated with measurements taken at four different times.
Work the following problems by Method I.

	X_1	f_1	f_2	f_3	f_4
1. Mean $X_1 f_1 = ?$	12	4	7	10	12
	17	6	9	15	16
2. Mean $X_1 f_2 = ?$	22	9	12	20	25
3. Mean $X_1 f_3 = ?$	27	14	16	15	20
4. Mean $X_1 f_4 = ?$	32	10	10	10	18
	37	7	6	5	9

Work the following problems by Methods II and III.

X_2	f_1	f_2	f_3	f_4
6	4	3	10	1
8	8	5	16	5
10	12	6	20	10
12	15	10	22	16
14	12	7	14	18
16	8	6	7	8
18	6	4	6	2

5. Mean $X_2 f_1 = $?
6. Mean $X_2 f_2 = $?
7. Mean $X_2 f_3 = $?
8. Mean $X_2 f_4 = $?

Work the following problems by Methods I and III.

X_3	f_1	f_2	f_3	f_4
15	3	6	8	2
20	4	10	12	3
25	6	12	20	7
30	8	14	10	15
35	12	12	8	19
40	8	8	6	10
45	6	5	4	6
50	3	3	2	3

9. Mean $X_3 f_1 = $?
10. Mean $X_3 f_2 = $?
11. Mean $X_3 f_3 = $?
12. Mean $X_3 f_4 = $?

Work the following problems by Method II.

X_4	f_1	f_2	f_3	f_4
9	10	16	20	2
12	15	18	25	4
15	20	25	30	6
18	30	40	45	8
21	40	50	56	10
24	30	35	40	12
27	20	30	32	10
30	18	15	28	8
33	10	12	14	6
36	5	6	6	4
39	2	3	4	2

13. Mean $X_4 f_1 = $?
14. Mean $X_4 f_2 = $?
15. Mean $X_4 f_3 = $?
16. Mean $X_4 f_4 = $?

3.7 The Median

The median is defined as the *value of the middle item in an array or frequency distribution*. In other words, one-half of all items in the group are smaller in value and one-half are larger in value than the median. Thus, the median is an "average" in the sense that it occupies a "middle" position in the set of data. It might also be noted that one simply finds the median in the data. Nothing else need be done.

In the process of locating the median it is necessary that the data be either in the form of an array—that is, ranked from lowest to highest—or in the form of a frequency distribution, which is itself a form of arraying the data. To determine the value of the median from an array it is only necessary to count the items in the array by moving through their position values $(X_1, X_2, X_3, \ldots, X_n)$ until the middle item is located. The X value of the middle item is then recorded as the value of the median. If no middle item exists, the two central items are averaged arithmetically, and this value is then considered to be the median. Thus, in the set of X data 2, 3, 4 the median is 3. In the set of X data 2, 3, 4, 5 the median is 3.5.

Ungrouped Data

When the values of a set of data are discrete, the median is the value of the middle item. However, should the data be continuous, the median would not necessarily be an item; rather it would be a "point" so located that one-half the items were on either side of that point. To locate the position of the median item in a set of discrete data, it is general practice to use the relationship $(N + 1)/2$ to locate the item. If the data were continuous, it would be proper to use $N/2$ to locate the item. When the middle item of the array has been located, the second step is simply to observe and record its value. *This is the median.*

Illustration 3.12 Location of the Median in Ungrouped Data When N is Odd

X	(Position) Item Number
2	1
5	2
8	3

Step 1. Locate the median item by

$$\frac{N + 1}{2} = \frac{3 + 1}{2} = \text{item 2.}$$

Step 2. The value of item 2 is 5. Therefore the median $= 5$

Illustration 3.13 Location of the Median in Ungrouped Data When N is Even

X	(Position) Item Number
2	1
4	2
6	3
8	4

Step 1. Locate the median item by

$$\frac{N + 1}{2} = \frac{4 + 1}{2} = \text{item } 2\tfrac{1}{2}.$$

Step 2. Since the data are discrete, item $2\tfrac{1}{2}$ does not exist. Therefore it is necessary to average the values of items 2 and 3. Therefore, the median is

$$\frac{4 + 6}{2} = 5.$$

Grouped Data

To find the median in grouped data, the procedure is slightly more complicated. Since the individuality of the original items is lost in the grouping process, it is necessary to (1) find the position at which the median is located, and (2) determine the proper X value to be associated with that location. When data are grouped, it is assumed that a continuous distribution results. This is not strictly correct for all distributions; nevertheless the assumption is made. Therefore, to locate the middle item in the distribution, the total frequency is divided by 2. Note that $N + 1$ is not used. These points are shown by Illustration 3.14.

Illustration 3.14   Location of the Median in Grouped Data

Class Intervals	f	(Cumulative Frequency) f_c
23 – 27	5	5
28 – 32	10	15
33 – 37	10	25—Cumulative frequencies up to the median
38 – 42	12	37—Median class (class containing median item)
43 – 47	10	Note: Here it is not
48 – 52	8	necessary to cumulate
53 – 57	4	frequencies beyond the
58 – 62	1	median class.
	$\Sigma = 60$	

Step 1. To find the median in grouped data, divide the sum of the frequencies by 2. This will locate the middle item whose value is desired. The middle item is number 30 in this case.

Step 2. Locate the class interval containing the median item. This is accomplished by finding in the f_c column the class interval which contains the middle frequency—that is $N/2$.

Step 3. Apply the formula for the median of grouped data:

$$\text{Med} = L + \frac{\frac{N}{2} - f_c}{f_m} \, i_m = 37.50 + \frac{\frac{60}{2} - 25}{12} \times 5 = 39.58,$$

where L is the lower class boundary of the median class,
 f_c is the cumulative frequency up to the median class,
 f_m is the frequency of the median class,
 i_m is the width of the median class interval.

Use of the formula given in step 3 for determining the median assumes that the frequencies in the median class are distributed evenly throughout the class. Further, it is tacitly assumed that the frequencies in the entire distribution are distributed evenly throughout each class.[1]   This point is

---

[1] It is, of course, highly unlikely that the items in the original raw data would be so accommodating as to distribute themselves in such a neat pattern.

shown in Illustration 3.16 below. However, it will be desirable first to look at the theory of median location in the simplified sketch shown in Illustration 3.15. This sketch shows the theory behind the median formula. Thus, it may be seen that the formula for obtaining the median in grouped data is essentially a means of discovering proportionality—that is, for the grouped data of the problem above, the sketch shows that 5/12ths of $5 must be added to $37.50 to obtain the median value. Thus:

$$\$37.50 + 5/12\text{ths of }\$5 = \$39.58.$$

Illustration 3.15 The Theory of Median Location—Sketch Based on Data of Illustration 3.14

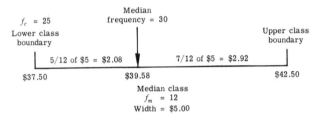

Using the data of Illustration 3.14 and observing only the median class to show the assumption of evenly distributed frequencies throughout the class, the result could be visualized in the detail shown in Illustration 3.16.

Illustration 3.16 Determination of the Median by Visual Example Employing the Data of Illustration 3.14

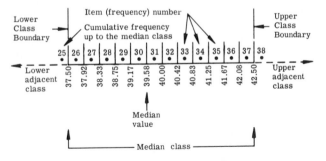

When locating the median item in grouped data, it is assumed the data are continuous. The appropriate median formula employs $N/2$ to locate the median point, from which the median class is then determined. Thus, in Illustration 3.15 and beginning with the lower class boundary of the median class, the median is located 5/12 of the distance between class boundaries. In Illustration 3.16 the locations of successive items in the class are shown as midpoints of the 12 smaller "classes" within the $5 interval. Because of the assumption that a frequency distribution is composed of continuous data, the median thus falls at the upper end of the interval containing item 30.

Brief Comments about the Median

The median is considered to be a highly useful tool in the business and economic statistician's tool box. For one thing, in sets of data which have a tendency to skewness—such as one generally finds with income data—the median is almost always a better measure of central tendency than the mean because the mean would be pulled in the direction of the extreme values.

In another sense, too, the median is often highly useful as a time saver because, when a central value is needed, the median can be obtained merely by finding the middle item.

Exercise 3.5. Find the median in the following practice sets of ungrouped data.

1.	2.	3.	4.	5.
10	24, 15	10, 25	55, 76	26, 14, 53
6	17, 18	14, 20	50, 85	28, 28, 58
4	12, 16	24, 22	20, 49	52, 31, 27
8	13, 20	21, 16	35, 31	64, 47, 31
1	25, 11	20, 11	45, 72	38, 60, 29
3	14, 10	21, 18	18, 28	79, 65, 17
2	28, 21	13, 13	27, 36	68, 18, 28
7			29, 39	69

Exercise 3.6 A filling station maintained records of the number of gallons of gasoline sold per auto on four consecutive Monday mornings between the hours of 7 and 10 A.M. The X_1 column represents the midpoints of class intervals measuring gallons of gasoline; the $f_1, \ldots, f_4$ columns represent the number of autos in each category for the four consecutive Mondays. Find the medians.

Class Boundaries	Midpoint X_1	f_1	f_{1_c}	f_2	f_{2_c}	f_3	f_{3_c}	f_4	f_{4_c}
	5	5		2		6		15	
	7	10		4		7		19	
	9	15		8		10		23	
	11	7		9		15		30	
	13	6		15		13		26	
	15	4		7		9		17	
	17	3		6		3		11	

1. Median $X_1 f_1 = ?$ 3. Median $X_1 f_3 = ?$
2. Median $X_1 f_2 = ?$ 4. Median $X_1 f_4 = ?$

Exercise 3.7. A manufacturer of a brand of wrapping string made a number of tests of the breaking strength in pounds as the production machinery was in the process of being adjusted. The X_2 column represents the breaking strength in pounds, and the $f_1, \ldots, f_4$ columns represent the four tests made after four consecutive adjustments of the equipment. Find the medians.

Class Boundaries	Midpoint X_2	f_1	f_{1_c}	f_2	f_{2_c}	f_3	f_{3_c}	f_4	f_{4_c}
	10	2		4		30		15	
	15	4		7		45		23	
	20	9		11		50		40	
	25	12		16		95		20	
	30	8		12		140		14	
	35	5		9		86		12	
	40	3		5		54		8	
	45	1		3		29		6	

1. Median $X_2 f_1 = ?$
2. Median $X_2 f_2 = ?$
3. Median $X_2 f_3 = ?$
4. Median $X_2 f_4 = ?$

Exercise 3.8
1. A manufacturer of flashlight batteries suspected that a product of one of his competitors was lacking in uniformity as measured by the length of time a battery would operate a bulb satisfactorily. A number of the batteries were purchased and tested. The midpoints of the hours of life are shown in the X column and the number of batteries falling in each category are shown in the frequency column. What is the median?

Class Boundaries	X	f	f_c
	2.5	12	
	3.5	16	
	4.5	23	
	5.5	31	
	6.5	28	
	7.5	20	
	8.5	14	
	9.5	10	

2. An agricultural experiment station planted a number of sunflower seeds and recorded the measurements of the height of growth attained after 10 days. The X column represents the midpoints in inches; the frequency column indicates the number of plants attaining the given height in inches. What is the median height?

Class Boundaries	X	f	f_c
	1.5	19	
	1.6	24	
	1.7	28	
	1.8	26	
	1.9	36	
	2.0	30	
	2.1	26	
	2.2	21	
	2.3	15	

3. A bottler of soft drinks states that the contents of each bottle is 8 ounces or more. The production machinery is set up in such manner as to assure that the contents will never fall below 8 ounces. However, the contents will exceed 8 ounces under these circumstances, and a study of the "overage" weight in ounces has been made. The results are shown below. The X column represents the midpoints of the overage weight in ounces; the frequency column indicates the number of bottles in each class. What is the median overage?

Class Boundaries	X	f	f_c
	.01	30	
	.02	45	
	.03	55	
	.04	70	
	.05	80	
	.06	71	
	.07	60	
	.08	48	
	.09	37	
	.10	28	

4. Researchers in a plywood veneer mill have experienced difficulty in obtaining a uniform thickness of veneer from a soft box-core wood used in some experiments. Repeated cuttings on their machines show the thickness in

thousandths of an inch as indicated by the midpoints in the X column, and the number of test cuttings at each thickness is shown in the frequency column. What is the median thickness of the veneer in this series of experiments?

Class Boundaries	X	f	f_c
	.005	12	
	.010	18	
	.015	21	
	.020	29	
	.025	32	
	.030	35	
	.035	30	
	.040	26	
	.045	19	
	.050	17	
	.055	12	
	.060	8	

3.8   Other Measures of Position

It is sometimes desirable to divide a distribution into more than two parts. When a distribution is divided into four parts, the partition values are called "quartiles." Five parts are known as "quintiles," ten parts as "deciles," and one hundred parts as "percentiles." Other measures may simply be referred to as, for example, "the eighth of twenty-five parts." Measures of position are sometimes known by the generic term "fractiles."

The method for finding partition values is exactly the same as that for finding the median. The following examples show how the formula for the median is modified to obtain any desired partition value:

$$\text{Med} = L + \frac{\frac{N}{2} - f_c}{f_m} i;$$

$$\text{First quartile} = L + \frac{\frac{N}{4} - f_c}{f_{Q_1}} i;$$

$$\text{Third quintile} = L + \frac{\frac{3N}{5} - f_c}{f_{quint_3}} i,$$

where i is the width of the class in question and the subscript for f in the denominator of the major fraction indicates the frequency of the class in question.

1. Observe that the denominator of the basic fraction (which is $N/2$ in the case of the median) represents the number of parts into which the distribution is to be divided.

2. The numerator of the basic fraction denotes the particular part of the distribution whose value is in question. For example, the *3rd* of 5 parts.

3. f_c is always the cumulative frequency *up to* the class interval containing the desired partition value.

4. The denominator of the major fraction (f_m in the case of the median) becomes the number of frequencies in the class containing the desired partition value.

5. In general, then, the formula for partition values is used for all fractiles, but appropriate modification must be made to yield the desired measure. Thus:
    (a) For the third quartile the basic fraction becomes $3N/4$.
    (b) For the second quintile the basic fraction becomes $2N/5$.
    (c) For the eighth decile the basic fraction is $8N/10$ or $4N/5$.
    (d) For the 32nd percentile (P_{32}) the basic fraction becomes $32N/100$ or $8N/25$.
    (e) And so on.

6. There is always one less partition value than the number of parts into which a distribution is divided. For example, the median (*one* partition value) divides a distribution into *two* parts.

Exercise 3.9. From the frequency distribution below, determine the partition values called for. The figures represent the number of minutes customers remain in a department store.

Class Boundaries	Class Limits	f	f_c
	3.5 – 5.4	60	
	5.5 – 7.4	80	
	7.5 – 9.4	105	
	9.5 – 11.4	125	
	11.5 – 13.4	140	
	13.5 – 15.4	180	
	15.5 – 17.4	200	
	17.5 – 19.4	205	
	19.5 – 21.4	170	
	21.5 – 23.4	145	
	23.5 – 25.4	110	
	25.5 – 27.4	80	
		1,600	

1. Median.
2. First quartile.
3. Third quartile.
4. First quintile.
5. Third quintile.
6. Fifth quintile.
7. Third decile.
8. Seventh decile.
9. Twentieth percentile.

Exercise 3.10. From the frequency distribution below, determine the partition values called for. The figures represent dollar values of invoices mailed by a wholesale hardware firm in a one month period.

Class Limits	f	f_c
20 but under 30	120	
30 but under 40	160	
40 but under 50	190	
50 but under 60	215	
60 but under 70	230	
70 but under 80	260	
80 but under 90	300	
90 but under 100	305	
100 but under 110	280	
110 but under 120	250	
120 but under 130	220	
130 but under 140	180	
140 but under 150	160	
150 but under 160	130	
	3,000	

1. Median.
2. First quartile.
3. Third quartile.
4. Second quintile.
5. The 14th of 15 parts.
6. The 13th of 20 parts.
7. The 4th of 8 parts.
8. The 30th of 32 parts.
9. The 61st percentile.
10. The 72nd percentile.
11. The 90th percentile.

3.9 The Mode

As used in statistics, the *mode* refers to *the value of the item which occurs most frequently in the set of data under consideration.* The mode is a measure of central tendency in that it is the item which, by occurring more frequently than any other item, provides a central value from which all other items diminish in frequency. *The mode is not calculated arithmetically; it is located.* Too, the mode is not necessarily a precise value, because it could be determined by slightly differing methods and the values thus determined would not be identical. The resulting values should, however, be reasonably close. It must, therefore, be concluded that the mode is the least stable and least useful of the major measures of central tendency. The mode does, nevertheless, provide, a "typical" value based on a frequency count. Thus mean, median, and mode are all typical or representative values *but all are based on different notions of typicality.* To obtain the greatest degree of understanding of a set of data it is frequently desirable to quote all three central values: mean, median, and mode.

Ungrouped Data

In an array, the mode is the value of that item which appears most frequently. Thus, in the array, 2, 4, 4, 6 the mode is 4. In the array 2, 3, 4, 5 there is no mode. In the array 2, 3, 3, 4, 4, 5, there are two modes 3 and 4. In the latter case the data would be described as *bimodal.*

Finding the mode in ungrouped data is hardly a difficult matter. It is merely necessary to locate that value (if any) which occurs most frequently. Since some sets of data will possess no clear mode and others will exhibit two or more modes, it is sometimes said that the mode should be located only from grouped data.

Grouped Data

In a frequency distribution the mode is, of course, the value of that item which occurs most frequently. Viewed in terms of a smooth frequency polygon, the mode would thus be located on the X axis at the point where the polygon attains its highest (Y) value. This is indicated in Illustration 3.17.

Illustration 3.17 Location of the Mode in a Smoothed Frequency Curve

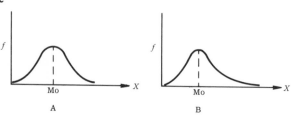

A

B

The actual process of locating the mode in grouped data is most satisfactorily accomplished by a formula based on the following theory: In a *symmetric distribution*, the mode is the midpoint of the class containing the greatest frequency, as shown in Illustration 3.18, or, if there is no center class, the mode is located directly between the two central classes.

Illustration 3.18   Location of the Mode in a Histogram Where the Distribution is Symmetric

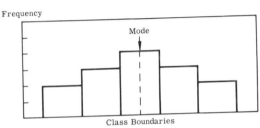

If the distribution is *not symmetric*, the mode will be located in the class having the highest frequency, but will be "attracted" towards both adjacent classes by a "force" proportional to the frequencies in the adjacent classes. This attraction of the mode towards the adjacent classes may be illustrated best by the graphic examples shown in Illustration 3.19.

Illustration 3.19   The Mode of a Frequency Distribution Located by Graphic Means

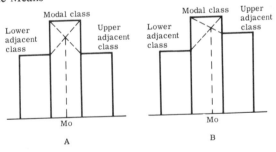

In calculating the mode from grouped data it is necessary to determine by inspection which class contains the largest number of frequencies and to establish the class boundaries. It is also necessary to know the frequency of the two adjacent classes. Since this is all the information required, the mode may be determined from open-ended distributions and from distributions of unequal intervals, although the method applicable in the latter case is not discussed herein. The general method for finding the mode in grouped data is shown in Illustration 3.20.

Illustration 3.20   Computation of the Mode from Grouped Data

Class Intervals	f	
23–27	5	
28–32	10	
33–37	10	(lower adjacent class)
38–42	12	(modal class)
43–47	10	(upper adjacent class)
48–52	8	
53–57	4	
58–62	1	

Solution:

$$Mo = L + \frac{A}{A + B} i$$

$$= 37.50 + \frac{12 - 10}{(12 - 10) + (12 - 10)} 5$$

$$= 37.40 + 2.50$$

$$= 40.00.$$

where L is the lower class boundary of the modal class,
   A is the difference between the frequency of the modal class and the lower adjacent class,
   B is the difference between the frequency of the modal class and the upper adjacent class,
   i is the width of the modal class interval (measured from boundary to boundary).

Relationships between Mean, Median, and Mode

It will be convenient to observe the manner in which the three major measures of central tendency are related in a distribution which is "skewed" slightly to the right. The word *skewed* means "nonsymmetric" or "out of symmetry," as indicated by Illustration 3.21.

Illustration 3.21   Location of the Mean, Median, and Mode in a Distribution Skewed Moderately to the Right

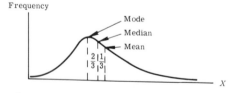

Observe that the median divides the distance between the mode and the mean such that two-thirds of this distance falls between the mode and the median. In general, this division will be approximately correct whenever the distribution is not too badly skewed.

It may be recalled that:

1. The mean divides the distribution into two parts such that the sum of the positive and negative arithmetic deviations measured from the mean is zero.

2. The median divides the distribution into two equal frequency parts. In the case of a frequency polygon, the median would divide the area under the curve into two equal parts.

3. The mode measures the highest point in the polygon; that is, the mode identifies the most frequently occurring value.

In the case of a symmetric distribution, the mean, median, and mode would be identical. Only in the case of skewness (defined as lack of symmetry) will the three measures be "pulled apart" as shown in Illustration 3.21.

Exercise 3.11. Find the value of the mode in the following problems. Assume that the X_1 column refers to the number of hours part time employees worked per week and represents midpoints of class intervals. The $f_1, \ldots, f_4$ columns are the number of employees working the given hours in four consecutive weeks.

X_1	f_1	f_2	f_3	f_4
5	5	2	6	15
7	10	4	7	19
9	12	8	10	23
11	7	9	15	30
13	6	10	13	26
15	4	7	9	17
17	3	6	3	11

1. Mode $X_1 f_1 = ?$
2. Mode $X_1 f_2 = ?$
3. Mode $X_1 f_3 = ?$
4. Mode $X_1 f_4 = ?$

Exercise 3.12. Find the value of the mode in the following problems. Assume that the X_2 column refers to the number of hours part time employees worked per week and represents midpoints of class intervals. The $f_1, \ldots, f_4$ columns are the number of employees working the given hours in four consecutive weeks.

X_2	f_1	f_2	f_3	f_4
10	2	4	30	15
15	4	7	45	23
20	9	11	50	40
25	12	16	95	20
30	8	12	140	14
35	5	9	86	12
40	3	5	54	8
45	1	3	29	6

1. Mode $X_2 f_1 = ?$
2. Mode $X_2 f_2 = ?$
3. Mode $X_2 f_3 = ?$
4. Mode $X_2 f_4 = ?$

Exercise 3.13

1. A manufacturer of small inexpensive electric motors has made heat-rise tests of the motors after 3 hours running time. The X column refers to degrees of temperature rise, and the frequency column to the number of motors exhibiting the rise. Calculate the mean, median, and mode.

Class Boundaries	(Midpoint) X	(Frequency) f	f_c
	2.5	12	
	3.5	16	
	4.5	23	
	5.5	31	
	6.5	28	
	7.5	20	
	8.5	14	
	9.5	10	

2. Mileage tests have been made with a new type of gasoline mix. One pint of gasoline is placed in the auto which is then driven at 25 miles per hour until the engine stops. The distance in miles is then measured. That distance is shown in the X column. The frequency column indicates the number of times the automobile attained the distance shown by the mid-point of the class interval recorded in the X column. Calculate the mean, median, and mode.

Class Boundaries	(Midpoint) X	(Frequency) f	f_c
	1.5	19	
	1.6	24	
	1.7	36	
	1.8	40	
	1.9	30	
	2.0	26	
	2.1	21	
	2.2	15	

3. A number of trainees in an industrial arts class are asked to measure the diameter of a piece of wire with a micrometer. The readings are given in thousandths of an inch and shown as midpoints in the X column. The number of trainees reporting the given measurements are shown in the frequency column. Calculate the mean, median, and mode.

Class Boundaries	(Midpoint) X	(Frequency) f	f_c
	.005	12	
	.010	18	
	.015	21	
	.020	29	
	.025	32	
	.030	35	
	.035	30	
	.040	26	
	.045	19	
	.050	17	
	.055	12	
	.060	8	

4. Customers who stop at a service station for a motor oil change are told: "Your automobile should be returned for its next motor oil change when you have driven approximately 2,000 miles." When the auto is next returned for the oil change, a record is maintained of the number of miles driven since the previous oil change. The X data represent the number of miles between changes, and the frequency column shows the number of autos falling in the given mileage classes. Calculate the mean, median, and mode.

Class Boundaries	(Midpoint) X	(Frequency) f	f_c
	1,000	4	
	1,200	8	
	1,400	13	
	1,600	19	
	1,800	21	
	2,000	23	
	2,200	20	
	2,400	18	
	2,600	14	
	2,800	9	
	3,000	6	
	3,200	4	

3.10   Summary

This chapter has discussed those statistical measures which yield valuable information relative to the "center" of the data. Such measures of central tendency are considered to be "representative" or "typical" values and may be used to summarize masses of data by substituting one number for many. Measures of central tendency are applicable to a broad range of informational uses, in part because they are representative statistics and in part because they are generally simple to compute and to comprehend.

Measures of central tendency are frequently used in conjunction with other statistical information to help provide a brief, yet clear picture of the data under consideration. In the following chapters we will observe other types of statistical measures which may be employed along with measures of central tendency to provide useful representations of sets of data.

Key Words and Concepts of This Chapter

Assumed mean (or origin)	Quartiles
Cohesive data	Quintiles
Correction factor	Reference point
Deciles	Representativeness (of a measure of
Deviation	central tendency)
Fractiles	Skewness
Mean (average)	Typicality (of a measure of central
Median	tendency)
Mode	Weighted average (or mean)
Origin	Weights
Percentiles	

Bibliography

Brumbaugh, Martin A., Lester S. Kellogg and Irene J. Graham, *Business Statistics*, chaps. 16 and 17. Homewood, Ill.: Richard D. Irwin, Inc., 1950.

Croxton, Frederick E., and Dudley J. Cowden, *Practical Business Statistics*, 3rd ed., chap. 16. Englewood Cliffs, N.J.: Prentice-Hall, Inc., 1960.

Leabo, P. A., and Smith, F. C., *Basic Statistics for Business and Economics*, rev. ed., chap. 3. Homewood, Ill.: Richard D. Irwin, Inc., 1964.

Neiswanger, William Addison, *Elementary Statistical Methods*, rev. ed., chap. 9. New York: The Macmillan Company, 1956.

Paden, Donald, W., and E. F. Lindquist, *Statistics for Business and Economics*, chap. 6. New York: McGraw-Hill Book Company, 1951.

Tuttle, Alva M., *Elementary Business and Economic Statistics*, chap. 10. New York: McGraw-Hill Book Company, 1957.

MEASURES OF DISPERSION

4

4.1 Introduction

The preceding chapter discussed techniques for measuring central tendency in a set of data. These measures (or statistics) made it possible to state numbers which, in and of themselves, provided useful information of a summary character. It was noted that the mean, median, and mode, while differing in conceptual form, were particular kinds of "typical" or representative values. For all the advantages of these statistics, however, they were unable to provide information as to the "scatter" of the items about a central point. In other words, these measures conveyed information about the center of the data, but revealed nothing about the "sides" or "ends" of the data.

It is the purpose of this chapter to discuss "measures of dispersion," that is, to consider statistics which reveal information about the scatter of the data around a central value—usually the mean. When the material of this chapter is completed, tools will then be available to describe, using only a few statistics, sets of data in such manner as to obtain the essential information without encumbering the presentation with all the items of the original group. Summarization will have been achieved; information can then be presented clearly and in compact form.

To illustrate the general nature of the problem of this chapter, suppose two sets of data possess a common arithmetic mean and median but differ markedly with respect to dispersion or scatter of the items, as shown in Illustration 4.1.

If only the mean and median were known for both sets of data in Illustration 4.1, there would be a tendency to conclude that the groups were identical. However, a glance at the items indicates the two sets are quite different with respect to scatter. Thus, if sets of data are to be adequately described and compared, some statistics in addition to the measures of central tendency will be required.

Illustration 4.1   Differences in Scatter of Two Sets of Data Having Identical Means and Medians

Set A		Set B	
48		20	
49	Note: the low-valued	30	Note: the low-valued
50	item is 48, the high-	50	item is 20, the high-
51	valued item is 52, a	70	valued item is 80, a
52	difference of 4 units.	80	difference of 60 units.

$\bar{X} = 50$ $\bar{X} = 50$
Med = 50   Med = 50
Spread or range = 4   Spread or range = 60

The problems involved in providing an adequate description of a set of data may also be shown in conjunction with the frequency distribution. In Illustration 4.2 two quite different frequency distributions are pictured.

Illustration 4.2   Two Frequency Distributions with Identical Means But Differing Widely in Scatter ($N_1 = N_2$)

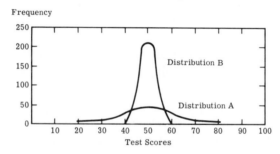

The value of the mean is identical in both cases and the N's are identical. However, observe that the distributions differ widely as to the scatter of the items along the X axis.

Note that the data of distribution B are substantially more "uniform" than those of distribution A. Suppose that both sets of data represented grade distributions of two groups of students, all of whom had taken the same examination; then it might be concluded that performance varied greatly in group A whereas performance was more uniform in distribution B. Too, it might be seen intuitively that if one item were to be drawn at random from distribution A, the value of that item could range anywhere from 20 to 80, whereas a random drawing from distribution B would always yield a value close to the mean of 50 since all items range between 40 and 60.

The concept of dispersion, then, is concerned with the "scatter" of the items about a measure of central tendency—usually the mean. The next task is to discuss the various methods for measuring and describing dispersion. After a section on symbols and notation, the following measures of dispersion will be discussed in turn: (1) the range, (2) the interquartile range and the quartile deviation, (3) the 10 to 90 percentile range, (4) average deviation, (5) standard deviation.

4.2 Symbols and Notation Used in This Chapter

The following symbols and notations are used throughout this chapter:

AD = average deviation. Also known as mean deviation.

f = frequency—the number of items in the class.

i = the width of a class interval.

N = the number of items in the group or distribution. The capital letter N is generally used throughout this book to refer to the *number of items in the universe* (*population*). This is done to distinguish universe values from sample values.

n = the number of items in the group or distribution. The letter n is generally used throughout this book to refer to the *number of items in the sample*. This notation distinguishes between universe and sample values.

P_{90}, P_{80}, P_{10}, etc. = percentile values. The particular percentile value is indicated by the subscript. Thus P_{90} equals the 90th percentile, and so on.

Q = the interquartile range, $Q_3 - Q_1$. The middle one-half of the items will fall in this range.

QD = quartile deviation, i.e., $(Q_3 - Q_1)/2$.

Q_1, Q_2, Q_3 = quartile values, the particular value being indicated by the subscript.

range = the difference between the highest and the lowest values in a distribution or a set of items.

S = the standard deviation of a set of *sample* values.

σ = the standard deviation of a set of *population* values.

V_{ad} = the coefficient of average deviation.

V_{sd} = the coefficient of standard deviation.

$|x|$ = an x deviation measured as $x = X - \bar{X}$, without regard to the algebraic sign of x, i.e., the 'absolute' value of x.

d.f. = degree of freedom.

Σ = an operational symbol meaning "take the sum of."

4.3 The Range

The *range* of the data is simply the value of the largest item in the set *minus* the value of the smallest item. Neither laborious to compute nor difficult to understand, the range clearly provides some indication of the "spread" of the data. In the case of an open-ended frequency distribution, the range cannot be computed because one or the other (or both) end values are unavailable.

The range is speedily calculated, gives a good notion of the spread of the data, and can be used to compare two or more distributions, particularly if the distributions have a common mean (see Illustration 4.1). However, the range is a crude measure of variability in that it reveals nothing whatsoever about the remainder of the data. The range may be misleading when the data exhibit extreme values. To illustrate these points, look at the two sets of data shown in Illustration 4.3.

Illustration 4.3 Sets of Data Having the Same Range But Differing in Internal Composition

Set A	Set B
10	10
10	14
10	15
11	15
15	15

The range of both sets of data is 5, but the items of Set A are concentrated near the lower values, while the items of set B are concentrated at the higher values. The range itself does not reveal this fact. Yet, even with the limitations imposed upon the range, it remains a useful measure. For example, stock market quotations provide the high and low values for each day's trading. When monthly or yearly summaries of stock prices are given, the range is almost always included. Perhaps it is now clear that if information consisting of the mean, the high and low values, and the range is provided for a set of data, a minimum description of the data is available.

Exercise 4.1
1. Distinguish between measures of central tendency and measures of dispersion.
2. The word "dispersion" and the word "variability" have been used in the paragraphs above. In what respect are the two words synonymous? In what respects, if any, are the words different?
3. What are the shortcomings of the range?
4. If the range were known for two different sets of data, would this knowledge be adequate to facilitate comparison of the sets of data? Why or why not? What else might you wish to know?

5. The range for two different sets of data is 2.0. Does this mean that the numbers in both sets of data have the same scatter (dispersion)?

6. Find the range in the following sets of data:
   (a) 12, 35, 22, 27, 31, 15, 25, 16, 10, 23, 36, 18.
   (b) 90, 87, 99, 84, 82, 91, 85, 98, 91, 98, 93, 95.
   (c) 50.6, 47.8, 52.3, 60.5, 43.5, 52.7, 57.9, 48.2, 53.6, 55.4, 60.1, 58.2, 48.3.

7. In the following sets of data tell whether the range is a useful measure of dispersion, or if the range is somewhat misleading and why.
   (a) 48, 58, 65, 69, 71, 50, 49, 55, 56, 55, 68, 57, 56, 49, 31, 51, 66, 68, 52, 56.
   (b) −.025, .037, .085, −.017, .099, .086, .073, −.001, −.011, .01, .03, .064, −.023, −.015, .10, .95, .063, .025.
   (c) 20.3, 18.2, 20.6, 15.0, 20.9, 20.8, 20.1, 24.9, 20.3, 19.9, 20.7, 19.8, 20.4, 19.9, 20.3, 25.0, 20.68, 21.0, 20.75, 20.63.

8. In the financial section of your newspaper or the *Wall Street Journal*, *Barron's*, or the *Commercial and Financial Chronicle* observe the manner of quoting the range of stock and bond quotations. What other measures of the day's trading are shown? What information do these additional measures provide?

4.4   The Interquartile Range and Quartile Deviation

As previously noted, the range suffers from a number of limitations. One of the most important limitations is that it conveys no information about the middle of a distribution. One way to overcome this limitation is to utilize the difference between the third and first quartiles as a measure of the scatter of items in a set of data. Thus, the *interquartile range* may be defined as: $Q_3 - Q_1 = Q$, where Q_3 and Q_1 are the third and first quartiles, as explained in Chapter 3, and Q is the interquartile range. Since the quartiles are based on positional values, the interquartile range necessarily includes the middle 50 per cent of the items in the group or distribution. Unfortunately, the interquartile range provides no information about the ends of the distribution, and its usefulness is limited to giving information about the dispersion at the center of the data.

A slightly different manner of treating the interquartile range makes use of one-half of the difference between the third and first quartiles. Thus, in formula form,

$$QD = \frac{Q_3 - Q_1}{2}, \qquad (4.1)$$

where QD = *quartile deviation.*

Notice the implications of QD. In a normal distribution (see Illustration 4.4) the mean, median, and mode coincide. For the present the normal distribution may be thought of as a symmetric distribution. It is presented in detail in Chapter 6. If $\pm QD$ were measured from the median of the distribution the end values of this range would be Q_3 and Q_1, and the middle (50 per cent) range of the items would have been identified. Thus, if a normal distribution has a median of 50, and $QD = 10$, the middle one-half of the data is 50 ± 10. In general, if QD is measured from the median it will include approximately one-half the items in the distribution. However, it is necessary that there be a sufficient number of items in the set to be able to clearly identify the quartiles before QD is appropriate. If the items in the data are bunched at one end of the distribution, QD is not appropriate to identify the range which includes the middle half of the items.

The measures Q and QD are limited in usefulness by the fact that they yield information relative to the scatter of the middle of a set of data, but reveal nothing about the ends of the data. To be most useful, Q or QD must originate in and be used with grouped data. In general, these measures should also be used only when the recipient of the information has knowledge of the original frequency distribution and the normal curve.[1] Otherwise, much of the value of the information in the distribution may be overlooked.

Illustration 4.4   Relationships between Q and QD in a Symmetric Distribution

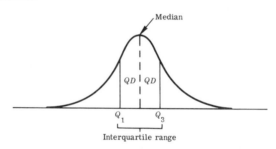

The graph of Illustration 4.4 provides a visual indication of the manner in which Q and QD may be used in conjunction with a symmetric (normal) distribution.

In the symmetric distribution of Illustration 4.4 the value of Q is the range within which the middle 50 per cent of the items are located and the median $\pm QD$ identifies this same range. This would not be the case with a skewed distribution. The more "skew" (lack of symmetry) the distribution displays, the more the median $\pm QD$ will fail to identify the middle 50 per cent of the items. In some respects Q tends to have a wider, more general applicability than QD.

---

[1] The normal curve is considered in detail in Chapter 6.

4.5   The 10 to 90 Percentile Range

The *10 to 90 percentile range* is relatively easy to describe and calculate. It is defined as the value of P_{90} minus the value of P_{10}. Thus the 10 to 90 percentile range includes the middle 80 per cent of the items in a frequency distribution. Because of the nature of the percentile calculation, a group of data constituting only a small number of items would be inappropriate for the 10 to 90 percentile range. In any case there should be enough items to facilitate percentile computation. The 10 to 90 percentile range is shown in Illustration 4.5.

Illustration 4.5   The 10 to 90 Percentile Range in a Symmetric (Normal) Distribution

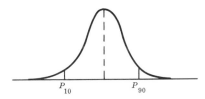

$$P_{10} \qquad P_{90}$$

Because of the nature of the computations, other partition values, the deciles, quintiles, octiles, etc., could be used for particular applications.

Exercise 4.2.   In each of the following frequency distributions, calculate the quartile deviation, the interquartile range, and the 10 to 90 percentile range.
(a)   In which of the distributions are the measures QD and the 10 to 90 percentile range most appropriate? Least appropriate?
(b)   Is it more accurate to calculate the interquartile range in distribution C than it is to calculate the 10 to 90 percentile range in the same distribution? Why or why not?
(c)   Under what conditions might the use of QD be inappropriate?

(A)		(B)	
Class Limits	*Frequency*	*Class Limits*	*Frequency*
25.0 – 34.9	80	.00 but under .01	10
35.0 – 44.9	150	.01 but under .02	15
45.0 – 54.9	210	.02 but under .03	23
55.0 – 64.9	290	.03 but under .04	32
65.0 – 74.9	330	.04 but under .05	38
75.0 – 84.9	350	.05 but under .06	34
85.0 – 94.9	380	.06 but under .07	23
95.0 – 104.9	350	.07 but under .08	19
105.0 – 114.9	330	.08 but under .09	10
115.0 – 124.9	290	.09 but under .10	6
125.0 – 134.9	210		210
135.0 – 144.9	150		
145.0 – 154.9	80		
	3,200		

	(C)		(D)
Class Limits	Frequency	Class Limits	Frequency
.5 but under .6	1	10 but under 15	15
.6 but under .7	3	15 but under 20	25
.7 but under .8	7	20 but under 25	45
.8 but under .9	10	25 but under 30	65
.9 but under 1.0	15	30 but under 35	90
1.0 but under 1.1	21	35 but under 40	65
1.1 but under 1.2	16	40 but under 45	45
1.2 but under 1.3	13	45 but under 50	25
1.3 but under 1.4	10	50 but under 55	10
1.4 but under 1.5	4		385
	100		

4.6 Average Deviation

The measures of dispersion heretofore examined in this chapter all make use of two values identifying the range between a "high" and a "low" point in the distribution. If, however, it is desired to allow each item in the entire set of data to exert its full impact on a measure of deviation, then some process of averaging is called for. One such measure is the *average deviation*, abbreviated AD.

Average deviation may be defined as the mean of the deviations of the items from a measure of central tendency, either the mean or the median. An arithmetic deviation, it will be recalled, is generally given the symbol x and is defined as $x = X - \bar{X}$. Since the median may also be utilized in calculating AD, x may also be defined as $x = X - \text{Med}$. The latter definition will be employed when AD is measured in grouped data.

In order to compute an average of deviations it is necessary to ignore the algebraic signs of the deviations, otherwise Σx would be zero if measured from the mean and might be a small positive or negative value if measured from the median. Thus, in ungrouped data the relationships are:

$$AD = \frac{\Sigma |x|}{N},\qquad(4.2)$$

where AD = average deviation,

N = the number of items in the group,

$|x|$ = the absolute value of the deviations measured as $x = X - \bar{X}$.

From this relationship it is clear that (1) each item enters into the calculation as a deviation measured from the mean, and (2) the information sought is an average of these individual deviations. Thus, the AD is a measure of the amount by which each item—on the average—deviates around its own mean. By use of the AD it is possible to compare the scatter of two or more distributions. By itself, AD is an "absolute" measure of dispersion stated in the units of the problem. Generally, however, comparison is facilitated by use of a relative measure of average deviation known as the "coefficient of AD" and is usually abbreviated V_{ad}. In order to convert AD to a relative measure, the following relationship may be employed:

$$V_{ad} = \frac{AD}{\bar{X}}, \qquad (4.3)$$

where V_{ad} = the coefficient of average deviation. Note: This ratio may be expressed either as a decimal or as a percentage.

To illustrate the use of average deviation with ungrouped data, consider the two sets of data shown in Illustration 4.6.

Illustration 4.6 Computation of Average Deviation, Ungrouped Data

Set A			Set B	
X	$\lvert x \rvert$		X	$\lvert x \rvert$
2	8		8	2
3	7		8	2
5	5		9	1
8	2		9	1
17	7		10	0
25	15		16	6
60	44		60	12

$\bar{X} = 60/6 = 10$ $\bar{X} = 60/6 = 10$

$AD = 44/6 = 7.3$ $AD = 12/6 = 2$

$V_{ad} = 7.3/10 = .73$ or 73% $V_{ad} = 2/10 = .20$ or 20%

In data Set A of Illustration 4.6 the AD is 73 per cent as large as the mean. Clearly, the items in Set A are widely scattered about their own mean. In contrast, the items of data Set B are more closely packed about their mean, a fact which is indicated by the relative dispersion V_{ad} of 20 per cent. The measure V_{ad} would also be useful when the two sets of data in question do not possess a common mean value. Comparisons of relative scatter would be facilitated by knowledge of V_{ad}.

When the data are ungrouped, the arithmetic mean is usually selected as the central value—as shown in Illustration 4.6. When the data are grouped and are not too badly skewed, the median is generally employed for ease in calculation, and the midpoint of the median class is chosen as the central value. Deviations are then defined around that central point.

Computation of AD from grouped data (equal class intervals) is a relatively simple matter. In terms of mechanics, (1) the median class is identified and its midpoint employed as the measure of central tendency, (2) the deviations (as absolute values) are measured in class intervals from the midpoint of the median class, (3) the class deviations are then weighted by the appropriate class frequency, and (4) the products are summed. Finally, (5) the formula $AD = i \Sigma f |x|/N$ is then used to obtain the AD value. These relationships are shown in Illustration 4.7.

Illustration 4.7   Composition of Average Deviation from Grouped Data

	Class Midpoint	f	$\|x\|$ in Class Intervals from the Median Class	$f\|x\|$
	25	5	3	15
	30	10	2	20
	35	10	1	10
Median Class	40	12	0	0
	45	10	1	10
	50	8	2	16
	55	4	3	12
	60	1	4	4
		60		87

$$AD = \frac{i \Sigma f |x|}{N} = \frac{5 \times 87}{60} = 7.25. \qquad (4.4)$$

As a final comment on the average deviation it may be pointed out that in a normal distribution (to be more fully described in Chapter 6) the range $\bar{X} - AD$ and $\bar{X} + AD$ will encompass 57.5 per cent of the items in the distribution. There is, however, no particular practical application for this range of items, as the standard deviation (to be considered next) is of greater usefulness and adaptability. Too, the AD is not subject to further treatment in an algebraic sense. The methodology and rationale of the AD is of practical value largely as an introduction to the technique of calculating standard deviation. It might be said that while the AD is a perfectly respectable measure of deviation, it is overshadowed by the standard deviation, which is subject to further algebraic manipulation and is applicable to a broad range of problems.

Exercise 4.3

1. Compute the average deviation (or mean deviation) in each of the following sets of ungrouped data.

Set 1	Set 2	Set 3	Set 4
3	3	7	.009
5	4	9	.017
6	6	10	.038
7	8	11	.043
8	10	13	.047
9	12	17	.049
11	13	21	.065
		23	.067
		24	.075
			.090

2. In sets 5 through 7 (sets 8 through 12 are optional) compute the average deviation from the midpoint of the median class. Also compute the coefficient of average deviation.

Set 5		Set 6		Set 7	
Midpoint	Frequency	Midpoint	Frequency	Midpoint	Frequency
5	1	6	1	7	1
7	4	8	9	10	5
9	14	10	36	13	23
11	28	12	84	16	60
13	35	14	126	19	105
15	28	16	126	22	126
17	14	18	84	25	105
19	4	20	36	28	60
21	1	22	9	31	23
	129	24	1	34	5
			512	37	1
					514

Set 8		Set 9		Set 10		Set 11		Set 12	
X	f	X	f	X	f	X	f	X	f
2	4	.05	1	.001	4	1,000	60	60	2
4	8	.10	8	.002	6	1,050	85	70	6
6	10	.15	28	.003	10	1,100	100	80	12
8	9	.20	56	.004	12	1,150	125	90	20
10	7	.25	70	.005	18	1,200	150	100	18
12	3	.30	56	.006	24	1,250	180	110	15
	41	.35	28	.007	17	1,300	200	120	9
		.40	8	.008	15	1,350	170	130	4
		.45	1	.009	9	1,400	155		86
			256	.010	7	1,450	140		
					122	1,500	100		
						1,550	80		
						1,600	55		
							1,600		

3. In which of sets 8 through 12 above is the use of the midpoint of the median class not particularly appropriate as a substitute for the mean in measuring AD? Why?

4.7 Standard Deviation

Of all the measures of dispersion, the most significant for analytical purposes is the *standard deviation*, for which the symbol is σ (sigma) or S. In general, σ is used to signify the standard deviation of a universe, while S is used to represent the standard deviation of a set of sample values; S is generally employed as an estimate of σ. *For the present it will be convenient to consider that the illustrative problem data represent universe (population) values.* Sampling applications will be considered after the basic features of standard deviation have been explored. The student should, at this point, be aware that there are a number of refinements of the standard deviation which will be introduced as the material of this section progresses.

Only the mechanics of the standard deviation (σ) will be explored to begin with, and for simplicity it will be assumed that only ungrouped data are to be considered. To derive σ for a set of data such as the X values 2, 3, 5, 8, 18, 25, the procedure is as follows: (a) each x value is squared—a process which makes all the deviations positive, and which emphasizes the larger deviations, then (b) the squared deviations are summed and (c) divided by the number of items in the set. To compensate for the squaring operation, (d) the square root is subsequently derived. The result is the statistic known as the standard deviation—that is, σ. In the form σ^2 this statistic is known as the *variance*.

Standard deviation may be defined as the square root of the mean of the squared deviations of the items measured from their arithmetic mean. In other words, standard deviation is a root-mean-square (RMS) value. In terms of formulae for ungrouped data,

$$\sigma = \sqrt{\frac{\Sigma x^2}{N}} \tag{4.5}$$

or

$$\sigma = \sqrt{\frac{\Sigma (X - \bar{X})^2}{N}}. \tag{4.6}$$

Illustration 4.8 indicates the derivations of AD and σ for a set of ungrouped data.

The differences between these two types of "deviation" are shown in Illustration 4.8. Clearly, the process of squaring deviations insures not

Illustration 4.8 Computation of Average and Standard Deviation (Ungrouped Data)

Average Deviation (AD)			Standard Deviation (σ)		
X	x	$|x|$	X	x	x^2
2	−8	8	2	−8	64
3	−7	7	3	−7	49
5	−5	5	5	−5	25
8	−2	2	8	−2	4
17	7	7	17	7	49
25	15	15	25	15	225
60	0	44	60	0	416

$\bar{X} = 60/6 = 10,$ 　　　　 $\bar{X} = 60/6 = 10,$

$AD = 44/6 = 7.33,$ 　　　 $\sigma = \sqrt{416/6} = \sqrt{69.33} = 8.33,$

where $AD = \dfrac{\Sigma |x|}{N}.$ 　　 where $\sigma = \sqrt{\dfrac{\Sigma x^2}{N}}.$

only that all values in the x^2 column will be positive, but that the more extreme deviations—as for example, the x value of 15 in Illustration 4.8—square to values that are relatively large in comparison with the remaining x^2 values. Too, it may be noted that the square root of $\Sigma\, x^2/N$ does not result in an answer identical to AD. In fact, σ will always be larger than AD because of the squaring operation.

At this point the student may question which measure of deviation should be utilized and under what conditions the measure would be appropriate, because the two measures, while similar, are obviously not identical. In general, it may be said that the standard deviation is the most useful in that it is applicable to a broad range of problems.

Before proceeding further, it will be worthwhile to indicate an alternative method of computing σ from ungrouped data. The method shown in Illustration 4.9 is often used when computational machines are available,

Illustration 4.9 Computation of Standard Deviation by the Direct Method (Ungrouped Data)

X	X^2
2	4
3	9
5	25
8	64
17	289
25	625
60	1,016

$$\bar{X} = \frac{60}{6} = 10.$$

$$\sigma = \sqrt{\frac{\Sigma\, X^2}{N} - \left(\frac{\Sigma\, X}{N}\right)^2} \qquad (4.7)$$

$$= \sqrt{\frac{1,016}{6} - \left(\frac{60}{6}\right)^2}$$

$$= \sqrt{169.33 - 100}$$

$$= 8.33.$$

although a table of squares may be used to provide the squared values. The X values of this illustration are simply illustrative; the student may, if he desires, think of them as the number of products sold year after year in a given retail outlet.

Computing Standard Deviation from Ungrouped Weighted Data

When ungrouped data are given in weighted form, the computation of σ, as shown in Illustration 4.10, is merely an adaptation of the basic formula for standard deviation (4.6) and is shown as formula (4.8). Observe the relationship between *weights* and *frequencies.* Weights can be regarded as frequencies; frequencies may be regarded as weights. An introduction to this transformation was given in Illustration 3.11, and in Chapters 5 and 6 it will be shown that frequencies may be converted to "relative frequencies," which may be defined to be probabilities. Illustration 4.10 shows the methodology for calculating σ when the problem is weighted.

Illustration 4.10 Calculation of σ from a Set of Weighted Data

X	w or f	fx	$X - \bar{X} = x$	$(X - \bar{X})^2$	$f(X - \bar{X})^2$
6	2	12	−4	16	32
8	4	32	−2	4	16
10	8	80	0	0	0
12	4	48	2	4	16
14	2	28	4	16	32
	20	200			96

$$\bar{X} = \frac{\Sigma fx}{\Sigma w} = \frac{200}{20} = 10.$$

$$\sigma = \sqrt{\frac{\Sigma f(X - \bar{X})^2}{N}} = \sqrt{\frac{96}{20}} = \sqrt{4.8} = 2.19. \qquad (4.8)$$

Computation of σ from Grouped Data

Computation of σ from grouped data employs the same principles as those shown in the ungrouped illustrations. Mechanically, the process is nearly identical to finding the mean in a frequency distribution (see Sec. 3.6, Method III). Illustration 4.11 indicates the method employed with grouped data; note, however, the deviations are in terms of class intervals measured from an "assumed origin," this origin being the midpoint of the class interval containing the median frequency.

In Illustration 4.11 it may be seen that the calculation of σ from grouped data is neither difficult nor particularly time-consuming. The use of Charlier's check is optional but is recommended as a means of making relatively certain that the arithmetic has been performed correctly. Of course, offsetting errors could have been made, but this is rather improbable.

Another method which could be used to compute the standard deviation of grouped data is shown in Illustration 4.12. This is not the most practical type of calculation to employ if only the simplest method of

Illustration 4.11 Computation of σ from Grouped Data (All Class Intervals Equal)

Class Limits	Midpoint	f	x	x^2	fx	fx^2	Charlier's Check $f[(x + 1)^2]$
23 – 27	25	5	−3	9	−15	45	20
28 – 32	30	10	−2	4	−20	40	10
33 – 37	35	10	−1	1	−10	10	0
38 – 42	40	12	0	0	0	0	12
43 – 47	45	10	1	1	10	10	40
48 – 52	50	8	2	4	16	32	72
53 – 57	55	4	3	9	12	36	64
58 – 62	60	1	4	16	4	16	25
		60			−3	189	243

Note: Charlier's check is an optional matter.

$$\sigma = i \sqrt{\frac{\Sigma fx^2}{N} - \left(\frac{\Sigma fx^2}{N}\right)} = 5 \sqrt{\frac{189}{60} - \left(\frac{-3}{60}\right)^2} = 5\sqrt{3.1475} = 8.87. \qquad (4.9)$$

Charlier's check on computations:

$$\Sigma f(x + 1)^2 = \Sigma fx^2 + 2 \Sigma fx + \Sigma f,$$

$$243 = 189 + 2(-3) + 60,$$

$$243 = 189 + (-6) + 60,$$

$$243 = 243.$$

The tabulations check.

The coefficient of standard deviation is

$$V_{sd} = \frac{\sigma}{\bar{X}} = \frac{8.8}{39.75} = .22.$$

finding σ is sought. However, the idea we wish to illustrate involves using the ordinary arithmetic deviations (x) of each class midpoint from the mean of the distribution, i.e., $X - \bar{X}$, squaring these deviations, and then weighting $(X - \bar{X})^2$ by the *relative frequency* of the class. The relative frequency of each class is f/N, and it must be computed for each class.

The important point to observe in Illustration 4.12 is the manner in which the relative frequencies serve as weights. These relative frequencies are, as will be noted in Chapters 5 and 6, essentially empirical probabilities for the frequency distribution. For the present, we are interested primarily in the method of calculation as shown in Illustration 4.12.

Illustration 4.12 Computation of σ from Grouped Data by the "Relative Frequencies" or "Empirical Probability" Method

Class Limits	X Mid-point	f	$(X - \bar{X})$	$(X - \bar{X})^2$	$\dfrac{f}{N}$	$\dfrac{f}{N}(X - \bar{X})^2$
22 – 27	25	5	25.00 − 39.75 = 14.75	217.5625	.0833	18.1302
28 – 32	30	10	30.00 − 39.75 = 9.75	95.0625	.1667	15.8437
33 – 37	35	10	35.00 − 39.75 = 4.75	22.5625	.1667	3.7604
38 – 42	40	12	40.00 − 39.75 = 0.25	0.0625	.2000	0.0125
43 – 47	45	10	45.00 − 39.75 = 5.25	27.5625	.1667	4.5937
48 – 52	50	8	50.00 − 39.75 = 10.25	105.0625	.1333	14.0083
53 – 57	55	4	55.00 − 39.75 = 15.25	232.5625	.0667	15.5042
58 – 62	60	1	60.00 − 39.75 = 20.25	410.0625	.0167	6.8344
		60				76.6874

$$\sigma = \sqrt{\Sigma (X - \bar{X})^2 \frac{f}{N}} = \sqrt{76.6874} = 8.87.$$

Exercise 4.4. *Computation of Standard Deviation, Ungrouped Data.* Instructions: For the following sets of data compute the variance (σ^2), the standard deviation (σ), and the coefficient of standard deviation (V_{sd}). Note: Save the worksheets for these problems: you will need them again in Exercise 4.6.

Set 1	Set 2	Set 3	Set 4	Set 5	Set 6	Set 7	Set 8
3	3	4.0	18	.009	−15	25	36
5	4	6.0	19	.017	−5	27	40
6	6	7.5	21	.038	−4	27	42
7	8	7.5	22	.043	−2	30	44
8	10	8.0	25	.046	0	32	53
9	12	9.0	27	.049	1	35	57
11	13	13.0	28	.065	3	39	71
—	—	17.0	30	.075	7	40	—
			35	.090	9	42	
					13		
					26		

Exercise 4.5. *Computation of Standard Deviation, Grouped Data.* Instructions: Using data sets 5 through 12 of Exercise 4.3, compute the variance (σ^2), the standard deviation (σ), and the coefficient of standard deviation (V_{sd}). Compare the standard and average deviations. Is the standard deviation always larger than the average deviation? Is this proper? Explain. As an extra exercise, apply the method of Illustration 4.12 to one or more of the problems of Exercise 4.3. Use sets 5 through 12.

Calculation of Standard Deviation from Sample Values

Thus far the standard deviation has been calculated on the assumption that the sets of data used as illustrations were composed of the entire universe of X values—that is, nonsample values. The phrase "entire universe of values" means that all possible measurements or counts of the variable have been made.

Now, under many conditions the X values do not include all universe values but rather are sample values—that is, only a portion of the universe is included in the set of data under examination. When the data are composed of sample values, rather than universe values, it is necessary to modify slightly the formulae used to calculate the standard deviation. These modifications will now be shown.

Standard Deviation, Sample Values, Ungrouped Data

When sample data are ungrouped, the following basic formula is applicable.

$$S = \sqrt{\frac{\Sigma x^2}{n - 1}},\tag{4.10}$$

where $x = X - \bar{X}$,

$\quad n =$ number of items in the sample,

$\quad S =$ standard deviation as calculated from the sample.

Use of $n - 1$ in the denominator of (4.10) means that the statistic S provides an estimate[2] of the corresponding population parameter σ. If it was desired to know the standard deviation of the sample items themselves only n would be used in the denominator.

When the sample data are ungrouped the standard deviation may be calculated without measuring the small x deviations—which can be tedious, particularly if the mean and/or the data involves decimals—by use of the following formula:

$$S = \sqrt{\frac{n(\Sigma X^2) - (\Sigma X)^2}{n(n - 1)}},\tag{4.11}$$

where $X =$ the X items,

$\quad n =$ number of items in the sample,

$\quad S =$ standard deviation, as calculated from the sample—that is, S is an estimate of σ.

The use of Formulae (4.10) and (4.11) in calculating S, the standard deviation of a set of sample values, will now be illustrated. Using the data

---

[2] Samples provide estimates of population values. Since estimates involve rather sophisticated knowledge of sampling and probability, the subject of estimates is taken up in detail in Chapters 8 and 9.

of Illustration 4.9 and assuming the data to be sample values, we have the result shown in Illustration 4.13.

Illustration 4.13   Calculation of S from Ungrouped Sample Data (Alternative Methods)

X	x	x^2	X^2
2	−8	64	4
3	−7	49	9
5	−5	25	25
8	−2	4	64
17	7	49	289
25	15	225	625
60	0	416	1,016

$$S = \sqrt{\frac{\Sigma x^2}{n-1}} = \sqrt{\frac{416}{6-1}} = \sqrt{83.2} = 9.121. \qquad (4.10)$$

$$S = \sqrt{\frac{n(\Sigma X^2) - (\Sigma X)^2}{n(n-1)}} = \sqrt{\frac{6(1,016) - (60)^2}{(6)(5)}} = \sqrt{\frac{6,096 - 3,600}{30}}$$

$$= \sqrt{83.2} = 9.121. \qquad (4.11)$$

Since either Formula (4.10) or (4.11) may be used to calculate the standard deviation of ungrouped sample data, it is merely a matter of convenience as to which is selected. In general, it is probably better to use Formula (4.11).

Standard Deviation, Sample Values, Grouped Data

When the sample data are grouped, the following formulae may be used to derive the standard deviation:

$$S = i \sqrt{\frac{\Sigma fx^2}{n-1} - \frac{(\Sigma fx)^2}{n(n-1)}} \qquad (4.12)$$

or

$$S = i \sqrt{\frac{n(\Sigma fx^2) - (\Sigma fx)^2}{n(n-1)}}, \qquad (4.13)$$

where x = deviations measured in class interval units from an assumed mean,

f = the class frequency,

i = the width of a class interval (all class intervals of uniform width),

n = the number of items in the sample.

The formulae are mathematical equivalents.

Use of standard deviation formulae for grouped data derived from values which are now considered to be sample values will be illustrated next. Using the information of Illustration 4.11, *and assuming that the set of X values are sample data, S* would be calculated as shown in Illustration 4.14.

Illustration 4.14 Calculation of *S* from Grouped Sample Data Showing Alternative Methods of Calculation

Class Limits	Midpoint	f	x	x^2	fx	fx^2
23 – 27	25	5	−3	9	−15	45
28 – 32	30	10	−2	4	−20	40
33 – 37	35	10	−1	1	−10	10
38 – 42	40	12	0	0	0	0
43 – 47	45	10	1	1	10	10
48 – 52	50	8	2	4	16	32
53 – 57	55	4	3	9	12	36
58 – 62	60	1	4	16	4	16
		60		44	−3	189

$$S = i\sqrt{\frac{\Sigma fx^2}{n-1} - \frac{(\Sigma fx)^2}{n(n-1)}} = 5\sqrt{\frac{189}{59} - \frac{(-3)^2}{(60)(59)}}$$

$$= 5\sqrt{3.20085} = 8.9455. \tag{4.12}$$

$$S = i\sqrt{\frac{n(\Sigma fx^2) - (\Sigma fx)^2}{n(n-1)}} = 5\sqrt{\frac{(60)(189) - (-3)^2}{(60)(59)}}$$

$$= 5\sqrt{3.20085} = 8.9455. \tag{4.13}$$

The student will observe by comparing Illustrations 4.11 and 4.14 that $S > \sigma$ (*S* is greater than sigma) *for the same set of data.* This is to be expected since the computations are slightly different. It should be repeated that a major purpose in calculating *S* from sample data is to employ *S* as an estimate of σ. When *S* is calculated as in Formulae (4.10), (4.11), (4.12), and (4.13), all of which employ $n - 1$ in the denominator, *S is considered an estimate of σ.*

Exercise 4.6
1. In your statistics notebook or other appropriate place, compare the formulae for standard deviation, distinguishing carefully between them.
2. The text material has distinguished between calculating standard deviation from universe (population) values and from sample values. What is the distinction and why?
3. Using the eight sets of problems of Exercise 4.4, calculate the standard deviation *S* and compare this value to the σ previously computed. About how much is the difference? If the problems used an *n* of 50, what would happen to the difference between *S* and σ? If *n* were 100? If *n* were 1,000?

4.8   Additional Comments on the Standard Deviation

Relationship of Standard Deviation to the Normal Curve

In Chapter 6 the normal curve will be explained in considerable detail. For the present, however, it will be desirable to indicate in brief outline certain features of the normal curve and the relationship of standard deviation to the normal curve.

The normal curve may be thought of as a particular type of frequency (also probability) distribution, one which conforms to a precise mathematical expression. The standard deviation is part of the mathematical formula for the normal curve and bears a definite relationship to the curve. In the broadest outlines, that relationship may be shown as in Illustration 4.15. Thus, in a normal curve:

Illustration 4.15 Relationship Between Standard Deviation and Area in a Normal Distribution

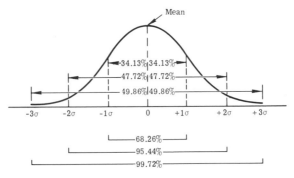

(a) The mean ± one standard deviation will be a range including exactly 68.26 per cent of the items in a normal curve.

(b) The mean ± two standard deviations will be a range including exactly 95.44 per cent of the items in a normal curve.

(c) The mean ± three standard deviations will be a range including exactly 99.72 per cent of the items in a normal curve.

(d) The table of areas for the normal curve (Appendix G) will provide intermediate values and percentages for standard deviation values not shown above.

(e) Since the range of the items in a normal distribution includes 100 per cent of the items, the mean ± three standard deviations will provide an estimate of the range. Said in another way, one standard deviation is about 16.62 per cent of the range. In still another way, it might be said that the range divided by 6 is approximately equal to the standard deviation in a normal distribution.

Relationship of the Standard Deviation to Other Measures of Dispersion

Two of the more important relationships are given below:

(a) In a normal distribution the average deviation is about 8/10 of the standard deviation, actually 79.79 per cent.

(b) The quartile deviation, in a normal distribution, is about 67.45 per cent of the standard deviation.

Explanation for the Use of $n - 1$ as the Denominator in Calculating Standard Deviation from Sample Data. Degrees of Freedom[3]

The reason for the use of $(n - 1)$ in the denominator of the formula for standard deviation when computed from sample data will now be explained.

Suppose someone placed a small box on a desk and explained that the box contained a large quantity of "chips" on which numbers were printed. Consider this box to contain a statistical universe. (Remember that "population" and "universe" are identical terms.) The assignment is to estimate the mean and standard deviation of this population. (a) Suppose one chip is drawn at random from the universe. The number on this chip will provide an *estimate* of the mean of the population, but will not provide any notion whatsoever as to the variability of the items in the universe. (If the mean were known then this one item would provide an indication of variability because the chip value could be subtracted from the mean to obtain the deviation x.) (b) A second chip is drawn. This chip, when compared to the value of the first chip, now will not only provide an estimate of the mean of the population, but will also permit the computation of x as the deviation of the first and second items from their own mean. Thus, some notion of the variability of the item is now available. Of course, the information is meager since only the value of two chips is known, but at least some information on variability is at hand. (c) Since the mean of the population is unknown, a minimum of *two* chips is required to provide an estimate of the standard deviation. One chip, by itself, will provide no information whatsoever as to variability, whereas the second chip does yield information as to the variability of the items in the universe. Therefore, one *degree of freedom* (abbreviated d.f.) is lost in calculating the standard deviation on the basis of sample values and the loss is accounted for by use of $(n - 1)$ as the denominator for calculating S. When working with population values, this degree of

---

[3] This topic is discussed further in Section 10.5.

freedom is not lost since the true mean can be calculated and every item in the population yields information as to the variability (variance) of the data.

4.9   Skewness and Kurtosis, an Introduction

Frequency distributions which approach a normal curve (shown in Illustration 4.16) but are not themselves normal curves may either exhibit skewness or kurtosis or both. When applied to a frequency distribution the word *skewness* refers to a sideways movement of the data—that is, the

Illustration 4.16   Skewness and Kurtosis

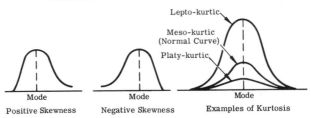

| Positive Skewness | Negative Skewness | Examples of Kurtosis |

the data are nonsymmetrical about the mean. In a manner of speaking it could be said the "hump" is misplaced. The word *kurtosis* refers to the degree of peakedness of the hump of the distribution. If a distribution is too peaked, it is said to be *lepto-kurtic;* if the peak of the distribution is too low, the condition is said to be *platy-kurtic*; if the distribution peaks as a normal symmetric curve (see Illustration 4.16) the distribution is *meso-kurtic.*[4] In measuring skewness and kurtosis, the criterion of comparison is the normal curve appropriate to the given data. The graphs of Illustration 4.16 will aid in visualizing these concepts.

Having described skewness and kurtosis, it might be asked why a frequency distribution should exhibit characteristics which cause it to be other than normal. In distributions resulting from empirical measurements, the basic reason for skewness may be traced to casual forces which are nonrandom, and the resulting distribution does not conform to the requirements of a normal curve.

Another reason why a particular frequency distribution may not be normal is simply that the normal curve is a mathematically precise continuous curve, whereas empirical distributions—that is, distributions resulting from actual measurements—are discontinuous and are not to be expected to duplicate a precise theoretical distribution. *Empirical distributions may frequently be assumed to approximate an appropriate theoretical distribution.* In this statement lies one key to understanding modern statistics—as well as much of modern science. Scientific inquiry has made

[4] The normal distribution is treated in detail in Chapter 6.

great strides through the ability to approximate empirical data by theoretical means, and to use this information even though it contains some
degree of error.

Knowledge that a distribution is skewed may provide a clue for
further inquiry. For example, is it logical that the set of measurements
comprising the empirical distribution be skewed? If it appears logical
that the distribution should be skewed, should it be slightly skewed?
Moderately skewed? Greatly skewed? Raising the question of skewness
may lead to the formulation of hypotheses which can be tested for correct-
ness. Too, skewness or kurtosis might well be a desirable situation.
For example, if workers are paid on a piece-rate basis, a distribution of the
weekly pay checks issued to such workers in a given week might be
skewed to the higher amounts. This could indicate either that employee
selection was generally good, or that many employees were performing
at an exceptionally high level of efficiency. In other cases it might be
desirable that a set of measurements be (say) lepto-kurtic, indicating a very
high degree of concentration about the mean.

Thus, the fact that a distribution exhibits skewness or kurtosis is
certainly not *prima facie* evidence that the causal forces resulting in the
empirical distribution require correction. Unfortunately, use of the word
"normal" to describe a particular curve type tends to carry the implication
that other curve types somehow reflect an undesirable state of affairs.
Normality is not necessarily a criterion of desirability. Normality is,
however, often desirable in the sense that tables of areas are readily
available for probability computations.

4.10   Computation of Skewness

There are several techniques for computing skewness. The least
complex methods make use of the fact that in a nonsymmetrical distribution the mean, median, and mode will not be identical in value. In a
distribution which is moderately skewed to the right (positive skewness), relationships will be exhibited as shown in Illustration 4.17. The discrepancies

Illustration 4.17   Position of the Measures of Central Tendency in
a Positively Skewed Distribution Where: Mode < Median < Mean

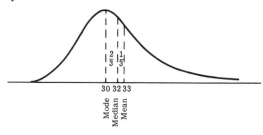

between the measures of central tendency will be greater as the skewness becomes more pronounced. When a distribution is moderately skewed to the left (negative skewness), the relationships shown in Illustration 4.18 will be exhibited. Again the discrepancies between the measures

Illustration 4.18   Position of the Measures of Central Tendency in a Negatively Skewed Distribution Where: Mean < Median < Mode

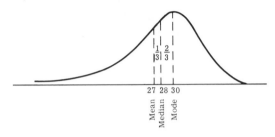

of central tendency will be greater as the degree of skewness becomes more pronounced.

Once it is seen that the three basic measures of central tendency will "pull apart" as a distribution skews, it is a logical step to formulate a measure of skewness based on this fact. Such a measure would be given in the absolute values of the problem by simply subtracting the mode from the mean. For purposes of comparison, however, skewness could be expressed in relative terms as follows:

$$sk = \frac{\bar{X} - \text{Mo}}{\sigma}.\qquad(4.14)$$

Use of this formula would yield the following characteristics:

(a)   The formula yields a value of zero for a symmetrical distribution.

(b)   The formula yields a negative value when the distribution is negatively skewed, and the value will move negatively away from zero as the degree of skewness increases.

(c)   The formula yields a positive value when the distribution is positively skewed, and the value will move positively away from zero as the degree of skewness increases.

Formula (4.14) has the desirable characteristic of being simple in application as well as yielding higher absolute values as the degree of skewness increases—that is, more positive or more negative, with zero for a symmetrical distribution. However formula (4.14) suffers from the fact that the mode is not a precisely determined value. To overcome this limitation an alternative formula may be used:

$$sk = \frac{3(\bar{X} - \text{Med})}{S}.\qquad(4.15)$$

Use of this formula yields the same general advantages as indicated for (4.14)—that is, a symmetric distribution yields zero; a skewed distribution yields a value moving away from zero in the direction of the skewness. Formula (4.15), however, does not suffer from the limitations imposed by the rather uncertain calculation of the mode. It will be noted that (4.15) makes use of the median—which is more precise in calculation than the mode—and that in a distribution which is not excessively skewed, the absolute distance between the mean and the mode is approximately $3(\bar{X} - \text{Med})$. The following examples indicate how skewness may be determined.

Example 1. Clearly, the requirements for determining skewness are that $\bar{X}$, S, or σ, the mode, and the median be known. If a distribution is characterized by the values $\bar{X} = 90.00$, $S = 29.86$, Med $= 89.86$, we have, by Formula (4.15),

$$sk = \frac{3(90.00 - 89.86)}{29.86} = +.014.$$

From these calculations it may be concluded that the degree of skewness is slightly positive.

Example 2. Consider next a frequency distribution exhibiting a considerable degree of skewness. The distribution is given in Table 4.1 and shown graphically (as a smooth curve) in Illustration 4.19.

Table 4.1

Class Boundaries	f
0 – 10	5
10 – 20	10
20 – 30	15
30 – 40	20
40 – 50	25
50 – 60	40
60 – 70	65
70 – 80	50
80 – 90	30
	260

$$\bar{X} = 53.46, \qquad \text{Med} = 62.31, \qquad \sigma = 16.39.$$

Illustration 4.19 Smoothed Frequency Polygon of the Data of Table 4.1

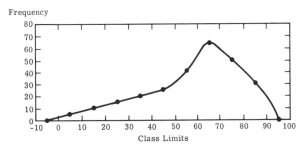

Computation of skewness:

$$sk = \frac{3(53.46 - 62.31)}{16.39} = -1.62.$$

Exercise 4.7

1. Given the following data, compute sk, the measure of skewness, by Formula (4.15) as described in the text. Tell whether the data are badly skewed, moderately skewed, slightly skewed, or symmetrical, and the direction of the skewness (if any).

Problem	S	$\bar{X}$	Median
(a)	5	14	14.5
(b)	9	27	30.0
(c)	16	40	37.5
(d)	14.5	80	70.0
(e)	600	1,580	2,230

4.11   Computation of Kurtosis

The measurement of kurtosis is somewhat more complex than the measurement of skewness. First, observe the formula for measuring kurtosis:

$$K = \frac{\dfrac{\Sigma fx^4}{N}}{\left(\dfrac{\Sigma fx^2}{N}\right)^2}, \qquad \text{where } x = X - \bar{X}. \qquad (4.16)$$

This formula will yield a value of 3 for a meso-kurtic curve, a value less than 3 for a platy-kurtic curve, and a value greater than 3 for a lepto-kurtic curve.

It should be observed that raising deviations to the fourth power places a very heavy emphasis on the deviations at either end of this distribution with a much lesser emphasis on deviations near the mean. Thus, the more peaked the distribution, the greater the ratio between the fourth and second powers of the deviations. Conversely, the less peaked the distribution, the smaller the ratio between the two values.

Example. Using the data of Table 4.2 as an illustrative frequency distribution, the necessary computations may be made as shown.

$$K = \frac{\dfrac{2,856,000}{3,200}}{\left(\dfrac{5,556,400,000}{3,200}\right)^2} = 2.18 = \text{kurtosis.}$$

Clearly, the measurement of kurtosis is a matter of some computational

Table 4.2

Computation of Kurtosis

Class Boundaries	f	x (Deviations)	fx^2	fx^4
25 – 35	70	−60	252,000	907,200,000
35 – 45	150	−50	375,000	937,500,000
45 – 55	230	−40	368,000	588,800,000
55 – 65	280	−30	252,000	226,800,000
65 – 75	340	−20	136,000	54,400,000
75 – 85	350	−10	35,000	3,500,000
85 – 95	370	0	0	0
95 – 105	360	10	36,000	3,600,000
105 – 115	310	20	124,000	49,600,000
115 – 125	300	30	270,000	243,000,000
125 – 135	200	40	320,000	512,000,000
135 – 145	160	50	400,000	1,000,000,000
145 – 155	80	60	288,000	1,036,800,000
	3,200		2,856,000	5,563,200,000

difficulty. The deviations are measured about the mean—a fact which can involve the student in a good many decimals. However, since the orientation throughout this book has been to emphasize the elementary aspects of business and economic statistics, we shall be content with the explanation and illustration given. Those who wish to explore the subject at greater length and to observe computational short-cuts by making use of an assumed mean are referred to other sources.[5]

4.12 Summary

The central theme of this chapter has been an explanation of measures of dispersion—that is, statistics which describe the "scatter" of items about a measure of central tendency. As explained in Chapter 2, measurements of a variable yield a number of X values, such values ranging over a particular arithmetic distance. For example, if the length of a number of standardized parts produced by a certain machine were measured, the measurements would be found to vary somewhat depending upon the

[5] Frederick E. Croxton, and Dudley J. Cowden, *Practical Business Statistics*, 3rd ed. (Englewood Cliffs, N.J.: Prentice-Hall, Inc., 1960), pp. 266–273. See also F. C. Mills, *Statistical Methods*, 3rd ed. (New York: Holt, Rinehart & Winston, Inc., 1955), pp. 166–173.

accuracy of the machine. These measurements would vary around a central value—usually taken as the mean—as some of the parts produced would be "short" and some would be "long." It is the purpose of measures of dispersion to describe this type of variability.

Throughout this chapter a number of statistics of value in measuring variability were discussed. Each of these measures has advantages and limitations. Each statistic must be used with full knowledge of its capabilities and its limitations. One of the extremely important points for the student to recognize is this: Statistics are used to provide and convey information. This information is often vital in the decision-making process which, in turn, is vital in the continued successful operation of the administrative unit. In the field of business and economics there are a large number of variables which may be considered influential as determinants of economic change. Stock market quotations are an example of a variable for which the range is a useful statistic. The prices of many goods and services are variables subject to a rather large range, while other prices, because of contracts or other rigidities, change less rapidly. Such economic indicators as "department store sales," "bank debits," "money in circulation," "consumer credit," and many others are examples of economic variables for which one or more of the statistics explained in this chapter are useful information tools. The materials of this chapter will also be valuable in studying sampling distributions at a later time.

Key Words of This Chapter

Absolute measure of dispersion	Relative measure of dispersion
Average deviation	Relative frequency
Coefficient of AD (or SD)	Sample
Degrees of freedom	Scatter
Dispersion	Standard deviation
Interquartile range	Variance
Population and universe	Weight
Quartile deviation	
Range	

Exercise 4.8. *Summary Exercise.* The following problem utilizes measures both of central tendency and of dispersion. Although the problem takes some time to compute, it does indicate relationships between the various statistical measures previously described and seeks to use the data to reach conclusions based on the empirical evidence at hand.

Extensive tests have been made with an experimental type of dry battery utilized as a source of power for portable equipment. The batteries were tested under actual operating conditions with the following results:

Hours of Life	Frequency for Type X_1	Frequency for Type X_2
7.5 and under 12.5	5	3
12.5 and under 17.5	10	8
17.5 and under 22.5	15	12
22.5 and under 27.5	35	20
27.5 and under 32.5	50	32
32.5 and under 37.5	85	75
37.5 and under 42.5	160	180
42.5 and under 47.5	200	193
47.5 and under 52.5	175	187
52.5 and under 57.5	140	162
57.5 and under 62.5	95	115
62.5 and under 67.5	60	96
67.5 and under 72.5	32	53
72.5 and under 77.5	15	27
77.5 and under 82.5	5	8
	1,082	1,171

Data for Experimental Battery X_1

$\bar{X}$ _____ S_____
Med _____ Coeff. AD _____
Mo_____
Q_1 _____ Coeff. SD _____
Q_3 _____ AD _____

Data for Experimental Battery X_2

$\bar{X}$ _____ S_____
Med _____ Coeff. AD _____
Mo_____
Q_1 _____ Coeff. SD _____
Q_3 _____ AD _____

(a) Which battery has the longest average life?
(b) Which battery is more uniform in its performance?
(c) Assuming the same price for both batteries, which do you recommend for purchase by your company? Why?
(d) If battery X_1 is priced 2 per cent below battery X_2, which do you recommend for purchase for your company? Why?
(e) If battery X_1 is priced 5 per cent below battery X_2, which do you recommend for purchase by your company? Why?

Bibliography

Bowen, Earl K., *Statistics, with Applications in Management and Economics*, chap. 6. Homewood, Ill.: Richard D. Irwin, Inc., 1960.

Croxton, Frederick E., and Dudley J. Cowden, *Practical Business Statistics*, 3rd ed., chaps. 1 and 17. Englewood Cliffs, N.J.: Prentice-Hall, Inc., 1960.

Downie, N. M., and R. W. Heath, *Basic Statistical Methods*, chaps. 5 and 6. New York: Harper & Brothers, 1959.

Freund, John E., and F. J. Williams, *Elementary Business Statistics: The Modern Approach*, chaps. 2 and 3. Englewood Cliffs, N.J.: Prentice-Hall, Inc., 1964.

McCarthy, Philip J., *Introduction to Statistical Reasoning*, chap. 5. New York: McGraw-Hill Book Company, 1957.

Mendenhall, William, *Introduction to Statistics*, chap. 3. Belmont, Calif.: Wadsworth Publishing Co., Inc., 1964.

Mills, Frederick C., *Statistical Methods*, 3rd ed., chap. 5. New York: Holt, Rinehart & Winston, 1955.

Neiswanger, William Addison, *Elementary Statistical Methods*, rev. ed., chap. 10. New York: The Macmillan Company, 1956.

Tuttle, Alva M., *Elementary Business and Economic Statistics*, chap. 11. New York: McGraw-Hill Book Company, 1957.

Wallis, W. Allen, and Harry V. Roberts, *Statistics: A New Approach*, chap. 8. New York: The Free Press of Glencoe, 1956.

5 AN INTRODUCTION TO PROBABILITY

5.1 Introduction

The subject of probability is central to the study of modern statistics, and it is also encountered by each individual every day in various ways. For example, if probability is considered to mean "chance," it may be seen that many daily events involve some degree of chance. Illustrations might include: (1) There is a chance you will receive a letter today. (2) There is a chance you will not get all your studying accomplished today. (3) If you are going on a picnic, there is a chance of rain. (4) There is a chance you will not find your favorite food at the lunch counter today. You could certainly extend this list in reviewing the various events of a typical day.

The study of probability actually encompasses more than the notion of chance; it is a challenging subject of almost universal interest, and many applications to ordinary situations can be discovered by the student. At this point we might list the following: (1) A knowledge of probability is basic to statistical understanding, since probability values are both numerical and informational in character. (2) A sound knowledge of probability theory enables the astute observer to make judgments and comparisons on the basis of probability. (3) Large amounts of information are gained by experimental methods, but the results are generally somewhat inexact and uncertain. Under these circumstances it is necessary to evaluate the degree of uncertainty (probability) attached to the results. (4) A knowledge of probability distributions permits the observer to identify and test empirical results against a mathematical model of the distribution. In this manner comparisons may be made, differences and similarities noted, and judgments made as to the value of the data for present or future purposes.

5.2   Symbols Used in This Chapter

C_r^n = the combination of n different things taken r at a time.

E = event. An event is one or more outcomes of an experiment.

$P(E)$ = the probability of an event E.

f = frequency.

H = a head showing on a coin.

T = a tail showing on a coin.

n = number of items in a set considered to be a sample.

N = number of items in a universe.

P = probability.

$P(A)$ = probability of outcome A.

$P(B)$ = probability of outcome B.

$P(A$ and $B)$ = probability of the joint occurrence of outcomes A and B.

$P(A$ or $B)$ = probability of either outcome A or outcome B.

r = the number of items to be drawn from a set. In certain kinds of problems the letter r refers to the number of outcomes of an experiment which fall into the category defined as r. For example, r may refer to the number of heads showing as the outcome of a coin-tossing experiment.

$n(S)$ = the number of sample points in a sample space. $n(S)$ may also be used to refer to the number of trials of an experiment. The data context will make clear which usage is intended.

$P(A \mid B)$ = conditional probability. The probability of outcome A given the fact that outcome B has already occurred.

P_r^n = the permutations of n different things taken r at a time.

$n < N$ = n is less than N.

$N > n$ = N is larger than n.

While probability knowledge is of wide application to many areas of human endeavor, its basic uses are in the areas of decision-making and the testing of hypotheses. Since the subject of probability is extremely complex and intricate, this text will attempt to develop only a basic understanding of probability notions applicable to an elementary statistical level. For more advanced studies in probability the student should consult one or more of the references given at the end of Chapter 7.

5.3   The Idea of an Experiment

Frequently, though not always, knowledge may be gained by performing an experiment. By itself, the word experiment suggests a trial or a process undertaken to discover or demonstrate some kind of knowledge.

For example, to physically demonstrate certain principles of probability, a coin-tossing experiment can be set up to determine if the coin will show heads one-half of the number of times it is tossed. Experiments of this type involving coins or other objects are readily utilized in probability studies because they lend themselves to simple demonstrations.

An Experiment Is a Supplier of Information

In the business world many important types of experiments—that is, experiments whose consequences are expensive—are continuously utilized. For example, a firm might wish to inspect the quality of incoming merchandise as received, but because of cost factors can only afford to inspect a fraction of the articles received. In this experiment, if the fraction passes inspection, the whole lot of merchandise is accepted; if the fraction fails the inspection, the whole lot of merchandise may be rejected and returned to the supplier. Thus the discovery of knowledge becomes a necessary and often a continuous process in the economic world where the purpose is not the demonstration of the principles of probability, but rather involves the hard necessity of making decisions.

Experiments May Take Many Forms

In some cases the possible results of an experiment can be predicted in advance. For example, if a single coin is to be tossed, it can be safely predicted that the outcome will be either heads or tails. Standing on its side is ruled out. It is not necessary to actually toss the coin to know these alternative outcomes (also called events).[1] In other types of experiments, the results may not be predictable until actual trials have been undertaken. For example, consider the problem of weightlessness and man's well-being in space travel. The results could not have been known until experiments were performed.

In the following paragraphs the word "experiment" will be met frequently. The word experiment will be used to mean that *some process has been established and that this process is allowed to operate until a definite outcome (event) is attained, at which point the process ceases.* It is convenient to assume that the experiment is capable of an infinite number of repetitions, each having a definite outcome.

As an illustration of an experiment, consider an industrial process which produces one-pound cans of coffee. A large quantity of this product is turned out each hour. Suppose a question arises as to whether the

---

[1] An event is defined to include more than one sample point in the sample space of an experiment—that is, an event is composed of one or more outcomes. This should be intuitively clear from the other materials of this chapter.

weight of the product is actually one pound plus the weight of the container. An experiment might be devised to answer this question. A container of coffee may be selected at random, placed on a sensitive scale, and weighed. This action constitutes one trial of the experiment and is frequently called a "simple" experiment. A simple experiment is the most elementary act in the experimental process. Now, even before the coffee package (or item) was selected, the prediction could be made that its weight will either be correct or incorrect. Thus, the simple experiment has two—and only two—possible outcomes. Each simple experiment will result in one of the outcomes and this one outcome will be a *sample point* in the *sample space*. A sample space includes all possible outcomes of an experiment and each outcome is a sample point in that space. For example, the experiment of tossing a single coin has two sample points H and T in the sample space. Sample spaces for an experiment can sometimes be constructed in several different ways depending upon how the outcomes are defined, the type of the experiment, and the purposes for which the experiment was designed.

In the coffee-weight example, when a trial of the simple experiment is performed—that is, a can of coffee is weighed—the outcome (either correct or incorrect weight) is one of the sample points in the sample space. If, say, ten containers of coffee were selected at random from the production process and the weight experiment performed on each item, then it could be said there were ten trials of the simple experiment—that is, $n = 10$—and these n trials of the simple experiment constitute a compound experiment. Now, consider another feature of this experiment, the *frequency* with which a particular outcome occurs. If ten items were weighed in performing the compound experiment, ten outcomes will result and these ten outcomes will be distributed over the sample space. Illustration 5.1 shows that eight of the items were of the proper weight, and two items were not of the proper weight. Thus, the overall frequency with which one outcome (correct weight) occurred is rather different from the frequency with which the remaining outcome (incorrect weight)

Illustration 5.1   Sample Space for the Results of an Experiment in Which Ten Cans of Coffee Were Weighted to Determine Whether the Weight Was Correct (C) or Incorrect (I)

Theoretical sample space for the simple experiment of weighing one can of coffee

Outcomes of ten performances of the simple experiment. Taken all together, these ten outcomes constitute the results of one compound experiment.

| C |
| I |

| C | C | C | I | C |
| C | I | C | C | C |

Sample space consisting of 10 sample points

occurred. To put the matter differently, the outcome (correct weight) for the compound experiment shows a relative frequency of 8/10, while the remaining outcome (incorrect weight) shows a relative frequency of 2/10. Clearly, the frequencies themselves are 8 and 2, and 10 trials of the simple experiment here constitute the compound experiment.

In the procedure just described, the experiment has yielded information to the effect that not all items are of the proper weight and suggests that the production process is turning out products which, on the average, are only 80 per cent proper with respect to weight. The responsible company official will now wish to assess this information to determine if corrective action should be taken. Too, the producer would find it desirable to repeat this experiment from time to time to check continuously on the performance of the production process.

Summary

An experiment is ordinarily established to yield knowledge applicable to a particular problem. To discuss the design of experiments here would carry the discussion too far afield, and simple experiments only have been suggested as illustrations. In these cases intuitive understanding is sufficient. When the experimental method was established for the coffee-weight problem, it was known that certain outcomes would result from each trial of the experiment. Each outcome of the experiment was termed a sample point and the set of all sample points in the compound experiment was termed a sample space. The final object of the experiment was to determine the relative frequency with which a given event, defined as one or more specific outcomes, occurred.

5.4   An Intuitive Understanding of Probability

From the preceding materials it is now possible to understand, at least on an intuitive basis, that *relative frequency in the long run is actually a probability*. If, for example, repeated experiments with the coffee-weight problem determined the relative frequency of correct weight to be 8/10, then it could be stated that the probability of correct weight on a random selection of a one-pound can of coffee from the process is .8. This could be shown in tabular form as in Table 5.1.

Table 5.1

Relative Frequency and Probability

Outcome	Relative Frequency	Probability
Correct	8/10	.8
Incorrect	2/10	.2

In the coffee experiment just described, the two sample points (correct and incorrect) of the sample space in Table 5.1 are not *equally likely*. That is to say, the sample points resulting from the experiment did not show equal probabilities; or said in another manner, the relative frequencies of the sample points were unequal.

Given another type of experiment, the sample points might have been equally likely. Thus, for example, if the experiment had been that of tossing a well-balanced single coin, where heads (H) and tails (T) constitute the sample points of the sample space, then each of the sample points would have been considered equally likely—that is, the relative expected frequency of each point would be approximately one-half.

By way of contrast, if each class of a frequency distribution be regarded as a sample point, then the relative frequencies of each sample point would form a distribution of probabilities over that sample space. As will be observed when the normal curve is discussed, knowledge of this normal distribution of probabilities can provide a most effective tool of analysis and serve as a basis for resolving decision-making problems.

A most useful generalization may now be stated. The empirically determined probability of a given outcome of an experiment, $P(E)$, is the actual number of times a given outcome $n(E)$ occurred, divided by the number of trials, $n(S)$, of the experiment. Thus,

$$\begin{pmatrix} \text{Empirically} \\ \text{determined probability} \\ \text{of an event } (E) \end{pmatrix} = P(E) = \frac{n(E)}{n(S)}. \tag{5.1}$$

Thinking in terms of the frequency distribution, this relationship could also be given as

$$P(E) = \frac{f(E)}{n} \qquad \text{or} \qquad P(E) = \frac{f(E)}{N}. \tag{5.2}$$

The relationships shown in Formulae (5.1) and (5.2) are a technique for empirically determining a probability—that is, the probability of a defined event (E) associated with a given experiment. In other words, *the actual experiment was performed and the probability of an event determined on the basis of relative frequency.* If, however, an experiment was such that all sample points in the sample space were equally likely, then the probability of a given outcome could be determined *theoretically* as

$$\begin{pmatrix} \text{Theoretically} \\ \text{determined probability} \\ \text{of an event } (E) \end{pmatrix} = P(E) = \frac{n(E)}{n(S)}, \quad (5.3) = (5.1)$$

where $P(E)$ = the probability of a given event,

$n(E)$ = the number of sample points included in the event,

$n(S)$ = the number of sample points in the sample space.

To illustrate Formula (5.3), consider an experiment where a single die is tossed. There are six sample points in the sample space and, as far as can be determined, let us say all points are equally likely. Then, the probability is 1/6 that on a single throw the die will show a one-spot. Obviously, the probability is the same for all other faces of the die.

Now, the experiment of tossing a single die may be viewed in a slightly different light. Suppose that not just one outcome of the experiment was considered important but rather an event was defined to include more than one outcome. As previously indicated, *an event is one or more outcomes of an experiment.* Thus, an event E associated with this experiment could be defined as "either a one- or a two-spot." In this case two sample points correspond to the event, since both sample points are included in the definition of E. If the theoretical probability of E were computed, the conclusion could then be drawn that 2 out of 6 sample points are included in E and the probability is 2/6. (Note: It is not always desirable to reduce probability fractions at this stage, as the unreduced fraction indicates the elements entering the problem. Technically such fractions should be reduced in any final presentation of data.)

It may now be repeated that *probability can be interpreted as relative frequency in the long run.* This statement is not offered as an elegant scientific definition of probability; nonetheless it can be readily interpreted and applied to realistic problems.

Probability Ranges from 0 to +1

It is now asserted, without any attempt at proving the assertion, that the numerical value of probability is always positive and ranges between 0 and +1.

An event with a zero probability is an *impossible* event when the experiment is performed. For example, the probability that a single ordinary die can land showing seven spots is zero. An event with a probability of one is *certain* to happen when the experiment is performed. For example, and even though man generally classifies only death and taxes as certain, if a die is tossed, it is certain to land somewhere. Thus, if E is defined as "the die will land," the probability value of one may be assigned.

In a realistic sense, few outcomes of experiments will yield values of 0 or 1. Of course, an event E may be defined in a manner which yields 0 or 1, but this is rarely a realistic kind of definition for practical problems. If the probability of an event E, is known, a judgment about that probability can be made on a scale ranging from 0 to 1. As $P(E)$ approaches 0, E approaches impossibility, which is to say that E rarely happens when the experiment is performed. As $P(E)$ approaches 1, the event E approaches certainty, which is to say E happens quite often when the experiment is performed.

5.5   The Addition Rule for Determining Probability

For certain kinds of problems, the probability associated with a given outcome of an experiment can be added to the probability of another outcome of the experiment to yield the desired answer. For example, in the experiment of tossing a single die, six outcomes are possible. Each of these outcomes can be thought of as an equally likely sample point whose probability is 1/6. If an event E be defined as "either a one-spot or a two-spot showing," then the event E includes two mutually exclusive sample points, and since both are included in E, the probability of E is $1/6 + 1/6$. This should check with your intuitive understanding of the experiment.

To be more technical, the *addition rule* of probability can be stated as follows: If A and B are mutually exclusive events associated with an experiment, then $P(A \text{ or } B) = P(A) + P(B)$.

The words "mutually exclusive" as used above, mean that no overlap exists between the sample points included in the event A and the sample points included in the event B. Perhaps it is easiest to understand the concept of mutually exclusive by thinking of a single die. The die has six faces and, when thrown, will land showing one and only one of these faces. The die cannot land showing two or more faces simultaneously. In this sense it can be said that the six sample points associated with this experiment are *mutually exclusive*.

However, in the situation where some of the sample points in A are common to the sample points in B, an "overlap" occurs and A and B are not mutually exclusive. In this case the addition rule becomes

$$P(A \text{ or } B) = P(A) + P(B) - P(A \text{ and } B). \tag{5.4}$$

To illustrate the addition rule in the case of non-mutually exclusive events, suppose we have a wage problem involving the employees of the ABC corporation. If the corporation employs 100 persons and 40 of these are female and 60 are male, and some of each group earn more than \$90 per week and some earn less than \$90 per week, a table such as Table 5.2 below may be constructed.

Table 5.2

Employees and Wages, ABC Corporation

Classifications	Wages Under $90 (C)	Wages Over $90 (D)	Totals	Row Probabilities
(A) Men	40	20	60	60/100
(B) Women	30	10	40	40/100
Totals	70	30	100	..
Column Probabilities	70/100	30/100	..	1.00

It is now asked: "What is the probability that a person selected at random from the universe of 100 employees will be a male (outcome A) or will be a person earning over \$90 per week (outcome D)?" The following set of relationships may be noted:

$$P(A \text{ or } D) = P(A) + P(D) - P(A \text{ and } D). \qquad (5.4)$$

Substituting:

$$P(A \text{ or } D) = \frac{60}{100} + \frac{30}{100} - \frac{20}{100} = \frac{70}{100}.$$

Observe that if the probability of A and B occurring jointly were not subtracted, there would be double counting of the 20 individuals who were both male and earned over \$90 per week. The overlap between outcome A and outcome D is often called the *intersection* of A and D.

Illustration 5.2 Diagram Indicating the Intersection of A and D as Shown in Table 5.2

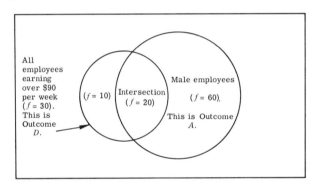

5.6   The Multiplication Rule for Determining Probability

For certain kinds of problems, the probability of an event associated with an experiment is the product of two or more separate—that is, independent—probabilities. For example, consider the experiment of tossing a single die twice and defining the event E as a one-spot on the first toss (outcome A) followed by a six-spot on the second toss (outcome B); then the probability of A and B occurring jointly is the probability of A, multiplied by the probability of B.

A more formal statement of the multiplication rule is as follows: Let an experiment E_1 be performed and, after E_1 is performed, let an experiment E_2 be performed. (E_1 and E_2 are independent, nonrelated events.) Let A be an event associated with E_1 and let B be an event associated with E_2; then

$$P(A \text{ and } B) = P(A) \cdot P(B). \qquad (5.5)$$

A less formal statement of the multiplication rule would be this: When two or more independent outcomes of experiments must happen in a given order or must happen simultaneously, the final probability is the product of the separate probabilities. Some examples will help make the multiplication rule clear.

Suppose a single die is to be tossed twice with outcome A defined as a one-spot on the first toss. Outcome B is defined as a six-spot on the second toss. What is $P(A$ and $B)$? Solution: The probability of a one-spot on a single toss is $1/6$; the probability of a six-spot on a single toss is $1/6$. Since A and B must occur in a particular order, their probabilities are multiplicative and $P(A$ and $B) = 1/6 \cdot 1/6 = 1/36$. Incidentally, if two dice, one red and one blue, were tossed simultaneously with A defined as a one-spot on the red die and B defined as a six-spot on the blue die, the probability calculation is the same as just given.

A second example using the multiplication rule may be useful. Suppose an experiment consists of tossing a coin three times in a row. The event E is defined as "a head showing on each toss." Find $P(E)$. Solution: Clearly the outcome of the first toss is quite unrelated to the outcome of the second or third tosses. Since a coin is an inanimate object, and (to state the obvious), it is possessed of no memory and no ability to control its own position, and no strings are attached, the tosses are said to be *independent* of each other. When the outcomes of a series of trials of an experiment are independent, the *probabilities* are multiplicative for a defined event E composed of two or more outcomes associated with the trials of the experiment. Thus, in this case if the coin is tossed three times, the defined event E (a head showing on each toss) involves a sequence of events—that is, all three coins must show heads. Thus $1/2 \cdot 1/2 \cdot 1/2 = P(E)$. Note that this problem could also be considered as if E were defined as the joint occurrence of $3H$, for which the *joint probability* is $(1/2)^3 = 1/8$. This is also known as a *compound probability*.

The word *independent* as used above should be clarified at this point, and to avoid a long technical discussion an interpretation of the concept will be given. Probabilities are multiplicative if an event is composed of a series of outcomes which must happen in a given order or must occur jointly, and each outcome in the event E is in no way influenced by any other outcome. To turn the matter around, outcomes of experiments are independent if and only if their probabilities are multiplicative.[2]

---

[2] More formally, it can be stated that A and B are independent outcomes if the probability of A given B [written $P(A \mid B)$] is the probability of A while the probability of B given A [$P(B \mid A)$] is the probability of B. Then A and B are independent outcomes. Or, stated slightly differently, independence is present if $P(A \mid B) = P(A)$ and, at the same time, $P(B \mid A) = P(B)$. Note, it is assumed that $P(A)$ and $P(B)$ are greater than zero. See the discussion of conditional probability, Section 5.8.

5.7   Use of Both the Multiplication and Addition Rules

In many applications, determination of the final probability for an event E associated with an experiment will require use of both the multiplication and addition rules. Consider a simple illustration requiring both rules. Suppose an experiment consists of tossing a single die twice. Outcome A is defined as "either a one- or a two-spot on the first toss." Outcome B is defined as "either a three- or a four-spot on the second toss." What is the probability of A and B—that is $P(A$ and $B)$? Solution: On the first toss $P(A) = 1/6 + 1/6 = 2/6$. On the second toss $P(B) = 1/6 + 1/6 = 2/6$. But, $P(A$ and $B) = P(A) \cdot P(B)$, so that $P(A$ and $B) = 2/6 \cdot 2/6 = 4/36$.

A second example of the use of both rules to determine the probability of an event E employs the experiment of tossing two coins simultaneously. Suppose, for convenience, that the two coins are a nickel and a dime. Too, it will be instructive to view the experiment in terms of its sample space.

Sample Space for Tossing a Nickel and a Dime
(Outcome of the Nickel Is Listed First)

H, H	H, T	T, H	T, T

To determine the probabilities of these outcomes, it may be seen that the probability of any sample point is $1/2 \cdot 1/2 = 1/4$. Or, it could be said that theoretically the relative frequency of each sample point is $1/4$. Now, up to this point only the multiplication rule has been employed. However, the addition rule would be used if an event E were defined as $E =$ a head and a tail in any order. In this case, two sample points conform to the definition of E—that is H, T and T, H, so that $P(E) = 1/4 + 1/4 = 1/2$. Note that if E should be defined as "two heads" or as "two tails," only the multiplication rule would be employed to find $P(E)$.

Exercise 5.1.   Note: In this exercise, answers to questions requiring a probability calculation are given in parentheses.

1.   Define or explain the following terms: outcome, sample space, sample point, trial, simple experiment, compound experiment, relative frequency.

2.   "An experiment is a supplier of information." Explain.

3.   An electrical relay admits water to an automatic washing machine on an impulse from a timer. Occasionally the relay will fail to function properly. How might an experiment be designed to determine the probability of relay failure during a washing cycle?

4. Given the sample space for a single die. What is the probability of:
   (a) a two- or a six-spot on a single throw of the die? (2/6)
   (b) a one-, three-, or five-spot on a single throw of the die? (3/6)
   (c) any face except the four on a single throw of the die? (5/6)

5. In each of the following experiments, list the elements of the sample space associated with the experiment.
   (a) Four coins are tossed. Note: Two sample spaces are possible. One will consist of 5 sample points and one will consist of 16 sample points. Explain.
   (b) Two dice are tossed. Show two sample spaces for this experiment.
   (c) Refer to the frequency distribution shown in Illustration 3.11. What is the sample space? Is each sample point equally likely? Why?

6. Two coins are tossed simultaneously. What is the probability of the event "a head and a tail are showing"? Why is this a compound experiment? Is the final probability a joint probability? Why? (2/4) (Two simple experiments) (Yes)

7. Given an experiment of tossing two dice. Why can we say that the event "sum of the faces is four" is a compound event? What simple outcomes comprise this compound event?

8. Given the experiment of tossing three coins:
   (a) What are the simple outcomes in the event "coins show at least two heads"?
   (b) What are the simple outcomes in the event "the coins show no heads"?
   (c) What are the probabilities for (a) and (b)? (4/8) (1/8)

9. An urn contains ten marbles of identical size. Four are red, one is transparent, and five are blue. On selecting one marble at random, what is the probability of red? of transparent? of blue? Now, if after each drawing the marble is replaced before the next drawing, are the probabilities you determined above "relative frequencies in the long run"? (4/10) (1/10) (5/10)

10. In a certain automobile race, ten contestants are entered. Assuming there are no distinguishable differences among the competitors, what is the probability that an auto picked at random will win the race? What is the sample space for this experiment? (1/10)

11. Given the information of problem 10 above. Now suppose that a distinguishable difference did exist among the ten contestants. What effect might this knowledge of differences among the competitors have on the likelihood of each sample point in the sample space? If, under this condition, the sample points are not "equally alike," how might probabilities be assigned to each of the sample points? Would these probabilities sum to exactly 1.0? Why?

12. What is the probability of throwing either a black or a white side with a six-sided block which has two sides painted white, two sides painted black, and two sides painted green? (2/6 + 2/6 = 4/6)

13. What is the probability of drawing either a black or a white marble from a bowl containing 1/2 black marbles, 1/4 white marbles, and 1/4 red marbles? (3/4)

14. Ten slips of paper numbered 1 through 10 are placed in a box. What is the probability that on a random drawing the slip will be numbered 4 or 6? What is the probability that the slip drawn will not be numbered 4 or 6? (2/10) (8/10)

15. Two dice are tossed. The event E is defined as "the sum of the faces is seven." What is the probability that the event E will not occur on a single trial of this experiment? (30/36)

16. A student about to graduate from college has completed five job interviews. On the assumption that each of the five opportunities is equally desirable and each of the five firms wishes to employ the student, what is the probability of the event "the student will accept either firm 1 or firm 3"? What is the probability that the student will not select firm 4? (2/5) (4/5)

17. Assume a single coin is tossed five times in a row. The event E is defined as "on each toss, the coin turns up tails." Find $P(E)$. $((1/2)^5)$

18. Five coins are to be tossed simultaneously. The event E is defined as "all five coins show tails." Does the calculation of $P(E)$ differ in any manner from the calculation you made in problem 17? Why, or why not?

19. On throwing a single six-sided die, what is the probability of throwing a two-spot on the first throw followed by a four-spot on the second throw? (1/36)

20. Over a period of one year, a corporation received 1,200 boxes of electron tubes from three different suppliers. Each box contained 100 tubes. The tubes were given a simple check to determine any defective items. Accurate records were maintained with the results summarized in the table below.

Defective Tubes per Box of 100 Units

Firm	0	1	2	3 or More	Row Totals
Supplier 1	250	100	100	50	500
Supplier 2	160	80	40	20	300
Supplier 3	300	50	25	25	400
Column Totals	710	230	165	95	1,200

Given the information above, answer the following questions. Answers may be expressed in fraction form to simplify calculations.

(a) If one box had been selected at random from this universe, what is the probability the box would have come from Supplier 1? From Supplier 2? From Supplier 3? (500/1,200) (300/1,200) (400/1,200)

(b) If a box had been selected at random, what is the probability that it would contain two defective tubes? (165/1,200)

(c) If a box had been selected at random, what is the probability that it would have no defectives and would have come from Supplier 1? (250/1,200)

(d) If a box came from Supplier 3, what is the probability it would have one defective tube? (50/400)

(e) If a box came from Supplier 2, what is the probability it would have two or less defectives? (280/300)

(f) What is the probability that a box selected at random came from Supplier 1 and had three or more defectives? (50/1,200)

(g) If a box selected at random had exactly two defectives, what is the probability that it came from Supplier 1 or Supplier 2? (140/165)

5.8   Conditional Probability

The fundamental notion of *conditional probability* is found in the following question: Given an event E composed of two outcomes, outcome A and outcome B. What is the probability of A *given the fact* that outcome B has already occurred? This is written $P(A \mid B)$, which means: What is the conditional probability of A *given B*? In the business and economic world, this type of question is not unusual. For example, a manager is considering introducing a modification of his product to the market. Clearly, any decision made will depend in part upon the course of action taken by his competitors and, in part, the decision will hinge upon what the manager conceives to be the state of the market for this product. Now, suppose the manager is considering the probability of success (defined as an increase in sales volume) to be assigned to the introduction of the new and modified product. The manager must take at least two unknowns into account: First, he does not know what his competitors will do and secondly, he does not know precisely how the market will accept his new product. Thus, he has two sets of probabilities to consider. As the manager ponders these factors, a telephone call informs him that one of his competitors has already introduced a new product this very morning and the action has been backed by a large-scale advertising campaign.

The new information may or may not be considered as "good news." In any case, the manager must now revise his probability calculations because he has *prior knowledge* of the occurrence of one of the two outcomes. Under these circumstances, the original question resolves itself into: What is the probability of success with the modified product *given the fact* that the competition has made a move? Certainly situations of this general type are by no means uncommon in the business world.

Many decision-making problems can be cast in the conditional-probability form—that is: What is the probability of outcome A given prior knowledge of outcome B? However, because of the complexity of real-life business decisions and problems, which involve a large number of interrelated facts, the points of conditional probability will be illustrated here by examples of greater simplicity.

As a very simple example of conditional probability, suppose two coins are to be tossed. The coins are a nickel and a dime, with the nickel being tossed first. If an event E be defined as "both coins land showing heads," we know that the probability of this event is $1/2 \cdot 1/2 = 1/4$. This is, of course, the probability of the joint occurrence of heads on both coins. Now, suppose the matter is viewed a bit differently and it is asked: What is the probability that both coins will land showing heads *given knowledge that the nickel has already landed heads*? Clearly, the fact that the first coin is already known to have landed heads permits the ready calculation that the probability of obtaining two heads now rests solely on the outcome of the second coin. Thus, given the fact that the first coin has landed heads, the probability of obtaining two heads *under these circumstances* is $1/2$, namely, the probability that the second coin will land heads.[3]

This general type of problem, the conditional-probability problem which contains the element of prior information, can be used to interpret a number of practical situations, and a slight digression may be in order at this point. For example, two armies oppose each other. The more each commander can learn about the other, the greater his own chances of success in an ensuing conflict. Prior knowledge about equipment, strength, strategy, and so on would be of immense value in raising the probability of a favorable outcome to the respective commanders. Or, if a sales person knows that each time a customer purchases product X, the customer's sales resistance to product Y is decreased, the probability of selling more of Y can be altered favorably by concentrating on product X. You can think of other examples.

To further illustrate the use of conditional probability, a more involved example may be used. Given the data of Table 5.3, it may first

Table 5.3

Education and Wages, XYZ Corporation

Grade Level	Wage Level after Five Years Experience			Row Totals
	(D) $0 – 5,999	(E) $6,000 – 11,999	(F) $12,000 and Over	
(A) 0 – 8	125	20	5	150
(B) 9 – 12	20	70	10	100
(C) 13 – 16	5	20	25	50
Column Totals	150	110	40	300

be asked: What is the probability that an individual drawn at random from this universe is in classification B, given that the individual is known to be in classification E? In other words, what is $P(B \mid E)$? Solution: Since the individual is known to be in class E, he must be one of the 110 individuals in that column. Therefore, all that is necessary is to calculate the

[3] The student may now review the concept of statistical independence given on page 112.

relative frequency of B as part of the 110 individuals in E. The probability we seek is 70/110.

As a second example, what is $P(F \mid C)$? Since the individual selected at random is known to be in classification C, he must be one of the 50 in that grouping. Again, the problem is viewed in terms of relative frequency. Out of the 50 individuals in C, some 25 are also in F. Therefore, the probability is 25/50.

Exercise 5.2. The following problems are designed to provide some practice in calculating conditional probability. Numerical answers are given in parentheses.

1. Given the wage table above, calculate the following conditional probabilities:
   (a) $P(A \mid F)$. (5/40)   (c) $P(A \mid E)$. (20/110)
   (b) $P(D \mid A)$. (125/150)   (d) $P(D \mid C)$. (5/50)

2. Given the data of problem 20, Exercise 5.1. Calculate the conditional probabilities for the following questions.
   (a) Given that a box selected at random came from Supplier 1, what is the probability that the box will show no defectives? (250/500)
   (b) It is known that a box selected at random has two defectives. What is the probability that it came from Supplier 1? From Supplier 2? From Supplier 3? (100/165) (40/165) (25/165)
   (e) The three probabilities you calculated in part (b) will sum to exactly 1.0. Why?
   (d) Given that a box selected at random came from Supplier 3. What is the probability that it contains three or more defectives? (25/400)
   (e) Given that a box selected at random came from Supplier 2. What is the probability that it contained one or two defectives? (120/300)

3. A die has been tossed and we are told it has not landed showing a six-spot. What is $P(2)$? (1/5)

4. Given a large and a small die. Let the event E be "small die turns up odd." Let the event F be defined as "large die turns up even." The dice are thrown. Find $P(F \text{ and } E)$. Find also $P(F \mid E)$. Are F and E independent? Why? (1/9) (1/3)

5. A dime is to be tossed three times in a row. On the first two tosses it turns up heads. What is the conditional probability that it will turn up tails on the third toss? Does this suggest that when all outcomes of an experiment are independent, $P(A \mid B) = P(A)$? (1/2)

5.9 Permutations and Combinations

When a sample of n items is drawn from a universe consisting of N different items $(n < N)$, the sample is only one of the combinations of items which could be drawn from that universe.[4] In order to explore the basic ideas of combinations it is necessary to consider both permutations and combinations.

---

[4] If the universe were single-valued, only one combination could be drawn.

Permutations

The word "permutation" refers to any *ordered arrangement* of the objects in a group or set. It is convenient to think of a permutation as an *ordered arrangement of objects in a line*. The key idea of permutation is this: "Order counts." For example, given the set of three letters, A, B, C, how many different ways may these three letters be arranged if all three are to be taken at one time?

To answer the question, simply arrange the letters in as many ways as possible. In due course it may be discovered that six different arrangements may be constructed: These are: ABC, ACB, BAC, BCA, CAB, CBA. Observe that it is the order which distinguishes one permutation from the others.

Now, suppose that a slightly different question were asked: Given a set consisting of the letters A, B, C, how many permutations can be constructed if only two letters are to be taken at a time? Actual enumeration will show that six different arrangements may be constructed: AB, AC, BA, BC, CA, CB. The student may now ask how many different permutations can be constructed using only one letter at a time. The answer, of course, is three.

A somewhat less obvious situation appears if we observe the case in which all of the objects or some of the objects we are to arrange in a line are indistinguishable from each other. Consider the objects to be the letters AAA. Is AAA one permutation and AAA another permutation? The answer is this: If the objects are indistinguishable, then AAA and AAA are *one* permutation. If, however, the objects should be made distinguishable in some manner, as for example, A_1, A_2, A_3, then six permutations of the three distinguishable letters are possible. By the same reasoning, the arrangement ABB is different from the arrangement BBA, and each is a separate permutation. However, BB taken by itself is one permutation.

By way of an additional illustration, suppose there were three new copies of this book on the bookstore shelf; then only one arrangement would be possible because the books are considered indistinguishable from each other (even though very small variations might be found here and there). On the other hand, if the three copies on the bookstore shelf were three different editions of the book, then six possible permutations of the three books would be distinguishable.

General Formula for Permutations

It would be most inconvenient if it were necessary to employ trial-and-error methods to discover how many permutations of *n* objects were possible. Fortunately, a very simple formula can rescue us from the need to use inefficient methods. The formula for the permutations of n different things taken r at a time is[5]

$$P_r^n = \frac{n!}{(n - r)!},\qquad(5.6)$$

where P_r^n = the permutations of n different things taken r at a time,
  n = the number of different objects in the set,
  r = the number of objects to be taken from the set of n things,
  ! = factorial (for example, $3! = 3 \cdot 2 \cdot 1 = 6$).

To illustrate Formula (5.6) suppose a set of five objects to be A, B, C, D, E. How many permutations of these five objects are possible when they are taken (a) five at a time, (b) four at a time, (c) three at a time, (d) two at a time, and (c) one at a time? The solutions for these questions are given below.

(a) $P_5^5 = \dfrac{5!}{(5 - 5)!} = \dfrac{5 \cdot 4 \cdot 3 \cdot 2 \cdot 1}{0!} = 120.$

Note: $0!$ is defined to be 1.

(b) $P_4^5 = \dfrac{5!}{(5 - 4)!} = \dfrac{5 \cdot 4 \cdot 3 \cdot 2 \cdot 1}{1} = 120.$

Note: $1! = 1$.

(c) $P_3^5 = \dfrac{5!}{(5 - 3)!} = \dfrac{5 \cdot 4 \cdot 3 \cdot 2 \cdot 1}{2 \cdot 1} = 60.$

(d) $P_2^5 = \dfrac{5!}{(5 - 2)!} = \dfrac{5 \cdot 4 \cdot 3 \cdot 2 \cdot 1}{3 \cdot 2 \cdot 1} = 20.$

(e) $P_1^5 = \dfrac{5!}{(5 - 1)!} = \dfrac{5 \cdot 4 \cdot 3 \cdot 2 \cdot 1}{4 \cdot 3 \cdot 2 \cdot 1} = 5.$

Clearly, when it is necessary to know how many permutations of n different objects can be distinguished, all that is required is a minimum bit of arithmetic. At a later point in this chapter, the relationship between permutations and combinations will be considered. But first the concept of combinations will be explained.

Combinations

The word *combination* refers to a collection of different objects taken without regard to order. The key idea of combinations is that *order does*

---

[5] Formula (5.6) is applicable only if the n objects are all different. Otherwise, modifications of the formula which are not considered in this book must be employed.

not count. What distinguishes one combination from another is that the composition of the *r* objects in one group differs from the composition of *r* objects in another grouping.

To illustrate, suppose we are required to select two elements from the set A, B, C. In how many ways can this be done? By actual trial three different groupings are discovered: AB, BC, AC. Suppose, however, a somewhat different question were asked: Given the objects A, B, C, how many different combinations can be made if these objects are taken all at once? Clearly, the objects A, B, C, taken all together, will form only one combination. The student may now ask how many different combinations can be made using only one letter at a time? The answer, of course, is three.

General Formula for Combinations

Again, it would be most troublesome if the trial-and-error method were to be employed each time we wished to solve a problem involving combinations. The general formula for combinations of *n* different things taken *r* at a time is

$$C_r^n = \frac{n!}{r!\,(n-r)!}, \tag{5.7}$$

where C_r^n = the combinations of *n* different things taken *r* at a time,
　　n = the number of different objects in the set,
　　r = the number of objects to be taken from the set of *n* things,
　　$!$ = factorial (for example, $3! = 3 \cdot 2 \cdot 1 = 6$).

To illustrate Formula (5.7), suppose a set of objects to be A, B, C, D, E. How many combinations of these five objects are possible when they are taken (a) five at a time, (b) four at a time, (c) three at a time, (d) two at a time, (e) one at a time? The solutions for these questions are given below.

(a) $$C_5^5 = \frac{5!}{5!\,(5-5)!} = \frac{5!}{5!\,0!} = 1.$$

(b) $$C_4^5 = \frac{5!}{4!\,1!} = \frac{5 \cdot 4 \cdot 3 \cdot 2 \cdot 1}{4 \cdot 3 \cdot 2 \cdot 1 \cdot 1} = 5.$$

(c) $$C_3^5 = \frac{5!}{3!\,2!} = \frac{5 \cdot 4 \cdot 3 \cdot 2 \cdot 1}{3 \cdot 2 \cdot 1 \cdot 2 \cdot 1} = 10.$$

(d) $$C_2^5 = \frac{5!}{2!\,3!} = \frac{5 \cdot 4 \cdot 3 \cdot 2 \cdot 1}{2 \cdot 1 \cdot 3 \cdot 2 \cdot 1} = 10.$$

(e) $$C_1^5 = \frac{5!}{1!\,4!} = \frac{5 \cdot 4 \cdot 3 \cdot 2 \cdot 1}{1 \cdot 4 \cdot 3 \cdot 2 \cdot 1} = 5.$$

A knowledge of combinations and permutations is indispensable to sampling theory and even though the subject of sampling will not be discussed at length until Chapter 7, it will be instructive to observe the relationship between permutations, combinations, and probability by use of the example given below.

Example of the Relationship Between Permutations and Combinations

Given the set of numbers: 1, 2, 3, 4, 5. The task is to discover how many permutations and how many combinations can be made from this set of numbers if they are taken two at a time. The permutation formula indicates 20 permutations will exist while the combination formula indicates 10 combinations may be formed. Suppose a listing is made, as in Illustration 5.3, to observe how the permutations and combinations will appear and how they are related.

Illustration 5.3   Permutations and Combinations for the Universe 1, 2, 3, 4, 5

Permutation Number	Permutation	Combination	Combination Number
1.	1, 2		
2.	2, 1	1, 2	1.
3.	1, 3		
4.	3, 1	1, 3	2.
5.	1, 4		
6.	4, 1	1, 4	3.
7.	1, 5		
8.	5, 1	1, 5	4.
9.	2, 3		
10.	3, 2	2, 3	5.
11.	2, 4		
12.	4, 2	2, 4	6.
13.	2, 5		
14.	5, 2	2, 5	7.
15.	3, 4		
16.	4, 3	3, 4	8.
17.	3, 5		
18.	5, 3	3, 5	9.
19.	4, 5		
20.	5, 4	4, 5	10.

$$P_2^5 = 20 \qquad C_2^5 = 10$$

Probabilities attached to permutations and combinations may also be observed from the foregoing example. Thus, if a universe consists of the digits 1 through 5 and the experiment is to draw two items at random from this universe, then there are 20 equally likely sample points for the experiment, and the probability of any permutation taken at random is 1/20. However, since each combination consists of two equally likely permutations, then the probability of any combination is 1/20 + 1/20 or 2/20. It might also be observed that if the experiment consisted of drawing two items from the universe and calculating the mean, then the probability of obtaining any given mean value within the scope of possible means is 2/20 = 1/10. This type of probability knowledge will be invaluable in the theory of sampling.

5.10 Summary and Looking Forward

The fundamental objective of the present chapter was to provide a background of understanding for the basic materials of probability applicable to elementary statistics. Throughout the chapter no attempt was made to provide an extremely sophisticated set of mathematically elegant materials; rather, the considerations were practical ones of the usefulness of this tool of thought to future types of statistical problems. We have attempted to understand the meaning of probability by considering relative frequency in the long run to be the probability that a defined event will occur. This concept of probability, simple though it may be, is a very powerful tool of understanding.

The next chapter will consider the application of probability concepts to yet another tool of understanding, the distribution of probabilities over a normal curve or over a binomially distributed variable. Once this is done, we will be in a position to understand sampling and statistical decision-making, which are among the central concepts of modern statistics.

Key Terms and Concepts of This Chapter

Combinations	Outcome of an experiment
Conditional probability	Permutations
Experiment	Prior knowledge
(a) Simple experiment	Probability
(b) Compound experiment	(a) Empirical probability
Equally likely	(b) Theoretical probability
Independent outcomes	Relative frequency
Joint occurrence	Sample point
Joint probability	Sample space
Mutually exclusive outcomes	Trial

Exercise 5.3. *Permutations and Combinations.* Numerical answers are shown in parentheses.

1. A retail clerk stacking the shelves has 8 different objects in his cart. How many different ways can he place these 8 objects in a line on the shelf? ($8! = 40,320$)

    (a) Suppose he lined up 7 of the 8 objects. How many different ways could he choose and line up 7 objects? (8! = 40,320)

    (b) How many different ways could he choose and line up 6 objects? (8!/2! = 20,160)

    (c) How many combinations of 6 objects could he make? (28)

2   A student about to graduate from college has 3 job interviews to schedule during a nine-hour period. Each interview requires one hour. How many different ways can he arrange (permute) these interviews? (504)

3.   A student must schedule 3 different class hours in a period from 8 A.M. to 3 P.M. inclusive. How many different class arrangements can he make—assuming he has full choice in the matter? (210)

4.   An automobile dashboard is to contain 5 different instruments in a line. How many arrangements of the instruments are possible? (5! = 120)

5.   An archery club has a membership of 20 persons. A committee of 4 is to be selected. In how many different ways might the members of the committee be selected from the membership? (4,845)

6.   From a reading list of 10 books, a student is to select 3 for a report. How many choices does this student have? (120)

7.   The chairman of the social committee is to purchase 4 prizes to be distributed at the next party. In a gift shop he finds 10 different acceptable possibilities. How many selections of 4 prizes can be made? (210)

8.   A specialty shop has been visited by 8 salesmen during the past 3 months. Each salesman has tried to persuade the shop manager to accept his particular line of merchandise. The manager has carefully considered the situation and decides to add four merchandise lines. In how many ways can he make his selection? (70)

9.   Given an experiment of tossing 4 coins at once. Draw up a sample space showing all the permutations. How might the permutation formula be applied in this case? Your sample space should show 16 permutations. How many combinations can be formed from these permutations? (5)

10. (Optional) An urn contains 3 red and 6 blue objects. If a random sample of 3 objects be drawn:

    (a) What is the probability the sample will contain exactly 2 red objects? (3/84)

    (b) What is the probability the sample will contain only red objects? (1/84)

    (c) Only blue objects? (20/84)

    (d) One red and two blue objects? (15/84)

Exercise 5.4. *Probability Review Problems*

1.   If your telephone is on a party line and the probability of finding the phone busy at any given time is .05, what does this statement imply in terms of the long run?

2.   Given the set of numbers 1, 2, 3, 4. Three of these numbers are to be selected at random. What is the probability that the mean of the sample will be exactly 3?

3. A production process produces parts which are known to be 5 per cent defective. If a random drawing of 100 items from the production line were made, how many of the items would be expected to be defective? Why?

4. Referring to problem 3 above, you probably indicated that five items could be expected to be defective. How "strong" is this expectation; that is, could you just as well have found three defectives? Four defectives? More than five? Explain.

5. On a certain campus, four student council offices are to be filled by a college-wide election. There are two candidates for each of the offices. Assume that the candidates for each office come from the campus and the academic parties. Make a list of the various ways in which the candidates can be elected to the four offices.

6. Given a set containing 1 black and 4 white marbles which are alike with respect to size and other characteristics except that the white marbles are numbered 1 through 4.
   (a) How many combinations of these marbles taken 5 at a time can be constructed?
   (b) What is the probability of drawing a random sample of 3 items such that the sample contains the black marble?
   (c) What is the probability of drawing a random sample of 3 containing no black marbles?

7. In a retail store there are some 15 varieties of breakfast foods. If a customer decides to purchase 5 packages of different cereals, how many combinations are available to him?

8. The university cafeteria menu contains 25 separate items available for lunch. Assuming a student selects six items for his tray, how many different combinations of items are available to him?

9. In a certain retail store display of convenience items, 20 different items are arranged. The probability that any given customer will purchase item A is .01; the probability that a customer will select item B is .03; the probability that a customer will select item C is .05. What is the probability that a customer will select all three items?

10. The 20 items mentioned in the question above are arranged on 4 shelves with 5 items to a shelf. How many ways may these 20 items be displayed?

11. In a firm the probability of being promoted three times after being hired is .6 for college graduates and .4 for noncollege personnel. After these first three promotions, the probability of the next two are .7 for college grads and .3 for noncollege personnel.
   (a) Out of a starting group of 20 college grads and 20 noncollege personnel, how many might we expect will be promoted three times?
   (b) How many of this starting group of 40 persons might we expect will ultimately be promoted five times?
   (c) What is the probability of a college grad's being promoted all five times?
   (d) What is the probability of a noncollege person's being promoted five times?

12. A farmer must harvest a crop before the first freeze in the fall. The probability that the crop will be ready for harvesting October 15 is .9. The probability of freezing weather on that date is .065. What is the probability that the crop will be ruined before it has ripened and can be harvested?

13. The manager of a large downtown department store conducted a study of the buying habits of "walk-in" customers. Over a period of weeks it had been determined that purchases varied with the day of the week. The manager felt that if he could establish a definite pattern of variation, it would be possible to allocate part-time help on the basis of this knowledge. The following table summarizes the results of the study.

Day of the Week	Per Cent of Walk-in Customers Making at Least One Purchase
Monday	30
Tuesday	15
Wednesday	35
Thursday	40
Friday	50
Saturday	70

(a) A walk-in customer enters the department store on an unspecified day of the week. What is the probability that he will make at least one purchase?

(b) Given that a person enters the department store on Friday. What is the probability that he will make at least one purchase?

(c) What is the probability that, if an individual walks into the store on Monday and on Saturday, that individual will make at least one purchase both days? Will not make any purchase?

(d) If an individual walks into the store on Monday and Tuesday, what is the probability that he will purchase one or more items during his two visits?

14. After bidding successfully on a new contract, a firm found it necessary to expand the working force by several hundred persons. Since much of the work to be performed was of a partially skilled nature, a training program was established for 300 of the new employees. Because it was impossible to know in advance the desirable amount of training per employee, it was decided to utilize a step approach. After the training period the employees were placed on the production line for one month. Their production records were then measured and the results recorded for guidance in future employee training programs. Thus, 100 persons were given three weeks of training, another 100 were given six weeks of training, and a final group of 100 were given nine weeks of training. The final results were tabulated as follows:

Production Rating	Training Period			Row Totals
	3 Weeks (L)	6 Weeks (M)	9 Weeks (H)	
Low (A)	50	20	10	80
Medium (B)	40	30	20	90
High (C)	10	50	70	130
Column Totals	100	100	100	300

(a) Given that an individual drawn at random has received nine weeks of training. What is the probability that this person has a production rating of C?

(b) Given that an individual drawn at random has received six weeks of training. What is the probability that this person has a production rating of C?

(c) Given that an individual drawn at random has received three weeks of training. What is the probability that this person has a production rating of C?

(d) On the basis of the table above, what can you say about the training program?

(e) Does the information in the table *prove* that nine weeks of training is the most desirable amount from the overall company point of view? Why?

(f) (Optional) Convert the frequency table above to a probability table.

(g) What is the probability that on a random selection of one individual from the set of 300, the person selected would be in:
   (1) subset A or subset B?
   (2) subset A or subset M?
   (3) subset B or subset L?

(h) Give the probabilities for the following: (1) (B and M). (2) (C and L). (3) (A and H). (4) ($A \mid M$). (5) ($A \mid L$). (6) ($B \mid H$).

(i) Make the following tests for independence between training and production rating: (1) A given L. (2) A given H. (3) C given L. (4) C given H.

(j) On the basis of your answers to question 9, is it clear that the production rating of the employees is not independent of the number of weeks of training? Explain.

Bibliography

See the bibliography at the end of Chapter 6.

THE NORMAL AND BINOMIAL DISTRIBUTIONS

6

6.1 Introduction

Among the most important concepts in modern statistics are those of the normal and binomial distributions of probability. Although the concept of the normal distribution was first formulated by De Moivre about 1733, only in more recent years has it been seen to have immense practical significance when applied to a whole cluster of related problems including those of quality control, sampling, and statistical decision-making.

It is the purpose of this chapter to provide an understanding of the fundamentals of the normal and binomial probability distributions. Actually, the degree of sophistication which is possible when these two distributions are studied in great detail would warm the heart of an Archimedes. The subject will not be studied to that degree of refinement, and it will be considered sufficient to provide an interpretative understanding of these distributions. Once this is done, that knowledge can be applied to some very practical kinds of problems. More than this must be left to advanced courses in statistics.

6.2 Symbols Used in the Present Chapter

The following symbols are used extensively in this chapter.

$\bar{X}$ = the mean of the X data. The X data are considered to be a random variable, just as in previous chapters. (See p below.)

$\sigma_{\bar{p}}$ = the standard error of a sample proportion or a percentage in a binomial-type (qualitative) universe. The concept of standard error is precisely the same as standard deviation used in previous chapters.

p = the mean of a sample proportion expressed either as a decimal or as a percentage. $\bar{p}$ may also be used.

P = the proportion of a universe which exhibits a defined characteristic. For example, if a universe of mass-produced parts is 1 per cent defective, $P = .01$.

Q = the proportion of a universe which exhibits the characteristic defined as not-P. For example, if a universe of mass-produced parts is 1 per cent defective, then $Q = .99$.

q = sample value for the proportion of a sample which is not-p. (See Q above.)

z = a standard deviation value from the mean of a distribution to a particular X value. The letter z is sometimes thought of as a "standard deviation distance." See Formula (6.1).

$P(X)$ = the probability that the random variable takes the value X. This is precisely the same usage as given in previous chapters.

X = a random variable. The letter X refers to the particular variable under measurement (for example, the number of heads showing on a toss of three coins).

$!$ = factorial. This is an operational symbol and may best be illustrated by an example. Thus, $4! = 4 \cdot 3 \cdot 2 \cdot 1 = 24$.

Y = the height of an ordinate. Ordinates are measured on the Y axis of a graph. In the material of this chapter, ordinates may be measured in terms of frequencies or in terms of probabilities.

x = a deviation measured as $X - \bar{X}$. This is precisely the same usage as employed in previous chapters.

Formulae for Use with the Binomial-Type (Qualitative) Universe

The standard error ($\sigma_{\bar{p}}$) for a distribution of sample values drawn from a binomial type universe may be expressed in three alternative ways. These are as follows:

(1)
$$\sigma_{\bar{p}} = \sqrt{npq}. \tag{6.6}$$

Example: If the standard error is to be expressed in terms of some attribute of the problem—for instance, the number of nonsmokers in an adult population—then this formula would express the standard error as a number of persons, perhaps 50 for a given problem.

(2)
$$\sigma_{\bar{p}} = \sqrt{\frac{pq}{n}}. \tag{6.9}$$

This formula expresses the standard error in decimal form. For example, the proportion of nonsmokers in an adult population might exhibit a standard error of .05.

(3)
$$\sigma_{\bar{p}} = \sqrt{\frac{pq}{n}}\,(100). \tag{6.9a}$$

This formula expresses the standard error as a percentage. For example, the percentage of nonsmokers in an adult population might be 5 per cent.

The mean of a set of sample items drawn from a binomial universe may be expressed as a number of items, say 700, and would be computed as as $\bar{p} = np$. For example, if $n = 1,000$ and $p = .7$, then the average number of nonsmokers in the sample is 700. If, however, it were desirable to express the mean of the sample as a proportion (decimal), the mean would be given simply by p, where $p = X/n$. To express the sample mean as a percentage, simply multiply by 100.

6.3   Description of the Normal Distribution

In the chapter concerned with the frequency distribution it was observed that the frequency column may be converted to "relative frequencies," which are really probabilities that a defined event E associated with the frequency experiment will occur. It was indicated that the class intervals of a frequency distribution may be regarded as sample points in the sample space. These sample points have a probability equal to the relative frequency of the class. What remains to be observed now is that the distribution of probabilities for a large number of empirical data situations can be generalized and converted to a single distribution known as the *normal distribution* or *normal curve*. Once a specific set of empirical data can be regarded as an approximation to a normal distribution, it becomes relatively simple to apply known tools of understanding to the specific problems for which the data were collected. The general appearance of a normal distribution is shown in Illustration 6.1.

Illustration 6.1   The Normal Distribution

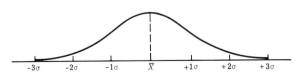

Strictly speaking, the normal distribution (also known as the normal curve) is applicable only to continuous data. The term "continuous data" was explained in Chapter 2 on page 19. Continuous data such as inches, miles, pounds, and so on may be considered as forming a *quantitative universe*. If the gap between values of discrete data are not too large, these data may be considered to be continuous as explained in Chapter 2. By way of contrast, a distribution of attributes—that is, characteristics which can be counted but not measured—will be known as a binomial-type or qualitative universe. The binomial distribution will be considered in Section 6.6.

Before an opportunity presents itself to become lost in a forest of normal curves, a bit of orientation will be in order. It would be well to remember that the final value of statistical tools lies in solving some type of practical problem. Thus, and first of all, *there exists some kind of problem* for which a solution is sought. This problem must be *defined* carefully. If conditions warrant and it is possible to *collect data* which throw light on the problem, that step should be undertaken. If the data collected are frequency data, they may then be subjected to *frequency distribution analysis*. If the frequency data approximate a normal distribution, it may be most appropriate to apply *knowledge of the normal curve* to further analysis of the problem. Finally, when all the information is collected and the analysis is completed, *some decision will be made* regarding the disposition of the problem. It is in this context that the normal distribution can be employed as a tool of analysis and understanding.

A wide variety of variables conform rather closely to the normal distribution. For example, if the numerical scores of a large number of students who completed an appropriate examination be grouped into a frequency distribution, the results tend to approximate a normal curve with mean $\bar{X}$ and standard deviation σ. Or, if the diameter of a large number of ball bearings produced by an industrial process be measured accurately and the measurements grouped in a frequency distribution, the results will approximate a normal curve—unless, of course, there is some basic flaw in the production process. To take another example, if the heights of Army inductees in World War II be grouped in a frequency distribution, the results would approximate a normal distribution. As a final example, suppose the weights of bars of soap produced by mass-production means were carefully determined and the results grouped as a frequency distribution. Here again, the distribution would be expected to be approximately normal.

Let us examine the soap-weight example a bit more closely. Given that an experiment has been performed—that is, the weights of a large number of bars (items) produced by a production process have been recorded and grouped as a frequency distribution. *Weight is here regarded as a random variable.* These recorded weights may exhibit an average of 3.00 ounces while the standard deviation is .03 ounces. Knowledge of the relative frequency of any given measurement in the range of the variable (say 2.96 ounces) makes it possible to determine the probability that a bar selected from the production process (assuming that the process has not changed meanwhile) would weigh the specified amount. The distribution could also be used to determine what percentage of the items weighed, say, more than 3.03 ounces or less than 2.95 ounces, or to determine the value of the 60th percentile, and so on. To make the example more specific, consider the distribution shown in Table 6.1.

Table 6.1

Frequency Distribution of the Weights of 300 Bars of Soap

X Midpoint (ounces)	f Frequency	P(X) Relative Frequency
2.90	3	.0100
2.92	7	.0233
2.94	10	.0333
2.96	18	.0600
2.98	57	.1900
3.00	110	.3668
3.02	57	.1900
3.04	18	.0600
3.06	10	.0333
3.08	7	.0223
3.10	3	.0100
	300	1.0000

From Table 6.1 the probability can be determined that a bar selected at random from the production process will weigh, let us say, between 2.99 and 3.01 ounces, as $P = .3668$. Or other probabilities could be determined —for example, the probability that the bar will weigh more than 3.05 ounces is $.0666 = .0333 + .0233 + .0100$. Other probability values could be determined as long as an *interval of weight* was stipulated and as long as the interval *began and ended at a class boundary*. But using class boundaries is a limitation. Methods can be devised which are more flexible and permit probability determination anywhere in the range of the variable.

The limitation that the interval begin and end at a class boundary can be removed if the distribution is considered to be a normal distribution and the variable considered *as if it were continuous*. Illustration 6.2 indicates how this transformation from the actual, discrete distribution to a continuous distribution may be visualized.

Illustration 6.2 Frequency Distribution of the Weights of 300 Bars of Soap

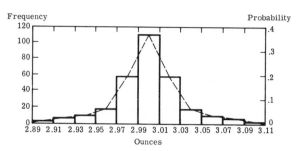

The dashed line in Illustration 6.2 is not precisely a normal distribution, but it can be assumed that the distribution is approximately normal. This assumption introduces the possibility of error, but the error will be relatively small if the original data do in fact approximate a normal curve. In any case it is a risk we will wish to take when the data justify making the assumption of normality.

6.4   The Standardized Normal Distribution

The standardized normal distribution or curve is a curve of unit area with a mean of 0 and a standard deviation of 1. The table of areas given in Appendix G provides proportionate areas (probabilities) for the standardized normal curve. The table of areas is used to facilitate the calculation of probabilities, percentages, and percentiles. These matters will now be examined.

If it is known or assumed that distribution of probabilities is approximately normal, then the distribution can be reduced to a *standard normal distribution* by a very simple process as follows: The mean of the empirical (actual) distribution is taken as the point of reference and assigned a standard deviation or z value of zero. Any X value on either side of the mean can be identified as a *standard deviation distance* from the mean (hereafter called z) by employing the following relationship:

$$\frac{X - \bar{X}}{\sigma} = z. \tag{6.1}$$

To illustrate some of the more mechanistic aspects of the standardized normal distribution, suppose the soap-weight problem were recast as follows: Assume that company officials have studied the production process carefully and know that the universe values are: $\bar{X} = 3.00$ ounces and $\sigma = .03$ ounces. The normal curve (not standardized at this point) would exhibit the general appearance shown in Illustration 6.2, with weights in ounces measured on the X scale. The height of the curve is not important, because in a normal distribution the only information required to answer probability questions is knowledge of the mean and standard deviation.

To convert the empirical data given above to a standardized normal curve, standard deviation is employed as the unit of measurement and all measurements are expressed as deviations from the mean. The mean itself is assigned a deviation value of zero. Any other point on the X axis can then be identified as a standard deviation "distance" from the mean. This point is shown by Illustration 6.3, on which both the X and the deviation values (z) appear.

Illustration 6.3 X and z Scales for the Data of Illustration 6.2

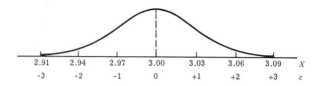

Conversion of the X values to z values transforms the distribution to a standardized normal distribution for which only one set of measurements, namely the z values, are necessary. Thus any distribution of empirical data *which is approximately normal* can be converted to the standard normal distribution. The conversion from X to z makes use of Formula (6.1). Two examples based on Illustration 6.3 are given below.

Example 1. When $X = 2.91$ and $\sigma = .030$, $z = -3$ because

$$\frac{2.91 - 3.00}{.03} = -3.$$

Example 2. When $X = 3.03$ and $\sigma = .030$, $z = +1$ because

$$\frac{3.03 - 3.00}{.03} = +1.$$

The great advantage of converting X values to z values is that it is now possible to calculate probabilities for any interval in the range of the distribution by use of a table of areas of the standardized normal curve.

How can probabilities associated with a normal distribution be determined by use of z values and a table of areas? A table of areas for the standardized normal curve is given in Appendix G. For simplicity assume the universe parameters for the soap-weight example are known ($\bar{X} = 3.00$, $\sigma = .03$) and it is essential to know the probability that an item drawn at random from the production process will fall in a certain interval in the range of the variable. To visualize this type of problem Illustration 6.4 and the examples which follow will be most helpful.

Illustration 6.4 Normal Distribution of Weights Where $\bar{X} = 3.00$ Ounces and $\sigma = .03$ Ounces

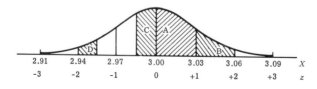

Example 1.   Using the data of Illustration 6.4, what is the probability that an item drawn at random from the production process will weigh between 3.00 and 3.03 ounces as shown in shaded area A? Answer: It is necessary to know the z distance of both 3.00 and 3.03 ounces. By Formula (6.1), the z value of 3.00 is 0, while the z value of 3.03 is +1. Thus, we are seeking an area which begins at the mean ($z = 0$) and extends to the right one z unit. Now turn to Appendix G and locate $z = 1$ in the left-hand column. Since $z =$ exactly 1, we move our eye one column to the right and observe the value .3413. This means that 34.13 per cent of the total area of the curve lies in the space between 3.00 and 3.03 ounces. The number .3413 is the probability that an item selected at random from the production process will weigh between 3.00 and 3.03 ounces. In percentage form 34.13 per cent is the relative amount of bars produced by the process and *which exhibit the weights specified.*

Example 2.   What is the probability that an item drawn at random from the production process will fall in area B and will weigh between 3.03 and 3.06 ounces? Answer: First of all, we need to keep in mind that the table of areas given in Appendix G only gives areas from the mean to a given z distance. Thus, in this case two stages of arithmetic must be employed. First, look up the z value of 3.06 ounces; z here $= 2$. The table value is .4772. Next, look up the z value of 1, which yields the table value of .3413. Then, by subtraction, $.4772 - .3414 = .1359$, which is the proportionate area between $z = 1$ and $z = 2$. Thus, the answer sought, namely the probability that an item drawn at random will weigh between 3.03 and 3.06 ounces, is .1359.

Example 3.   What is the probability that an item drawn at random from this universe will weigh between 2.985 and 3.03 ounces (that is, area C + area A)? Answer: For 2.985 ounces, $z = -1/2$: for 3.03 ounces, $z = +1$. Here is a case in which the area sought includes the mean. Addition is called for since the table of areas only yields answers for one-half of the standardized normal curve. However, since the normal curve is symmetric, it would be redundant to print the table twice. Thus, addition is used as follows: From the mean to distance $z = 1/2$, the area value is .1915. From the mean to $z = 1$, the area value is .3413. Thus, $.1915 + .3413 = .5328$. The probability sought is .5328.

Example 4.   Consider now the area shown in D of Illustration 6.4. To obtain the proportionate area bounded by 2.94 and 2.955 ounces, subtraction is again employed. The two z values are -2 and -1.5. The table value for $z = -2$ is .4772, while the table value for $z = -1.5$ is .4332. Subtracting, we have $.4772 - .4332 = .0440$, the answer we seek.

Example 5. What is the value of the 75th percentile? In this case the reasoning is as follows: The median in a symmetric distribution is identical to the mean. Therefore the 50th percentile is at $z = 0$ and $\bar{X} = 3.00$ ounces. The 75th percentile must be to the right of the mean. But how far to the right? Look at Appendix G and this time search the body of the table for the value .2500 or as near as possible to .2500. Here $z = .67$, the closest approximation in the table. Now, our answer must be expressed in terms of X. What is the X value of $z = .67$? It is $X = \sigma \cdot z = (.030)(.67) = .0201$. Finally, then, the median $= 3.00$, and we add .0201 to obtain 3.0201, the value of the 75th percentile.

6.5 Some Notes on the Normal Distribution

Up to this point the discussion of the normal distribution has been generally in the vein of "how to work the problem" rather than an explanation of the theory or "why the problem is as it is." It is now possible to look more closely, but briefly, at the theory of the normal distribution.

It is well to keep in mind the sequence of events which lead to the use of the normal distribution. First of all, we are attempting to deal with types of *practical problems arising out of business operations*. The solution of these problems often involves a good deal of theoretical apparatus. For example, it may be necessary to know whether or not an industrial process is producing a product which meets sales specifications. In solving the problem, it is necessary to *gather data* on the performance of the process. If the data are of the frequency type, an empirical distribution can be constructed. The empirical distribution tells us a good deal about the performance of the industrial process. For example, the mean, the standard deviation, the range, and the relative frequencies (probabilities) can be calculated. If there are irregularities or other difficulties, these can be spotted and checked out. As a result of this kind of knowledge, a process can be maintained at established standards throughout the production run.

In addition to the very practical knowledge originating in the empirical data, it is essential that there be some *standard of comparison*, some model, some theoretical norm or ideal against which the actual data can be compared. This model was here considered to be the normal distribution. But this is not to say that other theoretical distributions, such as the binomial distribution, might not be appropriate to other types of problems. At the moment our concern is with the normal distribution.

If the empirical distribution approximates a normal distribution, then a standard of comparison and a tool of decision-making is available in the normal distribution and all the known mathematical properties of that distribution. A technique is at hand by which certain kinds of problems and issues can be defined and decided. Obviously having such tools is a great advantage.

Notice, no assumption is made that any given empirical distribution is a normal distribution. All that is suggested is that *if the empirical distribution approximates the normal* then the normal can be used as a model. This transformation from the empirical to the theoretical introduces some error, but this is the price that must be paid for getting on with the tasks at hand. Techniques exist for determining *how closely a normal curve approximates the empirical data*, but such methods are not considered only briefly herein. (See, however, Chapter 10, Section 10.8.)

The normal distribution is a mathematically precise distribution. Since there is really an infinity of combinations for empirical distributions to exhibit different means and standard deviations and/or total frequencies, there exists an infinite number of normal distributions. For any given set of empirical data, the mathematical formula for a normal curve appropriate to those data is

$$Y = \frac{N}{\sigma\sqrt{2\pi}}\, e^{-x^2/2\sigma^2}, \tag{6.2}$$

where $Y =$ the height of an ordinate erected at x deviation from the mean,
$\quad x =$ a deviation from the mean—that is, $x = X - \bar{X}$,
$\quad N =$ the number of items in the distribution,
$\quad \sigma =$ the standard deviation of the distribution,
$\quad e =$ epsilon, 2.71828,
$\quad \pi =$ pi, 3.14159.

Armed with Formula (6.2), an empirical frequency distribution, and a generous quantity of patience, one can laboriously calculate the height of many ordinates, plot these on a graph, draw a smooth curve through the points, and derive a normal curve which precisely fits the empirical data. Ordinarily, however, there is no need for the statistician to undertake these calculations because his interest will not center in deriving a normal curve for the empirical data; rather he will wish to convert the empirical data to a standardized normal distribution. As observed, this conversion is a simple matter and does not require use of Formula (6.2).

The mathematical formula for the standardized normal curve of Appendix G is a good deal less cluttered in appearance than (6.2). Since the standardized normal curve has a mean of zero, a standard deviation of one, and is a curve of unit area, the formula becomes

$$Y = \frac{1}{\sqrt{2\pi}}\, e^{-x^2/2}. \tag{6.3}$$

Thus, Formula (6.3) yields *only one distribution, a standard normal distribution with mean 0 and standard deviation* 1.

By assuming that an empirical distribution approximates a normal distribution, it becomes possible to convert the original data to the standardized normal distribution and by-pass the mathematical calculations of either Formula (6.2) or (6.3). Since the table of areas for the standardized normal distribution is readily available in Appendix G, the matter of calculating probabilities turns out to be quite simple. This is generally considered good news by those who are not devotees of algebra and formula-solving.

How does the table of areas permit determination of probabilities? Probability has been interpreted as relative frequency in the long run. If, then, a frequency distribution exists which approximates a normal distribution, the probability of an event associated with the distribution must include all the frequencies and all the sample points so that $\Sigma f/N = 1$, or $N(E)/N(S) = 1$. What this means is that if a smooth curve be used to represent the distribution, the total area under the curve (see Illustration 6.3 for example) must represent all the probabilities of all the events associated with the experiment, and these must sum to exactly 1.0. The area of the curve includes all the probabilities.

Since the normal curve is a curve of probability, a small vertical portion or "slice" of the curve will also be a probability. The envelope of the curve reflects the manner in which the one unit of probability associated with the distribution is itself distributed over the range of the variable. Thus, the probability of an event near the end of the curve (such as $2.91 < X < 2.94$ in Illustration 6.3) will be a small number and the curve will be low—that is, near the X axis. On the other hand, an event which falls near the middle of the distribution will have a high probability since the envelope of the curve is relatively high in this range. In essence we are saying this: Since the total area under the curve represents the one unit of probability associated with the experiment, then a vertical portion or "slice" of the curve is a *portion of the total area*, and the proportionate area is the probability that an event will occur in the sample points bounded by that area. The table of areas is thus a table of probabilities. This is what Illustration 6.3 shows.

Although the normal distribution is mathematically precise, the probabilities derived for an empirical distribution by the area method will be approximate. Why should this be the case? In the first place, the empirical distribution of frequency data is necessarily a discontinuous distribution, as the realities of physical measurement suggest that rounding of numbers is a necessary fact of data collection. Because the distribution is discontinuous, the probabilities associated with specific outcomes are also discontinuous—that is, in graphic form, the probabilities would appear as a histogram rather than a frequency polygon. In contrast, the normal curve is a continuous curve—that is, it is like the frequency polygon. Secondly, empirical distributions are not likely to be precisely normal. Normality can be assumed, but applying a precise mathematical model to a set of somewhat imperfect empirical data will introduce some error. Thus, the probability calculations made by use of the standardized normal distribution are approximate. Finally, do not allow the ideal of "approximate" to mislead you. Approximations can be of immense value.

Exercise 6.1. *The Normal Distribution*
1. The standardized normal distribution is a curve of unit area with $\bar{X} = 0$ and $\sigma = 1$. Why is this so?
2. With reference to the frequency distribution and the normal distribution of probabilities:
    (a) In a frequency distribution problem, what is a simple experiment?
    (b) In a frequency distribution problem is it proper to think of N or n in terms of the number of simple experiments performed in a compound experiment?
    (c) What is the compound experiment referred to in (b)?
    (d) In a frequency distribution problem, how is it possible to speak of a measurement as the outcome of an experiment?
3. (a) By what reasoning is it possible to declare that an empirical distribution approximates a normal distribution?
    (b) Given this statement: An empirical distribution can, at its very best, only approximate a normal distribution. Why?
4. When Formula (6.2) is solved, the result is not a curve of unit area. What then is the area of a normal curve as derived from Formula (6.2)?
5. It has been said that if a distribution is normal and we are concerned with probabilities, all we need to know about the distribution is the mean and standard deviation. Why?
6. Two normal frequency distributions have the same mean and standard deviation but differ in respect to frequency. How would the graphs of these distributions differ?
7. Given two normal frequency distributions which have N and σ in common but differ with respect to their means. How would the graphs of these distributions differ?
8. The normal curve has been described by some students as a distribution of random errors. A description of the normal curve as a distribution of random errors was not, however, given in the text. Now, refer to Illustration 6.2 (the soap-weight example) and try to describe the distribution of weights about the mean as a distribution of errors. Could a normal distribution of examination scores be described as a distribution of errors?
9. A manufacturer of inexpensive wrist watches wishes to guarantee that the product will run 24 hours or more on a single complete winding. Production specifications are designed to allow the watches to run an

average of 26 hours on one complete winding. Repeated tests show that the watches have a mean running time of 26 hours with a standard deviation of 20 minutes.

(a) Does the manufacturer run a risk that the products violate the guarantee of 24 hours per winding?

(b) Is the manufacturer building more quality into these watches than he should? Explain.

(c) What percentage of the watches produced will have a running time in excess of:
   (1) 26 hours and 25 minutes?
   (2) 25 hours?
   (3) 25 hours and 40 minutes?

(d) What percentage of these watches will have running times between:
   (1) 25 hours, 40 minutes; and 26 hours?
   (2) 25 hours, 50 minutes; and 26 hours, 10 minutes?
   (3) 26 hours, 22 minutes; and 26 hours, 25 minutes?

(e) What is the value of the following:
   (1) the first quartile?
   (2) the 40th percentile?
   (3) the 90th percentile?

(f) What is the probability that any watch drawn at random from the production process would have a running time of:
   (1) between 25 hours, 30 minutes; and 25 hours, 50 minutes?
   (2) between 26 hours, 30 minutes; and 26 hours, 40 minutes?
   (3) exactly 26 hours?

10. A production process packages flower seeds at 1/8 ounce per package. Because of differences in seed sizes and moisture content, the actual count of seeds per package differs. Studies of this process yield the information that the average number of seeds per package is 100 and the standard deviation is 3. On the basis of this information, answer the following questions:

(a) What proportion of the seed packages will contain:
   (1) less than 91 seeds?
   (2) over 100 seeds?
   (3) 103 seeds or more?
   (4) 106 seeds or more?

(b) If a seed package were selected at random, what is the probability that the package would contain between 99 and 102 seeds inclusive?

(c) What is the probability that a randomly selected package would contain:
   (1) exactly 97 seeds?
   (2) more than 104 seeds?
   (3) between 96 and 99 seeds?

(d) Eighty per cent of the packages contain more than how many seeds?

(e) Thirty per cent of the packages contain less than how many seeds?

6.6   The Binomial Distribution—An Introduction

When a simple experiment results in one of two mutually exclusive outcomes, it can be said to be a binomial-type experiment. For example, when a coin is tossed it will land showing either heads or tails. No other outcomes are possible. Tossing one coin is a simple experiment, and if several coins are tossed simultaneously the experiment is a compound experiment in which each simple experiment (one coin) *must be independent of the other simple experiments* if the binomial distribution is to be applicable.

The binomial universe is a rather special type of universe because it is composed of attributes—that is, characteristics which can be counted but not measured.[1] For example, an adult population could be classified as "smokers" and "nonsmokers," and any adult group could be divided into these two categories. While it is true that the category "smokers" could be further subdivided into, say, "heavy" and "light" according to some criterion, the universe would still consist of two attributes and these could be counted in the same manner that heads and tails could be counted in a coin-tossing experiment. Thus a binomial universe is a population which can be divided into two mutually exclusive categories, the probabilities of which are usually designated as p and q. It makes no difference whether the letter p is selected for, say, "smokers" (because then q designates "nonsmokers"), or whether p is selected for "nonsmokers" (because then q would designate "smokers").

The binomial expression is $(p + q)^n$, where the letter p is the probability of one outcome of a simple experiment and the letter q is the probability of the remaining outcome of each simple experiment. The letter n indicates how many simple experiments are to be performed in each compound experiment. When the binomial expression is expanded the results are interpreted as "relative frequency" or "probability" for the events associated with the compound experiment. These matters will now be examined more closely.

The outcomes of binomial experiments are *random variables*. For example, if the experiment consists of the tossing of a single coin, the random variable may be designated as the number of heads showing after n trials—that is, after the compound experiment was performed. Conversely, the random variable could be considered as the number of tails showing upon the completion of n trials. Thus, whatever outcome is selected as the random variable is merely a matter of convenience. If a compound experiment consists of throwing a single coin twice ($n = 2$) and recording the number of heads per compound experiment, the outcomes are: 0 heads, 1 heads, or 2 heads. Conversely, the outcomes could have been listed as 2 tails, 1 tail, or 0 tails. Note that the number of heads (or tails) is the random variable.

The outcome of each compound experiment becomes one of the sample points in the sample space, and a probability can be determined for

[1] See also "attributes" as defined in Section 7.4, page 167.

each of the sample points. Thus, the probabilities of outcomes associated with the experiment distribute themselves over the sample space in a manner analogous to the distribution of probabilities in a normal distribution. It is *the distribution of probabilities* which becomes an important tool in solving many kinds of decision problems.

The binomial experiment may also be considered from a slightly different point of view. For example, suppose the simple experiment consisted of (a) taking a part at random from an assembly line and (b) checking to see if it is defective. When this inspection process is completed a second part is drawn at random from the assembly line, inspected, and assigned the attribute "defective" or "nondefective." Now, each of these inspections consists of a simple experiment, and the number of such simple experiments (*n*) to be performed in a given sequence or cycle will form the compound experiment.

When the compound experiment is completed the random variable, say "number of defectives," will be expressed as some integer: 0 defectives, 1 defective, 2 defectives, . . . , *n* defectives. Observe that the compound experiment, consisting of *n* simple experiments, really forms a sample of *n* items drawn from a larger universe. This larger universe consists of all the parts (items) produced by the production process under the currently existing circumstances of that process.

Observe also that if a large number of the outcomes of these compound experiments were considered to be the "raw data" of a frequency distribution, class limits and frequencies could be established so that a frequency distribution of the outcomes of the random variable could be constructed. This frequency distribution would, like all frequency distributions, have a mean, a standard deviation (hereafter to be known as a "standard error"), a mode, and percentile values just the same as those previously studied. Because of this ability to group the outcomes of binomial experiments in a frequency distribution, and because the characteristics of frequency distributions have already been studied, this knowledge can be applied just as well to the binomial experiment as to a universe consisting of quantitative values (inches, pounds, dollars, and so forth). Since probability has been defined as relative frequency in the long run, the relative frequencies of the outcomes of binomial experiments provide a distribution of probabilities for the random variable (say, the number of defective parts) of the experiment.

6.7 The Binomial Distribution

To illustrate the distribution of probabilities in a normal curve, the weights of bars of soap produced by a mass production process was previously employed. Now consider another production problem of the same manufacturer, namely the probability that the wrapper of the product will be torn or otherwise defective. The problem of the quality of the wrapper will illustrate the binomial distribution of probabilities. In this case either the wrapper is defective or it is not defective. Suppose further it is known from previous studies that *by very strict standards* 20 per cent of the wrappers are defective. These standards may, of course, be too high since the consumer is likely to be interested in the product and not the wrapper. Nevertheless, the example will serve to provide a good illustration of the binomial distribution.

In this situation the probability of a defective item is $p = .2$ (20 per cent). The probability of a nondefective item is $q = .8$ (80 per cent). Examining one bar of soap constitutes a trial of the simple experiment, and each trial of the simple experiment is independent of every other trial. Now, if the items are packaged three to a carton, it may be necessary to know the probability that any carton of three items will contain either 0, 1, 2, or 3 defectives. The random variable is X, the number of defective items. The task is to determine the probabilities of the values X can take—that is, $P(0$ defective), $P(1$ defective), $P(2$ defectives), $P(3$ defectives).

Example with Zero Defectives

Here the carton must contain no items having the characteristic "defective," so that the three items are all "nondefective" items. In other words, the characteristic "nondefective" must occur three times in a row. The multiplication theorem is appropriate. Since the probability of a nondefective item is $q = .8$, we have

$$(.8)(.8)(.8) = (.8)^3 = .512 = q^3.$$

The probability that a carton will contain no defective items is thus .512. Interpreted as relative frequency, it could be said that in the long run out of each lot of 1,000 cartons an average of 512 cartons will contain no defectives.

Example with Three Defectives

Here the carton must contain three items having the characteristic "defective" and again the three characteristics must occur in order—that is, the three times in a row. The multiplication theorem is appropriate so that $p = .2$ and

$$(.2)(.2)(.2) = (.2)^3 = .008 = p^3.$$

The probability that a carton will contain three defectives is thus .008. Interpreted as relative frequency, it could be said that in the long run out of each lot of 1,000 cartons an average of 8 would contain three defectives.

Example with One Defective

What about the situations in which the carton contained one or two defectives? This case merits close examination. A moment's reflection will bring to mind the question of permutations in the arrangements of the items in the carton. Since the items are packed three to a carton, it is possible that one defective could occur in any of the three positions in the carton as follows:

	Position 1	Position 2	Position 3
Case 1	Defective	Nondefective	Nondefective
Case 2	Nondefective	Defective	Nondefective
Case 3	Nondefective	Nondefective	Defective

As observed, if there is one defective in the carton, there are three ways this event could occur—that is, there are three permutations. Since "order counts," the multiplication rule is called for. But, at the same time since the interest is in one defective and there is no concern about the position of the defective, the addition as well as multiplication rule must be used. The following numerical example may help clarify the procedure.

What is the probability of Case 1? Multiplication is appropriate as follows:

$$P(D) \cdot P(ND) \cdot P(ND) = (.2)(.8)(.8) = .128 = (p)(q)(q) = pq^2.$$

What is the probability of Case 2? Multiplication is appropriate as follows:

$$P(ND) \cdot P(D) \cdot P(ND) = (.8)(.2)(.8) = .128 = (q)(p)(q) = pq^2.$$

What is the probability of Case 3? Multiplication is appropriate as follows:

$$P(ND) \cdot P(ND) \cdot P(D) = (.8)(.8)(.2) = .128 = (q)(q)(p) = pq^2.$$

Since the event "one defective" may occur in three ways, there are three sample points, each with a probability of .128 *and all must be included in the event*. Thus, the final probability is

$$.128 + .128 + .128 = 3(.128) = .384 = 3pq^2.$$

The probability that a carton will contain one defective is thus .384. Interpreted as relative frequency, it could be said that in the long run out of each lot of 1,000 cartons an average of 384 would contain one defective.

Example with Two Defectives

The reasoning in this situation is precisely the same as given in the example with one defective. To summarize: There are three ways the event "two defectives" may occur and each way has an identical probability, $P = p^2q = (.2)(.2)(.8) = .032$, but since there are three such ways the event can happen, the final probability is $3(.032) = .096$. Thus, the probability of two defectives is .096. Interpreted as relative frequency, it could be said that in the long run out of each lot of 1,000 cartons an average of 96 would contain two defectives.

The Final Probability Distribution

Now that the various parts of the problem of the number of defectives per carton have been considered, the problem may be viewed as a whole and shown in summary form (Table 6.2).

Table 6.2

Distribution of Probabilities for the Number of Defectives Packed per Carton of Three

X Defectives	Sample Points	Probability per Sample Point	$P(X)$ Probability
0	1	.512	.512
1	3	.128	.384
2	3	.032	.096
3	1	.008	.008
			1.000

Table 6.2 is a *distribution of probabilities* in exactly the same meaning of the term as a frequency distribution is a distribution of probabilities. The number of defectives is a random variable X, and the relative frequencies of the X values are $P(X)$. The distribution is, of course, skewed since it tails out towards the right. The binomial distribution of probabilities will be skewed whenever $p \neq q$. (The symbol $\neq$ means "not equal to.") Only in the case where $p = q$ is the binomial symmetric.

Two thoughts come to mind at this point. First, the values of p and q may be any decimal (or fractional) values subject to the restriction that $p + q = 1$. Secondly, it would be somewhat easier to compute binomial probabilities from a general formula than to tediously compute the number of permutations (sample points) and their corresponding probabilities. Each of these ideas will be taken up in turn.

With respect to the first point, namely that $p + q$ must sum to 1.0, a large family of binomial distributions exists because an infinite number of combinations of p and q are possible. Each different value of p (and thus of q) will yield a different distribution. Too, even though p and q were constant, changing n will alter the distribution, Thus, an infinite number of binomial distributions exist. The statistician could certainly have his work cut out for him. However, *if n, the number of independent simple experiments, is large, the binomial will approximate a normal curve.* In this case the normal curve can be substituted for the binomial. Even if p and q are unequal, but n is large, the normal approximation to the binomial distribution can be employed. A test as to whether the normal curve is appropriate may be employed as follows: If np and nq are both equal to or greater than 5, the normal approximation to the binomial may be used in lieu of the binomial distribution of probabilities. Thus, a table of areas rather than a binomial table can be used to calculate probabilities. The point to be emphasized is that many binomial-type experiments lend themselves to use of the normal curve and this is a highly desirable characteristic of the binomial distribution.

With respect to the second point, it was indicated that a general formula for the binomial would be useful for determining the probability of any value of the binomially distributed random variable X. This formula is as follows:

$$P(X) = \frac{n!}{X!(n-x)!} p^X q^{n-X}, \qquad (6.4)$$

where $X =$ the number of defined outcomes of the random variable (for example, the number of defective items in a carton),

$n =$ the number of independent simple trials in the compound experiment (for example, the number of items packed per carton),

$p =$ the probability of the outcome X,

$q =$ the probability of the outcome not X,

$! =$ factorial (for example, 3! means $3 \cdot 2 \cdot 1 = 6$; and incidentally, $0! = 1$ by definition).

To illustrate Formula (6.4), again let us use the soap-bar example. Suppose the question is raised: What is the probability that a randomly selected carton of three items will have exactly two defectives? Remembering that $P(D) = .2 = P$, and $P(ND) = .8 = q$, then

$$P(2 \text{ defectives}) = \frac{3!}{2!\,1!} (.2)^2 (.8)$$

$$= \frac{2 \cdot 1 \cdot 1}{3 \cdot 2 \cdot 1} (.04)(.8)$$

$$= (3)(.032)$$

$$= .096$$

—which is, of course, the same probability as obtained by the longer method shown on page 145.

In order to further clarify the use of Formula (6.4), some additional examples will be useful.

Example 1.   Four coins are tossed. The random variable is defined as the number of heads showing. Thus, $P(H) = 1/2$ and $P(T) = 1/2$. Since X is the number of heads, $p = 1/2$ and $q = 1/2$. What is the probability that, on a single toss of the coins, two heads will show? We have

$$P(2H) = \frac{4!}{2!\,2!} \left(\frac{1}{2}\right)^2 \left(\frac{1}{2}\right)^2$$

$$= \frac{4 \cdot 3 \cdot 2 \cdot 1}{2 \cdot 1 \cdot 2 \cdot 1} \left(\frac{1}{2}\right)^4$$

$$= \frac{6}{16}.$$

The student may now consider how the problem would differ if X were defined as the number of tails showing.

Example 2.   A sample of five items is to be drawn at random from an industrial process which produces a product known to be 1 per cent defective. What is the probability that the sample will show one defective item? Thus, $p = .01$ and $q = .99$, while $X = 1$. Then,

$$P(X) = \frac{5!}{1!\,4!} (.01)^1 (.99)^4$$

$$= \frac{5 \cdot 4 \cdot 3 \cdot 2 \cdot 1}{1 \cdot 4 \cdot 3 \cdot 2 \cdot 1} (.01)(.961)$$

$$= .04805.$$

Example 3.   A train arrives at a commuting station on time on an average of 8 out of 10 days. What is the probability that in a given week of 5 working days, the train will not arrive on time 2 of the 5 days? Thus, $p = .2$ and $q = .8$, while $X = 2$. Then,

$$P(X) = \frac{5!}{2!\,3!} (.2)^2 (.8)^3$$

$$= \frac{5 \cdot 4 \cdot 3 \cdot 2 \cdot 1}{2 \cdot 1 \cdot 3 \cdot 2 \cdot 1} (.04)(.512)$$

$$= .2048.$$

If the student should undertake to calculate the probabilities for other values of the random variable X, the answers, rounded to three decimals, will be:

$$P(0) = .328, \quad P(1) = .410, \quad P(2) = .205,$$
$$P(3) = .051, \quad P(4) = .006, \quad P(5) = .000+.$$

6.8   Some Notes on the Binomial Distribution

One of the significant features of the binomial distribution is that the mean and standard error (deviation) may be readily calculated by a simple form of computation as given in Formulae (6.5) and (6.6).

$$\bar{X} = np, \tag{6.5}$$

$$\sigma_{\bar{p}} = \sqrt{npq}. \tag{6.6}$$

The answers provided by Formulae (6.5) and (6.6) are expressed in terms of the attributes of the problem. For example, in a coin-tossing experiment, np = the average number of heads showing at the outcome of each experiment. Thus, if four coins are tossed simultaneously, the average number of heads showing will be two. Likewise, Formula (6.6) expresses the standard error of the binomial distribution expressed in terms of the attributes of the problem. For example, in a coin-tossing experiment, $\sqrt{npq}$ = the standard error expressed in units of either heads or tails—it makes no difference which attribute is under consideration as the standard error is the same for both. Thus, if four coins are tossed simultaneously, the standard error will be 1 since $\sqrt{(4)(.5)(.5)} = 1$.

Again, it may be worthwhile to emphasize that the terms standard deviation and standard error should not be matters of particular worry to the student. The standard error may be thought of in exactly the same manner as a standard deviation, the point being that a binomial universe itself has no variance, but a random variable which resulted from bi-nomial-type experiments would have a standard deviation. However, since the term standard deviation has been reserved for applications to universes—and there is no variance of a binomial universe from which to calculate a standard deviation—the term standard error is applied to the variability of the random variable which is recorded as the outcome of binomial-type experiments.

Another significant feature of the binomial distribution is the fact that it is a frequency distribution in exactly the same sense as any other frequency distribution. Thus, the knowledge previously developed in Chapters 2, 3, and 4 can be applied directly to the binomial distribution. For example, in Table 6.2 it may be noted that the X column can be thought of as representing the midpoints of class intervals for a discrete variable. The $P(X)$ column can be thought of as the frequency or weight column. If, for example, the mean of a binomial distribution were to be calculated, the method shown in Illustration 3.11 on page 55 would be employed. The assumed mean method shown also on page 51 could be used. It is suggested that the student try these methods with the data of Table 6.2. You will discover, of course, that the answer is identical to that of Formula 6.5.

The frequency distribution method of finding the standard error of the data is equally applicable to the binomial distribution. The method shown in Illustration 4.10 on page 86 may be employed to find the standard error. It is suggested that the student experiment with this method. At the end of the experiment, you will probably conclude that Formula 6.6—that is, $O_{\bar{p}} = \sqrt{npq}$ is really the preferred method since it yields the desired value with remarkable efficiency.

As indicated, the binomial $p = q = 1/2$ is symmetric. A graph of $(p + q)^n$, where $p = q = 1/2$, would display a symmetric distribution of probabilities about the mean. The graph would, however, be discontinuous since X is in integral value, and the probabilities would actually be "dots" rather than a continuous envelope (as was the case for the normal distribution). Now, if n is allowed to increase, the dots would come closer and closer together so that a continuous curve would be approximated. Yet, as n is increased the graph must spread to accommodate the larger n value, and as the graph spreads, it also flattens and the standard deviation increases while the mean moves to the right. As the graph flattens, the probabilities at either end of the distribution become almost zero. In fact, in many cases the probabilities at the end of the graph are so close to zero that it is appropriate to regard them as zero. The student may observe the spreading and flattening effects of the binomial by graphing one of the binomial distributions found in Appendix H where, say, $p = .1$ and where n is allowed to increase from, say, 5 to 10 to 15 to 20. See also Exercise 6.2, problem 3.

These "spreading" and "flattening" characteristics of the binomial suggest that a standardized distribution could be helpful by substituting one distribution for many. It would also be desirable if the standard distribution avoided the problems of spreading probabilities over a wide range. Fortunately, the undesirable characteristics of the binomial can be avoided by *substituting the standardized normal distribution when the value of n is large*—that is, when np and nq are both equal to or greater than 5.

Now suppose the binomial expression $(p + q)^n$ is skewed—that is, $p \neq q$. At first glance it does not appear that a normal distribution could be substituted for a skewed binomial—and in some cases the normal cannot be so substituted. However, if n is large, so that np and $nq \geq 5$, the graph of the binomial where $p \neq q$ has the curious characteristic of bunching on one end of the X scale. This property of probabilities refusing to scatter all along the X scale gives the interesting result that over the range in which probabilities do bunch together, *the distribution approximates the normal distribution.* This means that over the range of X values which the variable is most likely to assume, most of the probabilities fall in the range of $\bar{X} - 3\sigma$ and $\bar{X} + 3\sigma$. Thus, even a skewed binomial can be standardized if p and q are not extremely unequal—that is, close to 1—and if n is relatively large so that np and $nq \geq 5$. Clearly this characteristic of the binomial to approach normality is most desirable.[2] It is thus possible to apply approximation techniques and employ the normal standardized distribution as the basis for determining the probabilities of events which occur in the range of the variable. While some error is thus introduced, that error can generally be considered negligible if np and $nq \geq 5$.

In terms of methodology, how is the binomial standardized so that the normal standardized distribution may be substituted for the binomial? The technique is simple. Thus:

$$z = \frac{X - np}{\sqrt{npq}} . \tag{6.7}$$

But, employing the symbols to which we are most accustomed, (6.7) becomes

$$z = \frac{X - \bar{X}}{\sigma_{\bar{p}}} \tag{6.1}$$

and in this form the method is no different from that employed to standardize an ordinary frequency distribution, thus transforming the empirical data to a standardized curve with mean zero and standard deviation one.

At this point the student may well ask: "Under what circumstances would I need to use the actual binomial distribution of probabilities to evaluate $P(X)$, and when would I use the standardized normal distribution to evaluate $P(X)$?" The answer must be given in somewhat general terms since what one does depends in part upon the nature of the problem and the objectives to be served by the information. However, and speaking generally, if n is very small and regardless of the values of p and q, the

---

[2] The Poisson distribution may also be used where p, q, and n are small. However, the Poisson distribution is not discussed in this volume. See, for example, Frederick A. Ekeblad, *The Statistical Method in Business* (New York: John Wiley & Sons, Inc., 1962), pp. 155–163.

binomial distribution is the most appropriate distribution by which to determine the probability of the outcomes of the random variable. This means that either you may go ahead and solve the binomial formula (6.4) for whatever probabilities you require, or you may use a table of binomial probabilities (see Appendix H). On the other hand, if the problem for which information is sought does not require extreme accuracy and n is large so that np and $nq \geq 5$, the normal curve may be used.

As a specific example of the general methodology employed in evaluating probabilities, suppose you were concerned with the probability distribution where ten items were drawn at random from a universe in which $p = .4$. The binomial distribution would be used. But, if given the same universe and 50 items were to be drawn, the standardized normal distribution could be used. Again, this is a general rule and as such must be considered in light of the application of the information. If exact probabilities are required, a binomial table or a good deal of patient work would be necessary.

6.9   Percentages and the Binomial Distribution

In many types of problems the information sought is expressed not in terms of the number of X outcomes, but rather in the percentage of X outcomes. For example, in the previous soap-wrapper problem, it would be quite appropriate to speak of the percentage of defective items per carton. This could be viewed as a transformation in the manner of stating information and is shown in Table 6.3. One point should be observed now: namely, that if information is stated in percentage (or decimal) terms, the formulae required for the mean and standard error must be recast slightly. These formulae are shown below Table 6.3 and repeated subsequently in the paragraphs below.

As logic suggests and Table 6.3 indicates, there should be no difference in the probability distribution just because the random variable is expressed in alternative but equivalent terms. Percentage and proportion are merely equivalent methods of stating the outcomes of a binomial-type experiment. This flexibility of expression is a desirable characteristic. For example, in a good many problems, particularly those involving sampling in which the number of items examined for the X characteristic is large, it is easy to express the results in percentage terms. Thus, it is appropriate to say that a ton of taconite pellets is 60 per cent pure iron, or that the percentage of defective items in a box is $33\frac{1}{3}$ per cent. Applications will be seen in greater detail in the study of sampling theory.

One final point should be noted. If the outcomes of a binomial experiment are expressed as a proportion, how are the mean and standard

Table 6.3

Relationship Between Binomial Outcomes Expressed in Terms of X and in Terms of Percentages and Decimals (Soap-Wrapper Problem) $(p = .2; \ q = .8; \ n = 3)$

X Defective Wrappers in a Package of 3 Bars of Soap	$(X/n)100$ Percentage Defective	X/n Proportion Defective	$P(X/n) = P(X)$
0	00.00	.000	.512
1	33.33	.333	.384
2	66.67	.667	.096
3	100.00	1.000	.008
			1.000

Calculation of the mean:

$$\bar{p} = p = .2 \text{ or } 20\%.$$

Alternatively,

$$p = \bar{p} = \Sigma\left[\frac{X}{n} \cdot p(X)\right] = .2 \text{ or } 20\%.$$

Calculation of the standard error:

$$\sigma_{\bar{p}} = \sqrt{\frac{pq}{n}} = .23, \text{ or, } 23\%,$$

where p = Proportion of defective wrappers.

q = proportion of nondefective wrappers,

n = 3 (three bars of soap are packed per carton).

error for the number of defectives determined? The mean is given by the formula:

$$\text{mean} = \bar{p} = p = \Sigma\left[\frac{X}{n} \cdot p(X)\right]. \tag{6.8}$$

The standard error is given by the formula:

$$\text{standard error} = \sigma_{\bar{p}} = \sqrt{\frac{pq}{n}}. \tag{6.9}$$

It is easy enough to see that the mean of a proportion is $\bar{p}$ because, in the statement of the problem, it is noted that "the average number of defectives in the universe is (blank) per cent." It is not, however, quite so easy to see why $\sigma_{\bar{p}} = \sqrt{pq/n}$. An intuitive explanation may be given as follows: In terms of the units of the problem, $\sigma_{\bar{p}} = .675$ defectives. But, if it is desirable to express standard error in terms of proportion, the relationship $\sigma/n = .693/3 = .23 = \sigma_{\bar{p}}$ could be used. But .23 is precisely the value obtained by the formula $\sigma_{\bar{p}} = \sqrt{pq/n}$. Therefore, Formulae (6.6) and (6.9) are arithmetically equivalent.

6.10 Summary

The present chapter has examined two distributions of probability: the normal and binomial distributions. These distributions were a logical extension of the materials previously studied—the frequency distribution, measures of central tendency and of dispersion. Other types of probability distributions exist, of course, yet the binomial and normal distributions have long occupied a central position in the literature of statistics because of their extremely wide usefulness and adaptability to many kinds of problems. The objective has been to provide a basis for understanding these distributions.

Key Terms and Concepts of this Chapter

Approximation to the normal curve
Binomial distribution
Frequency model
Normal distribution

Proportion of the universe which
    may be characterized in a
    certain manner (as p or q).
Random variable
Standard deviation distance (z)
Standard error

Exercise 6.2
1. Using the binomial formula (6.4) derive a probability distribution for each of the following:
    (a) Three coins are tossed.
    (b) Four items are drawn from a universe where $p = .3$.
    (c) Five items are drawn from a universe where $p = .1$.
    (d) Six items are drawn from a universe where $p = .01$.

2. From a universe in which $p = .4$, what is the probability of each of the terms given below?
    (a) $n = 5, X = 0$.   (b) $n = 5, X = 2$.
    (c) $n = 8, X = 4$.   (d) $n = 10, X = 5$.

3. In order to demonstrate the spreading and flattening effects of a binomial distribution as n increases, draw graphs of the following four distributions for which the probabilities are shown in the body of the table at the top of page 154.

4. In order to demonstrate how the normal curve tends to bunch probabilities at one end of the X scale when the distribution is skewed, draw graphs of the following six distributions for which the probabilities are shown in the body of the table at the bottom of page 154.

Table of Probability Values of $P(X)$ Derived by Use of the Binomial Formula ($p = .5$)

X	n = 5	n = 10	n = 15	n = 20
0	.031	.001	.000	.000
1	.156	.009	.000	.000
2	.312	.044	.003	.000
3	.312	.117	.014	.001
4	.156	.205	.041	.004
5	.031	.245	.091	.014
6	.000	.205	.152	.037
7	.000	.117	.196	.073
8	.000	.044	.196	.120
9	.000	.001	.152	.160
10	.000	.000	.091	.176
11	.000	.000	.041	.160
12	.000	.000	.014	.120
13	.000	.000	.003	.073
14	.000	.000	.000	.037
15	.000	.000	.000	.014
16	.000	.000	.000	.004
17	.000	.000	.000	.001
18	.000	.000	.000	.000
19	.000	.000	.000	.000
20	.000	.000	.000	.000

Table of Probability Values of $P(X)$ Derived by Use of the Binomial Formula ($p = .1$)

X	n = 5	n = 10	n = 15	n = 20
0	.509	.348	.255	.121
1	.328	.387	.293	.270
2	.072	.193	.266	.285
3	.008	.057	.128	.209
4	.000	.011	.042	.070
5	.000	.001	.010	.031
6	.000	.000	.001	.008
7	.000	.000	.000	.002
8	.000	.000	.000	.000
9	.000	.000	.000	.000
10	.000	.000	.000	.000
11	.000	.000	.000	.000
12	.000	.000	.000	.000
13	.000	.000	.000	.000
14	.000	.000	.000	.000
15	.000	.000	.000	.000
16	.000	.000	.000	.000
17	.000	.000	.000	.000
18	.000	.000	.000	.000
19	.000	.000	.000	.000
20	.000	.000	.000	.000
21	.000	.000	.000	.000

5. From your graphs for problems 3 and 4, answer the following questions:
   (a) Describe what effect occurs as *n* is allowed to increase in a binomial distribution of probabilities. To what extent can you generalize and to what extent is it necessary to make separate statements about symmetric and skewed binomials?
   (b) Look at the graph of *n* = 20. Now, explain why the range of values which *X* can actually take is only a small portion of the possible 21 outcomes.
   (c) Considering the symmetric binomial, if *n* = 20, what appearance would the graph exhibit?
   (d) Now, does it seem reasonable to say that the normal curve may be employed as an approximation of the probabilities of a binomial distribution if the degree of skewness is moderate and if *n* is large? Is standardization of the binomial desirable when possible?

6. When you draw the graph of a binomial, the probabilities are "dots" at the ends of ordinates. Conversely, the probabilities of a normal curve are continuous and form the envelope of the curve. Why should these probabilities exhibit such different characteristics?

7. Use the binomial probability formula to calculate the probabilities of heads when six coins are tossed. When this is completed, determine the "expected frequencies" for an experiment consisting of tossing the coins 500 times—that is, performing the compound experiment 500 times.

8. An industrial process is known to be 2 per cent defective. What is the probability that, from a random drawing of four items, one will be defective?

9. A salesman finds from long experience that he obtains an order for his product on 20 per cent of his calls. What is the probability of two orders in a row? Could this problem be solved by the multiplication rule alone? Why?

10. Assume that the probability of a unit's being defective is .1. What is the probability that a sample of five units will contain one defective unit? That it will contain three defective units?

Bibliography

Excellent *extended* treatments of probability at a level appropriate to elementary business and economic statistics are, in the author's judgment, the following:

Goldberg, Samuel, *Probability: An Introduction.* Englewood Cliffs, N.J.: Prentice-Hall, Inc., 1960. 322 pages.

Lacey, Oliver L., *Statistical Methods in Experimentation.* New York: The Macmillan Company, 1953. 249 pages.

Mosteller, Frederick, Robert E. Rourke, and George B. Thomas Jr., *Probability and Statistics.* Reading, Mass: Addison-Wesley Publishing Company, Inc., 1961. 395 pages.

For the student who wishes to explore more fully the subject of "sets" see:

Hafstrom, John E., *Basic Concepts in Modern Mathematics*, chap. 3. Reading, Mass: Addison-Wesley Publishing Company, Inc., 1961.

Excellent treatments of probability for business and economic statistics may be found in:

Bowen, Earl K., *Statistics*, chap. 15. Homewood, Ill.: Richard D. Irwin, Inc., 1960.

Bryant, Edward C., *Statistical Analysis*, chap. 2. New York: McGraw-Hill, Inc., 1960.

Chernoff, Herman, and Lincoln E. Moses, *Elementary Decision Theory*, chap. 3. New York: John Wiley & Sons, Inc., 1959.

Croxton, Frederick E., and Dudley J. Cowden, *Practical Business Statistics*, 3rd ed., chap. 11. Englewood Cliffs, N.J.: Prentice-Hall, Inc., 1960.

Freund, John E., *Modern Elementary Statistics*, 2nd ed. chap. 7. Englewood Cliffs, N.J.: Prentice-Hall, Inc., 1960.

Grant, Eugene L., *Statistical Quality Control*, 2nd ed., chap. 9. New York: McGraw-Hill Book Company, 1952.

Hirsch, Werner Z., *Introduction to Modern Statistics*, chap. 5. New York: The Macmillan Company, 1957.

Kurnow, Ernest, and Gerald J. Glasser, *Statistics for Business Decisions*, chap. 5. Homewood, Ill.: Richard D. Irwin, Inc., 1959.

Mills, Frederick C., *Statistical Methods*, 3rd ed., chap. 6. New York: Holt, Rinehart & Winston, 1955.

Neter, John, and William Wasserman, *Fundamental Statistics for Business and Economics*, chap. 7. New York: Allyn and Bacon, Inc., 1956.

Rosander, A. C., *Elementary Principles of Statistics*, chaps. 6, 25. New York: D. Van Nostrand Company, Inc., 1951.

Schlaifer, Robert, *Introduction to Statistics for Business Decision*, chap. 1. New York: McGraw-Hill Book Company, 1961.

Tintner, Gerhard, *Mathematics and Statistics for Economists*, chaps. 20, 21. New York: Holt, Rinehart & Winston, 1953.

For a reference containing many probability experiments and suggestions, see:

Berkeley, Edmund C., *Probability and Statistics—An Introduction through Experiments*. New York: Science Materials Center, Inc., 1961.

An interesting and worthwhile reference for the general reader is:

Levinson, Horace E., *The Science of Chance*. New York: Holt, Rinehart & Winston, 1949.

The reader may be particularly interested in Chapter 16, "Fallacies in Statistics."

7 INTRODUCTION TO SAMPLING AND STATISTICAL INFERENCE

7.1 Introduction

Preceding chapters have discussed certain basic principles of probability, including probability distributions of random variables. All of this background is fundamental to the study of sampling. Now, in the present chapter, the principles of probability and sampling theory will be combined. The immediate task is that of exploring the nature of random sampling, the various problems of sampling, and some techniques for solving problems arising out of random sampling.

In approaching this new subject it may first be asked: Of what value is sampling? What is the process of sampling expected to accomplish? How does a knowledge of sampling fit into the overall framework of statistics, of the structuring of data and the use of information as studied up to this point? Some answers to such questions will now be suggested with the help of two examples.

Example 1. The basic goal of the sampling process is the supplying of usable information on which forward-looking decisions may be based. Sampling is thus an information-generating process. Suppose a business administrator faces this situation: His firm expects to produce a product for a market composed of thousands or millions of potential buyers. The administrator knows full well that the market is already being supplied by a number of firms whose products will be his competition. Before his firm definitely decides to enter this market the administrator will want to know the probable answers to many questions. Leaving aside the technical and engineering questions as to the feasibility of the firm's producing this new product, some information will be needed on the type (style, price, quality, and so on) of product salable in the market. How can such information be obtained? A direct analysis of the existing market and its products will answer many of these

157

questions, but some loose ends may remain. What attributes of the product does the market prefer? Is there a particular style, package, color, price, and type of outlet which the buying public prefers and will definitely absorb in quantities sufficient to permit mass production? The only avenue through which this kind of information may be obtainable could well be a scientifically designed random sample or samples. There is no need to dwell on the importance of such information to the decision-making process. The significance should be obvious.

The information supplied by a sample is subject to some degree of error simply because a sample is only a part of the universe (population) being sampled. Under these circumstances some kind of *inference* must be made from the sample information to formulate a judgement about the universe. The word "infer" means to reach a conclusion about an entity (that is, a universe) from an incomplete representation (sample) of the totality. Inference is a type of deductive reasoning—that is, reasoning from the known (sample information) to the unknown (the parameters of the universe). To move from the known to the unknown always involves a risk of making a mistake. However, since it is not always possible to possess complete information, incomplete information must be employed and inferences must be made in order to get on with the work at hand. And, as this chapter will try to show, inferences drawn from samples need not be haphazard but rather may be drawn in such a manner as to permit an evaluation of the inference in terms of the probability of its being correct.

Example 2.   To glimpse some of the mechanics of sampling without considering all the minutiae of the problem, consider next a case involving a television station in a particular community. The station telecasts a program of local interest to adults during the so-called prime viewing time in the evening. The manager of the station and the sponsor are understandably curious as to the number of people watching the local program. It would be nearly impossible to contact each individual in the local community and ask if he viewed the program. Some sampling technique therefore becomes essential.

The station manager knows one inexpensive method of obtaining the information sought. (1) Telephone a number of potential viewers on the evening of the telecast and ask if they viewed the program. (2) For each phone call completed the response will be "yes" or "no." If the answer is yes, the number 1 will be recorded for each adult viewer watching the program. If the answer is no, a zero will be recorded for each adult. (3) Now, if all the zeros and 1's are summed and divided by the total calls completed, the result will be the proportion of viewers who replied they were watching the program. (4) It will be assumed that the proportion of viewers in the sample is approximately the same as the proportion of adult viewers in the community. This knowledge, along with the assumption that the sample information is a good estimate of the universe information, is sufficient for the manager's and sponsor's purposes. (5) If, however, the manager wished to express the information in terms of number of persons rather than as a proportion, he could multiply the adult population of the community by the percentage of viewers in the sample and conclude that approximately X number of people watched this particular telecast.

Now, in this situation a number of variables are unaccounted for. Perhaps all television receiver owners do not have telephones and, since the survey was made by telephone, the non-telephone viewers are not represented in the sample. Or, possibly on the evening of the survey several community activities occurred that drew some persons away from their TV sets. There could have been a concert, a ball game, or bargain sales at local stores. Too, the survey may not have accounted for the fact that some viewers did not understand the questions and may have replied incorrectly. It is clear, without going into additional detail, that the survey supplies information but the information is subject to an interpretation involving possible errors, because sample information is incomplete information.

Some Basic Notions

A sampling inquiry involves, first, defining the problem and identifying general areas for which information is sought. The technique for obtaining the information must be selected. Here it has been suggested that sampling may be the proper method. The next problem is the proper interpretation of the sampling information as it has been obtained—that is, statistical inference. Once all of this has been accomplished, the final step involves deciding the issue (or issues) associated with the original problem.

Lest the hasty conclusion be drawn that sampling techniques to supply desired information are something quite new and different, it may be indicated that sampling is one of the oldest of ideas. The principle of tasting a bit of food or beverage to ascertain its quality has been used for centuries. As a matter of fact a good deal of our daily experience is really a sample drawn from a larger universe although the drawing may be haphazard. In contrast, the fundamental notion involved in scientific sampling is that an experiment can be designed in such manner as to provide sufficient information about the "universe" from which the sample was drawn to permit the making of correct decisions. For an ordinary example of one use of sampling, it is commonplace today to occasionally receive a free sample of toothpaste or foodstuff or swatches of cloth. In these cases it is inferred that the sample will be a true representation of the larger product and that the sample size is sufficient to convince a potential purchaser of the merits of the item.

While the notion of sampling is of ancient vintage, what is relatively new about the *process* and *theory* of sampling would fill several good-sized volumes. In the past two decades great strides have been made in sampling theory, and today the literature as well as the practice of supplying information by means of sampling is voluminous and sophisticated. Whereas a student of business and economics a generation ago might have by-passed sampling as unnecessary to his academic pursuits, knowledge of the process is today absolutely essential.

The basic reason for employing sampling techniques is, as has been observed, the necessity of making forward-looking decisions. These decisions require reliable information in order that the probability of "correct" decisions be as high as possible. Since samples are only a portion of larger universes from which they were drawn, samples are incomplete representations of the total information available in the statistical universe. Information supplied by samples is incomplete because *a portion—not the entirety—is studied.* This means that sample information supplies *estimates* of exact values of the information sought— that is, estimates of the parameters of the universe. A parameter is a statistic of the universe, and therefore an exact or "true" value, as contrasted to a sample statistic, which is an estimate of the true value. The estimates furnished by samples can be extremely close approximations— so close, in fact, that they can serve as the factual basis on which highly important decisions are made. When carefully designed and rigorously applied sampling techniques are employed under appropriate circumstances, the estimates will be extremely reliable. Sampling knowledge may be used in conjunction with a powerful technique for extending knowledge, namely statistical inference, the drawing of conclusions to which a high degree of probability may be attached even though the information on which the conclusion is based is incomplete.

The use of samples to provide reliable information demands that each step of the process be carefully designed and that the results be logically interpreted and applied with full knowledge of the possible sampling error. It is certainly a mistake to assume that reliable information can be provided by faulty samples; it would be equally fallacious and wasteful to use the results of excellent samples in a loose or ambiguous manner. None of the steps involved in designing and carrying out a sampling process can be slighted. The task of the analyst is to draw worthwhile conclusions from incomplete information. It is the task of the administrator or manager to make decisions based on this information. If the data are incomplete, they ought to be as reliable as time and costs permit.

Sampling Universe and Sampling Distribution

The distinction between a *sampling universe* and a *sampling distribution* will now be explained.

Suppose that on the desk before you there is a box containing a large but finite number of "chips"—that is, pieces of wood or paper on which numbers have been printed, one number for each chip. Consider this to be a *sampling universe*—a universe from which samples may be drawn. Now, it would be possible to draw each number from the universe, make an array of all the values, form the data into a frequency distribution, and by means of a table or graph express the sampling universe in visual form. This universe would exhibit a mean, median, mode, percentiles, range, and standard deviation, and in relative frequencies would also display the properties of a probability distribution.

However, suppose that instead of all chips being drawn from the box so that the universe values (known as parameters) could be determined, the chips were randomized by a vigorous stirring and then, at random, only a few chips were drawn. *Together these few chips form a sample.*

Each chip or item, as drawn, constitutes a simple experiment, and the several chips, taken together, constitute one compound experiment (sample) composed of n simple experiments. The outcome of each compound experiment can be determined as a mean, or a median, or a mode, or a range, or a standard deviation, or all of these. Suppose we concentrate only on the outcome "mean of the sample," and suppose the compound experiment was repeated a number of times. Clearly, the sample means resulting from the experiments become a random variable which takes the value $\bar{X}_1$, or more appropriately here, $\bar{x}_1$, $\bar{x}_2$, and so on.

If, when the first sample of size n has been drawn, the mean (say $\bar{x}_1$) is calculated and the items are then returned to the box, the entire process may then be repeated and a new sample composed of n trials of the simple experiment drawn. It is understood that n is constant for all samples of this particular experiment. The random variable now takes the value $\bar{x}_2$. The items are then returned to the universe and a third sample is drawn. The random variable now takes the value $\bar{x}_3$.

It is clear that if the compound experiment—that is, drawing a sample of size n—is repeated many times, the random variable $\bar{X}$ will have taken values $\bar{x}_1$, $\bar{x}_2$, $\bar{x}_3$, ..., $\bar{x}_k$. The values of the random variable are sample means. These means may now be: (1) arrayed, and (2) grouped

into a frequency distribution known as the *distribution of sample means.*
Clearly, this distribution of sample means will not be identical to the distribution of the original sampling universe. Thus *two* distributions now exist,
a *sampling universe* and a *distribution of sample means.* Each is a frequency
(probability) distribution but each has its separate identity, and the
principles discussed up to this point in the various chapters of this book
are applicable to both distributions.

The student is urged to keep this distinction between the sampling
universe and the distribution of sample means clearly in mind, as much of
this chapter depends upon a knowledge and elaboration of the distinction
between the two distributions.

Exercise 7.1

1. What, in a general way, are the objectives of sampling processes?

2. Considering Example 1, involving the business administrator and the new
   product, how would you, at this stage of your statistical knowledge, go
   about collecting information on consumer preferences for the new product—
   assuming the product to be a new style of men's dress shoes?

3. Considering Example 2, involving the television station manager, how
   would you go about setting up the telephone procedures? How many
   people would you employ on this project and for how long? What might
   be the cost of the survey information—supposing the city population to be
   250,000?

4. Is the general principle of sampling very new? To what extent have you
   observed the use of sampling techniques in relation to product, mail, or
   telephone surveys? To what extent are your own observations samples?

5. Explain the difference between a sampling universe and a distribution of
   sample means. What is the random variable in this situation? Why is it a
   random variable? Will the random variable have a frequency and a
   probability distribution? Why?

6. Check carefully on the meaning of the term "deduction" and the term "inference." Now, explain why inference always involves a risk of being
   incorrect.

7.2 Criteria for the Use of Sampling

As previous chapters have indicated, the statistician must first
formulate and define the problem or question clearly and in known
terms. Identification, formulation, and definition of a problem are not
simple tasks. The statistician should know precisely what questions the
sampling information will be asked to throw light upon. He should also
know what kinds of data are required and *if* the data may be obtained
through sampling methods. The statistician should also be conversant

with other studies of a similar nature—if such studies exist. If a sample survey was made a year or two ago along the same lines as are now proposed, the earlier study should be carefully examined before proceeding with the current survey. It is true that many tasks performed by the analytical statistician are rooted in common good sense and that an intelligent, experienced person would intuitively understand the general process. However, there are many technicalities of scientific sampling for which general knowledge and good sense are not in themselves sufficient. In the realm of sampling, it would take several lifetimes of experience to learn what current sampling theory already has to offer.

Some of the criteria on which the decision to use sampling may be based include the following:

1. The information may be available only through sampling.
2. The information may be speedily obtained by sampling methods.
3. Accuracy of the sampling information may be as good or better than that of information obtained from other sources.
4. Sampling methods may be considerably less costly than other information-generating techniques.
5. Sampling techniques have been developed and refined to the point where reliability is extremely dependable. However, reliability depends upon carefully designed samples in which each step of the process has been carefully carried out. Reliability refers to how closely the sample and parametric values agree.

The overall framework within which sampling methods are judged to be applicable is broadly part of the decision-making process. The following points indicate the methodology of sampling to be followed, once it has been decided to go ahead.

1. A problem has arisen for which clarification and possible answers depend upon information which is not readily available.
2. To obtain the required information the decision is made to utilize some variant of sampling.
3. A decision is made as to the particular type of sampling process or plan to be used.
4. The sample is then designed and the mechanical details are carried out.
5. Final results are tabulated and made available in summary form to those whose responsibility it is to decide the original issue or problem. Graphs, tables, and summary charts may be used for this purpose.
6. Insofar as possible this particular study may be used as the basis for future studies and for determining the possible improvements to be made should another similar sample be subsequently decided upon. If the information is filed, as it will be, it ought not to be permanently buried and lost. Valuable clues for future studies should be readily available in the files of past studies.

7.3   Sampling Notation and Explanation

The following symbols are of major importance; all other symbols remain as previously defined.

σ = the standard deviation of a quantitative universe. Note: a binomial (qualitative) universe does not have a standard deviation.

$\sigma_{\bar{x}}$ = the standard error of the mean—that is, the standard deviation of a distribution of sample means.

g = the expansion factor N/n.

f = the sampling fraction n/N.

N = the number of items in a clearly defined universe or set. These items could presumably be numbered from 1 to N.

n = the number of items to be included in the sample which will be drawn (or has been drawn) from the specified universe.

S = an estimate of the standard deviation of a universe as derived from calculating the standard deviation of a single sample of several items.

$S_{\bar{x}}$ = the standard error of a sampling distribution where S has been used as an estimate of σ, the standard deviation of the universe.

Notation for Binomial Populations

P = the proportion of items in a *universe* possessing some specified attribute. (An attribute is a characteristic which can be counted but not measured.) Suppose a finite universe consisted of ten parts, each of which was to be tested to discover if the part was defective or nondefective. As each part was tested, the number 1 would be assigned if the product was defective and the number 0 would be assigned if the product was nondefective. At the end of the ten tests, the 1's and 0's would be summed as ΣX. Thus, if ten parts were tested and two were found defective, the proportion P would be $2/10 = .2$. Thus $P = \Sigma X/N$, where N = the number of items tested and X is either 1 or 0 as defined above. In summary, then, P is defined as the proportion of items in a *universe* possessing a specified attribute. P is thus considered to be a parameter, a universe value.

Q = the proportion of items in a *universe* not possessing some specified attribute. For example, if P (as defined above) refers to defective parts, then Q refers to nondefective parts. In the example above where a universe of ten parts was examined, and two were found to be defective, eight parts must have been nondefective. Thus, $Q = 8/10 = .8$. Note that $P + Q$ must always sum to 1.

$p =$ the proportion of items in a *sample* possessing some specified attribute. When a sample is drawn from a universe, the object of sampling is, of course, to estimate the universe value P from the sample itself. Thus, p is an estimate of P. The calculation of p is exactly the same as the calculation of P as explained above. Thus, if in a sample of ten items two were found to be defective, $p = 2/10 = \Sigma\ X/n$. (Small n is used to indicate the number of items in the sample.)

$q =$ the proportion of items in a *sample* which do not possess some specified attribute. For example, if p (as defined above) refers to defective parts, then q refers to nondefective parts. In the example above where a sample of ten parts was examined and two were found to be defective, eight parts must have been nondefective. Thus, $q = 8/10 = .8$. Note that $p + q$ must always sum to 1.

Remember: Strictly speaking, a binomial-type universe has no mean and no standard deviation. The universe consists of a number of items possessing characteristic P (or whatever it may be designated as) and the remainder of the items possessing characteristic Q (or whatever it may be designated as). The universe does have a proportion P and a proportion Q which are the parametric values. Sampling distributions drawn from this universe will have a mean proportion and a standard deviation known as the *standard error of the distribution of sample proportions.*

$\sigma_{\bar{p}} =$ the standard error of a distribution of sample proportions. Technically, $\sigma_{\bar{p}}$ is the standard deviation of the distribution of sample proportions and measures the amount of sampling error inherent in the particular sampling experiment under consideration.

7.4   Definitions of Terms and Concepts

The following are important concepts in the theory of sampling.

1.   Universe and Set

A universe is a "set." In fact, a universe is the "universal set." Of this set there may be many "subsets"—that is, sets which themselves constitute only a portion of the universal set. (The empty set may be neglected.)

Thus, in sampling theory, a sample drawn from the universe constitutes a subset of that universe. Clearly, there may be many subsets of a given size (n), all of which constitute possible samples from the universe whose size is N.

The basic formula for combinations applies to samples drawn from statistical universes. To illustrate: If the universe is of size N, and if the sample is of size n, then:

The number of samples which may be drawn from this particular universe $= C_n^N = \dfrac{N!}{n!(N-n)!}$.

Example. Given the universe: 0, 1, 2, 3, 4. Make a listing of all possible different samples of size 3 which could be drawn from this universe. (Note: $C_3^5 = 10$.)

Table 7.1

All Possible Samples of Size 3 Which Could Be Drawn from the Universe: 0, 1, 2, 3, 4

Sample Number	Combination	Sample Number	Combination
1	0, 1, 2	6	1, 0, 4
2	0, 2, 3	7	1, 0, 3
3	0, 3, 4	8	2, 3, 4
4	1, 2, 3	9	2, 1, 4
5	1, 3, 4	10	2, 0, 4

The combination formula indicates there are ten different samples of size 3 which may be drawn from a universe of five items. If one and only one sample of size 3 were to be drawn from this universe, that sample must be one of the combinations shown in Table 7.1. The probability of drawing the first sample combination can be completely specified as $1/C_n^N$. If the sample items are drawn, recorded, and the items returned to the universe, then the probability of drawing each individual sample from the universe above is constant $(1/10 = .1)$. If, on the other hand, the sampling universe consisted of a small finite number of items, then as additional samples were drawn without replacement, the probability for such sequentially drawn samples would increase with each drawing and for the last sample drawn $P(X) = 1.0$.

2. Sample

The word sample refers to a subset of the universal set. The process of drawing a sample implies the selection of a fraction of the universal set, and it will be inferred that the subset is an accurate representation of the universe. In other words, the information contained in the universe is also thought to be contained in the sample. Thus, whatever information is revealed by the sample is also considered to be true of the universe. A sample serves as the basis for discovering information—that is, for formulating estimates of the characteristics or attributes of the universe.

The process of sampling does not, by itself, imply or specify any particular method to be employed in obtaining the sample. There are many "types" of sampling procedures, some of which will be mentioned below. However, throughout this book the concern is with *random* samples (meaning the items in the samples were selected by chance).[1] It is also necessary to be concerned with the probability that the sample information is actually a reliable estimate of the information contained in the population, and it will be important to study the means of drawing inferences from the sample data.

3. Attributes

The word attribute refers to "things" which can be counted but which are not subject to measurement. The random variable "number of heads showing" in a coin-tossing experiment would exemplify an attribute. Other examples of attributes would be years of college, true or false, red or green, defective or nondefective, and so on. Attributes may sometimes be expressed in terms of proportion; for example, the proportion of nondefective parts in a lot. Such variables are frequently referred to as "binomial," and this implies that the probabilities are binomially distributed.

4. Elementary Sampling Unit

The e.s.u. is the individual unit of the sampling population possessing the characteristic(s) of interest in the sample inquiry. The e.s.u. might be a person, an object, part of an object, or some other distinct entity forming part of the sampling set.

5. Primary Sampling Unit

The p.s.u. refers to a particular *whole unit* of the sampling population. It might or might not be an elementary unit. For example, the p.s.u. might consist of various city blocks which in turn are composed of various elementary sampling units, say housing units. In another case, the p.s.u. might be business firms or office buildings. The distinction between elementary and primary sampling units is not necessarily a sharp one. However, primary units are generally composed of a number of elementary units. Thus, for a given sampling inquiry, certain primary units may be selected (city blocks), and within each p.s.u. certain elementary units may be sampled.

---

[1] The word "random" as applied to sampling is defined in Section 7.5. At present the student may merely consider "random" to mean that the sample was selected through the operation of chance factors.

6. Sampling Frame

The sampling frame consists of a means or technique for identifying the sampling units which are to become part of the inquiry. The frame is really the universal set, the population. For example, a map of a city showing blocks and residences could constitute the sample frame. Other examples would be: (1) a firm's payroll by names, (2) a complete listing of grocery stores in a city, (3) a telephone book, (4) automobile registrations. Too, a sampling frame might be thought of as all the products from an assembly line, all the objects in a carton, or all the books in the library. However, in the latter situations, it is probably better to consider these things as a universe or set rather than a frame.

7. Sampling Bias

The term "sampling bias" is to be distinguished from "sampling error," which is defined below. Sampling bias refers to the difference between the value of the parameters and the corresponding sample statistics—such difference being due to some factor preventing true randomization of the items drawn. For example, if the wheat in a grain car is not sampled at random—say, the sample was all taken from the top—the grading would be biased. As another example of sampling bias, in designing a questionnaire to be completed by respondents the very design of the questions may solicit an answer which was "suggested" by the question itself. Obviously, under these circumstances, respondents tend to provide answers which are less than objective.

8. Parameter

A parameter is the true value of some statistics of the universe. The word parameter refers to a "true" value and is distinguished from sample values, which are "estimates" of parameters.

9. Sampling Error (Sometimes Known as "Sampling Variability")

When samples of size n are drawn from a universe of size N ($n < N$), there will tend to be slight discrepancies between the various parameters and the corresponding sample statistics. These differences are inherent in the very nature of sampling. This may be illustrated by observing the results of the ten possible samples previously considered in Table 7.1 and shown in Table 7.2.

Example. Using the data of the sampling combinations of Table 7.1, calculate the means of each of the ten samples and find the overall average of the ten sample means (Table 7.2).

Table 7.2

All Possible Mean Values for Samples of Size 3, Drawn from the Universal Set: 0, 1, 2, 3, 4

Sample Number	Sample Mean ($\bar{x}$)	Sample Number	Sample Mean ($\bar{x}$)
1	1.00	6	1.67
2	1.67	7	1.33
3	2.33	8	3.00
4	2.00	9	2.33
5	2.67	10	2.00
			$\Sigma \bar{x} = 20.00$

$$\frac{\Sigma \bar{x}}{N} = \frac{20.00}{10} = 2.0 = \bar{X},$$

where N = the number of samples.

Now that all possible means are known, suppose these are grouped in a frequency table as shown in Table 7.3.

Table 7.3

Distribution of Sample Means Based on All Possible Mean Values for Samples of Size 3 Drawn from the Universal Set: 0, 1, 2, 3, 4

Sample Mean Values $\bar{x}$	Frequency	Probability	$\bar{x} - \bar{X}$	$f\bar{x}$	$f(\bar{x} - X)^2$	$\bar{x}/\bar{X}$
1.00	1	.1	−1.00	1.00	1.00	0.50
1.33	1	.1	−0.67	1.33	0.44	0.067
1.67	2	.2	−0.33	2.34	0.22	0.083
2.00	2	.2	0.00	4.00	0.00	1.00
2.33	2	.2	0.33	4.66	0.22	1.16
2.67	1	.1	0.67	2.67	0.44	1.33
3.00	1	.1	1.00	3.00	1.00	1.50
	10	1.0		20.00	3.32	

Universe values:

$$\sigma = 1.41, \qquad \bar{X} = 2.00.$$

Sampling distribution values:

$$\bar{x} = \frac{\Sigma f\bar{x}}{\Sigma f} = \frac{20.00}{10} = 2.00,$$

$$\sigma_{\bar{x}} = \sqrt{\frac{\Sigma f(\bar{x} - \bar{X})^2}{\Sigma f}} = \sqrt{\frac{3.32}{10}} = .577.$$

Observe that $\sigma_{\bar{x}}$ could also be calculated from the formula

$$\sigma_{\bar{x}} = \frac{\sigma}{\sqrt{n}} \sqrt{\frac{N - n}{N - 1}} = \frac{1.414}{\sqrt{3}} \sqrt{\frac{5 - 3}{5 - 1}} = .577.$$

It may be observed that of the ten samples six are either the exact universe mean or are "very close." Of the four remaining samples, two are "fairly close" (2.33 and 1.67) and two (1.00 and 3.00) are a full point away. The eight sample means on either side of the true mean clearly display sampling error. It is to be emphasized, however, that this error is inherent in the nature of sampling. For example, the combinations C_n^N which yield a mean of 1.0 or 3.0 will each be drawn from the sampling universe one out of ten times on the average, and the probabilities of all other sample values can be determined in like manner. Actually, in the case of Table 7.3, the true mean will be drawn on the average of one out of five times.

It is also to be observed that the mean of the sampling distribution is identical to the mean of the universe from which the samples were drawn— that is, $\bar{x} = \Sigma f\bar{x}/\Sigma f = 20/10 = 2 = \bar{X}$. However, the standard deviation of the universe (1.41) is substantially larger than the standard deviation of the distribution of sample means (.557 = $\sigma_{\bar{x}}$). The value of $\sigma_{\bar{x}}$ may be calculated either from the distribution or by use of Formula (7.3).

The sampling error $\sigma_{\bar{x}}$ can, to some extent, be minimized. Observe that if samples of size 4—that is, larger samples than previously used— were taken from the universe 0, 1, 2, 3, 4, the results would be as shown in Table 7.4. (Note: $C_4^5 = 5$.)

Table 7.4

All Possible Mean Values for Samples of Size 4, Drawn from the Universe Set: 0, 1, 2, 3, 4

Sample Number	Combination	Sum	$\bar{x}$	$\bar{x}/\bar{X}$
1	0, 1, 2, 3	6	1.50	0.75
2	4, 0, 1, 2	7	1.75	0.87
3	3, 4, 0, 1	8	2.00	1.00
4	2, 3, 4, 0	9	2.25	1.12
5	1, 2, 3, 4	10	2.50	1.25

$$\bar{x} = 2.0, \quad \bar{X} = 2.0, \quad \sigma = 1.41, \quad \sigma_{\bar{x}} = .352.$$

The estimates of $\bar{X}$ provided by samples of size 4 show improvement over the estimates provided by samples of size 3. That is, all sample means here are "closer" to the true mean than was the case for samples of size 3.

If samples of size 5 be drawn from this universe, only one combination is possible and the sample estimates would turn out to be the universe values. In this case there could be no sampling error and $\sigma_{\bar{x}}$ = zero. Thus, from Tables 7.3 and 7.4 it may be seen that small samples tend to exhibit large sampling errors whereas large samples tend to display small sampling errors. Table 7.5 compares the standard deviation of the sampling means for all possible sample sizes that may be drawn from the universe 0, 1, 2, 3, 4.

Table 7.5

Comparison of the Standard Deviation of the Sample Means and the Range of the Sample Means for All Possible Sample Sizes from the Universe 0, 1, 2, 3, 4

Sample Size	Universe Mean	Universe Standard Deviation	Range of the Sample Means	Standard Deviation of the Sample Means
1	2	1.41	1.0–4.0	1.41
2	2	1.41	0.5–3.5	0.866
3	2	1.41	1.0–2.0	0.577
4	2	1.41	1.5–2.5	0.352
5	2	1.41	0	None

Note: The standard deviations were computed in the usual manner. Here, because the problems are short, Formula 4.5 on page 84 was employed.

Notice that in Table 7.5 the standard deviation of the two distributions of sample means has been calculated. There is something special about the interpretation of this standard deviation, for it measures the numerical amount of *sampling error* inherent in the distribution of means. It is necessary to distinguish carefully between the standard deviation of the universe and the standard deviation of a distribution of sample means drawn from that universe. The symbol σ or S will be used to indicate the standard deviation of a universe and a sample, respectively, but $\sigma_{\bar{x}}$ and $S_{\bar{x}}$ are employed to designate the *standard error of a distribution of sample means*. This is an important distinction and should be carefully noted.

When samples of size 3 were drawn in the illustrations above, the error of the estimates—such error being inherent in the sampling process—was measured as $\sigma_{\bar{x}} = .577$. When samples of size 4 were drawn, the error diminished to .352. This illustrates the point that sampling error diminishes as sample size increases. Observe that $\sigma_{\bar{x}}$ is at least partially under the control of the analyst, whereas the σ of an ordinary frequency distribution or array is not subject to control. Again, had samples of size 5 been drawn from this particular universe, the standard error ($\sigma_{\bar{x}}$) would have become zero—that is, no sampling error would then be present. To summarize: *Sampling error is inherent in the very nature of the sampling process but is subject to minimization by controlling the size of the samples drawn from a given sampling universe.* The sampling error may also be minimized by the design of the experiment, as for example in stratified sampling, a topic to be covered later in this section and also in Chapter 8.

10. Non-Sampling Error

The term *non-sampling error* refers to arithmetic mistakes and to errors in judgment, calculation, interpretation, instructions, and mechanics. To illustrate: If an interviewer misunderstood the sampling instructions and proceeded to interview ladies when the interviews were to have been conducted only with men, the sample design and variability of sample estimates (sampling error) is hardly at fault. The results of a sample infected by one or more mistakes will not be those for which the sample was originally intended. Mistakes and errors of this general type are neither sampling errors nor bias. They are simply errors.

By now it should be clear that the only permissible error in sampling is the error inherent in the very nature of the sampling process itself. Each step of the inquiry must be carefully designed and checked to insure that the sample information is as accurate as possible. Questionable methods, general sloppiness, and flouting of the spirit of exactness are to be rigorously avoided.

Exercise 7.2

1. An administrator requires a certain kind of information. Before deciding to use some sampling technique, what other avenues should he explore? What factors might cause the decision to be made in favor of sampling as the proper avenue of gathering information?

2. Explain briefly how the theory of sets and combinations is applicable to sample theory.

3. Distinguish between an elementary sampling unit and a primary sampling unit.

4. What is sampling bias and under what conditions may it be present?

5. Distinguish between a sample statistic and a parameter.

6. "Sampling error is due to the fact that the random variable X may take a range of values." Is this a true statement? Explain.

7. Referring to Tables 7.2, 7.3, and 7.4, why is the range of the random variable (that is, the sample means) less than the range of the universe from which the samples were drawn?

8. In Table 7.2, the mean of the sample means is 2.0. This is also the mean of the sampling universe. Why? The table shows that the mean of eight of the ten samples is either greater or less than 2.0. Why should this be?

9. Draw the graphs of the probability functions for the random variable in Table 7.5 for samples of size 3 and size 4. How and why do the graphs differ?

10. Distinguish between a standard deviation and a standard error. Are these two statistics different in principle? What criterion permits us to clearly distinguish between these two measures?

7.5   Types of Sample Design

There are several general types of sample design and a number of variations within each design type. The following descriptions provide both a classification and sufficient definition to acquaint the student with generic sample designs.

1. Judgment Sample

This general sample type is the simplest of all sampling designs because everything depends upon the judgment of some individual as to what units of the universe shall be sampled and how the sample will be drawn. For example, a firm might wish to know customer reaction to a new type of product before deciding to mass-produce the item. The chief of the marketing section might decide, based on previous knowledge of the market, that four persons will constitute an adequate sampling of opinion. He may then proceed to select the four individuals of the sample from his own acquaintances. In other words, when a judgment sample is used, someone decides that this (or that) will be included in the sample. There need be no application of scientific sampling principles except those known to and decided upon by the individual making the decisions.

In some respects it could be argued that every sample is a judgment sample because someone must decide what and how things are to be done. The distinction to be drawn is this: A true judgment sample ignores probability functions, is nonrandom, and is conducted on the basis of individually established sampling principles. In contrast, scientifically designed samples will follow rigorous theoretical principles, meticulously applied in all phases of the inquiry.

Judgment sampling is not "scientific" when evaluated by the criterion of highly sophisticated procedures and principles. However, under some circumstances judgment samples may be of excellent quality because of the expert background and intuitive judgment of an individual whose capabilities mark him as outstanding in making decisions of this type. An individual with a happy combination of personal traits may thoroughly understand the peculiarities and attributes of the universe to be sampled. Obviously, though, this type of sample design is only as reliable as its originator.

No matter how excellent a judgment sample may be, the results are not measurable against a probability distribution to determine the reliability of the sample. This implies that if the sample design does not conform to the principles of probability, then probability cannot measure the results. The judgment sample is also severely limited by the fact that knowledge so gained cannot be made comparable to the results of other sampling studies. Common denominators between the samples will be missing.

2. Quota Sample

Quota samples are "decision" samples. In drawing quota samples the decision is made to include only given percentages of units possessing common characteristics. As an illustration of the quota sample, a firm might ask its sales personnel to sample a number of customers during the day as to preference, grievances, or other factors. The sales force is instructed to secure responses from (say) five men, ten ladies, and two young people of high school or college age. The interviewing sales personnel may then obtain the particular interviews in whatever manner they decide. Obviously this is not a probability sample. The sample is open to various types of error and bias and cannot be checked for accuracy. On the other hand, the uses to which the information is put may require only modest accuracy. Thus, for the desired purpose, quota sampling may furnish the best (least expensive) means of obtaining the information.

Basically, a quota sample is determined by individual judgment and is therefore a judgment sample, possessing all the advantages and disadvantages peculiar to samples of this general variety.

3. Probability Sample

The term "probability sample" refers to a general classification of sampling types rather than to a special sample design. In a probability sample there exists a known probability for inclusion of any given item in the sample. It is not essential that the X items possess equal probabilities of inclusion, that is, $P(X_i) \neq P(X_j)$, although the probabilities may actually be identical.[2] Nor is it necessary that the probability of each sample item or sampling combination actually be calculated. The requirement is simply that such probabilities *may* be computed. A probability sample is not necessarily a random sample. (The random sample is explained below.)

The probability samples to be considered in this work are *random* samples. The great advantage in the random sample approach is that sampling results may be compared to the normal curve (where appropriate) and the amount of sampling error may be clearly specified.

---

[2] The subscripts i and j refer to particular items in the universe. In other words, if all the items in the universe could be numbered consecutively, X_i and X_j would be two specific items in the universe.

4. Random Sample

A sample is said to be random when *each unit as drawn has a probability identical to the probability of all the other units (or combinations) which might have been drawn in its place.* This point may be illustrated as follows. If units be drawn from an infinite universe in a manner such that each item of the universe has the same chance of being drawn as every other item, the sample is random. A modification of this principle is necessary when the universe is finite: when random samples are drawn from a finite universe, probabilities rise as the sampling sequence progresses. When the first item is drawn from a finite universe, the denominator of the probability ratio (mutually exclusive but equally likely events) $n(S)$ is reduced and the remaining items all have slightly higher probabilities. Therefore, when sampling from a finite universe, random sampling implies that all units have an equal chance of being drawn first, the remaining units all have equal probability of being drawn second, and so on to the n units to be included in the sample.

As an example of this matter of equal probabilities of inclusion in the sample, suppose a universe of five items exists. Let the items be numbered X_1, X_2, X_3, X_4, and X_5. Now a random sample of two items is to be drawn from this universe. When the first item is being selected, each of the five items has a probability of $1/5$ of being drawn. When the first item is removed from the universe, four items remain. At this point, selection of the second item for the sample must be made from the four remaining items. Thus, the probability of each of the four items being included in the sample is $1/4$. Observe that the two items actually drawn in the sample did not themselves have equal probabilities, since one had a probability of $1/5$ and the other had a probability of $1/4$. However, the point is this: As the items were being drawn, those items remaining in the universe all had an equal probability of inclusion—and it is this fact which makes the sample a random sample.

A random sample may be defined as follows: When samples of size n are to be drawn from a finite universe of size N, each set of n items has an equal probability of being drawn first if the sampling is random. That is, each combination C_n^N has an equal probability of being drawn. As the sequence of drawings progresses, the probabilities increase. This is similar to computing conditional probabilities, because the sample space shrinks as sampling progresses.

There are two general types of random samples: (1) simple random samples, and (2) stratified random samples. Most of the material relative to sampling theory considered in this book is concerned with the first of these two sample designs.

(a) *Simple Random Sample.*   When a sample of size n is to be drawn from a population by random methods such that each set of n items has an equal probability of being included, the sample is said to be a simple random sample. A major problem in this type of sampling is achieving randomization as the items are drawn. It is essential that the items be drawn "at random."

(b) *Stratified Random Sample.*   Where a universe may be subdivided into several strata (layers), each of which is more homogeneous than the original universe, and random samples taken from each stratum, the samples are described as both "stratified" and "random." Stratification is also appropriate when the original universe is badly skewed.

As an illustration of stratified random sampling, consider a sample drawn from the undergraduates in a certain college. The proportions of the student body as to class are known. Suppose these are: freshmen, 35 per cent, sophomores, 30 per cent, juniors, 20 per cent, and seniors, 15 per cent. Sampling could be undertaken as if four subuniverses were to be independently sampled. The four samples could then be drawn at random to include the known proportions of students in the universe.

5. Systematic Sample

In a systematic sample, items are chosen on the basis of their equidistant location in a row or line. For example, it might be decided to inspect the quality of every 50th item produced by a given machine process. The space between sample items is, of course, a decision based on what is determined to be an adequate sample for the purposes at hand. The smaller the distance, the larger the sample with respect to the population from which it is being drawn.

6. Area Sampling

Area sampling refers to a method for drawing samples on the basis of some geographic breakdown of a region. The frame for area sampling is usually a map. For example, the map of a state on which county boundaries and population are shown would constitute the sample frame. Then, on the basis of counties and population, enumerating teams could be apportioned and instructed in the mechanics of the sample. Because the various sampling units in the sample frame are known, a distribution of sample responses can be made to coincide with state or national geographic distribution. Area sampling may be one stage of multistage sampling.

7.6   Other Sampling Terms

1. Reliability

If many random samples of size n are drawn from a universe and the sample estimates of the parameters exhibit small differences between themselves—that is, they are grouped close to a central value—the samples (or any one of them) are said to supply reliable information. Sometimes the word "efficient" or "precision" is used in an identical sense. If the universe is badly skewed, reliability of the sample estimates may be seriously impaired unless very large samples are employed.

In general, the smaller the standard error of the distribution of sample mean estimates, the more reliable (efficient) are the estimates.

2. Sampling Fraction

Given a universe of size N, from which samples of size n are drawn, the sampling fraction is given by the relationship:

$$\frac{n}{N} = f \text{ (the sampling fraction).}$$

3. Expansion Factor

If samples of size n are drawn from a universe of size N, then the ratio of the size of the universe to the size of the sample is N/n. Thus,

$$\frac{N}{n} = g \text{ (the expansion factor),}$$

and when it is desired to raise a sample total to the universe total, the sample total, Σx, is multiplied by g. Thus,

$$\Sigma x \cdot g = \Sigma x.$$

4. Pilot Study

When it is necessary to obtain information about an unknown universe, a pilot study may be undertaken. The pilot study is an exploratory probing used to discover as many facts as possible about the universe. It is something of a "shot in the dark," for there is no *a priori* method of knowing what the sample size should be, whether the universe is skewed, what the parameters may be, and so on. It may be desirable to draw several items, calculate estimates of the parameter, then draw additional items, calculate the sample estimates, and observe whether the sets of estimates agree. The pilot study is considered completed when the various estimates of a parameter stabilize. However, a run of reasonably stable values does not necessarily guarantee—because of the probability of a run of values—sufficiency of the pilot study.

If it is possible to check the results of a pilot study with known results of similar studies, and if the results are in substantial agreement, the pilot study may then be considered complete.

Some General Comments about Sampling Terminology

Only a small, but essential, portion of sampling terminology relating to "background information" has been presented in these sections. As previously indicated on page 160, the literature of sampling is rich in many ways, including terminology and theoretical constructs. In this book, the objective has been to present only the terminology and concepts that might be most useful to the student of business and economics. With the present background in terminology and other basic notions, it is now possible to move on and observe some of the theory of sampling from a very basic, but highly rewarding, point of view. The next sections of the present chapter are designed to provide a foundation of theoretical knowledge about sampling and will build upon knowledge of the frequency distribution and knowledge of probability presented in previous chapters. Perhaps it is not amiss to be reminded that the frequency distribution that can be approximated by a normal curve will continue to be the mainstay of the analysis of sampling and statistical inference.

Exercise 7.3. The following questions refer to material in the first five sections of this chapter.

1. A certain universe has ten elements in the set. How many different samples of size 4 can be drawn from this universe?

2. Suppose that in a certain universe, $N = 1,000$ and samples of $n = 200$ are to be drawn. How many different samples could be selected? (Note: Unless you have a table of logarithms of factorials, merely set up the problem and estimate the answer.) Does this type of problem provide insights into the meaning of the following statement? "Variability of estimates is due to sampling variability." Can you explain this statement?

3. Given the following universe of five items: 10, 20, 30, 40, 50.
    (a) How many different samples of size 3 may be drawn?
    (b) Make a list of the different possible samples of size 3 and calculate their means.
    (c) Now rank the means; calculate their mean and median.
    (d) Is the mean of the sample means the mean of the universe? Why is the mean and median a single value?
    (e) Considering the sample means as a random variable, calculate the standard deviation of these several sampling means. Is this standard deviation larger or smaller than the standard deviation of the universe? Do you know or can you discover any reason why this should be so?

(f) The standard deviation of the sampling means (as calculated above) is called the "standard error" of the distribution of sample means. Will all the sample means fit between + and − 3 standard errors? Should they fit? Why?

(g) As you look at the ranking of sample means, do you feel they estimated the population mean rather well? If some means did not provide good estimates, why is this so?

(h) From the experiments of this problem explain why samples yield "estimates" of parameters. Explain why the sample means can be said to form a "distribution" of sample estimates.

4. Given a universal set of 20 values, samples of $n = 5$ are to be drawn without replacement. What is the probability to be attached to the first subset drawn? The second subset drawn? Is it clear that in sequential sampling from a finite universe without replacement, the probabilities of any given subset of being drawn are not equal in the sequence?

5. If the sampling population was infinite and samples of $n = 10,000$ were drawn, what is the effect on the probabilities of inclusion to be attached to succeeding samples?

6. In statistics (and certainly in this chapter) you find many "definitions." What is a definition?

7. Suppose there exists a universe consisting completely of ordinary pencils colored blue. What is the smallest sample which can be drawn from this universe which will accurately reflect the composition of this universe?

8. Suppose the universe referred to above were composed completely of ordinary pencils but these were of many colors. Would a relatively "large" or "small" sample be required to accurately reflect the composition of this universe? Why?

9. Why is it essential to keep in mind the cautions and limitations of sample results?

10. In a universe consisting completely of ordinary pencils what are some of the various attributes a sampling study might be interested in?

11. A study is to be made by a contractor in determining consumer preferences in modern housing construction. List several attributes of one-family dwelling units and indicate the means by which those attributes might be measured.

12. The following questions refer to various aspects of the concept of randomization.

(a) Define carefully the word "random."

(b) Why does randomization of the items of a variable bring about uniform sampling results?

(c) If the forces of chance alone are operating on a variable, does it appear reasonable that in drawing items from such a universe there would, on the average, be as many items with values below the mean as above the mean?

(d) If you were to draw a random sample of 75 items from 1,000 items produced by a machine process during one day, how might this be accomplished? Would the 1,000 items be a sampling frame?

13. Define carefully the word "sample." How would you say a "random sample" differs from a "sample"?

14. Distinguish between bias, sampling error, and non-sampling error.

15. Given the results of two samples drawn from the same universe. Without additional knowledge about the samples or the universe, one sample shows a standard error 8.5, the second sample exhibits a standard error of 12.1. Which sample is the most efficient? What would be the reason?

16. Samples of $n = 260$ are to be drawn from a universe of $N = 20,000$. What is the sampling fraction f?

17. A sample of $n = 500$ has been drawn from a universe of $N = 15,000$. This was a sample designed to estimate the total amount of money held in personal savings accounts. The sample total was $200,000. What is the total amount for the community?

18. (a) If a sampling fraction is .3, what is the value of g?
    (b) If $f = 2$ per cent, $g = $?
    (c) If $f = 10$ per cent, $g = $?

19. By what criteria may a pilot study be judged "complete"? To what extent do you suppose judgment enters into the decision that a pilot study is completed?

7.7   Types of Information Available from Samples

Most of the types of information available through sampling have already been examined in previous chapters. For example, a set of sample data may be used to calculate the mean, median, and mode. These values, when derived from sample data, are direct estimates of the corresponding population values. The standard deviation of the set of sample data may also be derived, but, as explained in Chapter 4, use of $n - 1$ in the formulae [(4.10) and (4.11)] is generally necessary when S is to be employed as an estimate of σ.

Information about the population parameters is furnished by the sample. The mean of the sample is an estimate of the mean of the population; the median of the sample is an estimate of the median of the population; the standard deviation of the sample is an estimate of the population standard deviation. In practice, the mode is seldom employed. The mean, median, and standard deviation are sometimes referred to as "point estimates" in that they supply one number, a point on the X scale of a graph.

Other "point" values may be derived from sample information. For example, the proportion of defective items produced by an assembly-line process, the proportion of a firm's employees with more than 12 years of formal education, the proportion of accounts delinquent, and many others may be estimated from sample information.

In order to identify and clarify the main features of a random sampling problem the student is urged to perform the following simple experiment. On small slips of paper write the numbers from 0 to 20. These numbers constitute the universe from which samples may be drawn. The parameters of the universe (here use only the mean and standard deviation) may be calculated as $\bar{X} = 10$ and $\sigma \approx 6.055$. (The symbol $\approx$ means "is approximately equal to.") Now, draw at random a sample of 5 items. Consider what information these 5 items reveal concerning the parameters of the universe: Can the range be estimated? The median? the mode? The mean? The standard deviation? From the 5 sample items compute the mean and standard deviation using $(n - 1)$ in the denominator of the formula for S [Formula (4.10)]. Compare these estimates with the known parameters. Consider "how well" the sample estimated the parameters and whether your estimates would be more correct were you to specify an "interval" rather than a point. In other words, suppose the sample mean turned out to be 9—which, of course, is not the true mean. Clearly, the sample mean of 9 is an estimate of the true mean. Now, suppose that instead of merely being satisfied with 9 as a "point" estimate, you were to form an interval by (a bit arbitrarily) adding and subtracting 1.5 from the sample mean of 9. As a result of this process you would make a statement such as the following: As a result of the sampling experiment, the true mean of the universe is expected to be between 7.5 and 10.5. Observe that this is a true statement.

At a later point in this chapter it will be possible to be more precise and to make interval statements with a known probability attached to the statement. For the present the student should note that sample estimates are point estimates and as such are almost never the exact—that is, parametric—value. However, by specifying an interval which is calculated according to known probabilities and by a precise method, statements can be made which have a high probability of being correct.

It will not be amiss to study this experiment carefully, as many of the fundamental principles of sampling and inference are already apparent in it.

7.8   Some Characteristics of Sampling Distributions

Suppose that a number of samples of size n have been drawn from a given universe and the mean of each sample has been calculated. As previously noted, the sample values will constitute a random variable and can be thought of as a probability distribution. Each individual sample where $n > 1$ constitutes a compound experiment whose outcome is a number $\bar{x}$ calculated from the n values in each sample. It is understood that n remains constant for all samples drawn in a particular experiment.

If samples of size n be drawn from a universe, recorded, and returned to the universe, as many samples as desired may be drawn, using replacement if necessary. From Tables 7.3 and 7.4 it can be seen that when samples are drawn from a universe whose x values form a variable,[3] the mean of each sample does not necessarily turn out to be the mean of the universe. Thus, the random variable $\bar{X}$ will range between the smallest and largest sample means which could be drawn. If the random variable $\bar{X}$ be shown as a frequency polygon, the base of the polygon must cover the range of the sample means and the height of the polygon will reflect the number of sample means drawn—that is, the number of experiments performed. These matters are shown graphically in Illustration 7.1.

Now, how does the frequency or probability function of the random variable $\bar{X}$ change if a set of 100 experiments be conducted with $n = 9$, and then a new set of 100 experiments be conducted with $n = 81$? The universe from which the samples are drawn is a very large universe and both sets of experiments refer to samples drawn from this same universe. The standard error of the mean of the resulting sampling distribution will be given by the relationship

$$\sigma_{\bar{x}} = \frac{\sigma}{\sqrt{n}} \; ; \tag{7.1}$$

thus the standard error of the sampling distribution will be large when n is small and small when n is large. This point may be observed in graphic form in Illustration 7.1.

Illustration 7.1 Relationship Between a Sampling Universe and the Distribution of 100 Sample Means for Samples of Size 9 and Samples of Size 81

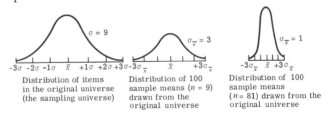

$\sigma = 9$	$\sigma_{\bar{x}} = 3$	$\sigma_{\bar{x}} = 1$
-3σ -2σ -1σ $\bar{x}$ $+1\sigma$ $+2\sigma$ $+3\sigma$	$-3\sigma_{\bar{x}}$ $\bar{x}$ $+3\sigma_{\bar{x}}$	$-3\sigma_{\bar{x}}$ $\bar{x}$ $+3\sigma_{\bar{x}}$
Distribution of items in the original universe (the sampling universe)	Distribution of 100 sample means ($n = 9$) drawn from the original universe	Distribution of 100 sample means ($n = 81$) drawn from the original universe

From Illustration 7.1 the following interesting characteristic may be observed: *The larger the sample size the better the estimate of the population parameter yielded by any given sample.* This fact is shown by the range of the possible sample means and illustrated by the size of the standard

---

[3] It may be well for the student to recall that x as used here means an item drawn as part of the sample. In other words, x is a sample item drawn from the universe of X values. Too, it may be worthwhile to recall that the statement "the random variable $\bar{X}$" is used to denote the fact that the sample means do form a random variable and the individual values (the sample means themselves) do form a cluster around the true mean of the universe. This cluster of sample means is, of course, a probability distribution.

error. In other words, larger samples provide better information than small samples but, as Formula (7.1) indicates, the relationship between size and informational yield is not linear. Yield is inversely proportional to the square root of the sample size.

A second characteristic of the distribution of sample means is known as the *central limit theorem*. This theorem states that *the distribution of sample means will tend towards normality whether or not the samples were drawn from a normal population and the larger the size of the sample n, the greater the tendency towards normality in the resulting sampling distribution.* In other words, this theorem says that the normal curve is generally appropriate as a description or model for the sampling distribution even though the samples be drawn from a nonnormal universe (where N is large). This is a most desirable theorem, for it permits use of the normal probability distribution as a tool or model for many sampling distributions and greatly simplifies the work of computing probabilities.

A third characteristic of sampling distributions is this: The mean of a random sample provides an unbiased *estimate* of the population mean. In other words, and in general, it may be said that $\bar{x} = \bar{X}$ (that is, the sample mean = the population mean) except for sampling variability. Too, the larger the sample, the closer the estimate $\bar{x}$ is expected to approach $\bar{X}$. Alternatively, as a large number of small samples is drawn, the better the estimate of $\bar{X}$ becomes when the many sample means are averaged. These points are shown in Tables 7.1 through 7.5.

Because it is extremely important to understand precisely what this third characteristic of sampling distributions actually implies, an alternative explanation will be provided. The mean of a random sample does provide an unbiased estimate of the population mean. The mean of a random sample would be equal to the population mean were it not for the fact that "errors inherent in the sampling process do occur." These errors of sampling cannot be avoided because the items drawn in the sample are drawn at random and the values of the items do not necessarily distribute themselves so nicely about the true mean that the sum of their deviations about that mean would be zero.

In practice then, the sample items distribute themselves about the true mean in a pattern which reflects the variability of the universe. Consequently the sum of the arithmetic deviations of the items in a sample from the true mean is almost always some positive or negative value. Now, what makes the sample mean unbiased is that the same probability exists that the sum of the deviations will be negative as that the sum will be positive. It is just as likely that the sample mean will be below the true mean as that it will be above the true mean. Therefore, the sample mean would equal the true mean except for sampling variability—that is, sampling error.

Fortunately, the error inherent in random sampling can be measured by calculating what is, in effect, the standard deviation of the distribution of sample means. It is this ability to measure the sampling error which allows probability judgments to be made according to a probability distribution.

7.9   Relationships Between Sample Size, σ, and $\sigma_{\bar{x}}$

The standard error $\sigma_{\bar{x}}$ of a sampling distribution for a continuous variable bears a definite relationship to the standard deviation of the population (σ) from which the samples were drawn. That relationship was given as:

$$\sigma_{\bar{x}} = \frac{\sigma}{\sqrt{n}} \quad \text{(infinite universe).} \tag{7.1}$$

The mathematics of this relationship stem from probability theory, but proof of Formula (7.1) is beyond the scope of this book.

Two points about this formula are of interest. For one thing, the formula clearly demonstrates the impact of sample size on the value of the standard error and shows that the first few items drawn in a sample furnish proportionately more information than later items (because of the square root of n). Secondly, the formula indicates the relationship between the value of the standard deviation and the value of the standard error. Thus if σ is increased, the $\sigma_{\bar{x}}$ increases only if n is constant. If σ is constant, then $\sigma_{\bar{x}}$ shrinks as n increases. Some insight into these matters is provided by Table 7.6, which shows σ as a constant. The student might experiment with situations in which σ is allowed to change.

Table 7.6

Table Illustrating the Impact of Increased Sample Size on $\sigma_{\bar{x}}$ in Both Absolute and in Relative Terms (Infinite Universe)

(1)	(2)	(3)	(4)	(5)	(6)
					Percentage Decrease in $\sigma_{\bar{x}}$ as n Increases from One Row to the Next
			Decrease in $\sigma_{\bar{x}}$ Due to Increasing n from One Row to the Next	Percentage Increase in Sample Size as n Changes from One Row to the Next	
n	σ	$\sigma_{\bar{x}}$			$100(\sigma_{\bar{x}_1} - \sigma_{\bar{x}_2})/\sigma_{\bar{x}_1}$
1	10	10.000	..	..	..
2	10	7.071	2.929	100.00	−29.29
3	10	5.774	1.298	50.00	−18.35
4	10	5.000	0.774	33.33	−13.00
5	10	4.472	0.528	25.00	−10.56
10	10	3.162	1.310	100.00	−29.29
20	10	2.236	0.926	100.00	−29.29
25	10	2.000	0.236	25.00	−10.56
40	10	1.581	0.419	60.00	−20.95
50	10	1.414	0.167	25.00	−10.56
100	10	1.000	0.414	100.00	−29.29

Table 7.6 has been constructed by holding σ constant and varying n. Column 4 shows the decrease in $\sigma_{\bar{x}}$ brought about by increasing n (10.00 − 7.071 = 2.929, and so on). Column 5 indicates the percentage increase in n from one row to the next (a sample size of 2 is 100 per cent larger than a sample of size 1). Column 6 indicates the percentage decrease occurring in $\sigma_{\bar{x}}$ as n is increased from one row to the next [100(7.071 − 10.000)/10 = −29.29 per cent]. The sign is negative because $\sigma_{\bar{x}}$ is shrinking.

An extremely interesting property of the relationship between n and $\sigma_{\bar{x}}$ is shown in column 6. There it may be noted that a constant percentage increase in n always yields a constant percentage decrease in $\sigma_{\bar{x}}$. For example, whenever n doubles, the standard error ($\sigma_{\bar{x}}$) decreases by 29.29 per cent. Thus, doubling the sample size invariably decreases the standard error by approximately 30 per cent. This relationship is, of course, precisely what Formula (7.1) shows.

It may also be observed in Table 7.6 that if the standard deviation of the universe was doubled for each given sample size, the standard error $\sigma_{\bar{x}}$ would also double, but the percentage results recorded in column 6 would remain as shown.

Exercise 7.4

1. Construct a graph showing the relationship between column 1 and column 3 in Table 7.6. Plot n on the X axis and column 3 on the Y axis. Draw a smooth curve.
   (a) Are the results those you would have expected by knowing that $\sigma_{\bar{x}} = \sigma/\sqrt{n}$?
   (b) Could you explain the table and graph to a fellow student who has not enjoyed the benefits of a course in statistics?
   (c) From the curve on the graph, interpolate the percentage decrease in $\sigma_{\bar{x}}$ for (1) a 10 per cent increase in sample size, (2) a 40 per cent increase, (3) an 80 per cent increase. Now, make the actual calculations necessary to observe the exact percentage change in $\sigma_{\bar{x}}$.

2. (a) If you drew a diagram of a sampling universe (suppose it was normally distributed) and then constructed a diagram of the distribution of sampling means taken from that universe, what would be the essential difference in the two diagrams?
   (b) Now double the number of samples drawn. In what manner would this affect the diagram of the distribution of sampling means?

3. (a) Suppose random samples of size n were drawn from a rectangular universe. The term "rectangular universe" means a universe in which all X values have equal frequencies. Explain why the resulting distribution of sample means would be expected to exhibit normality.
   (b) If the random samples of size n had been drawn from a lepto-kurtic universe, would the distribution of sample means be approximately normal? What would you expect and why?

7.10   Modification of $\sigma_{\bar{x}}$ to Account for the Sample Size, Finite Universe

The basic formula (7.1) for $\sigma_{\bar{x}}$ must be modified slightly if the size of the sample (n) is such that n/N is greater than approximately 5 per cent. In other words, if the sample constitutes a significant proportion of the universe, a correction must be made in the standard error. The correction is as follows:

$$\sigma_{\bar{x}} = \frac{\sigma}{\sqrt{n}} \cdot \sqrt{\frac{N-n}{N-1}} \qquad \text{(finite universe)}. \qquad (7.2)$$

When the sample size exceeds, say, 50 or more, the minus one in the denominator exerts but a small impact. Thus, for large samples the correction factor can be written:

$$\sqrt{\frac{N-n}{N}}. \qquad (7.3)$$

What is the reason for using the correction factor whenever the sample size exceeds 5 per cent of the universe? The basic formula (7.1) for the standard error ($\sigma_{\bar{x}} = \sigma/\sqrt{n}$) says nothing whatsoever about the size of the universe N but considers only the standard deviation of the universe σ and the size of the sample n. Since σ is not under the control of the statistician, the sole means of altering the value of the standard error is through changes in n. The larger n becomes, the smaller the standard error $\sigma_{\bar{x}}$ and the more efficient—that is, closer to the true mean (reliable)—the sample estimates become.

When sampling from a finite universe it is necessary to use the correction factor $\sqrt{(N-n)/(N-1)}$ in order to make allowance for the proportion of the universe included in the sample. Obviously, if

Table 7.7

Impact of the Correction Factor on the Standard Error

(1)	(2)	(3)	(4)	(5)
n	N	$\dfrac{n}{N}$	$\sqrt{\dfrac{N-n}{N}}$	Correction (Reduction in $\sigma_{\bar{x}}$, Per Cent)
50	1,000	5%	0.9747	2.53
100	1,000	10%	0.9486	5.14
300	1,000	30%	0.8366	16.34
500	1,000	50%	0.7071	29.29
750	1,000	75%	0.5000	50.00
900	1,000	90%	0.3162	68.98
1,000	1,000	100%	0.0000	100.00 (census)

the sample is a large percentage of the universe, the sample approaches a census, and a census cannot be subject to sampling error. The correction factor allows for this approach to a census.

Table 7.7 indicates the impact of the correction factor on the standard error as the sample size n approaches the universe size N.

Table 7.7 also indicates rather clearly that small samples (where n/N is small) hardly require correction for the standard error. Again, since samples are estimates, the small value of the correction factor (2.53 per cent at $n/N = 5$ per cent) might be disregarded. However, when the sample size as compared to the universe size is large, the correction factor becomes a matter of crucial importance. Thus, when sampling from a finite universe, it would be clearly in error to ignore this correction if the sample is relatively large (say over 5 per cent) when compared to the size of the universe.

7.11 Sampling Without Knowledge of Parameters

Frequently samples must be drawn from universes about which the statistican has little or no knowledge. As a matter of fact, one of the reasons for sampling is to discover new knowledge about unknown universes. For example, if an industrial process is designed to package 100-pound bags of sand, the process may operate well from an engineering point of view, but the question arises: "Are the bags of sand at any point in time actually averaging 100 lb?" In other words, the true mean is always supposed to be 100 lb, but is it? The true mean of the universe at any point in time is an unknown quantity and must, therefore, be estimated from sample information.

In this same situation the question may be raised: "What is the standard deviation of the weights of these bags of sand?" While it is true that a standard deviation does exist, its value is not known at any given point in time and must be estimated from a sample. Generally, in situations of this type the only knowledge of the universe is supplied from samples, and under these conditions minor changes are made in standard deviation calculations. Since knowledge of σ does not usually exist, the standard error of the distribution of sampling means must be estimated from the sample. Thus:

$$S_{\bar{x}} = \frac{S}{\sqrt{n}}, \tag{7.4}$$

where S is computed as

$$S = \sqrt{\frac{\Sigma x^2}{n-1}}, \tag{7.5}$$

where x = an arithmetic deviation. But, if S is to be computed from a frequency distribution composed of sample means, the assumed-mean method may be used with the following formula:

$$S = i \sqrt{\frac{\Sigma fx^2}{N - 1} - \frac{(\Sigma fx)^2}{N(N - 1)}}, \tag{7.6}$$

where N is the number of sample means in the distribution and x is the arithmetic derivation. There is no particular reason to overemphasize the minor differences between $\sigma_{\bar{x}}$ and $S_{\bar{x}}$ because (1) if the standard deviation σ is known, it will be used in the appropriate formula, and (2) if the standard deviation σ is not known, then S must be used. In either case the mathematical relationships of the formulas are essentially identical. The student may therefore treat $\sigma_{\bar{x}}$ and $S_{\bar{x}}$ as being *identical in application*.

7.12   Some Comments on the Standard Error of a Proportion (Binomially Distributed Populations)

The general method of sampling from a binomial population may be stated briefly at this point. (1) A random sample of size n is taken. (2) The number of items possessing the characteristic in question is noted. For example, this could be the number of defective parts in a shipment. (3) The ratio $\Sigma X/n = p$ is computed (where, for example, ΣX = the number of defective parts). (4) With the computation of the sample proportion there now exists an estimate of the universe value P.

The *standard error* (not standard deviation) of a distribution of sample proportions is given by the following formula:

$$\sigma_{\bar{p}} = \sqrt{\frac{pq}{n}}. \tag{7.7}$$

Note: This formula yields a decimal value, which may be converted to a percentage by multiplying by 100. Uses of the standard error of a proportion $\sigma_{\bar{p}}$ are: (1) estimating confidence intervals for P (the population mean); (2) testing the significance of a difference between P and p.

7.13   Estimate of Confidence Intervals for the Mean

In Section 7.7 a brief reference was made to confidence intervals. It was pointed out that when random samples are drawn from a universe, the values of the mean and standard deviation as calculated from the sample do provide *estimates* of the universe parameters. These estimates, however, are not likely to be the true values because of the sampling error inherent in the sampling process. Therefore, if it were stated unequivocally that the sample mean was equal to the true mean, such a statement would have an extremely high probability of being incorrect. It is expected that the sample value will be "close" to the true value, but will hardly be the parameter itself. It would therefore be desirable to formulate statements in such a manner that the statement would have a high probability of being correct.

To provide a basis for making statements which have a high probability of being correct, the standard error is employed as a measure of the variability of sample estimates and an interval is constructed by utilizing the sample mean as a central point and then adding and subtracting a multiple of the standard error to and from this sample mean. Since the standard error is related to the z values of the normal curve, probability coefficients may be attached to the interval statements. The method of making interval statements will be shown below.

First, however, it is essential that the need for a confidence interval be clearly understood. The sample mean provides a "point" estimate of the true mean. A point, however, is so small that the probability of having made an exact estimate is very tiny indeed. Technically, the probability that the sample mean will equal the true mean is zero if measured on a normal curve of probability since, in a continuous distribution, probability can be computed only with respect to an interval. Apparently then, what is required is an "interval" estimate in order to specify, with a high degree of probability, the range of values over which the true mean is expected to occur. Example: Rather than saying that in a given problem the population mean is 5.5, it may be stated that the population mean is is expected to fall between the values of 4.8 and 6.2. The numbers 4.8 and 6.2 define the confidence limits for this particular problem; these numbers form the interval.

The use of sample results to specify a range within which the true mean is expected to fall is known as the determination of "confidence intervals." The width of the confidence interval is not left to whimsical judgment, but is carefully calculated on the basis of a known and specified probability of being a correct statement. Thus, a confidence interval statement with an appropriate probability level may, for example, be stated as follows: "The confidence interval ranges from 4.8 to 6.2 at the 95 per cent confidence level."

Observe that when statements of this type are made, it is not specified that the true mean is actually in the interval. Either the true mean is in the interval or it is not in the interval. There is, however, a probability of .95 that the interval from 4.8 to 6.2 contains the true—but unknown—population mean. The probability applies to the interval and not to the mean. Said in another manner, if a large number of samples of the same size were taken from the same universe and for each sample the interval was calculated by use of the sample mean and the standard error for that sample, then approximately 95 per cent of these intervals would contain the true mean if $z = 1.96$. Clearly, in this situation, 5 per cent of the interval statements would not include the true population mean. If, then, the method of making confidence-interval statements is followed precisely, the "batting average" for correct statements will be an enviable one. Certainly any baseball player would like to do as well.

An example may be useful at this point. Suppose there exists an infinite universe and, for purposes of this illustration, the reader is informed that the true mean is 10, and the standard deviation is 3. Next, suppose a sample of size 100 is to be drawn at random from this universe and, on the basis of the sample values only, a confidence-interval statement is to be made with a 95 per cent confidence coefficient, that is, $z = 1.96$.

The central limit theorem states that if the sample size is large (consider $n = 100$ to be large in this case) the samples drawn from this universe will be normally distributed about the population mean. This feature of normality means that the relative frequencies with which various values of the sample mean will occur can be measured by the standardized normal curve. Thus, about 68 per cent of the sample means will fall within a range formed by adding and subtracting one standard error to the population mean. About 95.4 per cent of the sample means will fall between $\bar{X} \pm 2$ standard errors, and about 99.7 per cent of the sample means will fall between $\bar{X} \pm 3$ standard errors.

Now, in the example given above, the standard error of the sampling distribution of means is computed as $\sigma_{\bar{x}} = 3/\sqrt{100} = .3$. Calculating the ranges within which sample means are expected to occur at the given standard error values is readily accomplished as follows:

Calculations	*Range*
$\bar{X} \pm 1$ standard error $= 10 \pm (.3)(1) = 9.7 - 10.3.$	
$\bar{X} \pm 2$ standard errors $= 10 \pm (.3)(2) = 9.4 - 10.6.$	
$\bar{X} \pm 3$ standard errors $= 10 \pm (.3)(3) = 9.1 - 10.9.$	

In this particular problem, then, it is highly unlikely ($P = 3/1,000$) that a sample mean will be drawn to yield a value less than 9.1 or greater than 10.9. The error due to sampling variability thus is not likely to be more than $\pm.9$. Expressed in percentage terms, the maximum relative error at the 99.7 confidence coefficient (where $z = 3$) is $.9/10$ or 9 per cent.

To construct a confidence interval to compensate for the error which the sampling process cannot avoid, what is required is an interval statement which takes the error into account. The technique employed to take the error into account is almost self-evident at this point—namely, (1) use the sample mean as the central value to which (2) a multiple of the standard error will be added and subtracted. Since the normal curve is employed as a relative frequency or probability model, the standard error multiple can be selected to provide any level of confidence desired short of 100 per cent or 1.0.

It will now be desirable to illustrate the method of forming confidence intervals by the use of two examples as follows:

Example 1. Suppose we are considering the previously mentioned universe where the true mean was 10 and the standard deviation was 3. The variable is weight in pounds. While we are thinking about this universe, along comes a statistician and begins to draw some sample items. At this point we decide to "keep mum" and watch.

The statistician selects exactly 100 items from the universe and painstakingly weighs each item and records its value. Eventually he has 100 values of the variable. With a pocket adding machine, he calculates the mean and standard deviation as $\bar{x} = 9.7$ and $S = 3$. He "hit" the standard deviation and "missed" the mean. How did this come about?

Examining this matter from the background of knowledge we already have about the distribution of sample means, we would know that for a universe with $\bar{X} = 10$ and $\sigma = 3$, samples of size 100 would form a normal sampling distribution with a mean of 10 and a standard error of .3. ($\sigma_{\bar{x}} = 3/\sqrt{100} = .3$). A quick bit of arithmetic shows that almost all ($99 + \%$) of the sample means will fall between the mean $\pm 3z$, or here between 9.1 and 10.9 lbs. [$10 \pm (3)(.3) = 9.1$ and 10.9.] We now know the statistician did not take a faulty or biased sample since the mean of 9.7 is clearly within the range of values which may be expected from this sampling experiment.

Turning again to the statistician, he now calculates a confidence interval based on $z = 2$, i.e., the $95 +$ confidence level. The question we now raise is this: Will the confidence interval statement include the true mean?

The statistician calculates: $9.7 \pm (2)(3/100) = 9.1$ and 10.3. He then writes: "At the 95% confidence level, the universe mean is expected to fall between 9.1 and 10.3 lbs." To our surprise, perhaps, the statistician is correct since the stated interval does include the universe mean.

It may be observed from this example that although the statistician did not find $\bar{x}$ to equal $\bar{X}$, he did not expect to find such a neat equality. He only expected that if he repeated the experiment many times, about

95+% of his interval statements would be correct. (We gave the value of S as 3 to simplify the analysis.)

Example 2. Here, let us take the same situation and see what would happen if the results of the sampling experiment turned out a bit differently.

The universe values are still $\bar{X} = 10$, $\sigma = 3$, and $n = 100$. A sample ($n = 100$) is drawn yielding a mean of 10.7 lbs. and a standard deviation of 3. On the basis of this information, a confidence interval is constructed as follows: $10.7 \pm (2)(.3) = 10.1$ and 11.3. The confidence interval statement is: "At the 95+ level, the universe mean is expected to fall between 10.1 and 11.3." Clearly, this is a false statement even though the sample itself was a perfectly good sample.

It will be well to observe some implications of this problem. First, the statistician did not make arithmetic or sampling mistakes. The second interval was incorrect because the sample mean on which it was based came from the "upper end" of the sampling distribution—and in a normal distribution, sample means will be drawn from that portion of the curve on about 2+% of the experiments (if $z = 2$). Since it is just as likely the sample means will be drawn from the "lower end" of the curve, we conclude that about 5% of all interval statements constructed by the methods just explained will turn out to be incorrect. *This is the effect of sampling error.* And, from what was previously stated at the beginning of this section, the conclusion to be drawn from these two examples is that when $z = 2$, the experiments produce correct intervals about 95% of the time and incorrect intervals about 5% of the time.

Incidentally, the student may now inquire: If the standard deviation must be estimated from the sample and, under this circumstance, the standard deviation is a variable, will not the standard error also be a variable? If the standard error is a variable, the confidence intervals based on repeated sampling will also be variable and some intervals will be longer and some shorter. This reasoning is proper, but even with the variable standard error, the confidence-interval statements are still expected to be correct in approximately the proportion indicated by the confidence level—95 per cent in this case. This is true for large samples only because the normal curve is appropriate. (In the case of small samples, the "t" distribution is employed.)

Next, the selection of a confidence level (or coefficient) may be briefly examined. First of all, the student may inquire: Why not a 100 per cent confidence level? This notion may be dispelled by recalling that samples are incomplete representations of the universe from which they were drawn. Therefore, the only way to obtain perfect knowledge of that universe is to take a census—but this is not sampling. If it is

impossible to take a census, then something less than error-free information is the next best alternative. Under these circumstances, 100 per cent
confidence is impossible. Confidence levels of 99.7 per cent, for example,
are possible by the use of three standard errors, although such intervals
are generally quite wide. When the interval is narrowed by using, say,
1.96 standard errors, the confidence level decreases to 95 per cent. Further
narrowing the interval by the use of one standard error would reduce the
confidence value to about 68 per cent.

Now, the choice of a particular confidence coefficient depends upon
the uses to be made of the sample estimates. In practical problems the
confidence level to be specified depends upon the nature of the problem.
If, for example, the problem was to determine the mean useable mileage
of a given type of automobile tire, the confidence interval might be
relatively wide and still be highly useful. On the other hand, the confidence
interval for the mean weight of a process which produces one-pound cans
of coffee might necessarily be rather narrow.

Another matter may now be considered. If the 95 per cent confidence
interval is considered correct for a particular type of problem, but the
interval itself is too wide for the purposes of the problem, the only
alternative is to increase the size of the sample in order that the standard
error may be reduced. The 95 per cent confidence level may then be
maintained and the interval shortened to acceptable proportions.

Steps for Determining a Confidence Interval

The foregoing materials may now be presented in a somewhat
mechanistic manner by observing the steps required in the construction
of a confidence-interval estimate for the universe mean. The method is as
follows:

1. Draw a sample and calculate the mean. Parametric values are unknown.
2. Use the formula $S = \sqrt{\Sigma (x - \bar{x})^2/(n - 1)}$ to provide an estimate of the
   standard deviation of the universe. (Note: If the standard deviation σ
   were known, $\sigma_{\bar{x}}$ would replace $S_{\bar{x}}$.)
3. Determine the standard error by use of the formula $S_{\bar{x}} = S/\sqrt{n}$. (Or use
   σ, if known.)
4. Select a confidence interval, say 95 per cent or 99 per cent, for which
   $z = 1.96$ and 2.58, respectively.
5. Multiply $S_{\bar{x}}$ by z. (If $\sigma_{\bar{x}}$ is known, it will be used in this step.)
6. Determine the confidence interval as $\bar{x} \pm (S_{\bar{x}})(z)$.
7. Interpret the meaning of the confidence interval in this manner: When the
   confidence interval is set at, say, 95 per cent, this says that on the average,
   if 100 sample means of size n be drawn from the universe and intervals are

constructed, 95 intervals will include the true mean and 5 intervals will not. Note that, in terms of probability, if E be defined as the event "the 95 per cent confidence interval includes $\overline{X}$," then $P(E) = n(E)/n(S) = .95$.

To illustrate the steps outlined above, suppose we use the previous example in which the mean value of a given universe was 10 pounds, the standard deviation was 3 pounds, and the sample size was 100 so that the standard error would be .3. If it is assumed that a 95 per cent confidence interval is desirable, the following calculations would be made:

$$\sigma_{\bar{x}} = \frac{3}{\sqrt{100}} = 0.3$$

(note: $S_{\bar{x}}$ would be employed if σ were not known), and

or
while
$$\bar{x} \pm \sigma_{\bar{x}}(z) = \text{the confidence interval}$$
$$\bar{x} + \sigma_{\bar{x}}(z) = \text{the upper confidence limit}$$
$$\bar{x} - \sigma_{\bar{x}}(z) = \text{the lower confidence limit}$$

so that the confidence interval turns out to be

$$10 \pm 0.3(1.96) = 10 \pm .588 = 9.412 \quad \text{and} \quad 10.588.$$

The desired interval with a confidence coefficient of .95 may be stated as follows:

> The confidence interval ranges from 9.412 to 10.588 at the 95 per cent confidence level.

Confidence Intervals Other Than 95 Per Cent

Whenever the distribution of sample means may be related to the normal curve, as in the case of large samples it is not difficult to observe that confidence intervals other than 95 per cent may be chosen. The 99 per cent level is frequently used: a glance at the table of areas for the normal curve will indicate that if z is set equal to 2.58, the confidence level will be .99, and an interval of greater width will be obtained than if z equaled 1.96. Thus, in the illustration given above,

$$\sigma_{\bar{x}} = .3 \quad \text{and} \quad \bar{x} \pm 2.58(\sigma_{\bar{x}}) = \text{the 99 per cent confidence limits.}$$

Thus, $10 \pm 2.58(.3) = 10 \pm .774 = 2.226$ and 10.774, the 99 per cent confidence limits. The intervals thus established are, of course, somewhat wider than those at the 95 per cent level.

If the confidence interval is continually broadened, it must at some stage include the true mean. To take a rather absurd statement, it is true to say "the mean is between $+$ and $-$ infinity." However, a statement this broad is of no statistical value even though it may be correct. Somewhere between "point" estimates and "extremely broad interval statements" is to be found a range within which the information furnished by a confidence interval is adequate for the purposes at hand.

7.14   A Brief Look at Minimum Sample Size

At this point a simple approach to the problem of determining the sample size for a quantitative universe will be explained. A more detailed examination of the principles and problems of determining sample size may be found in Chapter 8.

The basic problem is how to determine the size of the sample which should be drawn from a given universe to provide an estimate of the true mean, such estimate having a maximum error of $+$ and $-$ some specified value. This error value may be designated E. Since the "error" due to sampling is the difference between the sample mean $\bar{x}$ and the true mean $\bar{X}$, and since the confidence interval makes allowance for this error at a specified confidence coefficient, the manner in which a confidence interval is constructed also indicates the manner for determining sample size.

The confidence interval is formed by adding and subtracting, say, $2.58\sigma_{\bar{x}}$ to and from the sample mean, as shown in the accompanying sketch.

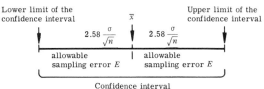

If the allowable sampling error is equated to $2.58\sigma/\sqrt{n}$ and the sample size is to be determined, then

$$n = \left(\frac{2.58\sigma}{E}\right)^2 \quad \text{(infinite universe).} \tag{7.8}$$

Clearly, here the problem is to know the value of σ, or at least to obtain an estimate of σ.

To illustrate the use of Formula (7.8), suppose a supermarket manager wishes to make a sample estimate of the average time a customer spends at the check-out cash register. He knows from past experience that the standard deviation is 4 minutes and he would like to estimate the mean waiting time within plus and minus one minute and specifies the confidence level of 99 per cent. The required sample size turns out to be

$$n = \left(\frac{(2.58)(4)}{1}\right)^2 = 106.5 \approx 107.$$

Now, if the population to be sampled is finite, the formula becomes somewhat more complex because of the correction factor. Under these conditions the required sample size is determined as

$$n = \frac{\sigma^2}{\dfrac{E^2}{z^2} + \dfrac{\sigma^2}{N}} \qquad \text{(finite universe).} \qquad (7.9)$$

To illustrate the use of Formula (7.9) suppose a test of a new type of packaging is to be made. A carload of large crates of apples is to be sampled at its destination to discover the average number of bruised apples per crate. The standard deviation is thought to be 4 as based on past experience, the allowable error is 1, the confidence level is .99, and $N = 400$. What sample size is required to estimate the mean number of bruised apples per crate for this experiment? Using Formula (7.9), we see that

$$n = \frac{(4)^2}{\dfrac{(1)^2}{(2.58)^2} + \dfrac{(4)^2}{400}} = 84.2 \quad \text{(round to 85).}$$

Exercise 7.5

1. What do we mean when we say the mean of a random sample furnishes an "estimate" of the population mean?

2. In discussing sample values we always speak of "estimates." What is being estimated and why?

3. (a) Using the following set of sample means, 4, 5, 6, 9, drawn from a given universe, explain what is measured by the standard error of these sample means.
   (b) Why is the standard error an objective measure of the error inherent in random sampling?
   (c) If you were to draw a very small sample from a one-valued universe, what could you say about the standard error?

4. If you were to determine the confidence level for each of the following problem situations, would you set the confidence coefficient at 95 or 99 per cent?
   (a) It is desired to know the average income of residents of City A as part of a marketing survey.
   (b) We need to know the average number of persons per year who will reach the age of 65 during the next decade.
   (c) A precision part is shipped in cartons of 1,000 units. We need to know the average number of defectives per carton.
   (d) We want to know the average number of hours worked per week in manufacturing industries.
   (e) We need to determine the average number of parts in an inventory bin.

5. In the five situations of the problem above, you probably set most intervals at .95. Does this level of confidence seem adequate for general policy and decision-making purposes?

6. If a confidence interval for a problem were computed for both the 95 and 99 per cent levels, how would the intervals differ?

7. In the making of very general statements, the confidence level is ordinarily very high. Why? State a 100 per cent confidence interval for the thickness of statistics textbooks.

7.15 Estimation of Confidence Intervals for Proportions

When constructing confidence intervals for binomial populations, the basic methodology is the same as that given for continuous variables. The standard error of a proportion is given by the formula:

$$\sigma_p = \sqrt{\frac{pq}{n}}. \qquad (7.10)$$

If percentages were desired, the formula would be:

$$\sigma_{\bar{p}} = \sqrt{\frac{pq}{n}}. \qquad (7.7)$$

But, in the case where n/N is more than 5 per cent, a finite correction factor should be as follows:

$$\sigma_{\bar{p}} = \sqrt{\frac{pq}{n} \cdot \frac{N-n}{N-1}}. \qquad (7.11)$$

The distribution of sample means will be approximately normal as long as the sample size n and either p or q are not extremely small so that np and $nq \geq 5$. This implies that the table of areas of the normal curve can be employed for most problems of this general type. If, however, p, q, or n is very small, then the binomial distribution must be used. In this case it will be necessary to calculate as many terms as are required to establish the desired probability.

Now let us take an example where it is desired to establish confidence intervals for the mean of a proportion. Suppose a random sample of 100 items has been drawn from an infinite universe (the correction factor $\sqrt{(N-n)/(N-1)}$ is not required in this situation) and that the sample proportion turns out to be .75. It is desired to know within what interval the true mean value P may be expected to fall at the 95 per cent confidence level. The standard error is computed first as

$$\sigma_{\bar{p}} = \sqrt{\frac{.75 \times .25}{100}} = \sqrt{.001875} = .043 = \sigma_p.$$

Then, to establish the 95 per cent confidence interval, the limits are computed as follows:

$$p \pm \sigma_{\bar{p}}(z) = \text{the interval};$$
$$p \pm (.043)(1.96) = p \pm .08428$$
$$= .75 \pm .084 = .666 \quad \text{and} \quad .834.$$

Thus, the 95 per cent confidence interval for this sample proportion could be stated as follows:

"At the 95 per cent confidence level, the confidence interval for P is .666 and .834."

Or the statement may be cast in terms of the statistics themselves, allowing the reader to choose his own confidence interval. Thus:

"The sample proportion is .75 and the standard error is .043."

Or, in terms of per cent,

"The sample mean is 75 per cent and the standard error is 4.3 per cent."

Binomial populations may, of course, exhibit values of P such that $0 < P < 1.0$. From the relationship $\sigma_{\bar{p}} = \sqrt{pq/n}$, it may be seen that populations in which p and q are close to .5 will exhibit a larger standard error than when p and q are farther apart in value—assuming n remains constant. Table 7.8, based on a sample size of $n = 100$, will indicate the changing standard error with various proportions of p and q.

Table 7.8

Examples of Changes in the Standard Error ($\sigma_{\bar{p}}$) as p Decreases ($n = 100$; Infinite Universe)

n	p	q	$\sigma_{\bar{p}}$
100	.5	.5	.0500
100	.4	.6	.0490
100	.3	.7	.0458
100	.2	.8	.0400
100	.1	.9	.0300
100	.01	.99	.0090

Table 7.8 indicates a basic principle of sampling from binomial populations which can be stated as follows: The more frequently items in the universe exhibit characteristic A, the smaller the sample size (n) required to detect its presence. For example, if 99 per cent of the universe items display characteristic A, even the smallest of sample sizes is likely to detect that characteristic as the standard error is very small. Table 7.9 shows the probabilities that a sample of size 3 will contain characteristic A, if $p = .99$.

Table 7.9

Probabilities of a Sample of Size 3 Detecting Characteristic A
When A is 99 Per Cent of an Infinite Sampling Universe

Sample Contains	Probability Computation	Probability	Cumulative Probability
$3A$	$1 \times (.01)^0(.99)^3$	.970299	.970299
$2A$	$3 \times (.01)^1(.99)^2$	.029403	.999702
$1A$	$3 \times (.01)^2(.99)^1$	.000297	.999999
$0A$	$1 \times (.01)^3(.99)^0$	.000001	1.000000
		1.000000	

From the table it may be observed that the probability of a random sample ($n = 3$) containing at least one item exhibiting characteristic A is .999999.[4] The probability that the sample will not exhibit A is .000001 ($1 - .999999$). In other words, it is almost impossible to draw a sample of size 3 or more which does not show A.

There is another facet of the principle illustrated above which is more subtle. Suppose it is known that at least 99 per cent of the population items exhibit characteristic A, but it is not known if characteristic B exists, or in what proportions B may exist, nor is it known if C and D exist; then a larger sample will be required to detect B and particularly to indicate the approximate proportion of B. However, moderately small samples will reveal the information that *if* B exists in the universe, its proportions are extremely small. Should this be sufficient information, additional sampling will not be required. On the other hand, if it is desired to establish the precise value of B, larger samples will be called for.[5]

Exercise 7.6. *Constructing Confidence Intervals for Proportions*
1. Explain why the standard error of a proportion is smallest when either p or q is largest in value (n being constant).

2. If you were sampling to detect characteristic B and it was known that B was an extremely small proportion of the universe, would large or small samples be required and why?

3. (a) In a certain sample of size $n = 190$, characteristic "1" occurred 50 times. What is the standard error of the proportion (infinite universe)?
   (b) What is the standard error of q?
   (c) What is the 95 per cent confidence interval for P?
   (d) What is the 95 per cent confidence interval for Q?

4. A sample of 200 items is drawn from an infinite universe with $p = .5$. What is the standard error and the 95 per cent confidence interval?

---

[4] The statement "containing at least one item exhibiting characteristic A" is interpreted to mean $P(1A) + P(2A) + P(3A)$, and in Table 7.9 these three probabilities sum to .999999.
[5] Determination of the minimum sample size for a binomial-type universe is explained in Section 8.6 and may be studied at this point if Chapter 8 is not to be assigned.

5. A sample of 400 is drawn from a universe of 1,200 items. It was found that $q = .8$. What is the standard error and the 99 per cent confidence interval for p?

6. Suppose you were sampling for characteristic "C" which was thought to constitute about 2 per cent of the universe. (The universe is of infinite size.) Suppose it cost 50 cents to draw each sample item. A sample of size $n = 100$ will have a standard error of about .045. A sample of size 500 will have a standard error of about .0063.
    (a) Is the ratio between the two n's and the two standard errors a constant ratio?
    (b) Is the ratio between the two sample costs better (from a money standpoint) than the ratio of the standard errors?
    (c) Does the increase in sample size appear to be a worthwhile expenditure (assuming considerable precision is required relative to characteristic "C")?

7.16   Summary

Sampling is an information-generating process. The basic objective is to obtain estimates of parameters (universe values) such as the mean and the standard deviation. These estimates may then be used in the decision-making process, or for further analysis, or may be recorded for future use, or perhaps put to all of these uses. Presumably, the information is sought because it is thought to be of sufficient value to make its acquisition worth the cost in time, effort, and money.

A substantial portion of this chapter was necessarily devoted to a definition of terms and to description of processes for the obtaining of sample information. As noted, sampling is not limited to one method, but the most scientific results are those of random sampling. Random sampling and probability theory are combined to forge a valuable set of information-supplying tools.

It has been necessary to distinguish between (1) the distribution of items in the universe from which samples were drawn, and (2) the distribution of sample estimates. Thus, we have discussed a "distribution of sample means," which is nothing more or less than a frequency distribution whose probability function may, by the central limit theorem, generally be considered approximately normal. On the basis of this kind of information, confidence intervals for the true parameter (usually mean) can be established. The information obtained from samples is never quite certain and must, therefore, be expressed in terms of probability. For this we have drawn heavily on the background of previous chapters.

The present chapter serves as an introduction to the fundamental principles of sampling. However, it should be understood that sampling is a far more complex subject than can be adequately treated in a few pages of an elementary text. The literature of sampling exists in great volume, and the student who would become expert in the field must expect to devote a large amount of time to specializing in this study alone. What has been presented here should introduce the student to the field and permit him to understand and interpret the results of sampling inquiries at an elementary but highly useful level of understanding.

Key Terms and Concepts of This Chapter

Area sampling	Parameter
Attributes	Pilot study
Binomially distributed population	Point estimate
Central limit theorem	Population (or universe)
Confidence interval	Primary sampling unit
(a) for continuous	Probability sample
distributions	Quota sample
(b) for binomial	Random sample
distributions	Relationship between sample size (n)
Confidence coefficient	and "simple experiment"
Distribution of sample means	Reliability
Efficient sample	Sample
Elementary sampling unit	Sampling bias
Estimate of parameters	Sampling error $(\sigma_{\bar{x}})$
Expansion factor	Sampling fraction
Experiment (How is this concept	Sampling frame
employed in sampling?)	Sampling universe
Interval estimate	Simple random sample
Judgment sample	Systematic sample
Non-sampling error	Universe (or population)

Exercise 7.7. *Some Sampling Experiments.* A great deal of theoretical knowledge may be gained by performing laboratory experiments in sampling. Listed below are a number of experiments which may be performed without a great deal of laboratory equipment. The list of experiments is suggestive only.

1. By use of random methods select ten pages in this book. On each of the ten pages count the number of times the word "and" appears. From this count, estimate the number of times the word appears in the entire book.

2. Secure approximately 100 chips (or other objects) of the same size but differing as to two or more colors. The proportions of different colors in this universe can of course be calculated. Establish a binomial-type experiment by drawing samples of (say) size 5, letting the random variable be a particular color, and let X be the number of occurrences of that particular color.
   (a) From the first sample drawn, estimate the proportion of chips of the identified color existing in the universe.

(b) Return the first sample to the universe, and repeat. Compare the first and second estimates. Combine the two sample results and compare to the known universe proportion.

(c) Repeat the experiment until the universe proportion has been "discovered" through the sampling procedure. How much sampling effort was required to establish the correct proportion?

3. Construct a sampling universe from the items listed in Universe A, Appendix B. Cardboard tags may be used for this purpose. Draw several random samples of size 5 from the universe, calculate the mean for each sample, and then return the items to the universe. Observe how closely each sample mean estimates the true mean of the universe. Observe, too, the manner in which the random variable (the sample means) actually does vary about the true mean.

(a) Compute the confidence interval for each sample.

(b) The sampling standard deviation may also be considered as a random variable and its variations about the true universe value may be noted.

(c) Larger samples (of 10, 15, 20, and 25) may be drawn (replacing the items as drawn) to observe the manner in which larger samples provide more efficient estimates of the parametric values. Standard deviations and confidence intervals may also be calculated.

Exercise 7.8.   The following questions are related to materials studied in this chapter.

1. If $\sigma = 70$ while $\sigma_{\bar{x}} = 7$, what was the size of the sample drawn?

2. If $\sigma_{\bar{x}} = 5$ and $\sigma^2 = 4.225$, what was the size of the sample drawn?

3. If $n = 8$ while $\Sigma (x - \bar{x})^2 = 729$, what is S? (Use $n - 1$.)

4. Using the data of problem 3 above, first calculate S by using $n - 1$, then by use of $S_{\bar{x}} = S/\sqrt{n - 1}$ calculate $S_{\bar{x}}$. Does this answer agree with the answer to problem 3?

5. If a sample of size 50 be drawn from a universe having $\sigma = 30$, what will be the standard error of the distribution of sample means. (Assuming a normal universe.)

6. Referring to problem 5, if σ is not known how could the standard error of the distribution be calculated?

7. How is the proportion (containing a given attribute) of a sample derived?

8. How is the universe proportion (containing a given attribute) derived? What symbol is used to signify this measure?

9. Explain by what procedures P might be established by hypothesis.

10. Suppose a sample of size 10 yielded a proportion p of .6. What is the standard error (σ_p) of the sample distribution?

11. What is the 95 per cent confidence interval for the data of problem 10?

12. Suppose 1,000 samples are drawn from a certain universe and the $\bar{x}$'s and S's are calculated. These $\bar{X}$'s and S's can now be used to form a
(1) _____ and
(2) _____ .

13. Would the mean of the sample means be equal to the mean of the population from which the samples were drawn? Why?

14. Would the standard error of a distribution of sample means be equal to the standard deviation of the population from which the samples were drawn? Why?

15. If a distribution of S's were constructed, what use do you suppose could be made of the standard error (S_s) of this distribution?

16. From a certain universe samples of size 10 were drawn, then samples of size 20, size 30, and so on.
   (a) Explain what happens to the standard error of the distribution of sample means as n increases.
   (b) Explain why this effect takes place.

17. Explain why $n - 1$ is used as the denominator for calculating the *variance* of small samples.

18. Suppose that the items of a universe are 2, 4, 6, 8, and 10. Make a table showing all possible different samples of size 3 that can be drawn. Arrange the items as shown below. Next, total each sample and find its mean and median.

Sample No.	Items	$\bar{x}$	Med
Totals			

19. From the table above, answer the following questions:
   (a) Is the mean of the sample distribution the mean of the population?
   (b) Is the mean of the medians equal to the mean of the population?
   (c) Does the sample distribution of means have a smaller standard error than the distribution of medians?
   (d) What is the standard deviation of the population?
   (e) By use of the formula $\sigma_{\bar{x}} = \dfrac{\sigma}{\sqrt{n}} \sqrt{\dfrac{N-n}{N-1}}$ could you have predicted the standard error of the means?

(f) Is the population a normal distribution?

(g) Does the degree of normality of a population affect sampling results? Why?

20. What is the purpose of "replacement" in sampling from a small universe? (As, for example, in the sampling experiments of Exercise 7.7.)

21. When only one sample is drawn (say $n = 100$), how is it possible for us to discuss a "distribution of sample means"?

22. How much information about a population can be gained from one sample?

23. Suppose we wanted to know the average age of the undergraduates in our particular college. By what methods could we obtain a truly *random* sample?

24. Why is it essential that data be randomized if uniformity is to be the end result of sampling procedures?

25. Explain the difference between standard deviation and standard error.

Exercise 7.9. *The Sampling Distribution.* This problem is designed to illustrate the sampling distribution and its deviation from a statistical population. (Note: This problem may also be used with Exercise 10.1.)

1. Look at Universe A, Appendix B. You will notice that this universe is composed of 386 items arranged in approximately a normal distribution. This is the *statistical universe.* It has population values of $\bar{X} = 50$ and $\sigma = 10$. From that universe samples of $n = 5$ were drawn. The values of the means of these samples are given below. Note that *these are the sample means which will be used to form the sampling distribution.* Now:

(a) From the sample means given below, construct the sampling distribution.

(b) Calculate the mean.

(c) Calculate the standard deviation of the sampling distribution. Observe that this standard deviation is the *standard error* of the distribution. Use Formula (7.6).

Distribution of Sample Means Drawn from Universe A (All Values Rounded to the Nearest Tenth)

47.8	53.2	38.8	56.2	50.8	49.6	50.2	59.6	51.8	49.0
54.8	52.2	49.8	47.8	53.0	54.8	54.4	50.8	50.2	49.6
43.4	45.8	52.6	47.6	50.6	43.2	48.1	51.4	44.8	47.8
43.6	46.4	47.0	43.8	52.0	49.4	55.4	51.8	45.0	51.6
52.8	47.8	46.2	50.0	49.0	48.0	50.6	49.6	53.6	47.0
50.6	51.0	43.8	48.0	46.4	49.0	50.4	46.0	57.2	50.4
47.2	42.0	55.8	52.8	50.8	47.6	54.6	54.8	50.4	47.8
48.8	52.0	59.0	54.4	46.4	56.6	46.6	52.0	44.4	54.0
43.4	51.4	48.6	49.8	48.8	51.4	43.6	45.6	54.4	52.8
54.8	49.0	52.6	45.0	50.6	52.6	47.2	42.2	50.0	52.6

2. Now, on ordinary graph paper plot the values for Universe A to form a normal distribution—that is, draw a smooth curve. (Note: You should stretch the Y axis by making the scale of frequencies less compact than the scale along the X axis. This will help emphasize the points made in this problem.)

3. Next, on the same graph paper and scales, plot the distribution of sample means as constructed in part 2 of this exercise. This should be a frequency polygon. You should now observe carefully the distinction between (1) the population and (2) the sampling distribution.

    (a) Do the two distributions appear about as you would expect on the basis of the theory of sampling distributions?

    (b) What factor accounts for the height of each graph?

4. Is the standard error approximately given by the formula: $\sigma_{\bar{x}} = \sigma/\sqrt{n}$. Should $\sigma_{\bar{x}}$ agree perfectly with the standard deviation of the distribution of sample means? Why?

Exercise 7.10. *Illustration of the Effect of Sample Size upon the Standard Error of the Means.* In the problem below it is assumed that samples of varying size n are being drawn from the same infinite universe. This universe has a standard deviation of 100. You are to pay particular attention to the changes in $\sigma_{\bar{x}}$. Fill in the blanks as indicated.

Prob.	(1)	(2)	(3)	(4)	(5)
	σ	n	$\sqrt{n}$	$\dfrac{\sigma}{\sqrt{n}} = \sigma_{\bar{x}}$	$\dfrac{\sigma_{\bar{x}}}{\sigma} \times 100 = \%$
a	100	4			
b	100	9			
c	100	16			
d	100	25			
e	100	36			
f	100	49			
g	100	64			
h	100	81			
i	100	100			
j	100	500			
k	100	1,000			

Illustration of the Changing Standard Error of a Proportion as n Increases. Compute the values as called for.

	(1) p	*(2)* q	*(3)* n	*(4)* $\dfrac{p(1-p)}{n}$	*(5)* $\sqrt{\dfrac{p(1-p)}{n}} = \sigma_{\bar p}$	*(6)* 95% *Confidence Interval for p*
a	.7	.3	4			
b	.7	.3	9			
c	.7	.3	16			
d	.7	.3	25			
e	.7	.3	36			
f	.7	.3	49			
g	.7	.3	64			
h	.7	.3	81			
i	.7	.3	100			
j	.7	.3	500			
k	.7	.3	1,000			

Bibliography

Excellent discussions of sampling procedures and theory are numerous. The following references are suggested for those who wish an additional source of sampling information in textbook form. See also the bibliography for Chapter 9.

Kurnow, Ernest, Gerald J. Glasser, and Frederick R. Ottman, *Statistics for Business Decisions*, chaps. 7 and 8. Homewood, Ill.: Richard D. Irwin, Inc., 1959.

> Chapters 7 and 8 describe the techniques and methods whereby the factors of risk and uncertainty may be considered in using sample information as the basis of decisions. A good introduction to sampling may be found in chaps. 3 and 4.

Paden, Donald W., and E. F. Lindquist, *Statistics for Economics and Business*, chaps. 9 and 10. New York: McGraw-Hill Book Company, 1951.

> These chapters will serve as a concise and lucid source of sampling information and techniques and may be recommended to the student who wishes additional study materials to supplement his assignments.

Rosander, A. C., *Elementary Principles of Statistics*, chaps. 9 and 19. Princeton, N.J.: D. Van Nostrand Co., Inc., 1953.

> A very thorough treatment of the subject of sampling.

8 SOME TECHNICAL PROBLEMS OF SAMPLING

8.1 Introduction

The preceding chapter discussed the fundamental principles of random sampling and statistical inference. The present chapter may be considered as an extension of the earlier materials. The major purpose of this chapter is to discuss problems of sample size, especially *how large the sample should be* to yield the desired information. A second purpose is to discuss briefly the nature of *stratified random sampling*. These topics conclude a brief formal survey of the subject of sampling.

A major problem in any sampling inquiry and one of the most perplexing is: What sample size n should be used in a given study? For one thing, if n is large, the cost of drawing and processing the sample results will be considerable. If, on the other hand, n is small, costs will be lowered but the sample results will be less reliable than if a larger sample were used.

The resolution of this enigmatic situation involves something of a compromise: Samples of a size just large enough to provide the requisite information at a specified level of sampling error can be drawn. The smallest acceptable sample will minimize the cost while maximizing the informational output for which simple random sampling is designed.

8.2 Symbols Used in This Chapter

Important concepts used in the present chapter are listed below. All other terms remain as defined in previous chapters.

E = the "allowable error." The concept of "allowable error" may be approached through an example as follows: In making a sample inquiry, the question naturally arises as to the amount by which the sample mean $\bar{x}$ may deviate from the true mean $\bar{X}$. When in terms of the informational requirement it is known how much error is permissible, E is then stated in absolute terms. For example, it may be decided that the sample mean could miss the true mean by

$5.00 but no more. Thus, E in *absolute* terms is $5.00. On the other hand, it is usually more convenient to state the percentage by which $\bar{x}$ may miss the parametric value $\bar{X}$. Thus, E may be stated in *relative* terms as 2 per cent, 5 per cent, 7 per cent, and so on.

V = the coefficient of standard deviation. In Chapter 4 the subscript V_{sd} was employed to distinguish between the coefficient of average deviation V_{ad} and the coefficient of standard deviation. In the present chapter, only the standard deviation value is employed and no subscript is necessary. You will recall that V was defined as $\sigma/\bar{X}$, and this definition continues. The coefficient of standard deviation as used here is identical in concept to the usage in Chapter 4. Here, V is expressed as a decimal.

$\sigma_{\bar{p}}$ = the standard error of a distribution of sample proportions.

$\bar{x}$ = the mean of a sample.

$\bar{X}$ = the mean of a quantitative universe.

P = the proportion of items in a universe possessing some attribute— for example, the proportion of defective products in a shipment.

8.3   Relationship Between Sampling Error and Sample Size

Suppose that samples are to be drawn from an *infinite* universe. The universe is so large that no matter what sample size is drawn, n will be an extremely small proportion of N. However, as samples are drawn the sample means will exhibit some variation around the "true" or universe mean.[1] This variation is measured by the standard error. For the sake of simplicity the present discussion will be concerned only with the standard error of the mean, $\sigma_{\bar{x}}$. The general formula for the sampling error of the mean when samples are drawn from an infinite universe is

$$\sigma_{\bar{x}} = \frac{\sigma}{\sqrt{n}}. \tag{8.1}$$

And from the formula it may be seen that the larger n becomes, the smaller is $\sigma_{\bar{x}}$ and therefore the more precise the estimate of the parameter $\bar{X}$ becomes. As long as $n < N$, then $\sigma_{\bar{x}} > \sigma$ provided $\sigma > 0$.

Now, suppose N is finite. In this case the size of the sample drawn could theoretically be so large that $n = N$. If the sample size were such that $n = N$, the sample would be "perfect." In other words, there could be no sampling error and $\sigma_{\bar{x}}$ should be zero. However, since in practice σ will be greater than zero, then $\sigma_{\bar{x}} > 0$ because $\sigma_{\bar{x}} = \sigma/\sqrt{n}$ (unless the

---

[1] The exception to this rule would be in the case of a single-valued universe. Obviously, each sample drawn from such a universe would show only the parametric value.

universe is single-valued). It might be argued that if $n = N$, the whole matter is a case of having taken a census rather than having drawn a sample. However, the point to be established here is that in the limiting case of $n = N$, there can be no sampling error and $\sigma_{\bar{x}}$ must be corrected to allow for that fact.

If, then, samples are drawn from a finite universe where $n < N$, a certain amount of sampling error will be present and is measured by $\sigma_{\bar{x}}$. When the samples are of such a small size that the ratio n/N is less than, say, 5 per cent, the sampling error as measured by $\sigma_{\bar{x}}$ is considered accurate and no correction factor is employed. However, as the ratio n/N approaches 1, the true sampling error as measured by $\sigma_{\bar{x}}$ will decrease; but when calculated by Formula (8.1), this error will be overstated. Thus, when n/N is greater than, say, 5 per cent, the correction factor is

$$\sqrt{\frac{N - n}{N}} . \tag{8.2}$$

To be technical, the denominator is $N - 1$, but since this generally makes only a very small change in the answer, the -1 has been dropped in the interest of simplicity. The complete formula will then be

$$\sigma_{\bar{x}} = \frac{\sigma}{\sqrt{n}} \cdot \sqrt{\frac{N - n}{N}} . \tag{8.3}$$

When n/N is less than .05, it is generally agreed the correction factor may be dropped. Quite probably there is enough sampling error in a sample whose size is less than 5 per cent of the universe to make it unnecessary or at least presumptuous to use a correction factor.

8.4   Determination of the Sample Size[2]

Once it has been decided that a given universe be sampled to determine the value of one or more parameters, the next decision to be considered is this:

(a) With what precision should the parameter be measured? How much error is acceptable? One per cent, 2 per cent, 5 per cent, 10 per cent, or more? This error refers to the difference between the parameter X and the sample estimate $\bar{x}$ of that parameter. In absolute terms:

$$\bar{x} - \bar{X} = E, \text{ the allowable error measured in the units of the}$$
$$\text{universe (dollars, employees, or whatever).}$$

[2] A brief discussion of sample size determination was presented in Chapter 7. The material in Section 8.4 develops the arguments at some length and employs an approach slightly modified from that of Section 7.14.

Actually, it would be difficult (or even impossible) to know $\bar{X}$ or $\bar{x}$ before the sample is taken, and in view of this difficulty a much better expression of allowable error makes use of relative (per cent) error. Thus:

$$\frac{\bar{x} - \bar{X}}{\bar{X}} = E, \text{ the percentage of allowable error.}$$

Now, the important thing in this case is that the allowable error can be specified as, say, 5 per cent without knowledge of the mean values. Considering error in the relative terms is the only feasible manner of answering the question, "How much error is acceptable?" The answer is given in percentage (decimal) figures. That is, "The allowable error is (say) 5 per cent ($= .05$)." Note: This implies ± 5 per cent.

(b) When the allowable error (E) has been decided, the question arises: At what level of confidence should the interval based on the sample estimate $\bar{x}$ be constructed? Can we afford to have $\bar{x}$ miss the true value of $\bar{X}$ by more than a given confidence interval once in a hundred times? Five times out of a hundred? Three times out of a thousand?

At this point the student who experiences a bit of fuzziness should review his knowledge of the normal curve and of sampling distributions which form a normal curve. For example, suppose in answer to the question of confidence it was decided the confidence interval be set so that in only one case out of a hundred on the average (the 99 per cent level) the true parameter $\bar{X}$ would not be included in the confidence interval. This interval would be formed by adding 2.58 times the standard error ($\sigma_{\bar{x}}$) to the sample mean ($\bar{x}$) and then subtracting this same value ($2.58\sigma_{\bar{x}}$) from the sample mean. The student will recall that if the confidence level is set at 95 rather than 99 per cent, the number of standard errors measured from the mean to achieve the lower confidence level will be substantially reduced from $z = 2.58$ to $z = 1.96$.

When the appropriate confidence interval has been decided, it is then necessary to use a table of areas of the standardized normal curve to establish the z value appropriate to this interval. Table 8.1 provides some frequently used values.

Table 8.1

Normal Curve Values

Confidence Interval	z	Confidence Interval	z
99	2.58	94	1.88
98	2.33	93	1.81
97	2.17	92	1.75
96	2.05	91	1.69
95	1.96	90	1.64

(c) Suppose it has been decided to use an allowable error of 5 per cent and that the sample estimate $\bar{x}$ should fall within the 99 per cent confidence interval.[3] For this interval, the standard error is allowed to range through ± 2.58 standard errors measured from the sample mean. In other words, and to place the problem in relative terms, what we have now accomplished is this:

$$\frac{5\% \text{ relative allowable error } (E)}{2.58 \text{ standard errors } (z)} = \sigma_{\bar{x}} = \text{The relative error to be allocated to each standard error of the sampling distribution—that is, } \sigma_{\bar{x}} \text{ is now in relative (decimal) terms.}$$

(d) This knowledge may now be applied to determine the sample size (n) necessary to achieve the specified accuracy. It will be recalled that the basic relationship between the standard error and the standard deviation of an infinite universe is given by the formula:

$$\sigma_{\bar{x}} = \frac{\sigma}{\sqrt{n}}. \tag{8.1}$$

But, it was just noted that $\sigma_{\bar{x}}$ may be equated to the allowable error (E) divided by the z value appropriate to the desired confidence interval. That is,

$$\frac{E}{z} = \sigma_{\bar{x}} \text{ (in relative terms)}. \tag{8.4}$$

Now that $\sigma_{\bar{x}}$ is in relative terms, it will be necessary to convert $\sigma/\sqrt{n}$ to relative terms. This may be accomplished by setting σ equal to V—defined as $\sigma/\bar{X}$—that is, the standard deviation divided by the parameter being estimated. Thus,

$$\sigma \text{ (in relative terms)} = \frac{\sigma}{\bar{X}} = V.$$

Note: Where σ is not known, S as derived from the sample may be used. Also $\bar{x}$ may be substituted for $\bar{X}$.

In relative terms Formula (8.1) becomes

$$\frac{E}{z} = \frac{V}{\sqrt{n}} \quad \text{or} \quad \frac{E^2}{z^2} = \frac{V^2}{n}. \tag{8.5}$$

[3] Caution is urged in the interpretation of "the 99 per cent confidence interval." What this interval means is that in 99 out of 100 sample estimates, and on the average, the confidence interval so established will include the population parameter in question. In general, then, the confidence interval will *not* include the true value in one out of a hundred times—on the average.

Solving for n, we have

$$n = \frac{z^2 V^2}{E^2}. \tag{8.6}$$

Example. If $z = 2.58$ (the 99 per cent confidence level) and $\sigma/\bar{X} = V = 10$ per cent, and the allowable error is 2 per cent, the necessary sample size is

$$n = \frac{(2.58)^2(.1)^2}{(.02)^2} = \frac{(6.6564)(.01)}{(.0004)}$$

$$= \frac{.06564}{.0004} = 164.1 \approx 164 = n.$$

If the sample was obtained from a finite universe, the correction factor (that is, finite multiplier) $\sqrt{(N - n)/N}$ must be used. Thus (squaring all terms):

$$\frac{E^2}{z^2} = \frac{V^2}{n} \cdot \frac{N - n}{N} \tag{8.7}$$

and, solving for n, we have

$$n = \frac{z^2 N V^2}{N E^2 + z^2 V^2}. \tag{8.8}$$

(e) Table 8.2 illustrates the use of Formula (8.5) in determining minimum sample sizes when the samples are drawn from an infinite universe.

Table 8.2

Minimum Sample Size (n) Required for Various Confidence Coefficients and Levels of Allowable Error. Here, $\sigma/\bar{X} = .1$. Values of n Are Shown in the Body of the Table (Infinite Universe)

Allowable Error (E)	Confidence Coefficients									
	99	98	97	96	95	94	93	92	91	90
1%	655	543	471	420	384	353	328	306	286	269
2%	164	136	118	105	96	88	82	77	71	67
3%	78	60	52	47	43	39	36	34	32	30
4%	41	34	29	26	24	22	20	19	18	17
5%	26	22	19	17	15	14	13	12	11	11

This table indicates several general principles of sampling. First, if the allowable error is relatively large (5 per cent might be so considered), then quite small samples will provide acceptable estimates. A comparison of row 1 with row 5 will clarify the point. Secondly, when the allowable error is reduced to a small quantity, the minimum sample size increases very rapidly, as a comparison of rows 1 and 5 will indicate. Lastly, it may be seen that with an increase of one confidence point (say from a confidence coefficient of 90 to 91) there is a relatively small increase in sample size. However, an increase of several confidence points does materially affect sample size and consequently sampling costs. Overall, the table indicates that it is possible to attain a relatively high information-producing sample—with specified maximum errors—by use of quite small sample sizes. On the other hand, almost any degree of accuracy may be obtained, if sufficient financial outlay is made.

8.5   Some Cautions and Limitations on Sampling from Infinite Universes

Referring to Section 8.3, the student will immediately question how σ and $\bar{X}$ may be known when this is precisely what the sample is supposed to discover. This seems to be another enigma. The answer is that there must be some information on hand prior to the inquiry. Unless previous studies have been made and are available to suggest values for σ and $\bar{X}$, there is no alternative but to undertake a pilot study to obtain estimates.

A pilot study may be undertaken even though small amounts of information relative to the universe are known. Here much depends upon the judgment of the investigator. However, a pilot study may be made in order to gain as much information and insight as possible. Then, on the basis of this information the necessary sample size may be determined. It has been suggested that a sample of size 50 is adequate to furnish the necessary σ and $\bar{X}$ estimates if the sample is random and the universe is approximately normal.[4]

A further question arises as follows: How much error may creep into the pilot study without unduly distorting the values being used to determine the sample size n? It has been suggested that if the error is not more than about 10 per cent, the pilot values may be utilized in the formulas without undue effect on the sample.[5] Unfortunately, when it comes to determining whether or not the pilot study is in error there are no unfailing criteria. All that can be said here is that the investigator must call upon his experience and judgment to "sense" incongruities of the data. It might be that in case of doubt, a second pilot probe be made and the results compared with the first one to test for variability of the sample estimates.

[4] Morris H. Hansen, William N. Hurwitz, and William G. Madow, *Sample Survey Methods and Theory*, vol. 1 (New York: John Wiley & Sons, Inc., 1953), p. 131.
[5] *Ibid.*, p. 130.

On the basis of the foregoing discussion it would seem desirable when a universe is sampled for the first time (if cost conditions permit) to determine the minimum sample size required on the basis of the pilot study and then increase n by perhaps 5 or 10 per cent. Under these circumstances it is highly unlikely that the sample would be too small to supply the desired estimate within the specific level of error. The size of any subsequent next sample drawn may be held to the minimum on the grounds that the general characteristics of the universe are now closely approximated.

Exercise 8.1

1. (a) When the answer to the question "How much error can be allowed?" is "The parameter estimate $(\bar{x})$ minus the parameter itself $(\bar{X})$—that is, $\bar{x} - \bar{X}$," explain how these values are or may be determined in absolute terms.
   (b) How may the question be answered in relative terms?
   (c) Why is the relative statement (generally) the preferable statement?

2. What factors, in a practical sampling situation, might influence the decision as to how high (or low) the allowable error should be set?

3. If the allowable error is 5 per cent and the confidence interval for the mean $(\bar{X})$ is 98 per cent, what z value should be used?

4. If the allowable error is 10 per cent and the confidence interval for the mean $(\bar{X})$ is 98 per cent, what z values should be used?

5. Why are the answers to problems 3 and 4 identical?

6. (a) Explain the meaning of the relationship:

$$\frac{\text{Relative allowable error}}{z} = ?$$

   (b) Draw a generalized graph of the normal sampling distribution and label the parts in accordance with the relationships of the formula given in (a) above.

7. If $\sigma_{\bar{x}}$ can be stated in relative terms by E/z, how may σ be stated in relative terms?

8. Write the formula which solves for the sample size n using an infinite universe, and explain satisfactorily each term of the formula.

9. When sampling from a finite universe explain in general terms the effect of the correction factor on n over what n would be if the universe were of infinite size.

10. Determine the sample size for an infinite universe where the allowable error is 1 per cent and the confidence coefficient is to be 97 per cent with a relative coefficient of variation of 10 per cent.

11. Using the data of problem 10 above, determine the sample size when the universe is finite and N is 2,000. How does this sample size n compare with the n for the infinite universe? Is the relationship what you might have expected?

12. Solve the following problems for n as indicated:

Problem Number	Confidence Coefficient z	Allowable Error E	Universe Size N	V	n
1	95	1%	∞	20%	
2	94	2%	1,500	10%	
3	99	5%	300	15%	
4	98	2%	∞	10%	
5	90	0.5%	∞	30%	
6	91	2%	∞	15%	
7	96	3%	600	20%	
8	92	3%	800	25%	
9	93	2%	∞	10%	
10	97	10%	200	50%	

8.6 Determining Sample Size for a Binomial-Type Population

The problem of determining sample size from a binomial population is essentially the same as for the quantitative population previously discussed. The essential notation has already been described in Sections 7.3, 7.12, and 7.15.

The objective of sampling from a binomial-type population is, of course, to estimate the parametric values P and Q. It is to be assumed that the estimates are to be made on the basis of a single random sample drawn from the population in question. Estimates made on the basis of this single sample will be subject to the same problems and limitations already discussed—that is, confidence coefficient for the interval within which the universe value is expected to fall, sampling error, allowable error, the possible need for a pilot study, and so on.

At this point the problem is to compute the minimum sample size required to provide estimates on which a confidence interval can be based. This interval should provide an estimate with a specified maximum amount of sampling error.

It will be recalled that the standard error of a distribution of sample proportions drawn from an infinite universe is given by the formula

$$\sigma_{\bar{p}} = \sqrt{\frac{pq}{n}}.$$

Now, in order to determine the sample size n for a given "allowable error" and given confidence interval, it is necessary to utilize the relationship:

$$\text{The relative} \atop \text{standard error} = \sigma_{\tilde{p}} = \frac{\text{the relative allowable error}}{\text{the } z \text{ value of the confidence interval}} = \frac{E}{z},$$

where E is expressed as a decimal. We have next

$$\frac{E}{z} = \sqrt{\frac{pq}{n}} \quad \text{or} \quad \frac{E^2}{z^2} = \frac{pq}{n}, \tag{8.9}$$

and, since p and q are already in relative terms, we may solve for n directly:

$$n = \frac{z^2 pq}{E^2} \quad \text{(when the universe is infinite).} \tag{8.10}$$

Example. Thus, suppose p and q for an infinite universe are thought to be .70 and .30, respectively, and it is desired to draw a sample with a 99 per cent confidence coefficient and an allowable error of 5 per cent. Thus:

$$n = \frac{z^2 pq}{E^2} = \frac{(2.58)^2(.7)(.3)}{(.05)^2} = \frac{(6.6564)(.21)}{(.0025)}$$

$$= \frac{1.397844}{.0025} = 558.13 \approx 559 = n.$$

However, if it is desired to be "almost certain" the sample size will be such that the estimates do not exceed the allowable error of 5 per cent, a z value of 3 could be used (rather than 2.58). Whether or not this step should be taken is purely a matter of judgment. In this case the sample size will be increased quite markedly. Thus:

$$n = \frac{z^2 pq}{E^2} = \frac{(3)^2(.7)(.3)}{(.5)^2} = \frac{(9)(.21)}{(.0025)} = \frac{1.89}{.0025} = 756 = n.$$

When sampling from a finite population, the correction factor must be used. (Note that the -1 has been dropped in the denominator of the correction factor.)

$$\frac{E}{z} = \sqrt{\frac{pq}{n}} \cdot \sqrt{\frac{N-n}{N}}. \tag{8.11}$$

Solving for n, the formula becomes

$$n = \frac{z^2 N pq}{NE^2 + z^2 pq} \quad \text{(when the universe is finite).} \tag{8.12}$$

Example.   Given a universe where $p = .7$ A sample is to be drawn with a 99 per cent confidence coefficient and an allowable error of 5 per cent. Determine n. The size of the universe is $N = 1,000$. The computations are as follows:

$$n = \frac{z^2 Npq}{NE^2 + z^2 pq} = \frac{(2.58)^2(1,000)(.7)(.3)}{(1,000)(.05)^2 + (2.58)^2(.7)(.3)} = \frac{(6.6564)(1.000)(.21)}{(2.5) + (6.6564)(.21)}$$

$$= \frac{1397.844}{2.5 + 1.397844} = \frac{1397.844}{3.897544} = 358.62 \approx 359 = n.$$

If however, the confidence coefficient where $z = 3$ were to be used, the sample size (under the conditions stated above) would be increased to $n = 435$. (You may wish to try the formula to discover how $n = 435$ was calculated.)

Table 8.3

Minimum Sample Size (n) Required for Selected Allowable Error Levels When the Population Is Binomial and Infinite. z is Constant at 3, i.e., the 99 + Confidence Level. Values of n Are Shown in the Body of the Table

Allowable Error (E)	\multicolumn{7}{c}{p}
	1 or 99%	5 or 95%	10 or 90%	20 or 80%	30 or 70%	40 or 60%	50%
.5%	3,564	17,100	32,400	57,600	75,600	86,400	90,000
1.0%	891	4,275	8,100	14,400	18,900	21,600	22,500
2.0%	223	1,069	2,025	3,600	4,725	5,400	5,625
3.0%	99	475	900	1,600	2,100	2,400	2,500
4.0%	56	267	506	900	1,181	1,360	1,406
5.0%	36	171	324	576	756	864	900
10.0%	9	43	81	144	189	216	225
20.0%	2	11	20	36	47	54	56

Table 8.3 illustrates the use of Formula (8.10) in determining minimum sample size to achieve given levels of allowable error and confidence when the sample is drawn from an infinite binomial-type population.

A study of Table 8.3 illustrates some of the general relationships and principles of sampling from an infinite, binomial-type universe. *First*, the sample sizes are minimum—that is, the smallest number of items which will yield the desired precision. If cost conditions permit, it might be desirable to increase the sample sizes slightly, particularly if the characteristics of the universe were uncertain. *Second*, the values selected for this table provide a high confidence interval (in excess of 99 per cent).

Other tables could be constructed for smaller confidence intervals and the net effect would be to show a reduction in sample size. *Third*, the table illustrates a general sampling principle which indicates that to reduce the allowable error to extremely small proportions requires very large samples. *Fourth*, it may be seen that any desired level of accuracy could be obtained if sufficient outlay were provided.

In addition, it is interesting to observe that as the values of p and q become more nearly equal, the sample size required to provide given levels of error increases rapidly. The reason for this effect is to be found in the behavior of the standard error of the sampling distribution.

Table 8.4

Changes in the Standard Error of a Distribution of Sample Proportions as p and q Become More Nearly Equal (Infinite Universe; $n = 100$)

(1)	(2)	(3)	(4)	(5)
p	q	pq	$\sqrt{pq}$	$\sqrt{\dfrac{pq}{100}}$
.01	.99	.0099	.0995	.00995
.1	.9	.09	.3000	.0300
.2	.8	.16	.4000	.0400
.3	.7	.21	.4570	.0457
.4	.6	.24	.4900	.0490
.5	.5	.25	.5000	.0500

To illustrate the change in the standard error for differing universe values it is necessary to study what happens when the values in the relationship $\sigma_{\bar{p}} = \sqrt{pq/n}$ are allowed to change. The best way to study these relationships is through a table such as Table 8.4. There, several values for p and q (infinite universe) are given in column 1 and 2. The product of p and q is given in column 3. Note how this product increases as p and q become more nearly equal (approach $p = q = .5$). Looking at column 4 next, observe that the square root of the product of p and q increases as these two values become more nearly equal. Consequently, when pq is divided by the sample size and the square root is taken, the result must be a standard error which increases as p and q become more and more nearly equal. To show this effect, column 5 assumes that the sample size is constant at 100, so that the numbers appearing in this column represents the standard error as computed for the values shown. Observe the rapidity with which the standard error increases as you move your eye down column 5.

The important point to be remembered from this discussion and from Table 8.4 is that as the values of p and q approach equality (where $p = q = .5$), the standard error for any given constant sample size increases to a maximum. Thus, larger and larger sample sizes are required to maintain a constant level of acceptable error as p and q approach equality.

Where the population is finite, use of the finite correction factor $\sqrt{(N - n)/N}$ will be required unless n/N is less than .05. The net effect of the correction factor will be to reduce the required sample size from what it would be if the samples were drawn from an infinite universe.

When computing the standard error of a distribution of sample proportions ($\sigma_{\bar{p}}$) the following formula should be used:

$$\sigma_{\bar{p}} = \sqrt{\frac{pq}{n}} \cdot \sqrt{\frac{N - n}{N}}.$$

Exercise 8.2

1. Why is the mean of a binomial universe conceptually identical to the mean of a quantitative universe?

2. Explain why the value either 1 or 0 may be assigned to each item in the universe in order to arrive at a population proportion.

3. If you were making a study of potential customers entering a retail outlet, list some of the ways this "population" would fall into the binomial mold. (Example: Adults and children.)

4. Make a table exactly like Table 8.3, except that the confidence level should be set at 95.545 per cent ($z = 2$).

5. (Optional for students acquainted with logarithms.) (You will need two sheets of 4-cycle semi-logarithmic paper for this problem.) On one sheet of 4-cycle log paper construct a series of curves for the data of Table 8.3. On the second sheet construct a series of curves for the table you made as part of problem 4 above. [Hint: On the arithmetic grid (the X axis) lay out the per cent of allowable error; on the logarithmic grid (the Y axis) lay out the sample size. Then plot a curve connecting all points possessing a common proportion (p) value. You will then have a "family" of curves or "isoquants" which will yield the approximate sample size for selected combinations of p and q, and various percentages of allowable error.]

   (a) Visually compare the two charts, observing the difference in sample sizes for the same p and q when the confidence level is lowered from 99 to 95 per cent.

   (b) Could you estimate the percentage savings in sampling costs which would be effected by using the 95 per cent rather than the 99 per cent confidence coefficient? Make the estimate where $P = .20$ and the allowable error is 3 per cent. Does this relationship appear to hold true in general?

6. Suppose you were working with an infinite universe where P (the universe proportion) is thought to equal .25. You require a 90 per cent confidence coefficient and an allowable error of 5 per cent.

   (a) What would be the correct minimum sample size in this case?

   (b) What would be the correct minimum sample size if the universe size were $N = 2,500$?

7. (a) If you had no notion whatsoever as to the proportions in a given universe, what would be the most logical assumption with which to begin a sampling inquiry?

   (b) On the premise that each sample item drawn costs $1.00, what might you do to minimize the sample cost insofar as possible?

8. Explain why the required minimum sample size grows larger as p approaches .5 from either side.

9. (a) What effect does the size of the universe exert on binomial-type population sample size?

   (b) Is this particularly different from the effect found in a nonbinomial, quantitative universe?

8.7   Stratified Simple Random Sampling

"Stratification" may be defined as "an arrangement of objects or things in layers." Stratification of a sampling universe implies that the original universe can be separated into two or more subuniverses (called strata) according to a logical definition or classification. Random samples will then be drawn from each stratum. The subuniverse or stratum will be more homogeneous than the original universe—unless, of course, the original universe is already homogeneous. A universe composed of all employees of a particular corporation might, for example, be stratified on the basis of skilled, semiskilled, clerical, and administrative personnel. If a study were to be made of weekly earnings, it might be expected that the income variation *within each stratum* would be less than the variation *within the entire universe* of employees.

In the process of stratifying a universe for sampling purposes, several significant problems and critical decision areas are encountered. *First*, it is essential that the original universe be capable of logical, nonoverlapping stratification. *Second*, there must be some gain in accuracy or precision as a result of establishing strata. *Third*, the cost of carrying out a study under these conditions must not be more than the value of the expected return of the information.

Stratified sampling procedures may be used efficiently either when (1) a sampling universe is composed of logical subuniverses so arranged that the means of the strata are of differing values, or when (2) the deviations of the items from the means (if the means in all were equal) are of various values. In either of these situations if (a) the means of the strata are not uniform or (b) the variance around the means is not uniform, then stratified sampling will provide better results than if the universe were considered as a complete entity. A third general situation which calls for stratified sampling is encountered when the original universe is badly skewed. The effect of skewness may be minimized by dividing the universe into several strata and drawing the desired universe information from the strata estimates rather than from one or two estimates covering the entire universe. For example, income data for large random groups of individuals tend to exhibit skewness and it might be desirable to obtain information, say for marketing purposes, by a stratified sample.

Another example of a stratified universe would be found in the student body of, say, a four-year college. Students will normally be classified as freshmen, sophomores, and so on, and these four classes could be considered strata for sampling purposes. In a study of grades, interest might center on values as determined for these strata. The universe might also be stratified by other criteria—over and under age 20, and so on. It might be that should the entire universe be considered as one unit, the diversity would turn out to be so great that a simple random sample would miss nuances of meaning and fail to reveal important variations within the universe. In this case, the stratified sample will provide more efficient estimates of the desired information than a simple random sample.

While a strong case may be built for the use of stratified sampling, there is certainly no reason to employ stratified sampling when the estimates either are not thereby improved or are improved only slightly. To repeat: stratified sampling is useful only when the universe itself is stratified along logical lines of classification or is badly skewed. Too, costs are always an important consideration. There are some universes from which stratified samples may be drawn at less cost than if simple random sampling were used, because the stratified sample may actually be of a smaller total size. However, decisions as to the use of stratified vs. simple random sampling (or other sample types) must be made on the basis of some previous knowledge about the universe and about costs as well as the end goals of the study.

8.8   Advantages of Stratification

Many universes may be subdivided into separate strata by defining certain distinguishing characteristics among the primary sampling units.[6] Stratification has at least three major advantages over simple random sampling:

1. Separate characteristics or attributes of the universe may be studied. For example, in the student grouping illustration previously used there might be some interest attached to the grade level of various majors and minors.

---

[6] The term "primary sampling unit" was defined in Section 7.4 and refers to a particular whole unit of the sampling population; the unit might be a person, a product, a single family dwelling unit, and so on.

In the illustration of corporate employees, interest might center on earnings and educational attainment, or earnings and age groupings.

2. The more closely grouped are the items of a stratum being sampled, the smaller the degree of sampling error (with a given n) because of the lack of wide differences among the items comprising the stratum. Thus, the statistician would likely discover smaller differences among, say, junior executives than among "all" executives. It would be expected that with respect to most economic criteria smaller differences would occur in each stratified group than would appear in the nonstratified universe.

   In the student grouping mentioned previously it would be expected that smaller differences might occur in the stratified grouping with respect to, say, academic interests of a group composed of business and economic majors than in a general group of college juniors and seniors.

   From the examples given above it may be seen that stratification—which is fundamentally logical classification—when properly used implies this: The standard errors of the various strata will each be smaller than the standard error of the universe considered as an entity. Too, stratification means smaller samples can be utilized, or better estimates are provided if sample size is held constant.

3. Where a universe is badly skewed, stratification allows the statistician to avoid the error which would be introduced in the estimates because of skewness. Too, when confidence intervals are based on an estimate from a skewed universe there will be a tendency to overstate the interval at one end and understate it at the other. Estimates based on homogeneous groupings from the skewed universe will overcome at least most of this difficulty.

8.9   Procedure in Stratified Random Sampling

The following outline provides an overview of the general process of stratified sampling.

1. The universe to be studied is divided into the previously determined and clearly defined strata. The ideal of "clearly defined strata" may or may not be completely achieved in practice. For example: In any college class of, say, sophomores, there are always some students who are almost juniors. However, recognizing this difficulty, it is still necessary to draw a line at a certain number of "credits," and the stratification is then carried out on that basis.

2. It is essential that something be known about the nature of the universe and the several strata. Ideally, it will be necessary to know N and the number of items in the various strata along with information as to means and variance in each strata.

   Certainly if little or no information about the universe is available, a pilot study will be required. From the pilot study values of the various parameters may be estimated. Fortunately, even though the estimates contain some margin of error, the actual results from the final sampling process will exhibit an even smaller percentage of error. To illustrate:

If the pilot study reveals a certain standard deviation for the universe and this turns out to contain an error of 20 per cent, the standard error will, because of the relationship

$$\sigma_{\bar{x}} = \frac{\sigma}{\sqrt{n}},$$

show a smaller percentage error than was true of the original estimate of σ.

Where a pilot study is unnecessary, it will generally be because some information is available from previous studies, or has resulted from internal information-generating procedures already established. In other cases samples may be taken periodically, and the necessary information for the universe is thereby maintained on a current basis.

3. The necessary sample size from each stratum can be determined according to the relationships and formulas for simple random sampling.

4. Samples are drawn and estimates of parameters calculated in the usual manner.
   (a) Each sample from a given stratum yields estimates of the parameters of that stratum only.
   (b) The strata may later be combined into totals for the universe or for estimation of the universe mean.

Exercise 8.3

1. Define the word "stratification" as used in sampling theory.

2. What criterion—that is, what method—is employed to divide a universe into strata? Suppose, for example, the universe consisted of tourists visiting a particular historical museum.

3. Look up the word "classify" in the dictionary. From the definition given there, does it seem logical that the strata of a universe will be more homogeneous than the original universe? (Assuming, of course, the original universe is subject to stratification.)

4. What is the reason for the general rule that a universe should not be stratified unless there is a gain in accuracy or precision because of stratification?

5. What are the general conditions under which stratification of a universe is a valuable sampling technique?

6. Consider a factory producing a wide assortment of wire nails. List some of the criteria by which product samples might be stratified.

7. A furniture company is planning a market study of consumer preference. The company produces all the ordinary types of furniture and a few specialized items.
   (a) What strata might be considered in the sample survey to provide useful information relative to potential customers?
   (b) If the survey employed a questionnaire, formulate at least five questions that might be asked in order to yield percentage (binomial-type) results.

8. One of the advantages of stratification (where applicable) is that separate characteristics or attributes of the universe may be studied. Suppose a study is to be made of the executives in a large corporation.

(a) How might "executive" be defined?
(b) If three strata were appropriate, what might these strata be?
(c) What separate characteristics of the three strata might be of value in such a study?

9. (a) Why is it necessary that the strata be "clearly defined" and "non-overlapping?"
    (b) If it were impossible to discover clearly defined strata in a universe, what type of sampling would be called for?

10. Explain briefly why the variance of a particular stratum might be much smaller than the variance of the complete universe.

8.10   Stratified Sampling—Cautions and Limitations

The following criteria are generally useful in considering whether or not to utilize the method of stratified random sampling.

1. Where a universe is already reasonably homogeneous, little or no gain in precision can result from stratification. To take a rather extreme case, suppose a universe *consisted of identical values*. The sample estimates would be identical whether determined from a random sample of the entire universe or on the basis of stratification. That is, $\sigma_{\bar{x}}$ and $\sigma = 0$. At the other end of the scale, suppose a universe consisted of the following values: 3, 3, 3, 6, 6, 6, 9, 9, 9. In this case stratification is clearly preferable to simple random sampling because the standard error for each stratum will be zero, while the standard error for the universe will be $\sqrt{54/9} = 2.449$. Stratified sampling provides improved estimates measured in terms of the variance only when the universe is itself stratified.

2. Stratification is useful when it is possible to clearly define the strata and, when these strata differ, the results will be of greater precision than if simple random sampling were used. Stratified sampling may be accomplished at a cost level which is either slightly greater than simple random sampling or else actually less (as is likely because of the fact that sample size may be reduced).

3. Samples taken in the various strata of a given universe must themselves be random samples. While judgment is exercised in the definitions of strata, the samples contemplated here are not judgment samples; they are random samples. It would, of course, be possible to use a stratified judgment sample, in which case the principles and limitations discussed in Section 8.7 are applicable.

8.11   Financial Costs of Sampling

Cost functions may be derived for sampling studies. In other words, if only a certain amount of money may be devoted to the sampling study, sample sizes will be limited in part by that factor. The following materials will briefly describe the costs of sampling studies.

Suppose the ordinary breakdown of costs as "fixed and variable" is used. As is customary, the fixed costs should include all costs such as overhead and those services which, in one manner or another, become part of the burden attributable to the sampling study. Thus it is necessary to know:

1. About how long the study will take from start to finish.
2. About how much light, heat, machinery, clerical help, and so on are required.
3. The allocation of salaries of service personnel used part-time on the sampling study.
4. Any other overhead costs associated with this study.

If these costs can be estimated with some degree of accuracy, the fixed-cost burden is now available.

The variable costs will increase (although not necessarily proportionately) as the size of the sample increases. While it is true that the cost charge is not always proportional to sample size, let us assume for the sake of simplicity that proportionality is the case. It is then possible to calculate the costs of drawing a single item and processing that value through to the conclusion of the study. Suppose that variable cost turned out to be 50 cents per item. On the basis of information relative to fixed and variable costs, a linear (straight-line) cost function may be derived as:

$$\text{cost} = \text{fixed cost} + .5n$$

(assuming each item costs 50 cents to draw and process). The cost function will not necessarily be constant for differing types of studies and will need to be calculated for particular studies or when the price elements have changed. However, this general method of cost calculation both serves to indicate the nature of and need for economy and also points up the fact that we can have estimates as precise as we are willing to pay for.

8.12   Summary

The subject of the present chapter has been the determination of sample size, the nature of stratified random sampling, and sample sizes in relation to the desired accuracy of the estimates. In general the discussion has been concerned with determining sample sizes just large enough to provide the requisite information at a specified level of tolerable error. While it may be considered desirable to draw large samples, cost considerations are important and must be carefully weighed in any sampling inquiry.

Stratified simple random sampling is useful only when the universe itself is stratified or badly skewed and when interest centers in discovering statistics for these strata, or when we wish to know the characteristics of the skewed universe by studying it in terms of strata. Stratified sampling employs the same sampling techniques as ordinary random sampling. Too, stratified sampling may be the most economical way to obtain the desired information about a universe if the stratification results in smaller standard errors than would otherwise be obtained.

Because of the great reliance placed upon sampling as a source of information in the modern world, it is essential for the student of business and economics to possess a workable knowledge of this particular portion of the science of statistics. The student whose interest may have been quickened by this brief tour of sampling will find a more thorough study of the field both challenging and rewarding. The references at the end of this chapter will provide a convenient starting point.

Key Terms and Concepts of This Chapter

Confidence interval	Strata or stratum
Fixed and variable costs	Stratification of a universe
Minimum sample size	Subuniverses
Pilot study	Allowable error in absolute units
(V)	Allowable error in relative units

Exercise 8.4

1. Under what general conditions is stratification useful? Set forth the advantages and limitations of stratification.
2. Along what lines would it be possible to stratify a universe of, say, automobile tires? Employees? Food products? Refrigerators? Men's clothing? Toys?
3. (a) Explain why a smaller total sample size may result from stratification than if the universe were not stratified.
    (b) Explain the conditions under which this condition would not hold true.
4. To what extent does judgment enter into a stratified random sampling process? Is there anything incorrect about using judgment in the sampling process? Why or why not?
5. A corporation with five plants located in different areas of the United States is considering a group life insurance policy to cover all employees. Formerly, the company offered group insurance only to employees in one of the plants. In deliberating the question, corporation officials wanted to obtain information as follows: What is the level of life insurance holdings of all employees in all the plants? Information is desired on each plant as well as the total corporate structure. It is believed a sample of 250 employees in each plant will provide at least a 95 per cent confidence level and an allowable error of no more than 10 per cent. Estimate the costs associated with this study at current price-wage levels and draw up a preliminary budget for carrying out the project.

6. In sampling from an infinite quantitative universe, what will be the percentage decrease in the standard error when the sample size is increased by (a) 10 per cent; (b) 30 per cent; (c) 50 per cent; (d) 75 per cent; (e) 100 per cent?

7. If a sample size (infinite universe) were allowed to increase by units from 500 to 1,000, draw a graph showing the accompanying cost increase (assume the overhead costs are $200 and each item costs 25 cents to draw and process) and the increase in accuracy of the estimates. (Hint: Although a smooth curve should be drawn for each variable, you will need to choose "steps" through which the sample size is actually increased.)

8. In the text it has been indicated that the correction factor $\sqrt{(N - n)/N}$ comes into use when $n/N > 5$ per cent. Try to present arguments to show: (a) that 5 per cent is too large; (b) that 5 per cent is too small; (c) that 5 per cent is about right.

9. Suppose you wanted to estimate the number of defective items produced by a continuous production process which has just been established. The requirements are that the sample estimate be within 1 per cent of the true mean value at the 99 per cent confidence level. What sample size should be utilized to provide this information?

10. A survey is to be made in a city served by two television stations. The information sought is to determine the percentage of available audience listening to each station. It is required that the estimate be within 2 per cent of the true proportion at the 95 per cent confidence level. There are 100,000 persons in the city. What sample size is required?
  (a) Should this problem be modified to confine the information to adults? Why?
  (b) Should this problem be further modified to account for various hours of the viewing day? If so, how might this be accomplished within the sampling study?
  (c) With the information and qualifications given, set up a program for obtaining the necessary information including type of audience and viewing times. Give a cost estimate. Is the information worth the cost as you consider these factors?

Bibliography

Bowen, Earl K., *Statistics*, chap. 16. Homewood, Ill.: Richard D. Irwin, Inc., 1960.

Croxton, Frederick E., and Dudley J. Cowden, *Practical Business Statistics*, chaps. 13 and 19. New York: Prentice-Hall, Inc., 1960.

Freund, John E., and Frank J. Williams, *Modern Business Statistics*, chaps. 7, 8, 9, and 12. Englewood Cliffs, N.J.: Prentice-Hall, Inc., 1958.

Hansen, Morris H., William N. Hurwitz, and William G. Madow, *Sample Survey Methods and Theory*, vol. 1. New York: John Wiley & Sons, Inc., 1953.
    This volume will be useful for the student who wishes to go beyond an introduction to sampling and study the subject in depth.

Mills, Frederick C., *Statistical Methods*, chap. 19. New York: Holt, Rinehart & Winston, Inc., 1955.

Mood, Alexander McFarlane, *Introduction to the Theory of Statistics*. New York: McGraw-Hill Book Company, 1950.

> For students whose mathematics background is adequate, chaps. 7, 8, 9, and 10 present a thorough treatment of the subject of sampling.

Neiswanger, William Addison, *Elementary Statistical Methods*, chaps. 11 and 12. New York: The Macmillan Company, 1956.

Neter, John, and William Wasserman, *Fundamental Statistics for Business and Economics*, chap. 11. Boston: Allyn and Bacon, Inc., 1962.

Tuttle, Alva M., *Elementary Business and Economic Statistics*, chap. 12. New York: McGraw-Hill Book Company, 1958.

Walker, Helen M., and Joseph Lev, *Statistical Inference*, chaps. 5 and 6. New York: Holt, Rinehart & Winston, Inc., 1953.

Wallis, W. Allen, and Harry V. Roberts, *Statistics, A New Approach*, chap. 11. New York: Free Press of Glencoe, Inc., 1956

9

STATISTICAL INFERENCE AND THE TESTING OF HYPOTHESES

9.1 Introduction

The central problem of this chapter is concerned with the testing of statistical hypotheses and statistical decision-making. The process and methods employed to arrive at a final decision are a logical extension of the sampling, inference, and probability materials of the preceding chapters.

The type of problem to be discussed may best be illustrated by an example. A production process produces a food product for sale in the market. This product has certain characteristics such as sight, color, taste, consistency, and so on. In order to sell continuously in the market, each unit of the product must meet certain specifications. If the food package specifies that the product inside should weigh 16 ounces *or more*, then the producer will wish to be certain the weight is *at least* 16 ounces. But how can the producer be certain that the process is actually turning out a product which meets these specifications? How can he decide when the process of production is correct and when it has gone astray with respect to, say, the characteristic of weight? The producer will have to make decisions about the quality of the product continuously—that is, simultaneously with the operation of the process itself. He cannot afford to let the weight fall below 16 ounces nor can he afford to allow the weight to rise much above 16 ounces. Some method must be devised to provide continuous measurement of the variable "weight" and to permit continuous decisions about whether the production process is operating properly.

This fundamental problem—that of determining whether or not a variable has changed and, if it has changed, whether it has changed so much that some kind of action should be taken—will be the major concern of this chapter. Essentially, then, the present chapter will discuss one type of statistical decision-making.

Statistical decision-making does not differ in principle from other types of decision-making. At many points in life an individual must decide what course of action is appropriate under a given set of circumstances. A general procedure for decision-making may be stated as follows: (1) recognition or detection of the problem, (2) defining the problem so that its outlines are clearly known and understood, (3) gathering information about the problem—such information may or may not be numerical in nature, (4) formulating alternative courses of action or hypotheses about the problem and its solution, (5) judging or deciding the issue. A final step is to go ahead and act on the basis of the decision made.

Although statistical decision-making does not differ in principle from other types of decision-making, two things do stand out. One facet of statistical decision-making is that the problem can be *quantified*—that is, it is capable of numerical expression; and second, the problem can be *evaluated* in terms of the risk of error, and this risk can be expressed as a probability. In this book the statistical analysis is not carried to the high degree of sophistication which would include the Bayesian approach, and perhaps game theory. The present volume is concerned only with the approach known as "classical." In the classical approach, probability is regarded as relative frequency in the long run (as explained in Chapter 5), which makes this approach particularly useful with experiments which are capable of repetition and thus can supply objective evidence of the existence of an event, principle, or value. The Bayesian school, on the other hand, allows probabilities which are essentially degrees of belief in the existence of an event, principle, or value. It is not here argued that the latter school is unimportant or of little value; rather the difficulty concerns the amount of material which can reasonably be included in an elementary work. In the author's view the classical approach has been chosen as being most generally applicable at the level intended herein as well as of substantial value in the general types of business and economic problems most frequently encountered.

9.2   New Symbols and Concepts Introduced in This Chapter

For the most part, the symbols and concepts required for the present chapter have already been developed in previous chapters. The following six concepts are, however, unique to the present chapter.

Type I error   A Type I error is defined as "rejecting a true hypothesis" and is explained at length beginning on page 224. A Type I error is sometimes known as an "alpha error."

Type II error

A Type II error is defined as "accepting a false hypothesis" and is explained at length beginning on page 244. A Type II error is sometimes known as a "beta error." (See Section 9.3 and Illustration 9.2.)

Alpha, α

Alpha is directly related to the concept of a Type I error. For example, if the confidence level (explained in Chapter 7) were set at .95, alpha would be .05. Under these conditions and on the average over a large number of trials, a Type I error will be made 5 times out of each 100 trials. An alternative explanation would be to say that alpha represents the decimal value of an area of the normal curve in which a given hypothesis will be rejected (declared false). Incidentally, note that the confidence level = $1 - \alpha$.

Null hypothesis

The term "null hypothesis" is used to refer to a situation in which there is deemed to be no difference between a sample value and the corresponding parametric value. In other words, the null hypothesis suggests that $\bar{x} - \bar{X}$ may be considered approximately zero. Note that the difference need not be zero, but only that the difference is considered so small that it is really not significant. (See also Section 9.4.2.)

$H_1, H_2, \ldots, H_n$

The letter H is used to refer to a particular hypothesis. Thus, H_1 refers to "hypothesis one," H_2 refers to "hypothesis two," and so on. Note that H_0 is used to designate the null hypothesis.

Random variable

Although this concept has been explained previously, it may not be amiss to review the essential points again. In an experiment which is capable of repetition and whose outcome is numerical, it is said that the outcomes of repeated experiments form a random variable. To specify a random variable, capital letters are used. However, when a particular outcome is specified, lower case letters are used. Thus, when the letter Z is used, the reference is to a variable measured in terms of the standard deviation units of the normal curve. But, when z is used, the reference is to particular values of the random variable Z. In any case, the meaning should be clear from the context in which the letters are used.

9.3   Some Illustrative Examples

Three examples will now be examined in which many of the issues and problems of decision-making are suggested and in which the main features of interest are pointed out for further discussion in later sections of this chapter.

Example 1. The following situation is nonstatistical in nature. Suppose a student is faced with the problem of deciding whether or not to take an elective course to round out a particular semester's (or quarter's) work. Several issues must be decided. There is the issue of whether or not he should take any elective course at this time. There is the question of whether he should choose a particular elective course or select another. Either decision involves at least some risks to his college career. Suppose the student is considering a particular course. He may consider that two hypotheses are tenable: (1) Let hypothesis H_1 state that the course would add much to his knowledge and would also be a pleasant and valuable experience. (2) Let hypothesis H_2 state that the course would add little to his knowledge because it would be uninteresting to him and he would not be motivated sufficiently to grasp the true meaning of the material.

Now, if the first hypothesis, H_1, is considered correct, the decision would be made to elect the course. But how can the student know in advance whether H_1 is the true hypothesis? In other words, if he selects H_1 and later discovers he made a mistake, he runs the risk of failing. If he selects H_2 and therefore does not elect the course, and later finds the subject was precisely what he wanted, it may now be too late in his career, or the course may not be offered again for two years. Either alternative causes the student to "risk" something of value to his college career.

However, the student may observe that his choice between H_1 and H_2 need not be made blindly. Courses of action are open in at least these respects: He could gather information about the course from students who have previously completed the work. He could seek information from the college catalogue and from the professor.

The questions he asks will be determined largely by his preconceptions and objectives. He may wish to ask questions such as the following: Is there a term paper? Is there a book report or reports? At what hour is the course taught? Is it open to undergraduates? In finding answers to such questions, the student gathers information. It is not here argued that these are the questions he necessarily "ought" to ask, but rather that these are questions he may ask and which he believes important in his own frame of reference.

Now, with the information collected and sorted out, the student begins to synthesize, to weigh, to evaluate, and after careful thought a decision is reached. No matter what the decision, there is a risk of being incorrect, although the final outcome can be known only after the passage of time. The consequence of either decision cannot now be precisely evaluated. On the fortunate side, there are guidelines the student may follow and these are largely based on past experience. For example, if the course is one which provides insights into traditional areas of knowledge, he is not likely to make a serious mistake. And, in any case, he will obtain some worthwhile benefits from the experience.

As the example suggests, even this rather common problem of college students is one which does not necessarily have an "easy" answer, and it is a problem whose ramifications are broader and deeper than appear at first glance. This type of problem is not, of course, a statistical problem even though it does indicate the areas of possible difficulty and points up the nature of problem-solving and decision-making.

Example 2.   Now take a different sort of problem. We have a coin before us. Someone states the hypothesis that the coin is not balanced—that is, it is not fair. Now the question arises: Is it or is it not a fair coin? If the question is "important" to us we may wish to devise some means of testing the coin. More precisely what we wish to do is to test the hypothesis, say H_1, which states the coin is fair. (This statement implies that if the coin is tossed a number of times, it will land showing heads about 1/2 of the tosses. This statement is, in effect, the null hypothesis.) Hypothesis H_2 then becomes: The coin is not fair.

Suppose it is decided to establish an experiment in which the coin in question is tossed 100 times. The random variable is the number of heads showing. Probability theory states that a fair coin may be expected to land heads np times. Thus, $(100)(1/2) = 50$. Probability theory also indicates that the outcome of a compound experiment of this type will not necessarily be precisely $r = 50$, where r is defined as the occurrence of a head, but the outcome ought to be "close" to $r = 50$. In other words, $P(r = 25)$, $P(r = 80)$, and so on are all low-valued probabilities for this experiment.

Now, suppose the coin is tossed 100 times and the outcome is $r = 50$. We then decide the coin is fair—that is, we accept H_1. Why should H_1 be accepted? We do so because the hypothesis is supported by what can be regarded as fairly clear evidence. After all, the expected value of X is $r = 50$. But does the outcome $r = 50$ make us *absolutely certain* the coin is fair? No, because even an unbalanced coin could, by chance, have landed showing $r = 50$. If we *did have an unbalanced coin* and decided it was fair on the grounds that $r = 50$, we would have made an error— that is, we accepted a false hypothesis (the coin is fair). On the other hand, if the hypothesis was that the coin is fair and *it really was a fair coin* and we accepted that hypothesis on the grounds that the experimental outcome was $r = 50$, no error would have been made. Of course, this is the result we seek to achieve, namely, selecting the correct hypothesis. Unfortunately, a record of a perfect selection among alternatives is highly improbable, and it will be necessary to be satisfied with the condition in which errors are minimized but not eliminated.

Table 9.1

Values of r, z, and P for the Experiment of Tossing One Coin 100 Times When $r \leq 50$ (Normal Curve Values)

r	z	$P(r \ or \ less)$
50	0.0	.50000
48	−0.4	.34458
46	−0.8	.21186
44	−1.2	.11507
42	−1.6	.05480
40	−2.0	.02275
38	−2.4	.00820
36	−2.8	.00226
34	−3.2	.00069

$$\bar{x} = np = (100)(1/2) = 50,$$

$$\sigma_{\bar{p}} = \sqrt{npq} = \sqrt{(100)(1/2)(1/2)} = 5,$$

$$z = \frac{r - np}{\sqrt{npq}},$$

where $\bar{x}$ = the mean of the sampling distribution,
$\quad \sigma_{\bar{p}}$ = the standard error of the sampling distribution.

Now, consider the same coin problem discussed above and suppose that the experiment was performed and the outcome was $r = 60$. Now, do we decide H_1 is a true hypothesis? Suppose the outcome was $r = 30$. Is H_1 true? If the outcome was $r = 20$, or $r = 80$, is H_1 correct? Clearly, outcomes of these numerical values begin to cast grave doubt on the validity of H_1. Too, from a knowledge of probability and random variables, outcomes other than $r = 50$ can be evaluated in terms of the normal curve approximation to the binomial. (See Section 6.7.) Suppose selected values of r, z, and $P(r$ or less) are computed as shown in Table 9.1.

Table 9.1 shows that $P(r$ or less) diminishes rapidly as r changes to the lower values so that $P(r \leq 34)$ is .00069. Clearly a fair coin is not likely to show 34 heads in an experiment where $n = 100$. We might agree that if $r \leq 34$ the coin is declared to be not fair and we would reject H_1. *But the* *point at which H_1 is rejected is somewhat arbitrary.* Why not reject H_1 if $r \leq 42$, or if $r \leq 46$?

While selection of the point of rejection for H_1 is somewhat arbitrary, *it is possible to select that point with reasonableness and with full knowledge of the likelihood of error.* For the moment, some other phases of the problem at hand may be examined.

Consider the situation in which $r \geq 50$. With a fair coin the expectation would be that $r \geq 50$ on one-half of the compound experiments of $n = 100$—that is, on the average, $r \geq 50$ one-half of the times the full

Table 9.2

Values of r, z, and P for the Experiment of Tossing One Coin 100 Times Where $r \leq 50$ (Normal Curve Values)

r	z	$P(r \text{ or more})$
50	0.0	.50000
52	0.4	.34458
54	0.8	.21186
56	1.2	.11507
58	1.6	.05480
60	2.0	.02275
62	2.4	.00820
64	2.8	.00226
66	3.2	.00069

$$\bar{x} = np = (100)(1/2) = 50,$$

$$\sigma_{\bar{p}} = \sqrt{npq} = \sqrt{(100)(1/2)(1/2)} = 5,$$

$$z = \frac{r - np}{\sqrt{npq}},$$

where $\bar{x}$ = the mean of the sampling distribution,
$\sigma_{\bar{p}}$ = the standard error of the sampling distribution.

experiment was performed. Probability theory indicates that the probabilities associated with outcomes in which $r \geq 50$ are exactly the same as outcomes in which $r \leq 50$. Therefore this problem of whether or not the coin is fair should be considered in terms of "both sides" of the standardized normal curve. A table constructed for positive values of $z = r$ is given as Table 9.2.

Since, in this experiment, outcomes in which $r \geq 50$ are as probable as outcomes in which $r \leq 50$, the problem of testing H_1 must be seen in terms of the probabilities supplied by "both sides" of the standardized normal curve. Further, a decision rule may be formulated by which a decision can be made as to whether or not the coin is fair. For example, a rule may be established as follows: If the random variable z takes a value between $+2$ and -2, consider the coin fair—that is, accept H_1. Otherwise, consider the coin not fair and accept H_2.

Observe what has been accomplished by employing this decision procedure. Limits are now expressed in terms of z, which permit us to decide whether or not the coin is fair. It must be admitted that the z limits are somewhat arbitrary, but at the same time the limits are deemed to be reasonable. Too, since the standardized normal curve is employed as the measure of probability, the limits of acceptance and rejection for H_1 and H_2 are in terms of z, which is independent of the sample size n. In other words, whether the test employs a sample of $n = 100$, $n = 50$, $n = 200$, or whatever, the z limits established will not affect the probability values. However, as subsequent sections will note, the sample size does have an important effect on the ability of the test to do what it is supposed to do—that is, lead to the correct decision.

By establishing z limits of $+$ and -2 for the decision rule, H_1 will be rejected on the average of about 5 per cent of the times the experiment is performed. The 5 per cent is calculated as follows: $P(z < 2) = .02275$ and $P(z > 2) = .02275$. Thus, $.02275 + .02275 \approx 5$ per cent. (Normal curve values.)

In terms of probability, then, the z value resulting from this experiment would actually be in excess of $+2$ or -2 about 5 per cent of the times that the experiment ($n = 100$) is performed. H_1 is rejected when z is greater than $+$ or -2 because the probability of z exceeding $+$ or -2 is so low as to cause us to believe H_1 is an incorrect hypothesis. Therefore, by rejecting H_1 under the decision rule established, an error, that of rejecting a true hypothesis, will be made about 5 per cent of the time. *Errors are the price to be paid for making decisions on the basis of incomplete—that is, sample—knowledge.* We expect, under the conditions described above, to make the correct decision with respect to H_1 about 95 per cent of the time and to make a Type I error about 5 per cent of the time. These percentages change if we use other values of z for the test. For example, a z value of $+$ or -3 would cause Type I errors about 3 times in 1,000 trials.

Example 3. Suppose a business firm is engaged in supplying a fine-quality, special-purpose sand in 100-pound bags. The production process has been designed to package each bag with 100.0 lb. Thus, 100.0 lb is the expected mean of the universe. However, since the production process which automatically weighs and bags the sand may, at some point, get out of control and provide too much or too little sand, it is necessary to make sampling checks of the weight of the bags as they emerge from the conveyor. Clearly, the firm is being inefficient whenever the weight falls much below or rises much above a mean value of 100.0 lb. Officials have decided that a sample mean falling between

100.0 ± 1/2 lb is a satisfactory weight range. The size of the sample has also been set at $n = 100$. Thus, if a sample of 100 sacks of sand is drawn at random and the mean weight is between 99.5 and 100.5 lb, the process is declared to be operating satisfactorily. The decision as to the size of the sample and the "range of acceptance" for the sample means (99.5 to 100.5 lb) has been somewhat arbitrarily established on the basis of past experience. However, the limits and sample size are believed to be reasonable.

The problem faced by the business in this situation is as follows. Once the production process has been set, the average weight of the bags of sand should be 100.0 lb. Some variation in the weights of individual bags is to be expected and the weighing process will be considered "in control" whenever the sample of 100 bags exhibits a mean between 99.5 and 100.5 lb. However, should the variables (machine settings, moisture, and so on) in the production process change, the mean weight will shift. If the mean weight, as determined by the sample, changes by more than .5 lb, action must be taken to correct the machinery which weighs and bags the product. Clearly, the business will be concerned if the sample mean shifts to either side of 100.0 lb (is too high or too low). Since it is too expensive to weigh each sack as a check on quality, a sampling process involving a random selection of 100 sacks at periodic intervals is to be employed.

The goal of the sampling process is to detect whether the mean weight of the universe has changed significantly from 100.0 lb. Therefore it has been determined that if the mean weight for the universe is between 99.5 and 100.5 no corrective action will be taken. If the sample mean is outside these limits, the production process must be shut down and reset to the proper value. *In general, then, "small" differences between sample values and the universe or standard value of 100.0 lb will be of no concern whereas "large" differences will call for corrective action.* H_1 could be the hypothesis that the mean of the sample *does not* differ significantly from the standard weight of 100.0 lbs. H_2 could then be the hypothesis that the mean of the sample *does* differ significantly from the standard weight of 100.0 lb. H_1 may be termed the *null hypothesis which states that there is no significant difference between the sample mean and the standard mean of 100.0 lb.* H_1 is the hypothesis to be tested.

Suppose now it is known from past experience that the standard deviation of the universe is 2.5 lb. Then if samples of 100 sacks are taken and weighed, the standard error of the sampling distribution of means will be $2.5/\sqrt{100} = .25$ lb. Since the acceptable mean weight for the sample is not to fall below 99.5 lb nor to exceed 100.5 lb, acceptance limits for the hypothesis H_1 will be $100.0 \pm 2\sigma_{\bar{x}}$. Thus, whenever a sample mean yields a value between 99.5 and 100.5 lb H_1 is accepted; otherwise H_2 is accepted. *If H_1 is accepted, the production process is allowed to continue; if H_2 is accepted, the process is shut down for corrective action.* Acceptance of H_2 will cause a shutdown in the production process and considerable expense may be encountered. It is obviously important that the samples lead to the correct conclusion as reliably as possible without incurring excessive cost in the sampling process.

The main features of the foregoing description may be summarized in a diagram as shown in Illustration 9.1.

Illustration 9.1 Graphic Illustration for the Decision Rule of Example 3. (Type of Error Shown in Roman Numerals.)

I	*II*	*I*
Rejection	*Acceptance*	*Rejection*
If sample mean falls in this area, decide the average weight is too low. Shut down process. Look for cause of trouble.	If sample mean falls in this area, decide the average weight is about correct. Continue the process.	If sample mean falls in this area, decide the average weight is too high. Shut down the process. Look for cause of trouble.

X

99.5   100.0   100.5   → X

Sample weight in pounds

It may be observed from Illustration 9.1 that a decision rule has been established in a manner such that the sample mean will indicate clearly "acceptance" or "rejection." The actual process of decision-making has now become rather mechanical but the process itself has been established in accordance with logic and known statistical principles. If the decision rule is followed carefully, the firm should be assured of turning out a product which—allowing for an occasional error—will meet established specifications. A brief indication of the errors which might occur under the conditions established for this particular problem will now be examined.

In the first place, knowledge of sampling variability indicates that if samples of $n = 100$ are drawn from a universe whose standard deviation is 2.5 and whose mean is 100.0 lb, approximately 95 per cent of all possible sample means will fall between $\bar{X} \pm 2\sigma_{\bar{x}}$. As long as these conditions hold true with respect to $\bar{X}$, σ, and n, H_1 will be accepted 95 per cent of the time and rejected 5 per cent of the time. However, as long as the universe mean is actually 100.0 lb, but H_1 is rejected on the basis of sampling information, an error is made. On the basis of the sample information leading to rejection of H_1 it is decided to shut down the process to determine the cause of the trouble, when in fact the production process is producing an acceptable product. *This type of error can be described as a Type I error.* (A true hypothesis was rejected.)

On the other hand, suppose the mean weight did actually shift to well below 100.0 lb. Such a shift in weight could occur and go undetected because the sample mean happened to be one from the upper end of the sampling distribution, one which fell within the acceptance range. In this case the process is declared to be within acceptable limits when in fact it is turning out an underweight product—that is, H_1 is accepted. Again an error is made. The process should have been shut down for correction, but on the basis of the sample information the process is allowed to continue. *This type of error can be described as a Type II error.* (A false hypothesis was accepted.)

To summarize: The hypothesis to be tested is, "The process is turning out a product whose weight is almost exactly 100.0 lb." In the first case the hypothesis was true but the sample information caused rejection of the truth. This is a Type I error. In the second case the hypothesis was false, but the sample information caused acceptance of the hypothesis. This is a Type II error.

Steps Involved in Making a Statistical Test

The method employed in statistical testing and decision-making may be structured as follows:

1. A problem exists for which some method of testing is required in order to permit a decision to be made about the problem. In the sand-weight example, the problem was to maintain an average weight of approximately 100.0 lb per bag of sand.

2. The problem is defined and stated in known terms. This implies that the principles of sampling and probability distributions be employed to establish a method by which decisions can be reached. This method should have a high probability of leading to correct conclusions. In other words, it is desired to run a low risk of error.

3. One or more tenable hypotheses are formulated. Each hypothesis provides a specific statement which can be tested by the methods employed.

4. A decision rule is formulated in such manner that the sample mean will fall within either an area of acceptance or of rejection. The rule is established in such manner as to minimize the risk of incorrect conclusions. In the sand-weight example, the rule was to accept H_1 if the sample mean fell between 99.5 and 100.5 lb. Otherwise, H_1 was rejected.

5. Each time a sample is taken, a decision is made on the basis of the decision rule. In the sand-weight example the decision was either to (1) continue the process or (2) close down the process and search out the trouble.

Exercise 9.1. The following questions are based on Section 9.3. You should assure yourself of understanding the point (or points) raised in each question.

1. In the coin-tossing experiment of Section 9.3 why do we state the outcome of 100 tosses "ought to be close" to $r = 50$? How certain can we be that r ought to equal approximately 50?

2. Refer again to the coin-tossing experiment of Section 9.3.
   (a) What is the purpose of hypothesis H_1, namely that "the coin is fair"?
   (b) Is it necessary to formulate the alternative hypothesis, H_2, which states the coin is not fair?
   (c) If it is not necessary to state H_2, is it already tacitly formulated when H_1 is stated?

3. Explain, in general terms, how errors may be made in accepting or rejecting hypotheses, and how the type of error is determined.

4. If $r = 50$ is the expected outcome of an experiment ($n = 100$) involving a fair coin, what is the probability that the outcome of a particular experiment will be $r \le 38$? What method is used to determine this probability?
   (a) Explain the role of the standardized normal curve in this situation.
   (b) Was it necessary to use the binomial $(p + q)^{100}$, where $p = q = 1/2$, to supply the probability information for this coin-tossing problem? Why?
   (c) On what grounds is it desirable to use the standardized normal curve rather than the exact probabilities as calculated from the binomial?

5. Refer to Example 2 beginning on page 233. In your judgment, what is the lowest and highest value of $X = r$ (number of heads showing) you would accept as "furnishing substantial evidence" that H_1, which states the coin is fair, is actually the correct hypothesis?

6. (a) How may the area of acceptance (as shown in Illustration 9.1) be "widened"?
   (b) How can it be "narrowed"?
   (c) As the area of acceptance is widened, what begins to happen to the possibility that we would declare the average weight to be correct when it was actually too small or too high?
   (d) As the area of acceptance is narrowed, what happens to the possibility that we would declare the weight to be over or under when in fact it was actually approximately correct?

7. (a) In example 2, as n increases, what do you think happens to the opportunity to reject H_1 in the coin-tossing experiment if the area of acceptance remains constant at $\bar{X} +$ and $- 2z$? For example, would you feel better about accepting or rejecting H_1 if $n = 200$ than if $n = 100$? Why?
   (b) Although you would probably prefer to have $n = 200$ in the coin-tossing experiment of Example 2, what considerations might prevent you from using $n = 200$ and thus finding yourself satisfied with a smaller n?

8. In the coin-tossing experiment of Example 2, how do we know that when $n = 100$, the random variable z would exceed $+$ or -2 about 5 per cent of the time the experiment was performed?

9. Why do we use incomplete knowledge as the basis for making decisions? In other words, why do we not use complete information?

10. Suppose you are in the process of deciding whether to borrow money to complete college or whether you should secure a part-time job. What are the risks, considerations, and factors you would consider in making your decision?

11. In Example 3 (the sand-weight example) the area of acceptance was set between 99.5 and 100.5 lb. If you were the official responsible for making decisions about the process:
    (a) Describe what action you would take if the mean weight of the sample was 99.3 lb. If the mean weight was 99.7 lb.
    (b) In what manner may the decision limits of 99.5 and 100.5 lb be considered arbitrary limits? In what sense are these limits not arbitrary? Are there any "better" limits to be set? Why or why not?
    (c) On what factors would the business base its decision to take action towards correcting the process when the sample mean exceeded or fell below a certain set of decision limits?

12. In our ordinary decision-making procedures, do we generally allow a little leeway from the precise standard? For example, if we invite guests to our home at 8 P.M. do we expect the guests to arrive at 8 o'clock sharp, or within a limit of, say, 8:00 to 8:20? Are these limits somewhat arbitrary? If we find it necessary to allow some leeway in daily affairs, is it any different in principle to permit a variance in manufacturing standards? Would you, however, say there are definite limits beyond which the variance cannot be permitted without some action being taken? In a manufacturing process what might determine the limits of acceptance and rejection?

9.4 Fundamental Concepts of Statistical Tests and Inference

The following concepts are fundamental to a study of statistical inference and the testing of hypotheses.

1. Inference

The word "inference" was defined in Section 7.1. There it was indicated that the sample provides information about a universe or population. The sample information is known, and the problem is to infer values for the universe. Thus, from specific information (sample values) generalizations about the universe are made. In making this jump from the known to the unknown there is always the risk of being in error, and the possibility of being in error must be taken into account. The preceding materials of the present chapter have suggested that it is usually possible to classify these errors as Type I or Type II.

Thus, the word *inference* suggests a conclusion or decision has been made or is to be made on the basis of existing knowledge. The existing knowledge or information at hand—usually derived from sampling processes—serves as the basis for conclusions about the universe from which the information was drawn. Why is this procedure employed? Because the universe values in which we are interested are unknown. If the universe values were known it would not be necessary to employ a sampling and inference process. On the other hand, since the universe values are not known, they must be inferred from the sample. In the process of inference the reasoning goes from incomplete, sample information to a generalization about the entire body of information—that is, the universe.

As an example of statistical inference, suppose the mean of a certain sample turns out to be 21. This fact can be made the basis of a statement (hypothesis) that the population or process mean is also 21. Note, however, we cannot be certain that the true mean is precisely 21, although we may tentatively hold that the true mean is close to 21. To indicate the degree of certainty attached to sample information, it is general practice to include a probability statement. Such a statement might take the form: "The sample mean is 21 and the 95 per cent confidence interval is 15 to 27."

2. Hypothesis

The word *hypothesis* refers to a statement or a proposition which is advanced to explain some set of facts or is used as the basis for a test. Hypotheses may be true or false, but as employed in statistics their function is to provide a definite statement which may be tested for truth or falsity.

A coin-tossing problem will serve as an example. A coin is tossed many times but does not show heads on approximately one-half of the tosses. It is therefore hypothesized that the coin is bent. Now, this hypothesis may or may not be true, but is currently accepted as a tentative explanation for the observed phenomenon, namely that the coin does not show heads as often as expected. This hypothesis can be subsequently tested by experimental methods.

A hypothesis may also be used to furnish a guide for further investigation of a problem. As such the statement is generally known as a *working hypothesis*. The hypothesis is, in many cases, merely a convenient starting point for further inquiry, a point from which an investigation can get underway.

Hypotheses may be tested by statistical means if the problem itself is statistical in nature. That is, statistical evidence may be employed to "prove" (accept) or "disprove" (reject) the hypothesis at some level of probability. The student should, however, be aware of the fact that "proof" is by no means a simple concept.

When a hypothesis is tested by sample information, the information will lead to the acceptance or rejection of the hypothesis. (A third alternative is open, namely to reserve judgment until further evidence is available.[1]) Thus, whether the hypothesis is accepted or rejected on the basis of sample information, the decision is really due to the chance factors of sampling. The universe from which the sample was drawn has a unique set of parameters and these, of course, are not chance values, but the information furnished by the sample is due to chance factors. Therefore as long as sample—incomplete—information is used to make inferences about the parameters, the statistician can only design the test and formulate the hypotheses in such manner as to achieve a high level of probability of judging the hypothesis (accepting or rejecting) correctly. However, a batting average of 1.00 (or 1000 if you prefer) is impossible in the long run because incomplete information is employed as the basis for inference. As previously noted, inference involves moving from the known to the unknown, and the risk of error is omnipresent.

A hypothesis of major importance in statistics is the *null hypothesis*. The null hypothesis is, strictly speaking, *a hypothesis of no difference between the values of a sample statistic such as the sample mean and the corresponding population mean.* The value of the universe mean may be established by hypothesis based on past experience. Too, the hypothesized value of the universe mean could be derived from an industry standard such as a customary size or weight, and the production process would then be geared to turn out products meeting this accepted standard. Thus, the null hypothesis would say there is no difference between the sample value and the hypothetical universe mean. Actually, it must be recognized that some slight differences will occur between sample and universe means (because of chance factors) and what is really implied by the null hypothesis is that *no significant difference* exists between the sample and universe value. Thus, in Illustration 9.1, the area of acceptance identifies the range within which the sample mean may fall without declaring the difference between the sample and the universe standard to be significant.

---

[1] It is impossible for an elementary text to go into all the sophistication which is attached to complex topics, but it may not be amiss to point out that if, for some reason, the sample information is felt to be inconclusive, the sample could be used as an estimate of the parameters of the universe, and with these data, the proper-sized sample could be calculated to achieve the goals of the test. Once this is done, the evidence should no longer be inconclusive.

3. Statistical Errors

There are many forms of statistical errors, as the student may have already observed. However, the errors to be discussed here are of two very specific and well-defined types.

The first is known as a *Type I error*, sometimes called an alpha error. A Type I error may be defined as *rejecting a true hypothesis*. Let us illustrate this error first by employing a nonstatistical example as follows: If a fellow student should make the statement that the statistics class for today has been canceled but you reject this statement and proceed to class, there discovering that the class is not being held, you have made a Type I error by rejecting a true hypothesis. Observe, however, that your only method of proof for the hypothesis was to go to the classroom and see for yourself.

Now, consider the Type I error in statistical terms. A hypothesis about a given universe has been formulated as, for example, "The mean of this universe is 25." A sample has been drawn yielding a mean which does not correspond with the hypothesis. Suppose the sample mean has the value 27. Now suppose the hypothesis is rejected on the basis of this sample information. It may well be that a true hypothesis has been rejected. The variance[2] of the universe may be such that it is quite possible to draw a sample mean with a value of 27 from a universe whose mean is 25. *In other words, a significant difference supposedly existed between the sample information and the hypothesis when actually the difference was not significant.* The result is a Type I error. A true hypothesis was rejected.

The average percentage of Type I errors made in testing statistical hypotheses is controllable by the statistician. If, for example, the range of the area of acceptance is set at $\bar{X} +$ and $-1.96z$, the null hypothesis will be rejected about 5 per cent of the times the experiment is performed. Should the z value of the area of acceptance be set at $\bar{X} +$ and $-2.58z$ the null hypothesis will be rejected 1 per cent of the times the experiment is performed. Unfortunately, the matter does not end here because as the area of acceptance is widened by increasing the value of z, thus reducing Type I errors, the area in which Type II errors may occur is expanded. This point is explained below.

The second type of statistical error to be discussed is known as a *Type II error*, sometimes called the beta error. A Type II error may be defined as *accepting a false hypothesis*. This type of error may be illustrated by the previous nonstatistical example. If a fellow student should make

---

[2] This term is defined in Section 4.7.

the statement that the statistics class for today has been canceled and you accept the statement and consequently do not go to class when, in fact, the class is being held as usual, you have made a Type II error by accepting a false hypothesis (statement). Again, proof requires that you go to the class to check the hypothesis.

Now, consider the Type II error in statistical terms. A hypothesis about a given universe has been formulated as, for example, "The mean of this universe is 25." A sample has been drawn yielding a mean which does not correspond with the hypothesis. Suppose the sample mean has the value 27. Now, suppose it is decided that because of the closeness of the two values, the null hypothesis should be accepted. It may well be that a false hypothesis is being accepted. The universe mean may not be even close to 25, but the sample was one of those few which fall at the end of the sampling distribution. *In other words, it was decided that the difference between universe and sample means was not significant when it should have been declared significant.* The result is a Type II error. A false hypothesis was accepted.

The foregoing material may be restructured as follows. The problem begins with a statement. It is not known whether the statement is true or false. However, some decision must be made about the statement; it must be either accepted or rejected. The decision may turn out to be correct or incorrect. This type of problem is diagrammed in Illustration 9.2.

Illustration 9.2   Diagram Showing a Two-Choice Decision Problem

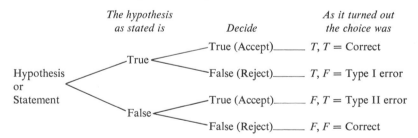

When a hypothesis about a problem is first formulated, the formulation generally is based on past experience or knowledge of similar situations. Interest in the "proper" outcome of an experiment makes it desirable to employ a decision-making process that entails a low risk of Type I errors. In other words, it is desirable to avoid rejecting a true hypothesis, particularly since it is one of interest or possibly one of substantial dollar value. Viewed in terms of Illustration 9.2, it would be desirable to have the probability of T, T be high, which is to say the risk of a Type I error (T, F) should be small. In this situation, a value of alpha would be selected at perhaps .05 or .01. Alpha specifies the risk of a Type I error. The alpha value is sometimes called the "size" of the test; $1 - \alpha$ may be called the "level of significance" of the test.

If, on the other hand, the hypothesis actually turns out to be false, the decision-making procedure ought to entail a low risk for accepting false statements. Thus, in Illustration 9.2 it would be desirable that the probability of choosing (F, T) be small. The probability of a Type II error cannot be determined as readily as for Type I, and no attempt will be made at this point to specify the exact risk. Ideally, the risk should be small. Preferably, the risk of both Type I and Type II errors should be small. There may, however, be a rather wide gulf between what is desired on ideal grounds and what is actually obtainable in practice. Obviously, if decisions could be made on the basis of complete information about all relevant variables, there would be far less concern about the risk of error.

The decision procedure described here involves the use of sample (incomplete) information. The possibilities of error creep in because the information on which the process is based is incomplete. Thus, the best possible opportunity to make correct choices lies in obtaining the greatest available amount of information. Unfortunately, this choice is not always available because of *data limitations* (the entire universe may not be available for study), *time limitations* (decisions must be made while they can be of benefit), and *cost limitations* (the budget permits only a certain sum of money to be spent on the project). Consequently, the conclusions reached in Chapters 7 and 8 about the information content of small and large samples are relevant in the decision-making context. Risks of error may be minimized by drawing large samples, but risks are not eliminated even by very large samples.

To summarize: A decision-making procedure which forces us to choose between two alternatives (for example, true or false) always results in one of two outcomes: the decision is correct or it is incorrect. If it is incorrect, an error has been made and the error is either of the Type I or Type II variety. The need is to design a decision procedure which minimizes the risk of both types of error.

4. Statistical Tests

A statistical test is a means of evaluating the probability that a certain outcome is consistent with a given hypothesis. Thus the test is a method for determining the "truth" or "falsity" of a given statement. For example, an engineer claims a new saw-blade design is such that this blade will not emit more than 100 decibels of noise at a constant speed of 3,600 rpm. Thus, H_1 says: "The noise level of the universe is 100 db or less." This statement may be designated as the hypothesis to be tested. Tests may now be made with the mass-produced blade. Perhaps 100 blades are selected at random and run at the specified speed, the decibel rating for each being measured and recorded. The average decibel level and the standard deviation may then be calculated. From this the standard error of the sampling distribution may be computed. Then the standardized normal curve will be employed to evaluate the probability that any given sample mean will show more than 100 decibels of noise. On the basis of this sample information, a decision is made as to the truth or falsity of H_1. Tests of this type are said to be *one-sided tests* in that the real problem occurs only when the decibel rating is *over* 100. In a one-sided test there is a single decision point and the sample mean falls either above or below that point.

The manner of making a one-sided test may be explained as follows. The problem is one in which the engineers are concerned only with a risk of the variable's exceeding (or falling below) some given standard. In the saw-blade example, only if the noise level exceeds 100 db will corrective action be taken. If the noise level is below this standard of 100 db, obviously that is all to the good and there is no problem. If, however, the noise level is too high (over 100 db), then the engineers will be concerned to take some action (if possible) to reduce the noise level. The method for the test is shown in Illustration 9.3.

Illustration 9.3   One-Sided Decision Rule as Explained in the Text

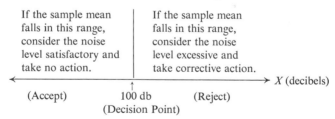

Now, suppose we discover somehow that the true mean decibel level is 96 db and that the standard error of a distribution of sample means ($n = 100$) drawn from the universe of saw blades is 2 db. The hypothesis H_1 to be tested is: "The noise level of the universe is 100 db or less." Under these assumptions, the diagram would now appear as shown in Illustration 9.4.

In the situation just described, no Type II errors would be made because the acceptance of H_1 occurs when it should occur—that is, below 100 db. However, Type I errors will be made whenever the sample mean exceeds 100 db, and this will happen on about 2.3 per cent of the samples (100 per cent − 97.72 per cent = 2.28 per cent).

Illustration 9.4   Distribution of Sample Means and the One-Sided Decision Rule as Explained in the Text

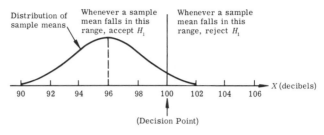

This same problem situation can be recast in terms of a *two-sided test*. Suppose the problem, as viewed by the statistician or engineers in charge, is to determine the true mean decibel level of the universe of saw blades produced by this particular process. Assume testing all of the blades produced is out of the question because of cost, and that a sample of size 100 is to be drawn at random from the production process. Assume further that we are let in on the knowledge that the true mean is actually 96 db and the standard error is 2 db. (In practice this would not be known, but the assumption is made here in order that the method of testing hypotheses may be shown.)

Now, hypothesis H_1 is stated as follows: *The true mean of the universe is* 100 db. Furthermore, a decision rule is formulated as follows: Draw a sample of 100 blades at random. Test each blade for noise level. Determine the overall sample mean noise in decibels. If the sample mean is less than 96 or more than 104, reject H_1. If the sample mean is between 96 and 104 db, accept H_1.

Illustration 9.5   Decision Rule for Two-Sided Decision Rule as Explained in the Text

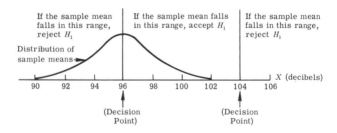

Notice that this type of test is a *two-sided test*. At this point the problem is not whether the test is a "good" one, but rather to observe how the test "works." Since the true mean is 96 (we know this but the person making the test does not know the true mean), sampling theory leads to the knowledge that 50 per cent of the possible sample means which could be drawn from this universe will exceed 96 db and 50 per cent of the sample means will be less than 96 db. When the sample mean is below 96, H_1 is rejected and no error is made. When the sample mean is above 96, H_1 will be accepted and the mean of the universe will be declared to be 100 db. This is clearly an error—and it is a Type II error because a false hypothesis has been accepted. In fact, the only errors made here will be Type II.

Now, the student may well observe: This test is not really very good because the same results could have been achieved by simply tossing a coin and declaring that if heads occurs, H_1 should be accepted, otherwise H_1 is rejected. Once this is seen, the next question becomes: How can the test be improved to raise the probability of a correct decision? Clearly, a larger sample would improve the decision-making process by shrinking the base of the normal distribution. Too, we have only postulated that the true mean is 96. If the true mean should either fall below 96 or rise above 96, the existing decision rule would be improved. However, unless complete information—rather than sample information—is provided, there will always be some risk of error. If a number of samples were drawn from the universe over a period of time, the average of the sample means would "zero in" on the true mean. Consequently, if the true mean did remain at 96, repeated sampling would clearly indicate that the true mean was not 100 db and the original hypothesis could be revised.

To summarize: Statistical tests are based on measuring the difference between an observed (sample) statistic and a given hypothesis (statement). Thus, if the sample statistic agrees with the hypothesis—that is, is close in value—the hypothesis is judged to be probable; if the statistic disagrees with the hypothesis by a large difference, the hypothesis is judged to be improbable. Whatever the judgment as based upon sample evidence, the final decision may be correct or incorrect. If the decision turns out to be incorrect, either a Type I or a Type II error has been made. The *test method*, however, is established in a manner designed to minimize the risk of error and maximize the probability of having made the correct decision.

9.5   General Considerations Bearing on Statistical Inference and the Testing of Hypotheses—A Summary

1. A sample provides *estimates* of population parameters and characteristics.
2. Statistical inference implies *drawing conclusions* from statistical estimates.
3. A statistical test is a means of *assigning probabilities* of truth to an estimate.
4. A statistical test never furnishes the investigator with empirical proof, but does provide *evidence* of truth or falsity.
5. The role played by a statistical hypothesis is to *formalize as a proposition* that which we wish to test.

6. Information provided by samples can be used to *generalize* (hypothesize) about an unknown universe.

7. Statistical inference is an extremely valuable method of increasing knowledge by allowing us to proceed from limited information provided by samples to conclusions about unknown universes. In the process of moving from the particular to the general, there is always the risk of error.

8. The purpose of assigning a level of significance (deciding to use .95, .99, or whatever) *before* making a statistical test is to maintain test objectivity. If the level were determined after the test was made, acceptance or rejection would be a matter of whim and the investigator would make the test rather than allowing the established standards to act as the criteria.

Exercise 9.2. *Formulation of Hypotheses.* In each of the following situations indicate, as precisely as you can, a hypothesis and an alternative hypothesis which fit the problem. The first statement is used as an illustration.

1. An automobile engine had been running smoothly for several minutes. Suddenly the engine coughed, sputtered, and stopped. The engine would not start by ordinary means.
    Hypothesis: The gasoline supply is exhausted.
    Alternative hypothesis: The ignition system has failed.

2. This clock has stopped running.

3. Last year the net profit of this (specified) business was $10,000. What might be estimated as the net profit of similar-sized, more or less identical business firms?

4. The present set of brand "A" tires on an automobile lasted 30,000 miles. What can be expected when a new set of identical tires is placed on this same auto?

5. A sample drawn from a universe whose parameters are unknown yielded a mean of 30. What can be hypothesized about $\bar{X}$, the universe mean?

6. A sample drawn from a universe whose parameters are unknown, yielded as S of 10. What can be hypothesized about σ, the universe standard deviation?

7. A sample ($n = 26$) has been drawn from a universe whose parameters are unknown. The sample values were $\bar{x} = 50$, $S = 10$. What can you hypothesize about the standard error of the sampling distribution?

8. Tests of electric light bulbs indicated a mean life of 80 hours for brand "A" with $S = 3$. The mean life for brand "B" was 90 with an S of 6. What can be hypothesized about these two distributions?

9. Is the following statement a hypothesis? Explain why or why not. "The population from which these (specified) samples have been drawn is believed to be a normal distribution."

10. Is the following statement a hypothesis? Explain why or why not. "Cost accounting technique A has been proven more efficient than cost accounting method B."

11. Are all hypotheses statistical hypotheses? What other classifications (types) of hypotheses might come to mind?

Exercise 9.3. *The Null Hypothesis.*   In the following problems you are to formulate a null hypothesis to fit the terms of the problem. The first problem is used as an illustration.

1. A single die is thrown 96 times. The five appears 15 times. What is the null hypothesis in this case?
   Answer: The null hypothesis would state that there is no significant difference between the empirical result and the expected results, which are $1/6 \times 96$ or 16. (That is, the five appears 16 times.)

2. The proportion of men to women drivers on the highway at a given time was computed to be 2 to 1. The owner of a filling station wishes to know the proportion of men and women drivers who stop at his station during some specified time. State the null hypothesis.

3. A sample is drawn yielding a mean of 45. What does the null hypothesis state about the population mean?

4. A certain sample was taken to determine the proportion of households planning to buy a new refrigerator this year. To the question, "Do you expect to buy a new refrigerator this year?" 95 per cent replied "no" while 5 per cent replied "yes." State the null hypothesis.

5. A sample of 100 persons chosen at random were asked whether they preferred the taste of brand "A" or brand "B" milk. Of the sample, 58 said they preferred brand "B". State the null hypothesis.

6. An urn contains 50 black and 50 red marbles. A sample of 6 is to be drawn. What is the null hypothesis?

7. A business statistics class may normally consist of 22 men and 3 women.
   (a) What is the null hypothesis with respect to the proportion of men and women in the overall college enrollment?
   (b) In this situation is the null hypothesis likely to be a correct hypothesis? Why?

8. A certain population has a σ of 10. A sample drawn from this population yields $S = 9$. What is the null hypothesis?
   (a) Why can the statement you made be considered a statement of "no difference"?
   (b) Is it desirable in this situation that the null hypothesis state "there is no *significant* difference"?

9. A certain universe has a median value of 30. A sample drawn from this universe yields a median of 25. What is the null hypothesis?

10. On the assumption that many large samples of a given n were drawn from an infinite universe, what would the null hypothesis say about the difference between any two successive sample means?
    (a) Would the null hypothesis change if the sample were relatively small?
    (b) Whether the samples were large or small, as long as n was constant, would the difference between successive sample means form a normal distribution of differences with a mean of zero? Explain.

Exercise 9.4. *The Mechanics of Statistical Tests.*   The curve below is a normal curve representing the distribution of sample means which would be expected to be drawn from a universe with a mean of 25 and σ of 20 ($n = 100$). Thus the mean of the sampling distribution is $\bar{X} = 25$, and the standard error is 2. On the basis of a 95 per cent confidence interval and a large number of sample means drawn from that universe about 2.5 per cent of the means would be expected to fall below a value of $21.08 = (25 - 1.96 \times 2)$ and 2.5 per cent of the sample means would be expected to exceed $28.92 = (25 + 1.96 \times 2)$. Remember that at the 95 per cent confidence level, $z = 1.96$.

In the problems below assume that each sample was drawn at random and the question to be answered on the basis of the sample information is whether or not the sample mean leads to acceptance of the null hypothesis H, which states there is no (significant) difference between the sample mean and the universe mean. Use the diagram below to make the decision about H.

Problem Number	Sample Number	Value of Sample Mean	Accept H?	Reject H?
1	1	20		
2	2	21		
3	3	21.1		
4	4	23		
5	5	28.9		
6	6	30		
7	7	32		

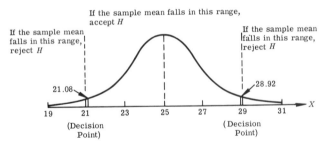

Exercise 9.5. *Type I and Type II Errors.* In the accompanying diagram, the curve drawn in the solid line is a distribution of sample means drawn from a universe where $\bar{X} = 25 = H_1$ and where the standard error is 2. The curve drawn as a broken line represents an identical distribution of sample means but is based on the hypothesis H_2 that $\bar{X} = 29$. In other words, the solid curve represents the sampling distribution based on the true mean of the universe, whereas the broken curve represents the sampling distribution based on an incorrect hypothesis. The confidence level (sometimes called the level of significance) is set at .95. Keep in mind that whenever a hypothesis is rejected, the possibility of a Type I error creeps in. Whenever a hypothesis is accepted, the possibility of a Type II error is open.

In the problems which follow, you are given a number of sample means and asked whether you would accept or reject the hypothesis that $\bar{X} = 25 = H_1$

and $\bar{X} = 29 = H_2$ on the basis of that particular sample mean. This is a two-sided test at the .05 level. Note that "two-sided" means to reject the hypothesis being tested when the sample mean is either *above* or *below* the range of acceptance. (It is assumed that n for all samples is identical.) Then indicate whether an error was made in accepting or rejecting the hypothesis, and if so what type of error occurred. Problem 1 has been completed as an illustration.

Problem Number	Sample Number	Sample Value	$H_1 = \bar{X} = 25$			$H_2 = \bar{X} = 29$		
			Accept	Reject	Error	Accept	Reject	Error
1	1	21		x	Type I		x	None
2	2	23						
3	3	25						
4	4	26						
5	5	29						
6	6	28.9						
7	7	21.1						

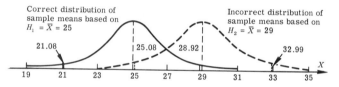

Correct distribution of sample means based on $H_1 = \bar{X} = 25$

Incorrect distribution of sample means based on $H_2 = \bar{X} = 29$

8. Within what range would sample means cause acceptance of $H_1 = \bar{X} = 25$?

9. Within what range would sample means cause acceptance of $H_2 = \bar{X} = 29$?

10. On the average if many samples of the given n were drawn from this universe, how often would $H_1 = 25 = \bar{X}$ be accepted?

11. On the average if many samples of the given n were drawn from this universe, how often would $H_2 = 29 = \bar{X}$ be accepted?

12. As a matter of actual fact, within what range would more than 99 per cent of all sample means fall?

13. Would it be theoretically possible to draw a sample mean of 17, given the postulates of this problem?

Exercise 9.6. *Effects of Changing α (the Rejection Region) Where a Two-Sided Test Is Used.* On the following diagrams you are to draw in ordinates for two-sided tests corresponding to the given α (the level of the test). Establish the necessary standard error distance from the mean in each case. The first problem has been given as an illustration. (The curves are normal probability functions.) You may wish to use a page from your notebook for actually completing this exercise.

1. Erect ordinates at the .05 level. Label the areas of acceptance and rejection. $\alpha = .05$. $z = $?

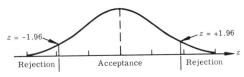

2. Erect ordinates at the .01 level. Label the areas of acceptance and rejection. $\alpha = .01$. $z = $?

3. Erect ordinates at the .02 level. Label. $\alpha = .02$. $z = $?

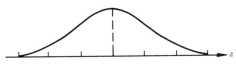

4. Erect ordinates at the .03 level. Label. $\alpha = .03$. $z = $?

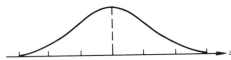

5. Erect ordinates at the .1 level. Label. $\alpha = .1$. $z = $?

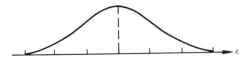

6. Erect ordinates at the .3 level. Label. $\alpha = .3$. $z = $?

7. Now go back to each of the diagrams above and indicate what proportion of times, on the average, the null hypothesis would be accepted and rejected.

8. Consider this problem: As the value of α is increased, what effect takes place regarding the number of correct null hypotheses being rejected?

9. Consider this problem: As the value of α is increased, what effect takes place regarding the opportunity to accept incorrect null hypotheses?

10. Is it clear that as Type I errors are minimized, the possibility of making Type II errors is _____? Is the opposite of this statement also true?

11. As a practical matter, explain how the level of significance is determined in a problem situation.

Exercise 9.7. *Effects of Changing α Where a One-Sided Test Is Used.* Assume that the curves below are normal curves of distributions of sample means, drawn from a universe whose values are given in minutes. The universe mean—and therefore the mean of the sampling distribution—is 10 minutes. Each standard error is 30 seconds. It will be convenient to assume that the universe is infinite and that the variable being measured is the time required by employees of an electrical firm to wind a high-voltage transformer. The objective of the testing process is to discover if the sample mean differs significantly from the 10 minutes established as the standard winding time. Therefore, the hypothesis being tested is this: "The average time required to wind a transformer is 10 minutes." The location of the decision point is specified in each of the problems. (Do not be concerned as to why the point was located in a given position in each of the problems.)

On the diagrams given below, draw in ordinates for one-sided tests at the points corresponding to the given α. Establish the necessary standard error distances from the mean in each case. Note that the 5 per cent level has been drawn in at 1.645 standard errors as an illustration. (The curves are normal distributions.) A page from your notebook may be used for actually completing this exercise.

1. Erect an ordinate so as to cut off 5 per cent of the area in the lower tail. Label areas of acceptance and rejection. $\alpha = .05$. $z = ?$

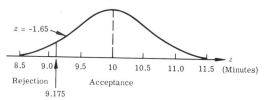

2. Erect an ordinate so as to cut off 10 per cent of the area in the upper tail. Label. $\alpha = .10$. $z = ?$

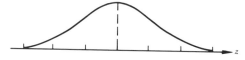

3. Erect an ordinate so as to cut off 20 per cent of the area in the upper tail. Label. $\alpha = .20$. $z = ?$

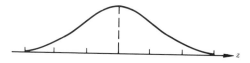

4. Erect an ordinate so as to cut off 30 per cent of the area in the upper tail. Label. $\alpha = .30$. $z = ?$

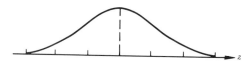

5. Erect an ordinate so as to cut off 1 per cent of the area in the lower tail. Label. $\alpha = .01$. $z = $?

6. Now, go back to each of the diagrams above and indicate what proportion of times, on the average, the given hypothesis would be accepted and rejected.

7. Consider this problem: As the value of α increases numerically, what effect takes place regarding the opportunity for the correct null hypothesis to be rejected?

8. Consider this problem: As the value of α is increased, what effect takes place regarding the opportunity to accept an incorrect null hypothesis?

9. Now, reverse the statements you made for problems 7 and 8. Are these reverse statements correct too?

10. What differences, if any, occur in the number and type of possible errors if a one-sided test is used rather than a two-sided test? Explain.

11. Do Type I and II errors have the same probability in the case of one-sided tests as in two-sided tests—assuming the same value of alpha in each case? Why?

12. Explain why a one-sided test is sometimes more appropriate to a given situation than a two-sided test.

Exercise 9.8*. *Effect of Sample Size on the Standard Error and the Range of Acceptance.* It has been observed that as the sample size n is increased, the standard error of the sample means decreases. It should now be clear that with z held constant, sample size will be an important factor in determining the "width" of the acceptance region (and, of course, of the region or range of rejection). The other important factor in determining this width of the acceptance region is the standard deviation of the universe from which the samples were drawn. The problems which follow are designed to indicate the manner in which "acceptance" and "rejection" depend on two variables: (1) standard deviation—and thus standard error—and (2) sample size. (Also keep in mind that α exerts an impact on the width of the range of acceptance.)

The following problems show different values for n and the two often-used values for alpha, namely .05 and .01. It is given that the population mean is 50 and the standard deviation is 20. Calculate the upper and lower values at which sample means would cause rejection of the null hypothesis $\bar{x} = \bar{X}$. Use the standardized normal curve (the z table) throughout. On a piece of graph paper, show the normal curve for each problem worked. Center all curves on a vertical line at the mean of 50.

Problem Number	n	Significance Level $= .05 = \alpha$		Significance Level $= .01 = \alpha$	
		Lower Value of Acceptance	Upper Value of Acceptance	Lower Value of Acceptance	Upper Value of Acceptance
1	4				
2	9				
3	16				
4	25				
5	36				
6	49				
7	64				
8	81				
9	100				
10	500				

The problems which follow are identical to the problems above except that the standard deviation of the universe is now 10 while the mean remains $\bar{X} = 50$. Calculate the upper and lower values at which sample mean values would cause acceptance of the null hypothesis $\bar{x} = \bar{X}$.

Problem Number	n	Significance Level $= .05 = \alpha$		Significance Level $= .01 = \alpha$	
		Lower Value of Acceptance	Upper Value of Acceptance	Lower Value of Acceptance	Upper Value of Acceptance
11	4				
12	9				
13	16				
14	25				
15	36				
16	49				
17	64				
18	81				
19	100				
20	500				

9.6 Statistical Testing Given the Parameter σ

When a process has been operating for a reasonably long period, it is likely that the past data record of the process will have established the value of the standard deviation of the universe. For instance, in the sand-weight example it was known that the weighing process generated a universe whose standard deviation was 2.5 lb. The question which the statistical test was designed to answer was this: Is the mean weight of the process as it is currently operating still approximately 100.0 lb? In other words, when a sample has been drawn, does the sample mean allow the inference that the universe mean is still 100.0 lb or should the conclusion be drawn that the universe mean has shifted?

In this problem, the standard weight is 100.0 lb. On the basis of a particular sample mean, should the null hypothesis be accepted? If the null hypothesis is accepted, the productive process is declared to be operating properly. If the null hypothesis is rejected, the process is declared to be operating improperly. (Remember that the null hypothesis would state there is no difference between the sample mean and the mean of the universe.)

The method for making a statistical test when σ is available is as follows. The sample size and σ are known, making it possible to employ the relationship $\sigma_{\bar{x}} = \sigma/\sqrt{n}$ to provide knowledge of the standard error. The desired probability values will be determined by use of the normal curve. Since the standard error is known, the acceptance interval formed by the sample mean plus and minus $1.96\sigma_{\bar{x}}$ will include the population mean 95 times out of 100 on the average. Consequently, if the test level of significance α is set at .05, and the test is two-sided, all the data necessary for establishing the acceptance region are available.

Mechanically, either of two techniques may be employed for the actual decision-making process. First, a graph of the normal curve could be drawn on which the two numbers are placed to indicate the acceptance region. Alternatively, the test could be conducted by utilizing the following relationships:

1. For a two-sided test at the .05 level:
   Reject the null hypothesis if $| z | > 1.96$.
   Accept the null hypothesis if $| z | < 1.96$.

2. For a one-sided test at the lower .05 level:
   Reject the null hypothesis if $z > -1.645$.
   Accept the null hypothesis if $z < -1.645$.

3. For a one-sided test at the upper .05 level:
   Reject the null hypothesis if $z > +1.645$.
   Accept the null hypothesis if $z < +1.645$.

Note: Students sometimes ask, "What happens if the z value as calculated turns out to be exactly, say, -1.645?" The answer is that this condition is highly unlikely because the value -1.645 is a "point" on the X scale. However, in the event that $z = -1.645$ (or whatever the value in question is), then it might be decided to flip a coin—or to draw a few more sample items. The latter would seem to be preferable.

The random variable Z is defined as

$$Z = \frac{\bar{x} - \bar{X}}{\sigma_{\bar{x}}}, \tag{9.1}$$

where $\bar{x}$ = the sample mean,

$\bar{X}$ = the universe mean or standard,

$\sigma_{\bar{x}}$ = the standard error of the distribution of sample means—
that is, $\sigma/\sqrt{n}$.

Illustrations 9.1 and 9.3 provide examples of the manner in which acceptance or rejection of the null hypothesis may be visualized mechanically. By use of Formula (9.1), the X scale can be converted to z units and the test carried out as explained above.

Exercise 9.9. *Testing the Difference Between $\bar{x}$ and $\bar{X}$ when the Value of σ Is Available*

1. The shipping department of a firm is known to prepare an average of 100 packages for shipment per hour with a σ of 7 packages. Over a period of time, a random sample of 49 hourly values was taken. The mean of this sample was 103 packages. The null hypothesis would indicate there is no significant difference between the sample and the universe means. Make a two-sided test of this hypothesis at the .05 level and interpret the results.

2. The average receipts per cash register in a supermarket are \$2,685 per day with a σ of \$280. A number of changes were made by the store manager including a new advertising campaign and a rearrangement of the personnel and store layout. After these changes were completed, the average receipts were \$2,785 on the basis of 49 observations. Employing a two-sided test, did the new policies have a statistically significant effect on receipts measured at the .05 level? At the .01 level? Explain why the .05 and .01 levels differ statistically.

3. (a) A machine which molds plastic parts ordinarily produces 1,000 parts per hour with a σ of 48 parts. After a new set of adjustments is made, the machine produced an average of 1,020 parts per hour over a 36-hour period. On the basis of the sample information and using a two-sided test, does a significant difference exist between the two means at the .05 level?
   (b) Does a significant difference exist at the .01 level?
   (c) Would a one-sided test be appropriate here? If so, is the difference between the means significant at this level?
   (d) Describe the Type I and Type II errors of this test.

4. (a) An industrial process is designed to package 8 ounces or more of food per package unit. The average weight per unit is known from past experience to be 8.05 ounces, with a σ of .15 ounces. Occasional samples are taken from this process and weighed as a quality control measure. One such sample weighed 100 units with the result that the mean was 8.01 ounces. Make a one-tailed test at the lower .01 level. On the basis of the sample information and this test, does a significant difference exist between the two means?
   (b) Describe the Type I and Type II errors of this test.

9.7 Statistical Testing on the Basis of Sample Information Only

Suppose an industrial process has only recently been placed in operation so that no historical records are available. In this case information is lacking as to the standard deviation of the product. However, because the process has been designed to turn out products which meet standard specifications, the product mean should be at the standard value. In the sand-weight example, this standard was 100.0 lb. The question before the officials of the firm is this: Is the process turning out a product whose mean weight is 100.0 lb? Because of possible errors in the setting of the machinery, the product mean could be above or below 100.0 lb. The hypothesis that the mean weight is 100.0 lb may be formulated and subjected to statistical testing on the basis of sample information.

It may be observed that the problem outlined here is identical to the problem situation in Section 9.6 except that information is lacking on the standard deviation of the product. Actually, the product mean is not known either, but it is known that *the mean should be almost exactly the standard value* (100.0 lb in the sand-weight case).

The procedure to be employed is as follows. A sample is drawn from the universe. From the sample, the mean and standard deviation of the universe will be estimated as $\bar{x}$ and S. As observed in Section 7.11 the value of S can be substituted for σ in the determination of the standard error. Since the sample size and S are known, the relationship $S_{\bar{x}} = S/\sqrt{n-1}$ is employed to provide knowledge of the standard error.[3] If the sample is relatively large, say in excess of 30 items, the probability values will be determined by employing the normal curve.[4] The test is carried out in the same manner as already indicated in Section 9.6. However, the random variable Z is defined as:

$$Z = \frac{\bar{x} - \bar{X}}{S_{\bar{x}}},$$ (9.2)

[3] If $n - 1$ had been used in the computation of S, then the -1 would not be used again. See Section 4.7, Formula (4.10).

[4] The t distribution is appropriate for small samples when σ is not available. Actually, the t distribution is accurate only when the samples have been drawn from a normal universe. Each value of $n - 1$ has a unique t distribution. For example, the distribution for very small samples (say $n = 2$) is similar to the normal curve except that the tails are somewhat more extended and the peak is flatter than a normal curve. The flatness of the curve is necessary because small samples exhibit substantial variability about the universe mean. However, as n increases, variability decreases and the t distribution tends towards the normal. Once n reaches 30, the difference between the two distributions is, for all practical purposes, negligible. At this point use of the normal curve is appropriate. (See also Chapter 10.)

where $\bar{x}$ = the sample mean,

$\bar{X}$ = the universe mean or standard,

$S_{\bar{x}}$ = the standard error of the distribution of sample means—that is, $S/\sqrt{n-1}$.

Illustrations 9.1 and 9.3 will again provide examples of the manner in which acceptance or rejection of the null hypothesis may be visualized.

Exercise 9.10. *Testing the Difference Between $\bar{x}$ and $\bar{X}$ When the Value of σ Is Unknown*

1. (a) A power shovel was designed to remove 31.5 cubic feet of earth per scoop. On a test run, some 145 sample scoops were made. The mean of the samples was 29.3 cubic feet. The standard deviation S as derived from the sample information was 6 cubic feet. On the basis of this information, is the null hypothesis which states that the universe mean is 31.5 cubic feet acceptable at the .05 two-sided test level? (Use $S_{\bar{x}} = S/\sqrt{n-1}$ in this and the following problems.)

   (b) Make a one-sided test at the upper .01 level. Is the null hypothesis now acceptable?

   (c) On the basis of this information alone, should the specifications for this equipment be revised?

   (d) Describe the Type I and Type II errors of this test.

2. A firm packaging a deluxe type of ornamental matches for fireplace use designed a process to place 18 matches per 10-cent box. The process was started and allowed to operate for 30 minutes. A sample of 37 boxes was then drawn. On the basis of this sample, the number of matches per box averaged 15.5 while the value of S was calculated at 6.

   (a) If a two-sided test be made at the .02 level, is the mean of 18 acceptable?

   (b) Would the mean of 18 be acceptable if the test level were .01?

   (c) Would a one-sided test at the upper level accept the mean of 18 if alpha were set at .05?

   (d) Where would alpha have to be set to accept 18 as the universe mean?

3. (a) A certain type of piecework in an assembly process comes from a universe believed to have a mean of 20 units per worker per minute. A survey team checks periodically on the performance of employees performing this task to determine if improvements suggested by the team have improved the process. During a given week a sample of 226 work-minutes was taken after some suggestions for improvement had been made. The sample mean was 19 units. S was 3.75 units. Is the mean for this type of work still 20 units at the .01 level using a two-sided test?

   (b) Can the universe mean be considered 20 units if the .05 level be used to set the limits of acceptance for the null hypothesis?

   (c) In this situation would a one-sided test be preferable? Discuss.

   (d) Describe the Type I and Type II errors of this test.

4. (a) The public relations department of a large corporation receives a number of letters from stockholders each week. Past estimates suggest that an average of 36 letters per day are received. A check of the files shows that an average of 40 letters was received during a sample period of 37 weeks. The sample indicates that the standard deviation S was 12 letters. On the basis of this information and using .01 and a two-sided test, is the universe mean of 36 a plausible hypothesis?

   (b) If .05 were used, would the universe mean be considered to be 36 letters?

   (c) Explain the differences between the results of parts (a) and (b).

   (d) Do the results of a test depend heavily on the criteria established for the test?

9.8   Summary

The material of this chapter has been concerned primarily with the problem of statistical decision-making. As such, it draws upon the theory of probability, sampling, and inference as discussed in previous chapters. When all of these things are brought together in the making of statistical decisions, we have at our disposal some very sharp tools for solving certain types of problems. It is important to understand both the sharpness of the tools and their limitations. Only problems which can be placed in a statistical mold are subject to tests of the type discussed in this chapter. The tests do not furnish complete proof or disproof of a given hypothesis. Tests of a statistical nature are open to the possibility of error, but as we have seen the errors are subject to minimization through the setting of the confidence level and the size of the sample. The tools of testing and decision-making must, like all tools, be used properly; it is always possible to abuse and misuse what is otherwise a valuable and worthwhile device.

In statistical testing we begin with a statement of the problem. A decision must be made. Information is used to throw light on those factors which will influence the decision, which when made may be correct or incorrect. Not all decisions, by themselves, have vital consequences attached to them—yet even a decision in a small matter, if the matter is repetitive, may result in ruin to the business or individual involved. Fortunately, the results of poor decisions often show up in the financial statement before bankruptcy or disaster overtakes the business, and thus the potential damage can be averted. The objective of statistical testing is to insure, insofar as possible, that errors, and particularly repetitive errors, are minimized and perhaps even eliminated. The value of this kind of knowledge to a business firm is obvious.

Key Terms and Concepts of This Chapter

Acceptance region (or interval)	One-sided test
Confidence interval for the mean	Proof of a hypothesis
Confidence level of the test	Range of rejection
Errors	Rejection point
(a) Type I (alpha)	Significant difference
(b) Type II (beta)	Statistical decision-making
Hypothesis	Two-sided test
(a) working	
(b) null	
(c) other	
Inference	

Exercise 9.11. *General Review Questions.* Some of the questions in this exercise require only a few words; some are more difficult and require considerable discussion.

1. What is the role of probability theory in the testing of hypotheses?

2. What are the risks involved in reaching a conclusion on the basis of sample information?

3. What is the role of a "working hypothesis" in experimentation and testing?

4. Suppose you are informed of an opportunity to purchase shares of stock in the XYZ Corporation. You are aware that the corporation is prospecting for gold in a remote corner of the world. It has prospected for a year with no tangible results but expects a real strike soon. Now, with reference to the decision to buy or not to buy, state the Type I and Type II error and the consequences of each to you.

5. Explain the steps or procedure employed in making a statistical (or nonstatistical) test.

6. In the ancient world, mankind learned many useful things although the modern technique of testing against a probability distribution was unknown. By what method do you suppose man learned survival, the number of days in a year, irrigation, principles of architecture, and so on? How, under primitive conditions, did he prove hypotheses?

7. What role do you suppose the human quality of curiosity plays in the process of learning through the testing of hypotheses?

8. (a) Why should the value of alpha be chosen before a statistical test is made?
   (b) What considerations have a bearing on the value of alpha?
   (c) What important risk can be controlled through the choice of a value for alpha?

9. In your notebook, draw a standardized normal probability distribution. Now, by using the curve, explain to your nonstatistics friend what happens as alpha is changed from .01 to .25 and explain this for a two-sided and a one-sided test.

10. The methodology of establishing confidence intervals was discussed in Section 7.14. In Exercise 9.8 you encountered a number of problems in which you were asked to state the lower and upper value of acceptance— that is, for accepting the null hypothesis. What is the basic difference, if any, between "confidence intervals" and the "range of acceptance"?

11. What are the basic differences in the methodology of testing the null hypothesis when σ is known and when it is unknown? (See Sections 9.6 and 9.7.)

12. What are the advantages and limitations of statistical tests?

Bibliography

The literature of statistical inference and decision-making is abundant; the list below merely offers some suggestions. These and other excellent references may be found in most college libraries.

The student who wishes to pursue the subject of inference and testing at greater length will find the following books very useful:

Kurnow, Ernest, Gerald J. Glasser, and Frederick R. Ottman, *Statistics for Business Decisions*. Homewood, Ill.: Richard D. Irwin, Inc., 1959.

This volume treats problems in the business and economics area in terms which the student of elementary statistics will find appropriate and useful.

Schlaifer, Robert, *Introduction to Statistics for Business Decisions*. New York: McGraw-Hill Book Company, 1961.

This volume offers quite sophisticated methods of decision-making appropriate to the area of business and economics.

Walker, Helen M., and Joseph Lev, *Statistical Inference*. New York: Holt, Rinehart & Winston, 1953.

A lucid and detailed treatment of the methods employed in statistical testing and in sampling. Chapters 1 through 8 are especially recommended since they include probability, sampling, inference, and testing.

Excellent treatments of statistical inference and the testing of hypotheses may be found in the following references:

Croxton, Frederick E., and Dudley J. Cowden, *Practical Business Statistics*, 3rd ed., chaps. 21, 22, and 23. Englewood Cliffs, N.J.: Prentice-Hall, Inc., 1960.

Dixon, Wilfred J., and Frank J. Massey, Jr., *Introduction to Statistical Analysis*, 2nd ed., chaps. 7, 8, and 9. New York: McGraw-Hill Book Company, 1957.

Freund, John E., *Modern Elementary Statistics*, 2nd ed., chaps. 11, 12, and 13. Englewood Cliffs, N.J.: Prentice-Hall, Inc., 1960.

Hirsch, Werner Z., *Introduction to Modern Statistics*, chaps. 11 and 12. New York: The Macmillan Company, 1957.

Lacey, Oliver, *Statistical Methods in Experimentation*, chap. 9. New York: The Macmillan Company, 1953.

Mills, Frederick C., *Statistical Methods*, 3rd ed., chaps. 7, 8, and 15. New York: Holt, Rinehart & Winston, 1955.

Neiswanger, William Addison, *Elementary Statistical Methods*, rev. ed., chaps. 11 and 12. New York: The Macmillan Company, 1956.

Neter, John, and William Wasserman, *Fundamental Statistics for Business and Economics*, chaps. 10 and 12. Boston: Allyn and Bacon, Inc., 1962.

Paden, Donald W., and E. F. Lindquist, *Statistics for Economics and Business*, chaps. 9 and 10. New York: McGraw-Hill Book Company, 1951.

Rosander, A. C., *Elementary Principles of Statistics*, chap. 24. Princeton, N.J.: D. Van Nostrand Co., Inc., 1951.

Smith, C. Frank, and D. A. Leabo, *Basic Statistics for Business Economics*, chap. 8. Homewood, Ill.: Richard D. Irwin, Inc., 1964.

Sprowls, R. Clay, *Elementary Statistics for Students of Social Science and Business*, chaps. 8 and 9. New York: McGraw-Hill Book Company, 1955.

Tuttle, Alva M., *Elementary Business and Economic Statistics*, chap. 12. New York: McGraw-Hill Book Company, 1957.

Weinberg, George H., and John A. Shumaker, *Statistics, An Intuitive Approach*, chaps. 11 and 12. Belmont, Calif.: Wadsworth Publishing Co., Inc., 1963.

10 ADDITIONAL METHODS OF TESTING HYPOTHESES

10.1 Introduction

The essential theoretical framework as well as methods for testing hypotheses and drawing inferences from sample data have been explained in the preceding chapters. A number of additional testing techniques are useful under proper circumstances, and the present chapter will discuss (1) tests which employ the "t" distribution, (2) the chi-square test, (3) tests for differences in means, and (4) an introduction to the analysis of variance.

Symbols Employed in This Chapter

The following symbols are used for the first time in the present chapter:

t = In theory, the t value is to be interpreted in exactly the same manner as the z value of the normal curve. In fact, z could be thought of as a special case of the t value.

χ^2 = chi-square. A special term associated with experiments whose outcomes are said to follow a chi-square distribution. As employed in the material of this chapter, chi-square is interpreted in terms of probability in the same manner as z is interpreted for a normal curve.

d = The difference between two sample means—that is, $d = \bar{x}_1 - \bar{x}_2$.

z_d = the z value of a difference between two sample means.

$S_{\bar{x}_d}$ = the standard error of the difference between two sample means.

$S_{\bar{x}_1}, S_{\bar{x}_2}$ = the standard error of sample 1 and sample 2.

10.2 The *t* Distribution for Small Samples

In significance testing and confidence-interval estimation the normal curve is not always an appropriate probability distribution. In some situations the *t* distribution will be appropriate when certain criteria are met. These criteria are now to be examined.

When samples are drawn from a normal universe whose standard deviation is unknown, the standard error as calculated from *S* is an estimate. Under these circumstances the true standard error is unknown, and to compensate for this deficiency the *t* distribution is an appropriate probability model for drawing inferences from the sample values. Technically, then, the *t* distribution is employed when (1) the universe from which samples are drawn is normal, and (2) the standard error is estimated —as is necessarily the case when *S* is used as an estimate of σ. However, the *t* distribution is so close to a normal distribution when the sample size is $n = 30$ or more that the normal distribution is almost always employed when the sample size exceeds 30 items. For this reason, the *t* distribution is generally associated with "small" samples where σ is unknown. If the value of σ is known, then the normal curve is employed regardless of sample size, because the standard error is not an estimate and is, therefore, the true value.

In essence, then, the following criteria apply to the use of the *t* distribution for testing hypotheses and construction confidence intervals.

1. If the population to be sampled is normally distributed but σ is unknown, the *t* distribution is appropriate regardless of the sample size. In practice, however, the *t* distribution is used with samples up to approximately size 30. For larger samples, the normal curve is used as a matter of convenience.

2. If the population to be sampled has a normal distribution and σ is known, the normal curve is appropriate for samples of any size because the standard error is not an estimate; it is an exact value. Under these conditions, the *t* distribution will *not* be used.

3. If the nature of the population distribution is unknown, but the samples drawn from that population are "large," the central limit theorem indicates that the normal distribution may be employed for making inferences about the population. If, however, the samples drawn from the unknown universe are small so that the central limit theorem is inapplicable, then the *t* distribution may be used to allow for the doubt associated with the value of the standard error. A question also exists concerning the difference between the sample mean and the value of the true mean.

Fortunately, the *t* distribution is similar to the normal curve and is used in exactly the same manner, so there is relatively little new for the student to learn regarding the theory of inference or the mechanics of testing hypotheses. Because this background of the normal distribution has already been presented, it will therefore be sufficient to explain the t distribution in a brief manner. Actually, there is a different t distribution for each size of sample—that is, degrees of freedom $n - 1$—but it is not necessary to explain this point at length because all t distributions may be thought of in terms of what is already known about the normal curve.

Illustration 10.1   The Normal Distribution and the t Distribution

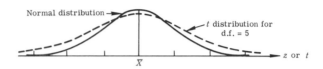

Illustration 10.2   Decision Rule Employing the 95 Per Cent Confidence Coefficient Expressed in Terms of the t Distribution

If the sample mean falls in this area reject the null hypothesis.	If the sample mean falls in this area accept the null hypothesis.	If the sample mean falls in this area reject the null hypothesis.
$-t_{.025}$	$\bar{x}$	$t_{.025}$

The t distribution was derived by W. S. Gosset (1876–1937), whose practical work with small samples led him to a fruitful study of the variance of sample means when n was small. His work was published under the *nom de plume* of "Student." Thus, the t distribution is sometimes known as *Student's t distribution*.

The t distribution is, in many respects, a first cousin to the normal curve. The t distribution is symmetric about the mean, and the spread of the curve to the right and left of the mean is measured in terms of standard deviations. (See Illustrations 10.1 and 10.2.) However, instead of employing the calculation $z = (\bar{x} - \bar{X})/(S/\sqrt{n})$, the letter t is substituted for z. Thus $t = (\bar{x} - \bar{X})/(S/\sqrt{n})$. Theoretically, t would be used in place of z whenever the sample size was small—that is, approximately where $n < 30$ (σ is unknown). The t table is shown in Appendix H.

In general, then, t can be employed as a replacement for z whenever the sample size is small and the universe to be sampled is known or assumed to be approximately normally distributed. Incidentally, it is possible even for knowledgeable persons to disagree about what size n should be regarded as "small" and what size n should be considered "large." In practical applications, what is small and what is large is really a matter of judgment based on known facts about a problem and a fund of knowledge about the theoretical considerations bearing on the problem. Here, it will be somewhat arbitrarily assumed that the dividing line is at $n = 30$. There are many t distributions, one for each value of $n - 1$, but the readily available tables provide integral values only from 1 to 30. For degrees of freedom over 30, the normal curve is generally employed as a probability model.

Now, to illustrate the use of the t distribution in constructing a confidence interval, the procedure is essentially the same as that given in Section 7.13. The steps to be followed are:

1. Draw a sample and calculate the mean. Parametric values are unknown.
2. Use the formula $S = \dfrac{\sqrt{\Sigma(x - \bar{x})^2}}{(n - 1)}$ to provide an estimate of the standard deviation of the universe.
3. Determine the standard error by use of the formula $S_{\bar{x}} = S/\sqrt{n}$.
4. Select a confidence level, say 95 or 99 per cent, for which $t_{.05}$ will be employed at the 95 per cent level, and for which $t_{.01}$ will be employed at the 99 per cent level. Observe the column headings in Appendix H. These are given in terms of probabilities for both sides of the distribution. Observe that the n column refers to the degrees of freedom. Thus, in confidence interval calculations, the degrees of freedom are always one less than the sample size. For a sample of size 5, and a confidence level of .95, the t value is found at the intersection of the row where $n = 4$, and the column headed .05. In this case, $t = 2.776$.
5. Now, multiply the t value by $S_{\bar{x}}$.
6. Determine the confidence interval as $\bar{x} \pm (S_x)(t)$.
7. Interpret the meaning of the confidence interval in the usual manner.

At this point, an example may be useful to indicate the overall methodology involved in using the t distribution as the basis for confidence interval statements.

Table 10.1

Confidence Interval Calculation

Sample Items x	Deviations d	d^2
39	−8.8	77.44
46	−1.8	3.24
48	+0.2	0.04
51	+3.2	10.24
55	+7.2	51.84
239		142.80

$$S = \sqrt{\frac{\Sigma(x - \bar{x})^2}{n - 1}} = \sqrt{\frac{142.80}{5 - 1}} = \sqrt{35.7} = 5.975,$$

$$S_{\bar{x}} = \frac{5.975}{\sqrt{5}} = 2.672,$$

$$\bar{x} = \frac{239}{5} = 47.8.$$

The 95 per cent confidence interval is calculated as:

$$(2.776)(2.672) = 7.415$$

and

$$47.8 \pm 7.415 = 40.385 \quad \text{and} \quad 55.215.$$

Use of the t Distribution to Test the Null Hypothesis

When an industrial process produces a product continuously and it is desired to check periodically on some characteristic of the product such as weight, small samples may be employed. The mean of the sample may be tested against the known process mean or standard to determine if the process mean is approximately correct. Thus, when a sample is drawn, the null hypothesis is to be tested against an appropriate probability distribution—in this case the t distribution. The test is made in terms of t rather than z as formerly, but the methodology is unchanged.

Example. Suppose the engineer mentioned in Section 9.4 is testing the noise level of saw blades selected at random from a production process. Five blades are considered to constitute the sample. The sample is drawn and the mean computed to be 95 decibels while the S value is computed to be 20 decibels. The test is two-sided and is made at the .95 level using 4 degrees of freedom at the t value for $t_{.05}$.

Step 1. Compute t as follows:

$$t = \frac{\bar{x} - \bar{X}}{S/\sqrt{n}} = \frac{95 - 100}{20/\sqrt{5}} = \frac{-5}{20/2.236} = \frac{-5}{8.94} = -0.559.$$

Step 2. Look up the value of $t_{.05}$ in Appendix H. This value is $t = 2.776$.

Step 3. If the computed value of $t < t_{.05}$, accept the null hypothesis. If the computed value of $t > t_{.05}$, reject the null hypothesis. Thus, $t = .559 < 2.776$. (Ignore the sign of t.)

Step 4. Conclude that the sample value of 95 decibels does not differ significantly from the standard level of 100 decibels.

Now, if the test were one-sided at the lower side, the value of $t_{.100}$ would be employed. Notice that while the test is being made at the 95 per cent confidence level, the t table *is given only in terms of both sides of the curve.* Therefore it is necessary to use the $t_{.100}$ value to obtain the 95 per cent level for a one-tailed test. Thus,

$$t \text{ as computed} = -.0559;$$

$$t_{.05} \text{ from the table} = -2.132$$

(the sign is minus because this is a lower-tailed test). Since $-2.138 <$ -0.559, the null hypothesis is accepted.

Exercise 10.1
1. Look back at Exercise 7.9 on page 204. Since the samples were of size $n = 5$, would the t distribution give a better probability description of the distribution of sample means than the normal curve? Why? Under conditions would the normal curve be appropriate in this problem?
2. Why is the t distribution frequently used with small samples where the value of σ is known, but the distribution of the universe is not known?
3. Explain how the t distribution for values of $n < 30$ compares with the normal curve.
4. Is the formation of a decision rule relative to the null hypothesis basically any different when t is employed rather than z?
5. How does use of the t table differ for the same confidence level when a one-sided test is used rather than a two-sided test?

10.3   Chi-Square.   General Considerations

Chi-square (χ^2) is an extremely useful type of test instrument and is used to provide a probability basis for testing the variation between sample values and values obtained from a frequency (probability) model. For example, the actual results of a coin-tossing experiment might be tested against the expected results of the experiment as predicted by the binomial theorem. The chi-square test for significance of the difference between the actual and expected results of the experiment would be appropriate for determining whether the differences between the results were significant.

Chi-square may thus be defined as a measure of the difference between an observed (experimental or sample) frequency and an expected (hypothetical or theoretical) frequency. Thus:

$$\sum_{i=1}^{h} \frac{(f_0 - f_t)^2}{ft} = \chi^2,$$

where f_0 = an observed frequency from a sample or experiment,

f_t = a theoretical frequency provided by an appropriate hypothesis,

h = number of classes in the problem.

One may easily discern that if $f_0 - f_t$ is equal to zero, then chi-square must be zero. On the other hand, the larger the difference between f_0 and f_t, the larger chi-square must be. Between these extremes, it may be seen that a small value of chi-square tells us that the two sets of frequencies are nearly alike, and if the two sets of frequencies are dissimilar, chi-square will be a high value. Thus, and in general, a large value of chi-square leads to rejection of the null hypothesis, while a small value leads to acceptance.

As used with chi-square, the null hypothesis would state: There is no difference between the frequencies as provided by the sample and those provided by the theory. As previously indicated this implies no *significant* difference between values.

Seen somewhat differently, chi-square is a means of measuring a frequency difference in a manner such that the difference may be tested against the probability function of an appropriate chi-square distribution (appropriate, that is, to the degrees of freedom involved; see below). Actually, use of the normal curve and the binomial as the basis of probability tests could be considered simply special cases of chi-square— although we will not herein be concerned with this fact.

Use of the chi-square test of significance provides an answer to the question: Are the differences between the sample frequencies (f_0) and the theoretical frequencies (f_t) too great to be attributed solely to chance? From sampling theory it is understood that random fluctuations (sampling differences) will occur—these are to be expected—but are the fluctuations so great as to allow us to draw the inference that chance alone was not operating and the cause of the differences must be sought in some other determinant? A small chi-square indicates (but does not prove, of course) minor chance fluctuations, whereas a large chi-square indicates that reasons other than chance explain the variations between sets of frequencies.

The general idea of chi-square may be illustrated with an example as follows: Given a single die. The question is this: Is the die well balanced? To answer this question an experiment is set up to toss the die a large number of times. If the die is well balanced, the actual frequencies for each outcome in the six sample spaces of the experiment would be expected to be in the ratio of 1:6. Minor differences may, of course, occur without causing rejection of the null hypothesis. But how large can the differences be before the null hypothesis is rejected? Before this question is answered, suppose the experiment was conducted and the die was tossed 180 times. The results are shown in Table 10.2.

If the chi-square test is made at the .05 level of significance, the calculated value of 3.0667 will be compared with the table value (see Appendix J) for 5 degrees of freedom.[1] Since the table value is 11.07 and the actual chi-square value is well below this, it may be concluded on the basis of this test that the die is well balanced. If the actual chi-square value had exceeded 11.07, the null hypothesis would have been rejected, with the inference that the die was not well balanced.

---

[1] The "restriction" in this problem which cost one degree of freedom came about because the data were forced to agree only on the total frequencies. See Section 10.5.

Table 10.2

Chi-Square Calculation for Tossing a Single Die 180 Times

Face	Observed Frequency f_0	Theoretical Frequency f_t	$f_0 - f_t$	$\dfrac{(f_0 - f_t)^2}{f_t}$
1	29	30	-1	1/30
2	31	30	$+1$	1/30
3	33	30	$+3$	9/30
4	27	30	-3	9/30
5	24	30	-6	36/30
6	36	30	$+6$	36/30
	180	180		92/30

Calculation of chi-square: $92/30 = 3.0667 = \chi^2$.

10.4   Characteristics of Chi-Square

Some of the more important characteristics of chi-square are the following:

1. The term "chi-square" refers to a value computed as shown in the formula above.

2. The term "chi-square distribution" refers to a probability function in which the degrees of freedom provide the only parameter. Actually there exists an entire family of chi-square distributions, one for each d.f. (degree of freedom) value.

3. If a graph is drawn for a chi-square distribution, the mean is the number of degrees of freedom; the mode is always d.f. minus 2, except the mode cannot be less than zero. There are no negative values of chi-square.

4. Where the d.f. exceeds 30, the value of chi-square obtained may be substituted in the following formula:

$$z = \sqrt{2\chi^2} - \sqrt{2(\text{d.f.}) - 1}, \qquad (10.1)$$

where χ^2 is computed as shown in Formula (10.1) and d.f. is the number of degrees of freedom in the problem. The results are then compared to the normal probability function—that is, a two-tailed test may be made at the .01 and .05 levels, and so on, as explained in Chapter 9.

5. The chi-square distribution itself is a continuous function, but where the frequencies involved are small, the discreteness of small numbers introduces an error similar to that of considering the binomial as a continuous function at small values of n. To overcome this difficulty, a general rule is that if any given call frequency is less than 10, Yates' correction should be used. *Yates' correction involves adding 1/2 to the frequency of the small classes and subtracting 1/2 from the larger classes.* Thus the row and column totals remain unchanged.

10.5   Degrees of Freedom

Two disturbing questions to the neophyte in statistics are: "What does the term *degrees of freedom* mean, and how are the degrees of freedom determined?" Degrees of freedom were first introduced in Section 4.8, but a more detailed explanation will now be given.

1. Degrees of freedom may be defined as the number of free choices in a given problem. In other words, it is necessary to answer the question: "With the total frequencies of the problem as a given fixed quantity, how many classes (or groupings) are actually able to take any frequency value whatsoever?" When the question is answered, the d.f. value is known.

   (a) Chi-square problems are ordinarily set up much like an ordinary table with rows and columns. There may be several rows and several columns in the table. Thus:

	2 columns		Σ
			14
3 rows			20
			36
Σ	40	30	70

   Note that by supplying frequencies to some of the cells—and since the row and column totals are fixed—it soon becomes clear that at some point you are no longer free to supply any value, but must supply a certain value to some cells to obtain the fixed totals. Thus, the degrees of freedom are the number of values which may be freely selected. (Two in the illustration.)

   (b) Fortunately for the neophyte, formulas can be devised to obtain the proper d.f. for ordinary problems.

   (1) In a row-and-column problem (physical outlines illustrated above) the d.f. may be calculated as:

   $$\text{d.f.} = (R - 1) \times (C - 1); \qquad R = \text{rows}; \quad C = \text{columns}.$$

   (2) In a problem involving the correspondence of two frequency distributions, the d.f. may be calculated as:

   $$\text{d.f.} = \text{number of classes} - 3.$$

   (c) While students are often desirous of using formulas as crutches, this should not excuse one from knowing how to reason through to the answer. Some additional background for approaching the matter logically is given in the following paragraph.

2. Degrees of freedom available start with n, the sample size. However, when the sample data have been grouped in a frequency distribution, the number of classes provides the starting number of d.f. available. Beginning from either of these points, one d.f. is subtracted for each restriction—a restriction being a manner in which one set of data is forced to agree with the other. Sets of data may be forced to agree as to n, as to *means*, and as to *standard deviation*. Each restriction subtracts one d.f. Actually, in using $n - 1$ as the denominator for calculating the variance of small samples, the formula recognizes the loss of one d.f. because the variance was computed from the sample mean rather than the true mean. By way of summary, then, start with the total available numbers (or classes) and subtract one d.f. for each restriction placed on the data. Whatever remains constitutes the d.f. for the problem. Where the data have been grouped into classes, the d.f. begins with the number of classes.

Exercise 10.2. *Determining Degrees of Freedom*

1. Given the accompanying cell table, observe that the marginal totals are fixed. The number of degrees of freedom will be as many as the values you are free to select.

a	b	c 10
d	e	f 15
g 12	h 13	i 25

Conditions: $c = a + b$; $f = d + e$; $i = g + h$, or $c + f$.

Instructions: You are to place values in a and b and d and e. How many values can you freely choose so the conditions given will apply?

—————— = d.f.

2. Given the accompanying cell tables, the marginal totals are fixed as given. The number of degrees of freedom will be as many as the values you are free to select.

		Sum
		30
		60
		45
		35
		50
Sum 90 230	220	

Degrees of freedom—————

				Sum
				100
				120
				90
				230
				180
				145
Sum 200	150	180	335	865

Degrees of freedom—————

3. In problem 2 could you use the formula: $(R - 1) \times (C - 1)$ to provide the correct d.f. answers?

4. In the accompanying table you are given a frequency distribution along with the frequencies to be expected if the distribution were a normal curve. Given that the mean of the original frequency distribution is 11.82 and $\sigma = 3.38$.

Class Limits	f	Calculated f
3.0 – 4.9	6	5.7
5.0 – 6.9	15	14.7
7.0 – 8.9	34	33.3
9.0 – 10.9	46	53.1
11.0 – 12.9	70	59.3
13.0 – 14.9	41	47.8
15.0 – 16.9	27	27.4
17.0 – 18.9	14	10.9
19.0 – 20.9	3	3.8
	256	256.0

(a) What is the total d.f. available before calculation of the expected frequencies?

(b) When the expected frequencies were calculated, how many d.f. were lost?

(c) How were these d.f.'s lost?

(d) How many d.f.'s remain?

(e) Now calculate $\bar{X}$ and S on the basis of the expected frequencies. Do these values actually agree with the given values?

(f) Obviously, the n's agree. Why? Is this a restriction placed on the data? Does this restriction lose one degree of freedom too?

10.6   The Chi-Square Test of Independence

The chi-square test for independence is a test to discover whether a significant difference exists between the frequencies provided by sample (or experimental) data and frequencies which would be expected on the basis of a hypothesis of independence with respect to one classification criterion. In such problems, a high value of chi-square will indicate that the discrepancies between expected and actual frequencies are too great to be attributed to chance factors alone and thus indicate independence of the variables in the classification. Conversely, a low value of chi-square would indicate that no significant difference exists between the variables in the classification. The following example will help clarify the facets of this type of problem.

Example. Suppose it is desired to know whether there is any significant difference between educational achievement and life insurance ownership of male adults. Both education and life insurance ownership are variables. Suppose education were classified on the basis of college and noncollege graduates; suppose further that life insurance ownership were classified on the basis of ownership or nonownership. The result would then be a dual classification, as follows:

Education	Insurance Ownership	
	Own Life Insurance	*Do Not Own Life Insurance*
College		
Noncollege		

Once this classification basis has been established, it is possible to design a sample to provide the actual frequencies which may then be tested against the hypotheses of independence. Chi-square may then be employed to test the difference in frequencies. What is being tested? The test is to determine whether or not educational achievement and life insurance ownership are independent; that is, the null hypothesis would state that there is no significant difference in life insurance ownership between the college and noncollege groups, and it is the null hypothesis which is to be tested.

Calculation of the expected frequencies: The actual frequencies are determined by taking a random sample of male adults. But how (by what hypothesis) can the theoretical frequencies be determined? Basically the method is this: Assume that the *proportion* of college and noncollege male adults in the population will be given by the sample. Using the values in the illustration below, the proportion of college graduates was 41.2 per cent of the total sample = (140/340) × 100; noncollege graduates formed the remainder of 58.8 per cent = (200/340) × 100. (1) Now, assume that if no relationship existed between education and insurance ownership the 232 persons *who do own life insurance would be distributed in this same proportion*—That is, 41.2 per cent of 232 = 95.5 and 58.8 per cent of 232 = 136.5. On this basis, insurance ownership is related to the proportions of college and noncollege male adults. (2) Next, assume that those *who do not own life insurance are distributed according to the same proportions*—that is, 41.2 per cent of the 108 persons not owning such insurance are college graduates, 58.8 per cent are noncollege. Simple multiplication will provide the expected frequencies (41.2 per cent × 108 = 44.5 and 58.8 per cent × 108 = 63.5). Note carefully the assumption that ownership and nonownership are distributed exactly in proportion to educational achievement. Now it is possible to test that hypothesis by assuming the actual frequencies do not differ significantly from the theoretical frequencies. The rationale of the test itself is identical to testing the significance of the difference between a sample mean and a universe or process mean.

Education	Own Life Insurance	Do Not Own Life Insurance	Total
College	$f_0 = 112; f_t = 95.5$	$f_0 = 28; f_t = 44.5$	140
Noncollege	$f_0 = 120; f_t = 136.5$	$f_0 = 80; f = 63.5$	200
Totals	232	108	340

Utilizing the basic formula for chi-square

$$\sum_{i=1}^{h} \frac{(f_0 - f_t)^2}{f_t} = \chi^2,$$

we have

$$\frac{(112 - 95.5)^2}{95.5} + \frac{(28 - 44.4)^2}{44.5} + \frac{(120 - 136.5)^2}{136.5} + \frac{(80 - 63.5)^2}{63.5}$$

$$= \frac{(16.5)^2}{95.5} + \frac{(16.5)^2}{44.5} + \frac{(16.5)^2}{136.5} + \frac{(16.5)^2}{63.5}$$

$$= \frac{272.25}{95.5} + \frac{272.25}{44.5} + \frac{272.25}{136.5} + \frac{272.25}{63.5}$$

$$= 2.85 + 6.13 + 1.99 + 4.29 = 15.26 = \chi^2.$$

Now that chi-square is known, check the chi-square table in Appendix H for a distribution with d.f. = 1 and alpha = .01. From the table it may be determined that χ^2 for $n = 1$ at .01 = 6.635. Since 15.26 > 6.635, the difference is declared to be significant at the .01 level, and the conclusion is drawn that educational achievement and life insurance ownership are independent. The null hypothesis must be rejected.

Notice that the χ^2 test is a one-tailed test. That is to say, the test was based on large differences between frequencies. Had the differences in frequencies been extremely small the null hypothesis would have been accepted, but here it is necessary to be very careful because where the variables are randomly selected it would be unlikely that chi-square would be extremely small. Therefore, on the basis of logic, the null hypothesis ought to be rejected if χ^2 is too small. Actually, the nature of the problem should indicate whether it is logical to reject the null hypothesis at either extreme (at a very small or a very large difference).

Exercise 10.3. *Calculating Chi-Square.* In the following problems you are to calculate chi-square primarily as an exercise in methodology. Later problems are designed to provide practice in actual testing of hypotheses.

1.

15	20	35
22	28	50
37	48	85

Chi-square_____

2.

10	5	15
7	14	21
17	19	36

Chi-square_____
(Use Yates' correction)

3.

115	230	345
83	70	153
198	300	498

Chi-square_____

4.

15	6	21
12	14	26
27	20	47

Chi-square_____
(Use Yates' correction)

10.7   The Chi-Square Test of Dependence

The chi-square test for dependence is the opposite of the test for independence. If it is desired to know whether the data of two or more samples have been derived from the same universe (with respect to the characteristic in question) the chi-square test may be used to provide a measure of the correspondence between f_0 and f_t frequencies. If the resulting test yields a low value of chi-square, the indication is that the frequencies are in close correspondence, and we would conclude that the two sets of frequencies were derived from (dependent upon) the same universe. Conversely, a high value of chi-square would indicate that the two sets of frequencies were not derived from the same universe, and the null hypothesis would be rejected.

Since the chi-square test is applicable to any number of columns and rows, it is not limited to two classifications, and the test described above may be used with (at least theoretically) any number of variables.

10.8   The Chi-Square Test of Goodness of Fit

Because chi-square values are based on differences between observed and theoretical frequencies, this measure is easily adaptable to frequency functions. Thus, suppose there exists a frequency distribution based on experimental or sample data, and it is desired to know how closely this distribution approximates a normal curve or some other appropriate distribution. Since the observed frequencies are already available, all that remains is to calculate the theoretical frequencies. An example was shown in Table 10.2 and another in the example of Section 10.6. A small value of chi-square will indicate a closeness of fit between the two distributions; a large value of chi-square will indicate a small degree of agreement.

Note, however, it would be unreasonable to expect that sample values comprising the frequency distribution would conform exactly to a normal curve or other theoretical distribution, because of chance factors. In other words, some variations are expected to occur, but the question then arises: Is the variation between frequencies too great to be attributed to chance (sampling) factors? The chi-square test is made on the basis of probability as measured by the appropriate chi-square distribution. If the test is to be made at the .05 level and the chi-square value computed from the problem is less than that expected at .05, it may be concluded that the agreement between frequencies is good enough to cause acceptance of the null hypothesis. On the other hand, if it should be discovered that the probability of disagreement between frequencies is more than .05, the null hypothesis is rejected and the conclusion is drawn that the two distributions do not exhibit a good fit.

Exercise 10.4.   *Chi-Square Problems*
1. Suppose there are two radio stations in a given community. The two stations are equally powerful and thus blanket the same market area. A sample survey of 1,000 radio listeners provided the following information: 400 listeners preferred Station A. Is this significant at the .1 level?

$$\chi^2 \underline{\qquad}; \quad \chi^2 \underline{\qquad} \text{ (from table)}; \quad \text{d.f.} \underline{\qquad}.$$

(a) What hypothesis is being tested?
(b) What theory provides the expected frequencies?

2. A certain machine used in an industrial process produces, under normal conditions, products of which 5 per cent are defective. After modifications were made in the machine a trial run was made of 1,000 units. There were 35 defectives in this run. Is this significant at the .05 level?

$$\chi^2 \underline{\hspace{2em}}; \quad \chi^2 \underline{\hspace{2em}} \text{ (from table); d.f. } \underline{\hspace{2em}}.$$

   (a) What hypothesis is being tested?
   (b) What theory provides the expected frequencies?
   (c) Is it now certain that the machine has been improved? Why?
   (d) If you were the plant manager, what might you wish to consider before taking additional steps?

3. The industrial relations department of a certain firm was considering the desirability of introducing a new type of job-classification procedure but questioned whether the employees would prefer the new or the old plan. To this end, the department conducted a survey of some 84 employees. The replies were 32 favorables and 52 opposed. Is this difference significant at the .1 level?

$$\chi^2 \underline{\hspace{2em}}; \quad \chi^2 \underline{\hspace{2em}} \text{ (from table); d.f. } \underline{\hspace{2em}}.$$

   (a) What hypothesis is being tested?
   (b) What theory is used to provide the expected frequencies?
   (c) If you were the plant manager of this firm would you put the new plan into effect?

4. From a bowl containing a large number of red and white beads in the proportion of 20 per cent red and 80 per cent white beads, a sample of 50 beads is drawn. The beads are as follows: 15 red and 35 white. Was the sample random?

$$\chi^2 \underline{\hspace{2em}}; \quad \chi^2 \underline{\hspace{2em}} \text{ (from table); } \alpha \underline{\hspace{1em}.01\hspace{1em}}; \text{ d.f. } \underline{\hspace{2em}}.$$

   (a) What hypothesis is being tested?
   (b) What theory provides the expected frequencies?

5. An industrial process is organized to produce certain parts of a toy assortment. When these parts are packaged, 60 per cent are supposed to be "long" and 40 per cent should be "short." One-half of the parts are to be colored green and the remainder blue. After the production process had been underway for some time a random sample was drawn with the following results: 130 parts were long, 70 parts were short; 70 of the long parts were green and 60 were blue; 20 of the short parts were green and 50 were blue. Make a chi-square test.

$$\chi^2 \underline{\hspace{2em}}; \quad \chi^2 \underline{\hspace{2em}} \text{ (from table); } \alpha \underline{\hspace{1em}.01\hspace{1em}}; \text{ d.f. } \underline{\hspace{2em}}.$$

   (a) What hypothesis is being tested?
   (b) What theory provides the expected frequencies?
   (c) Has the production process been performing as expected? Explain.

6. The manufacturers of Automobile A and Automobile B both claimed their products would average 16 miles per gallon of gasoline in ordinary city driving. A test of the two automobiles yielded the following results:

Automobile A averaged 14.5 miles per gallon whereas automobile B averaged 15.5 miles per gallon. Are these results significantly different from the manufacturers' claims?

χ^2 _____; χ^2 _____ (from table); α __.05__; d.f. _____ .

(a) What hypothesis is being tested?

(b) Is the test conclusive? What variables would have to be rigidly controlled in such tests?

(c) What factors might account for the differences between the manufacturers' mileage figures and those of the test?

7. Given the following experimental information: Three coins were tossed 1,200 times with the following results:

Coins Showing	f_0	f_t	
h^3	120		d.f. _____
h^2t	440		χ^2 _____
ht^2	465		α __.01__
t^3	175		χ^2 _____
	1,200		(from table)

(a) Provide the theoretical frequencies.

(b) What hypothesis is being tested?

(c) What theory provides the expected frequencies?

(d) Is this a test of independence? If not, what type of test was made?

8. A retail outlet wished to determine whether ladies or men were predominant shoppers in their hardware department. It had always been assumed that the department catered largely to men, but a sample taken at various random times throughout one week revealed the following results: Men, 1,675; ladies, 1,425.

(a) Calculate χ^2 and test at the .05 level.

(b) What conclusions may be drawn on the basis of the sample and test?

9. During a period of changeover for retooling and remodeling a certain firm found it necessary to furlough part of its labor force. The question then arose as to whether the proportions of skills temporarily unemployed differed from those whose employment continued. It was considered too costly to take a census of all the personnel files, but a random sample was taken and yielded the following results:

Classification	Unemployed	Employed	Totals	
Skilled	15	80	95	d.f. _____
Semi-skilled	25	100	125	χ^2 _____
Unskilled	30	120	150	χ^2 _____
Totals	70	300	370	(from table) α __.05__

(a) What type of test is appropriate in this case? What is being tested?

(b) Was the proportion of employed and unemployed significantly different?

10. Go back to Exercise 10.2 and, utilizing the data of problem 4, calculate the chi-square value for the goodness of fit between the actual and the expected (calculated) frequencies.
    (a) Is the fit sufficiently good to allow the conclusion to be drawn that the actual frequencies are really a normal curve—except for minor deviations?
    (b) If the data of this problem were sample means, would you conclude that the distribution of sample means was normal?
    (c) Might chi-square be used to test the central limit theorem for practical problems where this information was necessary to further applications of the data?

10.9 Testing Differences Between the Means of Large Samples

In statistical work, the question sometimes arises as to whether two samples may have actually originated in the same universe. For example, an automobile tire manufacturer makes two types of tires, and one type is believed to be somewhat superior to the other when judged by the criterion of average mileage. Mileage tests show that samples from each tire type (universe) yield slightly different means. Suppose that one tire type is designated as originating in universe 1 and the other as originating in universe 2. Sample tires from the first universe yield a mean of 22,900 miles, and from the second universe the mean value is 23,000 miles. At first glance this difference does not appear to be significant. However, before jumping to any conclusions, it may be well to examine this matter from a statistical point of view. The issue is whether the difference in means is actually a *significant* difference. It is possible that the observed mileage difference is due to random variations rather than to quality differences. It would be desirable to have some technique by which to judge, on objective grounds, which of the alternative explanations (chance variations or quality differences) is really correct.

At this point a brief review of the theory of significant differences and a bit of repetition may be in order. When two sample means are drawn and a difference exists between the two values, it is desirable to know whether the difference is merely due to chance fluctuations originating from sampling, or whether the difference is due to some fundamental cause other than sampling variation—that is, to differences in the means of the two universes. If the difference can be attributed to sampling (chance) variations, then the difference between the sample means is declared "not significant." On the other hand, if the difference between the two sample means is so large as to cast doubt on the sampling explanation, the difference is then declared to be "significant" and the cause of the difference must be sought in something other than sampling variation.

In order to test the difference between the two sample means, the null hypothesis is formulated, stating that "there is no difference between the two mean values." The observed difference is then tested against a standard error to determine if the observed difference is "small," in which case the null hypothesis is accepted. But if the observed difference is "large" when measured against the standard error, the null hypothesis is rejected and the difference declared significant.

Applying the theory of significant differences to sample means, the reasoning is as follows. If large samples are drawn from a given universe, the sample means will vary normally around the true mean according to the central limit theorem. The standard error of the distribution will be equal to $\sigma/\sqrt{n}$. Thus, if many samples were drawn from this same universe and the differences between each sample mean and the mean of the universe were calculated, these differences would sum to zero—since the distribution of sample means is, according to the central limit theorem, symmetric. Expressed somewhat differently, the *distribution of differences* would be symmetric around a mean of zero. The standard error of this distribution could, of course, be calculated in the usual manner. Thus, random *sample means drawn from a given universe will show only deviations due to sampling fluctuations and these deviations are measured by the standard error of the sampling distribution.* The differences between sample means will form a random variable with mean zero.

By way of contrast, suppose sets of sample means are drawn from two different universes with different-valued means so that $\bar{X}_1 \neq \bar{X}_2$. Now let a sample be drawn from the first universe and a sample be drawn from the second universe. The means of these samples are subtracted to obtain the difference: $\bar{x}_1 - \bar{x}_2 = d$. Now, let this process be repeated a number of times so that several d values are obtained. The mean of the d values is now obtained. The mean of the differences would be expected to be a value equal to the actual difference between the means of the two universes. In other words, the mean of the sample differences is not zero and its value is not due to sampling variability—the mean difference is due to the difference in the universe means.

Now, suppose that there was no logical way to know whether the samples were drawn from two different universes or were actually drawn from the same universe. This is a situation akin to the tire example previously explained. If the samples were drawn from a single universe, any differences between two sample means would be due purely to sampling variability, whereas if the samples were drawn from two different universes, the differences between any two sample means would be due to differences between the universe means. The problem is to know when $\bar{x}_1 - \bar{x}_2$ reflects a difference due to chance and when the difference is due to other causes. Too, this problem is clearly one of inference because a conclusion is to be reached on the basis of incomplete (sample) information.

Consider next the more customary practical problem which gives rise to the need for testing mean differences. Suppose it is believed that two separate universes do exist and they are thought of as universe 1 and universe 2. A random sample is drawn from each universe and the mean is computed for each sample. (Incidentally, the sample sizes need not be identical in this type of problem.) Now if $\bar{x}_2$ be subtracted from $\bar{x}_1$, sampling theory suggests that the difference is not likely to be zero even though universe 1 and 2 were actually subuniverses of the same universe. Since a difference of zero between the two sample means is not to be expected, how large can the difference be before the decision is made that the difference is significant? If the difference is declared to be significant, the inference is then drawn that universe 1 and universe 2 are not the same universes. In the tire example, this would be interpreted to mean that the tires produced by process 2 are superior to those produced by process 1. (See below.)

The problem at this point, then, is to determine on the basis of these two samples whether or not a *sampling distribution of differences* would actually have a mean of zero. The null hypothesis provides one of the necessary tools to help decide the issue. The null hypothesis would be formulated to state: "There is no difference between the two sample means." Expressed a bit differently, the null hypothesis says, $d = \bar{x}_1 - \bar{x}_2 = 0$. As previously observed, it is understood that d is not likely to be precisely zero.

At this point some standard is required by which d can be judged as "large" and thus significant, or "small" and thus not significant. In other words, the truth or falsity of the null hypothesis is to be judged by this standard. But what is the standard? As the student might expect, the standard employed in making the judgment is the *standard error of the difference between two means*, and is identified by the symbol $S_{\bar{x}_d}$. Thus, the test of the null hypothesis in this case takes the form:

$$\frac{\bar{x}_1 - \bar{x}_2}{S_{\bar{x}_d}} = \frac{d}{S_{\bar{x}_d}} = z_d,$$

where $z_d =$ the z value of a difference between two sample means. The normal curve is used to evaluate the probability value of z_d. And, to complete the test of the null hypothesis, the z_d value is tested against the normal distribution at a given level of significance. In other words, the test of the null hypothesis is made according to the usual two-sided decision rule.

Calculating the Standard Error of the Difference Between Two Means

The calculation of the standard error required in this type of problem is very little different from the techniques of calculation explained in previous chapters. What is required in this particular situation is: (1) Calculate the variance of each sample. This is, of course, S_1^2 and S_2^2. (2) Now, divide each variance by the appropriate sample size, i.e., $S_1^2/n_1 = S_{x_1}^2$ and $S_2^2/n_2 = S_{x_2}^2$. (3) Now add the two standard error variances: $S_{x_1}^2 + S_{x_2}^2$. Take the square root of the sum of the standard error variances. Thus,

$$S_{\bar{x}_d} = \sqrt{S_{x_1}^2 + S_{x_2}^2},$$

where $S_{\bar{x}_d}$ = the standard error of the difference between two sample means. S_1^2 and S^2 were calculated from the usual formula for estimating the variance of the universe from the sample—that is,

$$S^2 = \frac{\Sigma x^2}{n - 1},$$

so that

$$S_{\bar{x}_{1 \text{ or } 2}} = \frac{\frac{\Sigma x^2}{n - 1}}{n} = \frac{\Sigma x^2}{n(n - 1)}.$$

The values so obtained are then substituted in the formula:

$$S_{\bar{x}_d} = \sqrt{S_{\bar{x}_1}^2 + S_{\bar{x}_2}^2}.$$

Now, to illustrate the method of testing the difference between two sample means, the following example involving tire mileage will be employed. For the sake of simplicity, only the essential calculations are shown.

Universe 1	Universe 2
$\bar{x}_1 = 22{,}900$ miles	$\bar{x}_2 = 23{,}000$ miles
$\Sigma x^2 = 490{,}000$	$\Sigma x^2 = 512{,}000$
$n = 50$	$n = 65$
$S_1^2 = 10{,}000$ miles	$S_2^2 = 8{,}000$ miles
$S_{\bar{x}_1}^2 = \dfrac{10{,}000}{50} = 200$ miles	$S_{\bar{x}_2}^2 = \dfrac{8{,}000}{65} = 123.1$ miles

To calculate the standard error of the difference between the two means:

$$S_{\bar{x}_d} = \sqrt{S_{\bar{x}_1}^2 + S_{\bar{x}_2}^2} = \sqrt{200 + 123.1} = \sqrt{323.1} \approx 18.0.$$

To test the null hypothesis at the 95 per cent level, a test rule would be formulated as follows: "if z_d is equal to or less than 1.96 (ignore the sign of z_d), the null hypothesis is accepted and the difference is to be declared not significant. Otherwise, the null hypothesis is rejected and the difference is to be declared significant." Thus:

$$\frac{\bar{x}_1 - \bar{x}_2}{S_{\bar{x}_d}} = \frac{22,900 - 23,000}{18.0} = 5.55 = z_d.$$

Clearly, in this problem $z_d > 1.96$, and the null hypothesis is rejected. What this test implies is that tires produced by process 2 do have a mileage life which differs significantly from the mileage life of tires produced by process 1. Observe, however, that this conclusion has been inferred from incomplete information, and the conclusion could be erroneous.

Summary

The methods just described provide a means for objectively testing differences between two sample means (large samples) where it is uncertain whether the two samples were drawn from the same or from different universes. In general, this type of test is applicable to many types of experiments. Whenever two processes are to be compared, and where the processes lend themselves to random sampling, this method of testing differences between means can be utilized. In addition to industrial experiments, agricultural experiments often involve testing two types of seed, or fertilizer, or moisture, and this type of experiment tends to lend itself to testing significant differences between means. Educational problems often lend themselves to this method in testing the effects of differing teaching approaches, or types of tests, or specific differences in groups of students.

It may not be amiss at this point to observe that an experiment to be carried out in a scientific manner might well lend itself to the type of test described in this section. In other words, the experiment might be designed to utilize a test of significance between two sample means. The results of the experiment would then be interpreted in terms of a generally recognized and accepted test method.

It may also be observed that when experiments are designed to test two methods or processes in order to determine whether one is better than the other, the usual preference is that the null hypothesis be rejected in order to reveal a significant difference. This would mean that the research could be considered fruitful. Obviously, however, such idyllic results are not always achieved and, in fact, the general rule in experimentation is probably to the contrary.

Exercise 10.5

1. Explain the basic reason(s) for employing a test for the significance of the difference between two means.

2. Why might the individual or department conducting an experiment which involves a test of the difference of two sample means desire the test to actually result in rejection of the null hypothesis?

3. Why is the test for the significance of the difference between two sample means a problem in inference?

4. A production process is designed to fill iron-ore cars with 50 tons per car. Two operators are responsible for filling the cars, with one operator working one shift and the second operator working the second shift. A sample of 65 cars filled by operator 1 shows a mean weight of 51.2 tons and a standard error of 2 tons. A sample of 100 cars filled by operator 2 shows a mean of 48 tons and a standard error of 1 ton. At the 95 per cent level, does a significant difference exist between the mean tonnage values of these two operators?

5. Given the following information on two samples which are thought to have been drawn from different universes.

$$\bar{x}_1 = 43 \text{ bushels}, \qquad \bar{x}_2 = 40 \text{ bushels},$$
$$n = 25, \qquad\qquad n = 49,$$
$$S_1 = 3, \qquad\qquad S_2 = 2.$$

At the 99 per cent level, did the samples originate in the same universe, or were the universes actually different?

10.10   Testing Differences among Several Means. The Analysis of Variance

The methods applicable to testing the differences between two means as explained in Section 10.9 are inapplicable to larger problems where three or more means are to be tested for significant differences. A method which may be employed for the more complex problem makes use of techniques which are part of a broad statistical area known as "the analysis of variance." In the present section, it will be desirable to look carefully at the method for testing the differences among several sample means. For simplicity of presentation only the one-way classification will be shown.

Suppose that three samples have been drawn and it is not known whether they all came from the same universe.[2] Suppose further that to supply a working hypothesis, it is assumed that the samples did come from normal universes and that the sample size n is uniform for all samples. Too, only one characteristic is to be studied, and in the following example

---

[2] The methods shown in this section may be applied to three or more samples, but all must be of the identical size n. For simplicity of presentation, only the "three sample" examples will be shown.

this characteristic will be retail store location. The basic problem then becomes one of testing the differences between the means of the samples.

In testing the differences between three (or more) means under the assumptions outlined above, the question to be asked of the data is basically the same as if only two means were being tested. In other words, *are the differences between the sample means so large as to lead to the conclusion that the three means actually were drawn from three different universes*? To make the test, the null hypothesis is again employed and would state: "There is no difference between the sample means."

In theory, if the three samples came from the same universe, their means and standard deviations would be identical except for sampling variation. Thus, any variation among the three samples is due only to chance factors (not causative factors). Each sample mean is an estimate of the universe mean. All other statistics, too, would be estimates of the corresponding population parameters.

Next, it may be reasoned that if the three sample means are averaged, the resulting mean will be a good estimate of the population mean—but this is true only if the three samples came from the same universe. The identical reasoning could be applied with respect to the standard deviations of the samples—that is, the average standard deviation should be equal or close to the value of the universe standard deviation if all samples originated in the same universe. Presumably, then, the three (or more) samples drawn from a single universe should, as a group, lead to reliable approximations of the universe parameters.

To turn the matter around, if the three sample means differ substantially from each other, then it can be assumed the samples *did not come from the same universe*. In this case the variation among the three means and among the three standard deviations will be "large." The variations among the means will be emphasized by the squaring operation used when computing the variance, S^2. Incidentally, computation of the variance is carried out in precisely the same manner as previously explained in Chapter 4.

At this point, an example will be useful. The example will employ only a few data in order to keep the details to a minimum. Suppose that a new type of merchandising for frozen foods is being considered by a large retail grocery chain. It is not known whether this method will appeal equally to customers in different parts of a given large city. The statistician therefore selects three stores known to be about equal in sales volume, and the new merchandising technique is employed in these stores for a six-week period. Total weekly frozen-food sales are reported in dollars and, for the purpose of this example, it may be assumed that two zeros are omitted. The sales data are given in Table 10.3.

Table 10.3

Effect of a New Merchandising Approach for Frozen Foods in Three Retail Stores in a Given City (Data in Dollars; Two Zeros Omitted)

	Store 1	Store 2	Store 3
	48	48	44
	40	46	52
	36	42	54
	50	50	52
	51	48	50
	45	48	60
	270	282	312
$\bar{x}$:	45	47	52

Calculation of the overall mean of the samples:

$$\bar{X} = \frac{45 + 47 + 52}{3} = 48.$$

The null hypothesis to be tested states that $\bar{x}_1 = \bar{x}_2 = \bar{x}_3 = \bar{X}$. If this hypothesis proves tenable, it may be inferred that the new merchandising method has the same effect in all stores regardless of location. If, on the other hand, the null hypothesis is declared false, it will be inferred that the stores draw their frozen-food customers from different universes as far as this one characteristic (frozen-food sales) is concerned.

Clearly, the means of the samples shown above are not identical, and some method must be devised to measure the differences between these values. The method to be employed utilizes a comparison between the variance computed in two different ways; one variance will be computed as the variance *among the means*, and the second will be computed as the variance *within the samples*. The method of calculation will be shown in the example below. The theory of the test is that if the samples all came from the same universe, these two estimates should be relatively close in value; if the samples came from different universes, the variance estimates should be relatively far apart. To complete the test of the difference in variances, the F table (see Appendix I) will be used.

The method for calculating the *variance among the means* is as follows:

(1) $\bar{x}$ Sample Means	(2) $\bar{X}$ Overall Mean	(3) d (1) – (2)	(4) d^2
45	48	−3	9
47	48	−1	1
52	48	+4	16
			26

Next, the squared standard error is computed as:

$$S_{\bar{x}}^2 = \frac{\Sigma d^2}{n-1} = \frac{26}{3-1} = \frac{26}{2} = 13.$$

However, the measure required is S^2, which may be computed by noting that

$$S_{\bar{x}} = \frac{S}{\sqrt{n}},$$

so that $S^2 = S_{\bar{x}}^2 \cdot n$ and

$$S^2 = (13)(3) = 39 = \text{variance among the means.}$$

The next operation is to determine the variance *within the samples*. If the sample data really did come from the same universe, the samples should all exhibit an identical variance—except for chance sampling factors. Thus, if the variance of each of the samples is obtained and the three variances averaged, the average variance should be close to the value of S^2 obtained by the previous calculation. In other words, the variance *among the means* and the variance *within the samples* should be close in value *if the samples all came from the same universe*. If the variances are not close in value, the inference is that the samples came from different universes.

To determine the variance *within the samples*, it is necessary that each sample variance be calculated so that the three variances can be averaged. Thus:

Store 1				Store 2				Store 3			
x	$\bar{x}$	d	d^2	x	$\bar{x}$	d	d^2	x	$\bar{x}$	d	d^2
48	45	+3	9	48	47	+1	1	44	52	−8	64
40	45	−5	25	46	47	−1	1	52	52	0	0
36	45	−9	81	42	47	−5	25	54	52	+2	4
50	45	+5	25	50	47	+3	9	52	52	0	0
51	45	+6	36	48	47	+1	1	50	52	−2	4
45	45	0	0	48	47	+1	1	60	52	+8	64
			176				38				136

The S^2 values are calculated for each sample by the usual formula. Thus:

$$S^2 = \frac{\Sigma d^2}{n-1}$$

and

for Store 1:   for Store 2:   for Store 3:

$$S^2 = \frac{176}{5} = 35.2, \qquad S^2 = \frac{38}{5} = 7.6, \qquad S^2 = \frac{136}{5} = 27.2.$$

The average variance *within the samples* is

$$S^2 = \frac{S_1^2 + S_2^2 + S_3^2}{3} = \frac{35.2 + 7.6 + 27.2}{3} = \frac{70.0}{3} = 23.3.$$

A slightly more efficient means of calculating the value of S^2 *within the samples* would be

$$S^2 = \frac{\Sigma d_1^2 + \Sigma d_2^2 + \Sigma d_3^2}{(n-1)(3)} = \frac{176 + 38 + 136}{(5)(3)} = 23.2.$$

The final step is to compare the variances by determining the ratio between them and then comparing this ratio to the F table. The ratio of the variances as calculated by the two different methods is

$$F = \frac{S^2 \text{ among the means}}{S^2 \text{ within the samples}} = \frac{39}{23.3} = 1.67.$$

Clearly, the ratio of the variances appears small, but nevertheless for the sake of certainty it must be tested against the F distribution of probabilities.[3] The F distribution of probabilities depends upon the degrees of freedom in the numerator of the ratio shown above and also upon the degrees of freedom in the denominator of the ratio. Since there were three means in the numerator, the degrees of freedom are $3 - 1 = 2$. Since there were six items per sample in the denominator, the degrees of freedom are $6 - 1$ per sample, and since there were 3 samples, the degrees of freedom are calculated as $(6 - 1)(3) = 15$.

Turning to the F table in Appendix I at the .05 level, and checking for two degrees of freedom in the numerator across the top of the page, and for 15 degrees of freedom in the denominator along the side of the page, the F value turns out to be 3.68. Now, since F calculated was 1.67, which is obviously smaller than the table value of 3.68, the null hypothesis is accepted. The differences among the sample means are declared not significant, which then leads to the inference that the three means did originate in the same universe.

The conclusion is now reached that the merchandising method affects the three stores about equally. On the basis of this information, the retail chain may decide to utilize this new method of merchandising in all of its stores.

To show the other side of the problem, *suppose the differences had been declared significant.* This information would now lead to a search for the cause(s) of the differences in customer reaction to the new merchandising method for frozen foods. At this point no numerical information

---

[3] The F table was originated by Professor R. A. Fisher and was named the "F table" in his honor.

exists by which to isolate the cause or causes of the observed differences. These causes must be sought on other grounds. For example, if one of the stores was located in a suburban area where many potential customers are accustomed to do home gardening and preserving as a hobby, this might explain at least some of the difference between mean sales in the three stores. Or, if one of the stores was located near a large apartment complex, it might be that customers from that area were more attracted to the new merchandising methods than customers for the other two retail outlets. Clearly, more would have to be known about the characteristics of the customers in these stores before the cause or causes of the significant differences could be discovered. The statistical test has indicated that a difference between means exists, but at this point the statistical methods of the test reach their limitations. The next step is to search for assignable causes with the use of other methods.

Exercise 10.6
1. What are the basic assumptions in the one-way classification analysis of variance with regard to:
    (a) normality of the sampling universe,
    (b) sample sizes,
    (c) characteristics by which the samples are classified?
2. What is the role of the null hypothesis in the test made by the analysis of variance?
3. Is the use of the null hypothesis any different in the type of test made by analyzing the variance of several samples than in the other types of tests explained in this chapter and in Chapter 9?
4. Is there anything unique about the computation of the individual variances of the samples—that is, different from the methods outlined in Chapter 4?
5. Why is it necessary to say that, once the F test for significance is completed, the cause(s) for similarities or differences among the means must be sought out on other than statistical grounds? Might there be any exceptions to this general rule?
6. Suppose that, instead of the data shown in Table 10.1, the following sales figures had resulted from the frozen-food experiment:

Store 1	Store 2	Store 3
46	49	48
38	47	56
34	43	58
48	51	56
49	49	54
43	49	64

(a) Using the analysis-of-variance method of testing the differences between the means, compute the F ratio and decide whether the differences are significant.

(b) Why is the F ratio just computed considerably higher in this problem than in the text example? What accounts for the change? Was this change due to a change in the sample variances, or in the means, or in both?

(c) Is the test outlined here—that is, a test for mean differences—actually a test of the differences in variances? Explain.

7. A training program given by the personnel department of an electronics firm to new women employees was designed to permit assembly of a complex subsection. Since some of the new recruits learned more readily than others, it was decided to test whether age differences could account for the differences in learning times. Personnel records were sampled with the following results:

Number of Hours Required to Pass the Subassembly Test by Age Groups (Female Employees)

18–21	22–25	26–29
15	16	11
18	16	14
20	17	14
21	18	15
21	23	16

(a) Using the analysis-of-variance method of testing the differences between the means, compute the F ratio and decide whether the differences are significant.

(b) Does the test show a significant difference between the age groupings? Interpret this difference or lack of difference in terms of the hiring policy of the firm for this type of subassembly work.

10.11   Summary

The materials of this chapter have briefly presented some specialized techniques for testing the null hypothesis and drawing inferences from sample data. The discussion necessarily leaned heavily upon the background developed in Chapters 7 and 9 (sampling, testing, and inference). The methods employed in the present chapter to test the null hypothesis are either adaptations of the methods previously presented or provide alternative means to test the null hypothesis.

With the exception of the chi-square test, all of the test and inference methods presented both in the present chapter and in Chapter 9 are parametric methods. That is, the basic issue was to determine, on the basis of sample evidence, whether a universe actually had or did not have a particular parameter within a specified confidence level. From this decision concerning the parameter other inferences could be drawn about the universe, or decisions of a practical nature could be made—for example, deciding whether to accept or reject a shipment of parts from a supplier, or whether a production process was "in control." These tests all required an assumption of normality about the universe, or assumed that the distribution of sample means was normal or could be identified as a "*t*" distribution. In essence, these are the classical methods of statistical testing and inference. Properly applied and interpreted, they are valuable tools in the statistical spectrum.

Key Terms and Concepts of This Chapter

Almost all of the concepts of this chapter were developed and explained in the preceding nine chapters. However, the following concepts are of especial significance in the present materials.

The chi-square distribution
Degrees of freedom
Expected (or theoretical) frequency
The *F* table
The *t* distribution
Yates' correction
Variance
Variance among the means
Variance among the samples

Bibliography

See the bibliography at the end of Chapter 9.

II THE USE AND CONSTRUCTION OF INDEX NUMBERS

11.1 Introduction

In the modern world a great deal of economic information is conveyed to the ultimate consumer through index numbers. By themselves, index numbers are percentagelike computations measuring *relative change* in one or more economic variables or groups of variables. Included in the variables currently being measured by index-number techniques are prices, economic activity, cost of living, industrial production, and many others. A partial listing is given in Section 11.13.

Index numbers are as small in size as percentages; theoretically they are relatively simple to calculate. Index numbers are flexible in that they are appropriate to a wide variety of situations and purposes. Too, index numbers are readily utilized with graphic methods. These points add to the general conclusion that while simple to construct and use, index numbers are an important technique of measurement and they are excellent informational devices. A study of index numbers thus constitutes one major phase of a concentrated study of statistics as applied to the business and economic environment of the modern world.

Since index numbers are percentagelike computations, they are subject to the same techniques of interpretation applicable to percentages. Thus, index numbers can be thought of as *ratios* resulting from a comparison of one measurement value (wages, prices, and so on) at one time or place with the same variable measured at another point in time or space. A fundamental objective of the use of index numbers is the reduction of complex sets of data to a single number or to a small set of ordinary numbers. Like percentages, index numbers focus attention on *relative* change rather than on *absolute* amounts of change.

Index numbers are part of *descriptive* statistics. That is, index numbers are a means of measuring, summarizing, and structuring data. They are not considered to be part of statistical inference, although it could be argued that many indexes are really samples from a larger universe and that the theory of sampling is essential to the construction of index numbers in such situations. However, the samples are generally judgment samples, even though the sample items may be randomized wherever possible. Thus, while a knowledge of probability is essential to devising methods for the construction of some index numbers, the use of a probability distribution, such as the normal curve, to provide a confidence interval is normally not undertaken.

As a result of these considerations, it will be best to think of index numbers as descriptive statistics, and to avoid any inferential considerations. In practice, index numbers are used to make comparisons, to simplify more complex data, and to provide easy-to-understand quantitative results. This is the approach followed in the present chapter.

The materials presented in this chapter involve basic methods, issues, and concepts in the construction and use of index numbers. The goals of this chapter include showing the nature of index numbers, describing the more widely used methods of computation, and suggesting some criteria by which to interpret and understand the advantages and limitations of index numbers. It is impossible, in an elementary text, to provide all of the business and economic understanding which would be desirable as background for a complete understanding of the environment within which problems exist and for which index numbers may provide a useful solution. As a matter of fact, most index numbers constructed today, it would seem, have been the result of applying specific techniques of measurement to specific problems. Thus, to understand a specific index number, the student should also have at least a general understanding of the practical problem and the environmental factors which led to the construction of the index-number series.

Index numbers are among the most useful tools in the statistician's kit. In general, it may be said that index numbers are used to make decisions or to form judgments based on a comparison between two or more values of the index. Alternatively, comparisons may be made between different but comparable indices. Thus, decisions to buy or not to purchase stock for inventory might be determined, in part, by information obtained from recent changes in the index of construction costs. A businessman may wish to form an opinion of the level of a specific commodity price in terms of the general level of prices for the group to which the commodity belongs. An economist may wish to form some notion of recent changes in productivity. For agricultural policy purposes it is necessary to judge the relationship between prices received and prices paid by farmers. Every individual has a stake in the value of the consumer dollar. A paper mill executive is keenly interested in making a comparison between the change in the sales of his mill compared to the change in sales for the industry as a whole. There are so many uses of index numbers that it would be impossible to do more than simply suggest what some applications might be.

As an example of one of the many indices prepared by business firms, the Research Department of the Security First National Bank of Los Angeles prepares an "Index of Business Activity in Southern California." As the title indicates, this index is constructed to measure business activity. Included as components of the index are the following statistical series: bank debits, department store sales, industrial power used, manufacturing employment, payrolls in manufacturing, petroleum production, motion picture production and distribution employment, building permits issued, engineering construction, contracts awarded, real estate sales activity, railroad freight volume, and telephones in use. These components represent the items which, taken together and assigned appropriate weights, result in the final index published by the bank. Some of the components are also available separately as index numbers.

With this background in mind, the basic construction principles for an elementary type of index number may be illustrated by assuming that a firm's balance sheet last year indicated a net profit of $10,000 whereas this year's net profit is $12,000. It is perfectly clear that net profit has increased and that the relative increase is 20 per cent. If index numbers were to be used for this calculation, the arithmetic would be as follows. (Note that while these are percentage calculations, the per cent sign is not attached to the final result.)

Index Computation Year 1:

$$\frac{\text{Net Profit (Year 1)} = \$10,000}{\text{Net Profit (Year 1)} = \$10,000} \times 100 = 100.0.$$

Index Computation Year 2:

$$\frac{\text{Net Profit (Year 2)} = \$12,000}{\text{Net Profit (Year 1)} = \$10,000} \times 100 = 120.00.$$

Observing this method of calculation, it may seem a bit strange that Year 1 should be compared to itself because, as anyone could see, the result must be 100 per cent or unity. But this is just the point. The net profit figure for Year 1 has become the "standard" or "base" by which other years will be compared. The index number of Year 2 (120.0) may be compared with the index number for Year 1 (100.0) indicating a rise of 20 "points" occurring in the span of one year. This example also illustrates one of the major advantages of index numbers: it is possible to observe relative changes in the variable quickly by simply scanning the figures. The required information is conveyed briefly, succinctly, and rapidly.

As a further example of index numbers, suppose we look at a set of consumer price indices. The index numbers given in Table 11.1 are the yearly values of the consumer price index as compiled by the Bureau of Labor Statistics. The years selected include the World War II period, the postwar period, the Korean conflict, and the subsequent years through 1964. Thus, if the index numbers shown actually reflect the overall

Table 11.1

The Consumer Price Index, 1940–1964 (1957–1959 = 100)

Year	Index	Year	Index	Year	Index	Year	Index	Year	Index
1940	48.8	1945	62.7	1950	83.8	1955	93.3	1960	103.1
1941	51.3	1946	68.0	1951	90.5	1956	94.7	1961	104.2
1942	56.8	1947	77.8	1952	92.5	1957	98.0	1962	105.4
1943	60.3	1948	83.8	1953	93.2	1958	100.7	1963	106.7
1944	61.3	1949	83.0	1954	93.6	1959	101.5	1964	108.1

SOURCE: *Economic Report of the President.* An excellent booklet, *The Consumer Price Index, A Short Description,* is available from the Bureau of Labor Statistics of the United States Department of Labor.

consumer price changes for the United States in this period, a great deal of information on the behavior of this particular economic variable is at our disposal.[1] Observe that the information in Table 11.1 is in brief yet readily understandable form. The consumer price index, in graphic form, is shown in Illustration 11.1.

Given this set of index numbers and the chart, it is possible to compare the *relative* price movements of consumer items for the two decades

Illustration 11.1   The Consumer Price Index, 1940–1964 (1957–59 = 100)

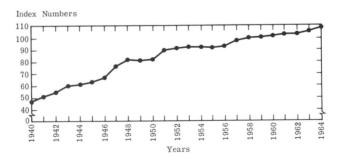

---

[1] The index measures changes in price of the goods and services bought by families of city wage earners and clerical workers.

shown. Observe that the index numbers are based on the 1957–1959 *average* of consumer prices. In other words, the "yardstick" of measurement is the average of consumer prices during those years. All yearly prices are then stated *relative* to the 1957–1959 average. From the table it is possible to quickly observe the periods of time during which the consumer price level was moving up rapidly; for example, from 1945 through 1948 the index gained 21.1 points, whereas from 1953 through 1956 the index remained "fairly stable." This information could then be related to other economic information of those periods to form a picture of the general economic situation existing at that time.

If index numbers are widely used as a basic technique for measuring economic change, what are some of the major reasons why such measurements have become commonplace? Certainly, as for any type of measurement, one basic reason is the ability to specify a particular "thing" or "concept" in standardized numerical terms. In measuring the length of an object, one has a particular thing to measure, but in measuring a price level, there is only a concept, for no such object as a price level exists in concrete form. That part of the world which centers around the marketplace and around the processes of trade and exchange is a world characterized by a multiplicity of forces, each of which acts as a "determinant" of one or more variables. Such variables would include price levels, production, income, taxes, sales, product types, market patterns, employment, wages, interest rates, expenditures, savings, consumer credit, demand deposits, and so on. Index numbers are one technique by which variables of the economic world may be measured and their relative strengths estimated. Knowing these forces, the policy-maker, the decision-maker, and the interested person may form reasonably accurate notions of and draw warranted conclusions about the economic world.

The measurement of economic quantities frequently involves highly abstract concepts. When working in the world of abstract quantities, we are considering matters which are understandable but are not represented by physical form. The mind of man must first "conceptualize" these notions, define and refine them until they can be made clear and precise. Fortunately, however, it is not always necessary to reach the purest form of the concept before it becomes valuable as a tool of thought or as a means of providing important information.

Consider now the problem of measuring a price level. There exists no concrete object which may be recognized as a price level. There are only individual prices, and these are expressed in an abstract unit of account—money. Yet it is necessary to gain some perspective as to changes in a price level; otherwise how can judgments be made relative to the future? How is it possible to analyze the successes and errors of the past unless relatively accurate knowledge is available? If man were to wait until he could refine these concepts to perfection, the whole matter would be useless. Therefore, it is necessary to decide certain issues and get on with the work at hand. For example, someone must decide what price level is relevant to the problem under consideration. Does the problem involve agricultural prices? consumer prices? wholesale prices—or some other price level? Once a clear notion of where the problem is centered is formulated, methods and techniques of securing the desired information must be devised. Here decisions must be made as to what items should be classified as agricultural or wholesale or consumer, and when this is done these items must be grouped into a meaningful whole or entity. Then, by successive refinements it is possible to begin to measure the concept which was once so abstract and apparently so far removed from the physical world around us. These matters form much of the content and substance of index-number theory. It is a major scientific development that we can make these measurements at all.

Individuals responsible for making economic decisions will wish to keep informed of changes in the general level of economic activity and particularly those changes closest to their own businesses. Certainly the issue is not whether the managerial and analytical functions call for keeping informed of changes; rather the issue is "how" to keep informed. Some intuitive knowledge of changes will be possessed by responsible officials, but this knowledge often must be supplemented by more precise information. Among the statistical techniques for storing and transmitting information, index numbers occupy an important portion of the spectrum. This is not to say that index numbers are more or less important than another type of information, but rather that part of all economic information received will be in the form of index numbers. It is, therefore, essential to know precisely what information is—and is not—being relayed through an index-number series. It is also essential to understand *where* index numbers are appropriate, *how* they were constructed, and *why* they are useful in particular circumstances.

Symbols and Notations Used in This Chapter

$p_w = p_0 =$ a price computed at some period identified as the "base period."

$q_w = q_0 =$ a quantity or number of items existing at a "base period" of time.

$p_1, p_2, \ldots, p_n =$ prices computed at the time period indicated by the subscript.

$q_1, q_2, \ldots, q_n =$ quantities computed at the time period indicated by the subscript.

Exercise 11.1

1. What is the end result achieved by the use of index numbers as a technique of measurement?

2. Define the term "economic variable." Define "index number."

3. Why do you suppose the text material makes a point of emphasizing "relative change" in discussing index numbers?

4. Given that a wage-earner receives a gross pay check of $105.63 in a particular week. One week later his check is $110.91. Are those relative numbers? If not, how may they be changed to relatives?

5. Why is the "base period" always equal to 100.0? In what sense is the base period a standard of measurement?

6. What are the basic reasons for the process of measurement? Suppose man had not yet learned how to measure. Under these conditions what do you estimate he would know about his environment?

7. Is the value of information minimized because the information may be presented in a simple number? Would information gained through counting and expressed as a natural number be any less valuable because the result is simply expressed?

8. What do we mean when we "conceptualize" a price level? How would you conceptualize a price level for books? Is your definition of a book a completely precise concept in that you can decide without doubt what is a book and what is not a book? Would your concept need to be absolutely perfect to make it useful?

9. In this section we have touched upon some of the general notions of decision-making as discussed in Chapter 7. In the earlier chapter it was noted that we first need to know "what the problem is." In this chapter it has been pointed out that when we are measuring something we must know "what we are measuring." What do these two concepts have in common?

10. Using a recent issue of the *Federal Reserve Bulletin*, or the *Economic Report of the President*, estimate the proportion of statistical (numerical) information presented in the form of index numbers.

11.2   The Simple Index Number

The simplest general type of index-number construction may be demonstrated with a single series of measurements. Suppose a series of data shows the dollar value of new housing in a certain community by years as given in column 1 of Table 11.2. To convert these dollar values to index numbers as shown in column 3, it is only necessary to: (1) select a base period, (2) divide the values shown per year by the base, (3) multiply by 100, and (4) round to one digit at the right of the decimal.

Table 11.2
Construction of the Simple Index Number

Year (1)	Value of New Housing Laid Down per Year in City "A" (2)	Index Numbers (1961 = 100) (3)
1961	$15,675,290 (base)	100.0
1962	16,932,450	108.0
1963	17,251,600	110.0
1964	12,945,370	82.6
1965	18,263.510	116.5

In constructing this type of index, one does not normally encounter particularly difficult problems—assuming the dollar value of new housing is already available. All that was required by way of arithmetic processes was division and multiplication. Yet the resulting index-number series was in no way diminished in usefulness by its ease of construction. Relative changes are clearly shown by the index numbers. If one may assume the dollar values given actually measure what they are supposed to measure, then conversion to index numbers provides a facility and ease of reporting change not possessed by the original data. For example, the dollar value for the year 1962 (as shown in column 2) is larger than the value for the year 1961 (the base year), but can you discover at a glance how much the two values differ? Of course the difference can be computed quickly, but the question of relative change would not be answerable directly from that computation. The index number readily yields this information. If we seek absolute values, we consult column 2; if we seek relative change, we consult column 3.

Since all index numbers of this example are related to one base value, 1961 in this case, there is some question as to the degree of change between years other than the base. For example, the index number is 108.0 for the year 1962 and 110.0 for the year 1963. Did the value of new construction change by 2 per cent in this period, or by 2 index-number points? The answer to this question is as follows:

$$\text{percentage change} = \left(\frac{\$17,251,600}{\$16,932,450} \times 100\right) - 100 = +1.9 \text{ per cent}$$

or

$$\frac{(110.0 - 108.0) \times 100}{108.0} = 1.9 \text{ per cent.}$$

whereas the index-number change was 2 points. Thus *it is not correct to say that the percentage change between any two index numbers is the numerical difference of the numbers.* This point should be clear from the manner in which index numbers are constructed; that is, index numbers all relate to changes from a given base and therefore would not show percentage change (except approximately) between any two selected index numbers.

11.3   General Nature of More Complex Index Numbers— The Market Basket

Some years ago a popular feature of certain newspapers was the "weekly market basket column" in which food price changes were noted and briefly analyzed. Thus, each Thursday or Friday an enterprising

Table 11.3

Market Basket of Food Products—An Illustrative Example

Item	Price, Week 0 (cents)	Price, Week 1 (cents)	Price, Week 2 (cents)
Bread (lb)	18	18	19
Butter (lb)	65	66	69
Whole milk (qt)	17	17	17
Eggs (doz)	22	20	26
Ground beef (lb)	37	40	37
Potatoes (10 lb)	50	49	52
Sugar (lb)	12	12	11
Medium oranges (doz)	45	48	45
Breakfast cereal (lb)	20	20	20
Totals	$2.86	$2.90	$2.96

young reporter would be given a shopping list by his editor and instructed to shop local grocery stores for the prices of the items comprising the market basket. The list of items was constant from week to week. When the necessary footwork was accomplished, current information on prices would be assembled, printed, and commented upon. Presumably the readers were interested in following this feature week after week and by so doing received interesting and worthwhile information on food price changes affecting their budgets. Many index numbers are constructed in a similar manner—that is, a market basket of products or services is priced periodically, and the sequence of market basket costs is then converted to an index for the express purpose of portraying changes through time.[2]

Suppose now the market basket approach to measuring price changes is illustrated by a hypothetical example as shown in Table 11.3. (Since the year and specific week are not important for illustrative purposes, no dates need be given here.)

[2] Items comprising the consumer price index are sometimes referred to as a "market basket." See *Consumers' Price Index*, Hearings Before a Subcommittee on Education and Labor, House of Representatives, 82nd Congress, 1st Session (Washington, D.C.: Government Printing Office, 1952), pp. 2, 23, 37, *et seq.*

From Table 11.3 several distinct features of the market basket may be observed: (1) It is a "standard" package or basket which is "purchased" each week with the price purpose of measuring how the total cost of the package changes through time. (2) In the basket shown, no attempt has been made to allow for the fact that families actually purchased these items in varying quantities—that is, a particular family might use 20 quarts of milk per week, three dozen eggs, four pounds of sugar, and so on. In other words, the market basket shown does not provide standard "weights" for the products in accordance with some "average" family consumption. (3) In the example the reader's attention is drawn to the *total* cost of the market basket. Comparison is facilitated by the fact that the numbers are small and the whole presentation is simple and un-cluttered. This factor of ease in comparison and comprehension is, after all, one of the virtues of statistical presentation. (4) The totals do not indicate the relative change in market basket costs but rather are expressed in absolute amounts. (5) The totals given represent *composites* in that they are the *sum* of the individual components comprising the market basket. (6) No information is given as to the method utilized to collect the prices. It may be that all prices were obtained in one particular retail outlet, or it may be that the prices quoted were obtained by averaging the prices at several outlets, or perhaps only small (or large) stores were shopped for prices. Clearly, *how* the prices were obtained would have an impact on the final results.

Many of the problems faced in the construction of index numbers are identical to the considerations raised by the example of Table 11.3. However, before exploring these issues in greater detail, observe that the market basket could have been presented in the form of an index-number series, rather than an expenditure series, by selecting one week as the "base" (denominator of the index-number ratio) and dividing all totals by that base. Thus:

$$\text{Week } 0 = \frac{\$2.86}{\$2.86} \times 100 = 100.0,$$

$$\text{Week } 1 = \frac{\$2.90}{\$2.86} \times 100 = 101.4,$$

$$\text{Week } 2 = \frac{\$2.96}{\$2.86} \times 100 = 103.5.$$

In constructing index numbers in this way, a question is raised as to which week ought to be selected as the *base period* and why. The student should keep this point of the base period in mind, as it is one of the major problems in index-number construction. Section 11.4 will consider this "base" problem in detail. In the market basket case the earliest week was selected to be the base for illustrative purposes.

With reference to the market basket shown above, another set of questions emerge in considering the technical and theoretical problems encountered in assembling the original market basket. For example, what is to be measured? Do we wish to measure the effect of food price changes on the family budget? If so, then the market basket, as shown, makes no allowance for quantities used per week by an average family. On the other hand, what are the characteristics of the average family? If the items in the market basket are not purchased (weighted) in accordance with some average pattern of consumption, comparison between weekly baskets certainly does not reflect the exact impact of price changes on the family budget. Too, is the market basket complete? Does it contain only high-priority items? What about items other than those shown (such as canned goods, frozen foods, and so on)? Clearly, *what* we are attempting to measure (perhaps changes in the average family expenditure on food) will determine the composition of the market basket.

On the assumption that definitions and procedures to be used in measuring food prices are now clearly stated, there remains the question of how and where the prices are to be obtained. Should the price shopping take place in small food stores? Large food stores? A combination of food stores? Large cities? Small cities? Cities of various sizes? Should the prices be taken on weekends? Should occasional "bargain" sales be included? Here again it appears that some compromises (averaging) must be reached if the issues are to be settled. Once the procedure is set, it then remains firmly in place for the period under consideration. Procedure is changed only when conditions warrant such change.

An additional set of problems arises in connection with the *quality* of items included in the market basket. If week-to-week changes are to be measured over a short period of time, there is likely to be scant evidence to suggest that quality has either improved or deteriorated. However, over a period of years it is clear that the quality of some products will have changed. How should the market basket take account of this fact? Once again it appears that a great deal of difficulty will be encountered if the procedure attempts to take account of quality changes, which are very difficult to measure. In general it may be said that most indices necessarily ignore the problem of quality change.[3]

---

[3] The problem of quality changes and the difficulties of trying to take account of such changes during World War II and the Korean conflict are discussed briefly in *Consumers' Price Index*, *op. cit.*, pp. 8–34.

To summarize: The market basket example introduces many of the basic problems involved in index-number construction. One of the interesting points is that a matter as simple as a market basket designed to measure total price change has raised so many important issues. Clearly, many concepts must be defined and problems settled if the totals used for comparison are to provide a consistent measurement of what the market basket purports to measure. If, however, the market basket does consistently provide a measure of price or expenditure change in this particular variable, then the market basket approach is certainly a most convenient and rapid means of assessing the significance of that change. In other words, while a host of problems emerge, the problems are not insoluble and the final results turn out to be well worth the effort of collecting and presenting the information. Thus, a market basket (or a market basket in index-number form) is a valuable technique for gaining certain types of desired information.

Exercise 11.2

1. Convert the following series to simple index numbers.

Year	XYZ Corporation Persons Employed	Index (Year 1962 = 100)
1960	32,684	
1961	33,791	
1962	35,800	
1963	31,259	
1964	37,470	

   (a) In your judgment, does the index number make the changes in employment clearer to the understanding than the original series?
   (b) Does the index-number series contain any information not found in the original employment series?
   (c) How would the relationships between the employment series change if the base were 1961 rather than 1962?
   (d) If you were calculating percentage change between various employment values, would this change be equal to the change in index numbers if you compared: (1) 1960 to 1962? (2) 1961 to 1962? (3) 1964 to 1960? (4) 1964 to 1962? In each case explain why the changes were equal—or were not equal.
   (e) Explain in general terms why changes in index numbers are not necessarily identical to percentage change.

2. What is the unifying concept in a "market basket" of items?

3. It should be clear that a market basket need not be composed only of tangible items. It could also be composed of services. Devise a market basket of commercial "family recreational services." State clearly the criteria used to decide whether or not particular service items should or should not be included.

(a) Would your market basket be quite appropriate to (a) persons between the ages of 15 and 25? (b) persons between the ages of 26 and 35? (c) persons of low-income groups? (d) persons of high-income groups?

(b) Who could best utilize your market basket as an indicator of changing costs of commercial recreation? Would the use of your index be subject to careful interpretation? How and why?

(c) Would your market basket change if you were in a small city? Large city?

4. What method would you use to collect the prices of the services included in your market basket?

11.4   Selection of Base Period

The following points may be considered criteria of base-period selection.

1. Since the major purpose of index numbers is to provide a comparison between some standard (the base) and other values of the variable, it follows that the base selected should represent some typical or average value. The word typical here suggests a "standard of measurement" on which reasonable agreement would be reached by individuals familiar with the particular set of measurements under consideration.

2. If no one time period can be found which could be considered typical, then an alternative is to average several values of the variable and utilize the mean for the base. Thus in Table 11.2 it would have been possible to compute the arithmetic average of all five values and then compare each yearly total to that average. Too, the years 1962, 1963, and 1964 might have been averaged and this value used as the base in making the index-number comparisons.

3. Generally speaking, the base to be selected is a past-time period, preferably several "years" removed from the present. The question is, how far back should the base be established? For example, to use (say) 1910 as a base for measurements today may be stretching the concept of typicality a bit too much—at least for most index-number series. Certainly a comparison between products, consumption patterns, incomes, and prices a decade ago and a year ago leaves something of a large gap between the two periods. While it may be true that many variables did not change one whit during this period, others will have changed considerably and we find ourselves comparing two things which, strictly speaking, are not comparable. Choice of a base period in terms of the past, therefore, involves some arbitrariness, but we ought not to introduce more unrealistic elements than are absolutely essential. Therefore, it is desirable to select as a base period some past "year" but a year not too far removed from the present. A nice bit of judgment is involved in base-year selection. The base period must, however, meet the test of objective judgment, and the base period selected should be defensible against reasonable criticism.

4. In some index-number series it might well be that the base period chosen is selected to agree with other indices. For example, if a particular firm

maintains or has access to various indices of maintenance costs, it would be desirable for each separate index to be related to the same base period. Thus, if indices were available for changes in the prices of brick, glass, lumber, electric fixtures, roofing, and so on, estimates of current maintenance costs might reasonably be made. If, however, each index was computed on a different base, the indices could not be combined in a manner to provide accurate cost estimates. (Note: It is sometimes possible to shift the base of index numbers in order to obtain a comparable series. This point is further explained in Section 11.11.)

11.5   Uses of Index Numbers

We are now in a position to examine some of the inherent advantages gained by the use of index numbers as an informational device. Knowledge of the ends sought by utilizing index numbers should not only be interesting and valuable in itself, but is also of assistance in exploring the more complex forms of index-number computation. Among the advantages of index numbers are the following:

1. Index numbers provide a means of simplifying data—that is, of reducing complex forms of measurement to simple numbers which reflect the relative changes in the variable through time or space. Because the absolute measurements (in dollars, pounds, tons, bales, or whatever) are reduced to a simple relative, comparison between different values of the same variable is facilitated.

2. Measurements taken at various points in time and space are readily compared as to relative change. For example, a firm composed of several retail outlets could compare the relative change in sales and other variables among its stores by the index-number method.

3. Index numbers provide a useful method of combining units of dissimilar nature into one meaningful value. Thus, tons, books, oranges, pins, automobiles, and so on may be combined by multiplying their respective prices by corresponding quantities and summing to a total dollar value. The total value may then be compared to the same measurement made at an earlier (or later) date. This method of combining dissimilar units is nothing more or less than the rationale of the market basket.

4. When a variable has been measured periodically and converted to a set of index numbers, the resulting "time series" forms a useful set of informational values from which trends, seasonal and cyclical movements may be dissected. Such matters are the subject of the next two chapters.

11.6   The Composite Index Number

The composite index refers to a combination of commodities and/or services grouped in a market basket arrangement. There are three general types of composite indices; (1) the price index, (2) the quantity index, and

(3) the value index. Examples of these three indices will be given in following paragraphs. An unencumbered example of a composite index for measuring price changes is shown in Table 11.4. Once the index numbers are calculated, they may then be presented in tabular form as shown in Table 11.5.

Table 11.4

The Composite Price Index—An Illustrative Example

		Prices		
Commodity	Year 0	Year 1	Year 2	Year 3
A (lb)	$0.12	$0.13	$0.17	$0.17
B (doz)	0.75	0.75	0.90	1.35
C (units)	0.80	0.90	1.00	1.25
D (box)	1.00	1.25	1.30	1.85
Totals	$2.67	$3.03	$3.37	$4.62
Computation	2.67	3.03	3.37	4.62
	2.67	2.67	2.67	2.67
Index	100.0	113.5	126.2	173.0

The example of a composite price index as shown in Table 11.4 was simplified to take into account only a few commodities. The significance of the composite aspect of this calculation is that *many dissimilar items have been combined into one meaningful total.* The resulting index numbers then reflect relative changes in these totals.

In the illustration of Table 11.4 each commodity enters the index once.

Table 11.5

Index Numbers

Week	Index (Year 1 = 100)
0	100.0
1	113.5
2	126.2
3	173.0

SOURCE: Table 11.4.

No cognizance is taken of the fact that these commodities might have been weighted in proportion to their average use or by some other criterion. Thus, this situation raises the same question of weighting previously encountered in the market basket illustration of Table 11.3.

The illustration of a composite price index in Table 11.4 demonstrates the general nature of composite index construction. Now, observe that commodity A enters the index with relatively little importance since its price is low relative to the other commodities, whereas commodity B enters the index with roughly eight times the importance of A (1.00/ .12 ≈ 8). In other words, the ratios between the prices of the commodities are acting as weights. This type of weighting may (or may not) be appropriate to the objectives of measurement in question. Clearly we are not going to be able to proceed very far in this direction until we have fully explored the whole matter of "weighting" within the composition of an index.

11.7   Use of Weights in Index-Number Construction

Suppose now that the commodities of Table 11.4 are widely used and it has been determined that the objective of measurement should be to measure the impact of price changes for these commodities insofar as

Table 11.6

Consumption of Commodities A–D

Commodity	Weekly Quantity Consumed
A	20
B	5
C	15
D	10

price changes affect the average family budget. We need to know the average consumption of these commodities by an average family. Remember, the example has been made extremely simple to illustrate the basic features of an index without unnecessary clutter. Suppose it is discovered (perhaps from a recent study) that the average household during an average week consumes the quantities of each commodity shown in Table 11.6. Many families, of course, will purchase the commodities in differing proportions, but we can conveniently ignore the deviations because we are dealing with averages and assume the quantities consumed remain stable during the period of our illustration. With these matters disposed of, all that remains is to (1) price the commodities each year according to a standardized pricing plan, (2) multiply the yearly price by the quantity consumed for each commodity, (3) sum the products, (4) compare the summations to the base period. (5) The results are then expressed as index numbers. Thus, observe the method as shown in Table 11.7. (Again, specific time periods are not essential to the problem.)

If the results of the weighted index of Table 11.7 are compared with the "unweighted" index of Table 11.4, we observe the indices are not identical, although the values are similar. The degree of correspondence between the two "market baskets" would depend upon the manner in which weighting affected the items. However, if our interest in measurement centers in the total impact of price changes on the family budget, then the weighted index may be considered more appropriate. For purposes of simplification the index accounted for only four commodities,

Table 11.7

The Composite Price Index Number (Quantity Weighted)—An Illustrative Example

Commodity	Average Consumption q_0	Year 0 Price (p_0)	(p_0q_0)	Year 1 Price (p_1)	(p_1q_0)	Year 2 Price (p_2)	(p_2q_0)	Year 3 Price (p_3)	(p_3q_0)
A	20	0.12	2.40	0.13	2.60	0.17	3.40	0.17	3.40
B	5	0.75	3.75	0.75	3.75	0.90	4.50	1.35	6.75
C	15	0.80	12.00	0.90	13.50	1.00	15.00	1.25	18.75
D	10	1.00	10.00	1.25	12.50	1.30	13.00	1.85	18.50
			28.15		32.35		35.90		47.40

Indices:
(Year 0 = 100)

$$\frac{28.15}{28.15} = 100.0 \qquad \frac{32.35}{28.15} = 114.9 \qquad \frac{35.90}{28.15} = 127.5 \qquad \frac{47.40}{28.15} = 168.4$$

SOURCE: Tables 11.4 and 11.5.

and it should be clear that many more commodities would be included in a practical problem. Too, it should be clear from this example that if the weights were shifted—that is, if the high weights were associated with rapidly changing prices—this fact would tend to pull the resulting index in the direction of change. Conversely, if low weights are associated with low-priced items, then even a reasonably large price change (say from 20 to 22 cents—a 10 per cent change) would not exert much impact on the index.[4]

When indices are computed for weeks or months, it is often desirable to use differing weights for each time period. The reason ·for periodic alteration of the weight structure is to account for seasonal changes in the use of commodities or services. Thus, during the summer a good many truck garden crops will be readily available which are almost totally

[4] In economic theory it is generally pointed out that a change in the price of an item whose consumption is small in contrast to the use of more frequently consumed items has a "low income elasticity." Salt would be an example of this type of item. Even if personal incomes change greatly, the consumption of the product remains about the same as previously. Items with low income elasticities are not likely to affect the family budget greatly.

absent in winter months. Too, certain types of products tend to be consumed in summer rather than in winter (insect sprays, charcoal, ice cream cones, and so on). As the consumption pattern changes during the winter months, if a consumption index is to accurately reflect changes, it must account for seasonal use of the priced items.

The absolute values of the weights utilized in the example of Table 11.7 are not, in and of themselves, of significance in determining the index. The significance of weighting lies in the ratio of the weights to each other. Thus, it may be seen that the weights are in the ratio of $4:1:3:2$. Had the weights been used in their ratio or decimal form, the following calculations would have been made:

Table 11.8

The Composite Index Number (Quantity Weighted by Ratios)

Commodity	Weights (w_0)	Year 0 P_0	(p_0w_0)	Year 1 P_1	(p_1w_0)	Year 2 P_2	(p_2w_0)	Year 3 P_3	(p_3w_0)
A	0.4	0.12	0.048	0.13	0.052	0.17	0.068	0.17	0.068
B	0.1	0.75	0.075	0.75	0.075	0.90	0.090	1.35	0.135
C	0.3	0.80	0.240	0.90	0.270	1.00	0.300	1.25	0.375
D	0.2	1.00	0.200	1.25	0.250	1.30	0.260	1.85	0.370
			0.563		0.647		0.718		0.948

Indices:
(Year 0 = 100)

$$\frac{0.563}{0.563} = 100.0 \qquad \frac{0.647}{0.563} = 114.9 \qquad \frac{0.718}{0.563} = 127.5 \qquad \frac{0.948}{0.563} = 168.4$$

SOURCE: Table 11.7.

It is to be observed that the results of Table 11.8 are identical to those of Table 11.7. The point to be emphasized is that the resulting set of computations *do not depend upon the absolute value of the weights*, but rather are dependent upon the *ratios between the weights*. Thus, problems of computation may frequently be simplified by using ratios which total 1.0, 10.0, or 100.0. Too, the use of 100.0 for the sum of weights provides a ready means of understanding the relative importance of one or more items in the index by comparison with the weighted importance of other items comprising the index.

Exercise 11.3

1. Compare the weights of Table 11.7 with those of Table 11.8. Since the final index numbers are identical, defend the point that the weights in Table 11.8 are generally preferable to those in Table 11.7.

2. In index-number construction, why should the base period ideally be a typical period? Carefully define the word "typical." Is the definition easily applied to a wide variety of situations?

3. Now, think back over the past decade. What year or years would you think are typical from an economic point of view and why?

4. Why is the base period of an index-number series generally selected to be at least a few periods in the past? Does base selection involve "hard and fast" rules? Could the rules be more firm on this point? Why or why not?

5. Compared with a market basket of items ten years ago the same market basket composed of today's items may introduce variables (such as quality) for which prices do not fully account. Now, given the following items, indicate which ones you believe have changed in the past ten years, how they have changed, and whether the change would make any difference in constructing a ten-year series of index numbers. (a) Auto tires, (b) soap, (c) eggs, (d) gasoline, (e) electricity, (f) light bulbs, (g) television sets, (h) watches, (i) cameras, (j) lawn mowers.

6. Explain the general process for combining unlike items into a meaningful total as is done in index-number construction.

7. Can there be an unweighted composite index? Why or why not?

8. Explain the theory of using weights in a composite index by indicating (a) the purpose of weights, (b) how weights are selected and used, (c) how the final resulting series of index numbers is affected by weighting, and (d) whether the results succeed in achieving the purposes of weighted index numbers.

9. Attach weights to the following products in accordance with your own expenditure for the products per average week. Choose numbers so as to total ten. (a) Clothing, (b) food, (c) books, (d) rent or cost of housing, (e) entertainment, (f) general school supplies, (g) transportation.

10. Explain the uses of index numbers to your critical, but intelligent, non-statistics friend. Assume he has asked you a question similar to, "What good are index numbers?"

11. A firm with retail outlets in cities A, B, C, and D wishes to make up a series of index numbers on monthly sales for each city. City A is itself about as large as B + C + D. However, D is the smallest with 10 per cent of the total sales for all outlets. How might index numbers be established from a mechanical point of view? Defend your reasons for choosing the particular methods and process you selected.

11.8 Quantity Indices

Another of the many uses of index numbers is found in the measurement of quantity changes. If, for example, a trade association wished to measure hardboard production and express the result as an index number, no particular theoretical problems would be encountered. The board feet of hardboard production could be determined per week or month and the data then converted to indices. The process would be much the same as that illustrated in Table 11.2.

A more difficult set of problems is encountered when the quantity index is a composite, and a number of items are to be combined in one index. Suppose a quantity index was designed to measure the physical production of a multiproduct firm. The firm might produce pliers, wrenches, bolts, and drills. How may these differing products be combined? Certainly some kind of weighting process must be employed, as it is obviously incorrect to count one bolt and one pair of pliers as equal items.

The problem of weighting can be solved by the process of valuation— that is, multiplying the quantity of each item produced by its price so that a dollar or value figure is obtained. The items can then be combined into one meaningful total simply by summing the values. This approach is illustrated in Table 11.9.

Table 11.9

Construction of the Quantity Index—Illustrative Example

		Year 0		Year 1		Year 2		Year 3	
	Average	Production							
	Price	(Thousands)		Production		Production		Production	
Commodity	(w_0)	(q_0)	(w_0q_0)	(q_1)	(w_0q_1)	(q_2)	(w_0q_2)	(q_3)	(w_0q_3)
Pliers	1.00	62	62.0	65	65.0	66	66.0	90	90.0
Wrenches	1.50	138	207.0	120	180.0	110	165.0	80	120.0
Bolts	0.25	500	125.0	540	135.0	580	145.0	800	200.0
Drills	2.25	10	22.5	10	22.5	10	22.5	10	22.5
			416.5		402.5		398.5		432.5
Indices (Year 0 = 100)		$\dfrac{416.5}{416.5} = 100.0$		$\dfrac{402.5}{416.5} = 99.6$		$\dfrac{398.5}{416.5} = 95.7$		$\dfrac{432.5}{416.5} = 103.8$	

The quantity index is but a special variant of the market basket. In the case of the quantity index the market basket has a variable load of commodities, whereas in the price example the market basket always returns from the shopping trip with exactly the same number of items.

Table 11.9 indicates how these various products are combined in the construction of a quantity index. Notice that this is a new problem and is not the food index utilized in previous examples, and that specific years are not necessary for the computations.

Problems encountered in the construction of a quantity index are essentially the same as those involved in constructing any composite index. The choice of a base period, periodic modernization of the base, considerations as to what commodities should be included in the index, the problem of occasional adjustment of the weights to conform to existing conditions—all of these are matters of primary importance in the quantity index just as they are in a price index.

The example given in Table 11.9 will indicate some of the fundamental facets of a quantity index. For one thing, the index is a composite since it includes many differing items. The resulting index is essentially in the form of an average in which the denominator of the formula is akin to N in computing the arithmetic mean. Thus:

$$\bar{X} = \frac{\Sigma f(X)}{N},$$

while the index-number computation is

$$\frac{\Sigma w_0 q_n}{\Sigma w_0 q_0},$$

where q_n is the physical quantity in any year n,

   w_0 is the average price used to weight the series,

   q_0 is the physical quantity in the base period.

In compiling an index number the individuality of each component is submerged by grouping—a situation analogous to the computation of the arithmetic mean. Too, in the example of Table 11.9 we may note that the production of wrenches is declining over the four-year period and, since this commodity has a relatively high weight, $\Sigma w_0 q_n$ is consistently affected by this factor. At the same time, the production of pliers and bolts is rising and since the weights of these commodities are relatively low, they are insufficient to offset the decline in wrench production. The production of drills remains constant throughout and therefore does not exert an impact on the changes of the index. Drill production does exert an impact in that the index numbers would be more variable if production were changing. But, of course, the fundamental purpose of the index is to measure quantity change, and the changes shown here therefore originate in the commodities other than the production of drills. By the nature of its construction the resulting index must measure relative change in the *overall* package of commodities. However, since price is held constant, the index measures relative changes in quantities entering the market basket.[5]

---

[5] Note on the Federal Reserve Index of Industrial Production: One of the most prominent quantity indices is the Federal Reserve Index of Industrial Production. The basic objective of this index is to measure changes in the overall level of industrial production which, by definition, excludes agricultural and service industries. Thus, when the index is constructed, it is a simple matter to observe at a glance the general level of industrial production in the United States. While this measure is a most useful one, it is also desirable to be able to observe interindustry shifts within the general framework of the index; to this end, indices are prepared for various industrial segments, including iron and steel production, machinery, transportation equipment, lumber, leather, food products, and many others. In this manner both the overall index and the components may be studied for changes through time. The student should consult a recent *Federal Reserve Bulletin* for detail concerning this index. See particularly the issue for December 1959. See also the issue for October 1962.

A Note on Index-Number Types

The weighted composite price and quantity indices explained in this chapter are of the Laspeyres type and, in general, are obtained by employing the formulae as indicated below. Observe that both elements of the denominator are constant:

LASPEYRES-TYPE INDEX

Price Index   Quantity Index

$$\frac{\Sigma\, p_n q_0}{\Sigma\, p_0 q_0}$$ $$\frac{\Sigma\, p_0 q_n}{\Sigma\, p_0 q_0}$$

This type of index-number construction allows any two or more time periods to be compared with each other because the base is constant throughout the series.

An alternative type of construction is known as the Paasche index number. In general, this type of index is obtained by allowing one of the factors in the denominator to take the value of the current time period. The general formulae are indicated below. Observe that the denominator is not a constant:

PAASCHE-TYPE INDEX

Price Index   Quantity Index

$$\frac{\Sigma\, p_n q_n}{\Sigma\, p_0 q_n}$$ $$\frac{\Sigma\, p_n q_n}{\Sigma\, p_n q_0}$$

The Laspeyres index employs fixed weights for the base (the denominator is constant) and therefore the index may get somewhat "out of touch" with current conditions when these are changing, particularly if conditions change rapidly. However, this problem may be mitigated by relatively frequent changes in the base period. Changes in the base period do, nevertheless, raise other problems of comparability.

The Paasche index, which solves the problem of a constant base and keeps the index current in this respect, suffers from the defect that the index for a given time period can only be compared to the base index number. Interperiod comparisons are not valid with the Paasche-type index.

11.9   The Value Index

In economic terms "value" may be defined as $V = (P)(Q)$. In the construction of a price index, quantity is held constant, while in the construction of a quantity index, price is held constant. Now, in a value index, both terms are allowed to vary and the resulting index reflects such changes as occur in *both* factors. Thus, in the value index itself, the observer could note at a glance that a value change had occurred, but the index would not indicate whether change was due to an increase in the quantity factor, or a revaluation of the product to higher (or lower) prices, or both. Clearly, when a value index is constructed, the center of interest is *total valuation* rather than price or quantity taken separately.

Table 11.10 indicates how the value index is constructed. Prices and quantities in this example have been selected in such a way as to indicate how various combinations of price and quantity for high- and low-valued items (in terms of either price or quantity) will affect the resulting index.

The value index may be viewed from the standpoint of a "total-expenditure index." After all, expenditure on the various items would be the sum of $(P) \times (Q)$ for all items. In this case each commodity entering the index bears a weight equal to the percentage the value of the commodity bears to the total expenditure (for the items included) in the base period and the period in question. By examining the relationships between the variables in Table 11.10, it may be noticed that the commodities are weighted by both P and Q, and the impact of commodity value (both in price and quantity) may be observed on the resulting expenditure total and thus on the index itself.

The value index needs to be carefully interpreted. For one thing, a common view or understanding of the word "value" would seem to imply that if value increases, one is receiving "more for one's money." Observe that this notation is not necessarily correct in interpreting the value index. The value index may rise because of a rise in quantity or a rise in price—or both. The value index does not indicate which factor was responsible for a change in the index—or if *both* factors were responsible. What the index does indicate is change in total expenditure for both a set of variable quantities and a set of variable prices. One might thus expect that the value index should be used only when the possibility of misunderstanding is minimized.

Exercise 11.4

1. In what manner, if at all, does:
   (a) a price index differ from a composite index?
   (b) a quantity index differ from a price index?
   (c) a value index differ from quantity and price indices?
2. If value is $(P)(Q)$, explain why it is that exactly the same quantity could at one time and place have a higher (or lower) value than at another time or place.
   (a) Is the process of valuation relative? Relative to what?
   (b) Would high prices necessarily mean high value? If so, from what point of view? Would low prices mean high value? If so, from what point of view?

Table 11.10

Construction of the Value Index—An Illustrative Example (Prices Given in Dollars; Quantities Given in Thousands of Units)

Commodity	Year 0			Year 1			Year 2			Year 3		
	p_0	q_0	p_0q_0	p_1	q_1	p_1q_1	p_2	q_2	p_2q_2	p_3	q_3	p_3q_3
A	1.10	94	103.40	1.15	85	97.75	1.20	74	88.80	1.00	99	99.00
B	0.20	1,700	340.00	0.25	1,800	450.00	0.25	1,800	450.00	0.20	1,900	380.00
C	0.70	154	107.80	0.70	184	128.80	0.75	195	146.25	0.75	193	144.75
D	3.00	300	900.00	3.10	350	1,085.00	3.20	400	1,280.00	3.15	400	1,260.00
			1,451.20			1,761.55			1,965.05			1,883.75

	Year 0	Year 1	Year 2	Year 3
Indices: (Year 0 = 100)	$\dfrac{1,451.20}{1,451.20} = 100.0$	$\dfrac{1,761.55}{1,451.20} = 121.4$	$\dfrac{1,965.05}{1,451.20} = 135.4$	$\dfrac{1,883.75}{1,451.20} = 129.9$

(c) Do index numbers account for the pricing process involved in value computations?

(d) In view of the questions raised above, what do value indices measure?

3. Explain how it is in a quantity index that the market basket returns from its periodic shopping trips with a variable load of commodities?

4. What process or processes (if any) may be used to weight a quantity index. Is the quantity index weighted?

5. In what sense is an index number a special case of averaging?

6. If there has been an increase in a value index, is it possible to know where the increase originated?

7. Might the relative importance of an item change from period to period in a value index? Why?

8. Given the following data:

Commodity	Period 0		Period 1		Period 2		Period 3	
	p	q	p	q	p	q	p	q
A	12	20	18	10	6	30	24	40
B	72	4	108	2	36	6	144	8
C	32	16	48	8	16	24	64	32
D	40	22	60	11	20	33	80	44
E	100	10	150	5	50	15	200	20

(a) Construct a price index using period 1 quantities as weights. Explain changes in the index by reference to the original data.

(b) Construct a quantity index using period 3 prices as weights. Explain changes in the index by reference to the original data.

(c) Construct a value index from the original data. Time period $0 = 100$.

(1) What is the relationship between prices in periods 1 and 2? How should this fact affect the value indices? Was the "expected price effect" offset by quantity changes? If so, how, and to what degree was it offset?

(2) What is the relationship between quantities in periods 1 and 3? How should this fact affect the value index? Was this "expected quantity effect" offset by price changes? If so, how, and to what degree was it offset? Is this what you should have expected?

11.10 Use of Index Numbers in Deflating a Value Series

The process of deflating a value series may be defined as dividing the value equation by an appropriate price index. The result ($Q = V/P$) will then be a quantity series in which the impact of price changes will presumably have been removed. The word "presumably" is used here to call attention to the fact that the index chosen for deflation must be consistent with the market basket of items comprising the value series. Ideally, the deflating index would have been constructed from the same market basket

utilized in the value computations. The point may be illustrated this way:
It would not be appropriate to use a wholesale price index to deflate
personal income data nor would the index of agricultural prices be used to
deflate the sales figures of an industrial firm.

The process of deflation is sometimes used with the dollar to produce
a set of values known as "the purchasing power of the dollar." The
purchasing power of the dollar refers, in terms of an average, to the quantity of things purchasable by a current dollar as contrasted to the
quantity of things purchasable by a dollar at some past period.

If purchasing power is thought of in terms of the most general of
cases, it would refer to consumers, although special indices have been
devised for other purposes. While it is true that a dollar always equals
100 cents, it is clear that 100 cents at various times and places will purchase
a variable amount of goods and services. Since a dollar is always a dollar,
it is unvariable. If, however, a consumer price index indicates a rise in the
level of prices, this means the consumer dollar will now purchase less than
formerly. Conversely, if the level of consumer prices falls, a current dollar
will purchase more than formerly. What is required here is knowledge of
the consumer price index and the relationship:

$$\text{purchasing power of the consumer dollar} = \frac{100 \text{ cents}}{\text{consumer price index}}.$$

Thus, if at the time the computation is made the consumer price index
stands at 125.0, it may be said that the purchasing power of the dollar
at that particular point in time was 100 cents/1.25 = .8 = 80 cents.
Note, however, that the 80 cents is relative to the base period of the index.
If the base of the index used was ten years ago, then the assumption is that
a dollar ten years ago was a "full dollar" and relative to its purchasing
power ten years ago a dollar is now "worth" 80 cents. It must be clearly
understood that a purchasing-power computation always implies that in
some past period the dollar was "full-bodied," and that the selection of the
past period (base) is itself an arbitrary origin from which measurement is
now made. If these points are understood, then the usefulness of a
purchasing-power computation is in no way diminished by the selection
of an arbitrary, but appropriate, origin. It is only in misuses of such
computations that misleading information is derived, and incorrect
conclusions or decisions constitute the unfortunate result.

Among the major reasons why it would be desirable to deflate a
value series would be the need to analyze the "real" changes taking place
in the variable. Thus, in a period marked by inflationary tendencies
sales figures may rise simply because prices are rising, and for analytical purposes it might be desirable to know, in real terms, whether

the sales volume is actually changing. In other words, is the firm actually selling and delivering more goods or is it merely experiencing revaluation from a constant sales base? Certainly it would be within the realm of possibility, for example, that in a period of rising prices an industrial concern shows increasing sales but is actually delivering *less* goods than formerly. For some phases of economic and business analysis the deflating process is a prerequisite to understanding actual changes in terms of real goods and services.[6]

As is inevitable in analytical situations, a number of significant questions arise when one begins to apply the general principle of deflation

Table 11.11

Deflating a Value Series—An Illustrative Example

Year (1)	Total Sales (P)(Q) (thousands) (2)	General Price Index Appropriate to the Business (Year 0 = 100) (3)	Sales in "Real" Terms (thousands) Col. (2) Col. (3)/100 (4)
0	$1,300.0	100.0	$1,300.0
1	1,500.0	109.8	1,366.1
2	1,600.0	115.3	1,387.7
3	1,625.0	125.0	1,300.0
4	2,000.0	125.0	1,600.0

to more specific situations. An example of the use of a price index in deflating the sales figures of an industrial corporation is shown in Table 11.11. Note that total sales are given in thousands of dollars and that a price index appropriate to the business is given in column 3. Column 4 is the result of dividing column 2 by column 3 expressed as a decimal.

Observe the impact of general price changes on the real (deflated) sales figures of column 4. Now note in column 2 that sales measured in current prices increased from $1,300 in year 0 to $1,500 in year 1. Simultaneously, the price index also increased from 100.0 to 109.8. The question, then, is this: To what extent did the sales effort of year 1 actually yield new sales and to what extent was this sales effort absorbed through price advances? The deflated figures of column 4 show that the real quantity of sales did advance, although the increase is actually quite small compared

---

[6] It may be well to recall that the term "real" as used in economics refers to actual quantities of goods and services which may be purchased with a given sum of money. Thus, one may speak of a "real wage" as contrasted to a "money wage." The concept may be utilized to measure other quantities, too. One could also speak of "real profits" or "real sales." The terms would imply a deflated valuation, which in a period of declining prices might well be an increase in "real wages," "real wealth," "real sales," and so on.

to the corresponding increasing value (in thousands of dollars)—that is, $1,500 − $1,300 = $200, whereas $1,366.1 − $1,300.0 = $66.1. Clearly, the sales figures of column 2 reflect not only volume but also price change. The student may now compare years 2 and 3, as well as years 3 and 4 for other examples of the manner in which deflation of value figures alters the original sales values.

Certain significant questions raised by the deflating process may now be examined. Is it essential that the base period in the value series be identical to the base period of the price index utilized in deflation? One might well assume that it would be desirable to have both bases anchored at an identical point in time. On the other hand, it is not necessary that the base periods be identical if the informational requirement is primarily to observe the relative changes in real product. As a matter of fact, when a value series is deflated, that series is changed to the base of the price index because the period selected to equal unity (100.0) assumes the dollar to have been worth 100 cents at that time, and the deflation of a value series essentially places the deflated result on the price index base period. Generally speaking, this issue of base periods' being in correspondence need not be of substantial concern *as long as* the information required is primarily for the purpose of indicating relationships among the real changes taking place. However, price indices should not be used in an indiscriminate manner. Certainly there should be a logical and defensible basis in fact for the choice of a price deflater to be used with a value series.

Many other significant questions arise out of the selection of an "appropriate" price index for deflating a value series. If a particular firm wishes to analyze its internal operations from the point of view of real product, real wages, and other "real" changes, it will be necessary to have price indices which actually reflect changes in the particular series under analysis. Unless the firm should possess indices especially constructed for this purpose, it would be necessary to select an index computed by some other agency such as a trade association, or by one of the government statistical bureaus. While it is true that many price indices are available from government and trade associations, perhaps none of the indices are precisely appropriate to the particular analytical situation at hand. This, then, raises the question of whether or not subsequent analysis should be undertaken. Obviously, the answer depends upon the accuracy demanded from the information and the importance of that information measured in terms of its cost. In other words, is the cost of the information in excess of its informational value? Certainly, the use of an index which is only partially appropriate will furnish only partially correct information and this may be quite undesirable.

Deflating a Wage Series—An Illustration

Suppose it were desired to know the impact of price changes on the average weekly gross wage of persons employed in the durable-goods industry of the United States. A glance at column 2 of Table 11.12 will indicate that during the period under consideration, the money wage has been rising; too, the consumer price index (CPI) has been advancing in the same period. The question to be resolved is, what was the net impact of consumer price changes on the purchasing power of the wage dollar in this industry?

Table 11.12

Purchasing Power of Wages in the Durable-Goods Industry Deflated for Changes in the Consumer Price Index

Year	Average Gross Weekly Earnings, Current Dollars (1)	Consumer Price Index (1957–59 = 100) (2)	Average Gross Weekly Earnings in Constant 1957–59 Dollars (3) = (1) ÷ (2)
1954	$76.19	92.8	82.10
1955	82.19	93.1	88.28
1956	85.28	94.7	90.05
1957	88.26	97.9	90.15
1958	89.27	100.7	88.65
1959	96.05	101.5	94.63
1960	97.44	103.1	94.51
1961	100.35	104.2	96.30
1962	104.70	105.4	99.34
1963	108.50	106.7	101.69
1964	112.19	108.1	103.78

SOURCE: *Economic Report of the President, 1965.*

The consumer price index may be considered appropriate for deflating the wage series of Table 11.12. However, the CPI is itself an average for the nation as a whole and does not specifically take into account changes inherent in consumption patterns for various sections of the United States or variations in consumption patterns among wage-earners in the same wage group. Thus, whatever result is obtained, it is an average result and must be interpreted in that light.

If the data of Table 11.12 be shown graphically, the net impact of price changes on the consumers' real income appears as in Illustration 11.2.

In the interpretation of an original value series and the accompanying deflated series care must be exercised. The background against which the series and the deflator index have been constructed should be known, and it must be kept in mind that the results are average results and that change

Illustration 11.2   Weekly Wages in the Durable-Goods Industry Shown in Constant Dollars and in Dollars of Constant Purchasing Power (1957–59 = 100)

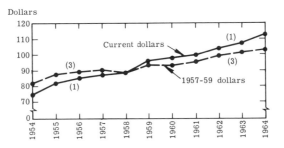

is brought about by many determinants. A statistical series alone is insufficient to provide analytical answers to many of the analytical questions which may be raised. On occasions the statistical series or charts may seem to point to obvious conclusions, but one should not jump to such conclusions until they have been firmly established in logic and coincide with common good sense about the problem itself. Deflating techniques for value series are useful, but they are not informational panaceas.

11.11   Shifting the Base of Index Numbers

The problems involved in deflating a value series suggest that on some occasions it might be desirable to use a base period other than the one already established in the index series. For example, an index might be constructed on the base 1957–1959 when it would be useful to possess a base of (say) 1955. Such problems would arise when several value series (sales, wages, costs, and so on) are to be related to a common base period but the indices used for deflation are computed on differing bases.

The mechanical technique for shifting the base of an index-number series is extremely simple in principle. Table 11.13 shows a material cost index with a base period of years 1953–55. Now, consider it desirable to show this series on the base year 1961, and also on the base year 1965. To achieve the base shifting, simply *divide each of the original indices by the index value for the base year selected*. When this has been accomplished, the base of the series has been shifted from the former to the latter period. The mechanics of the base-shifting process are shown in Table 11.13.

In order to indicate the relationships among the series of Table 11.13, the chart in Illustration 11.3 has been constructed.

Notice in Illustration 11.3 that base shifting does not alter the relative

Table 11.13

Shifting the Base of Index Numbers—An Illustration (Demonstration Data)

Year (1)	Materials Cost Index (Years 1953–55 = 100.0) (2)	Index of Col. (2) with Base Shifted to Year 1961 (3)	Index of Col. (2) with Base Shifted to Year 1956 (4)
1951	76.9	76.9/1.145 = 67.2	76.9/1.245 = 61.8
1952	83.4	83.4/1.145 = 72.8	83.4/1.245 = 67.0
1953	95.5	etc. 83.4	etc. 76.7
1954	102.8	89.9	82.6
1955	101.8	88.9	81.8
1956	102.8	89.8	82.6
1957	111.0	96.9	89.2
1958	113.5	99.1	91.2
1959	114.4	99.9	91.9
1960	114.8	100.3	92.2
1961	114.5	100.0	92.0
1962	116.2	101.5	93.3
1963	120.2	104.9	96.5
1964	123.5	107.9	99.2
1965	124.5	108.7	100.0

Illustration 11.3 Chart Indicating the Relationships Between an Original Series of Index Numbers and the Identical Index with the Base Shifted to New Periods

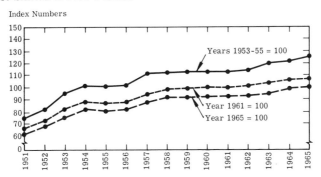

changes portrayed by the original index series. Altering the base period "raises" or "lowers" the valuations for each year, while leaving the relationships unchanged. This is, of course, the basic purpose of base shifting.

Exercise 11.5

1. In deflating a value series the price index used must be consistent with the value series. Why? What does the term "consistent" mean in this case?

2. When a value series is to be deflated, is it essential that the base periods of the two series be identical? Are there really *two* base periods? What factors would be most influential in choosing a base for deflation?

3. If a series of dollar sales figures are deflated by an appropriate price index, the result is a dollar figure. How are the deflated results to be interpreted? Specifically, what has been achieved through deflation?

4. The statement: "A dollar is worth 75 cents today," has a very specific meaning if properly interpreted. Explain the above statement to your critical nonstatistics friend.

5. What basic considerations must be taken into account to avoid misleading calculations and/or misleading interpretation of the deflation process?

6. Do you suppose it would be possible to take a value series and make the figures show almost any result you wished? Use the purchasing power of the dollar and the consumer price index to illustrate this particular point by showing that the dollar is worth 100 cents and that it is worth only 60 cents. What is the truth?

7. Deflate the following value series and graph both the original and the deflated series. Explain the technical process and the results to your nonstatistics friend.

Year	Consumption Expenditures (Billions of $)	Index (Year 5 = 100)	Deflated Consumption Expenditures at Year 5 Prices
1	195.0	89.9	
2	209.8	96.0	
3	219.8	98.0	
4	232.6	98.9	
5	238.0	100.0	
6	256.9	100.3	
7	269.9	102.1	
8	284.8	105.2	
9	293.0	107.2	
10	311.4	108.3	

8. Using the data of problem 7, deflate the consumption series so as to place the figures on the base year 1. Graph.

9. Using the data of problem 7, deflate the consumption series so as to place the figures on the base 10. Graph.

10. You now have a graph indicating the value of consumption expenditures in current dollars and in dollars of constant purchasing power for years 1, 5, and 10. Explain why the four lines appear as they do—that is, provide the logical rationale for the appearance of your graph.

11. Shift the base of the following index-number series to year 6. Graph.

	A				B	
Year	Index	Base Shifted to Year 6		Year	Index	Base Shifted to Year 6
1	100.0			1	182.0	
2	124.0			2	171.0	
3	159.0			3	152.0	
4	193.0			4	133.0	
5	197.0			5	124.0	
6	207.0			6	120.0	

12. When the base of an index-number series is shifted, what effect does this have on the relationships between the various values of the series?

   (a) Are the two lines in your graph(s) above exactly equidistant when these lines indicate the same index series on different bases? Should the values be equidistant, or is it the relative change which remains constant?

11.12 Some Readily Available Indices

Many index-number series are readily available to the general public. The following index-number series may be found in *Survey of Current Business*.

Industrial Production	Help Wanted Advertising
Prices Received and Paid by Farmers	Foreign Trade—Exports
	Foreign Trade—Imports
Consumer Prices	Restaurant Sales
Wholesale Prices	Steel Production
Purchasing Power of the Dollar	Industrial Materials Handling Equipment
Construction Costs	
Construction Contracts, Total Valuation	Output of Refrigerators and Home Freezers
Total Sales, United States	Sales of Insulating Materials
Total Stocks, United States	Paper and Paper Products
Indexes of Weekly Payrolls	

In addition to many of those listed above, the *Economic Report of the President* also contains the following index series:

Indexes of Output Per Man Hour	Farm Production Indexes
Indexes of Farm Inputs	Farm Output and Productivity

The *Federal Reserve Bulletin* also lists many of the indexes shown above. The *Monthly Bulletin* of the United States Department of Labor carries some of the series listed above and frequently includes special series as well.

The *Morgan Guaranty Survey* (published monthly) includes an index of business activity for the United States.

Business Week magazine publishes the Business Week Index of Business Activity.

The *Monthly Summary of Business Conditions in Southern California*, published by the Security First National Bank of Los Angeles, gives an index of business activity for Southern California.

The Wall Street Journal publishes the Dow-Jones averages of stock prices.

Many bureaus of business research in American colleges publish information relative to their own areas and make use of index series as appropriate. Examples of these publications include the *Kansas Business*

Review, the *Iowa Business Digest*, the *Illinois Business Review*, and the *Business News Notes* of the University of Minnesota. Also, *Duluth Business Indicators*, published by the Department of Economics, University of Minnesota, Duluth, in cooperation with the Minnesota Department of Employment Security.

11.13   Summary

The present chapter has explored one of the most useful means yet devised for measuring some of the intangible variables of the economic world. Through the use of index numbers, relative change of a variable through time can be measured and charted. In this way the index numbers provide information of value to the problem-solving and decision-making process. Index numbers are a form of averaging a heterogeneous set of data in which the result is expressed as if it were a percentage. The basic problems of index-number calculations are primarily conceptual—that is, defining what is to be measured and then determining what elements should be included in the index. The arithmetic computations may be lengthy but they are ordinarily not difficult.

The usefulness of an index number is found in its ability to measure and state relative changes in a variable. Properly used, index numbers may also be employed to deflate a value series, to provide a means of expressing changes in purchasing power, and to indicate quantity changes. To the individual interested in observing and analyzing broad economic areas such as the structure of farm prices, wages, consumer prices, wholesale prices, national product, and others, index numbers will be a required part of the study.

Key Terms and Concepts of This Chapter

Base period	Weighting
Base shifting	Index numbers
Consumer price index	Simple
Deflation of a value series	Composite
Dollars of constant purchasing	Price
power	Quantity
Market basket	Value
Price relative	

Bibliography

Bowen, Earl K., *Statistics, With Applications in Management and Economics*, chap. 13. Homewood, Ill.: Richard D. Irwin, Inc., 1960.

Croxton, Frederick E., and Dudley J. Cowden, *Practical Business Statistics*, 3rd ed., chaps. 32 and 33. Englewood Cliffs, N.J.: Prentice-Hall, Inc., 1960.

Hirsch, Werner Z., *Introduction to Modern Statistics*, chap. 13. New York: The Macmillan Company, 1957.

Mills, Frederick C., *Statistical Methods*, 3rd ed., chaps. 13 and 14. New York: Holt, Rinehart & Winston, 1955.

Mudgett, B. D., *Index Numbers*. New York: John Wiley & Sons, Inc., 1951.

Neiswanger, William Addison, *Elementary Statistical Methods*, chap. 13. New York: The Macmillan Company, 1956.

Neter, John, and William Wasserman, *Fundamental Statistics for Business and Economics*, chap. 12. Boston: Allyn and Bacon, Inc., 1962.

Paden, Donald W., and E. F. Lindquist, *Statistics for Economics and Business*, chap. 3. New York: McGraw-Hill Book Company, 1951.

Smith, C. Frank, and D. A. Leabo, *Basic Statistics for Business and Economics*, chap. 11. Homewood, Ill.: Richard D. Irwin, Inc., 1964.

Stockton, John A., *Business Statistics*, chap. 16. Cincinnati: Southwestern Publishing Company, 1958.

Tuttle, Alva M., *Elementary Business and Economic Statistics*, chap. 13. New York: McGraw-Hill Book Company, 1957.

U.S. Government Publications

Since the U.S. Government is a major supplier as well as a major user of statistics, there are literally hundreds of Government publications dealing with statistics in one form or another. The following references are of especial interest in relation to the topic of index numbers.

Consumers' Price Index, Hearings before a Subcommittee of the Committee on Education and Labor, House of Representatives, 82nd Congress, 1st Session, pursuant to H.R. 73. Washington, D.C.: U.S. Government Printing Office, 1952.

Government Price Statistics, Hearings before the Subcommittee on Economic Statistics of the Joint Economic Committee, Congress of the United States, 87th Congress, 1st Session, Pursuant to Sec. 5(a) of Public Law 304 (79th Congress), Parts 1 and 2. Part 1 contains the National Bureau of Economic Research Report Number 73: *The Price Statistics of the Federal Government*, 1961. Part 2 contains a transcript of the testimony of experts relative to Government price statistics.

It should also be observed that many U.S. Government Bureaus and Departments issue publications of interest to users of statistics. The Bureau of Labor Statistics publishes the *Monthly Labor Bulletin* as well as special publications on an occasional basis. The U.S. Department of Commerce publishes *Survey of Current Business* as well as special publications. The Federal Reserve Board of Governors publishes the *Federal Reserve Bulletin*. Statistics, as well as information on their rationale and collection, are published by many specialized agencies of the Government.

12 TIME SERIES AND TREND FITTING

12.1 Introduction

Time series and trends occupy a prominent place among the means of meeting certain types of informational and analytical requirements because they provide a *picture of change, yield a knowledge of the direction of change,* and show *repetitive movements* in the data. Time series are a systematic and orderly manner of presenting information. The methods shown in this chapter are largely techniques for structuring time-series information. However, once changes in a variable are detected and measured, questions arise as to the *cause* of the changes.

Searching for the cause or causes of economic change is one of the most difficult analytical problems in business and economics. The individual seeking causative factors must possess a good deal of background information about the specific problem under consideration. This information plus the individual's knowledge, training, and experience will provide clues which can then be methodically explored. Some hints as to what may be important in the business and economic world are provided in this chapter, but a complete analysis of the causes of change would be beyond the scope of this book.

12.2 Symbols Introduced in This Chapter

The only new symbols introduced in this chapter are:

Y_c = the computed trend values.

a = the origin of a straight-line trend.

b = the slope of a straight-line trend.

$\sum_1$ = sum of part 1 of the data.

$\sum_2$ = sum of part 2 of the data.

330

12.3   The Nature of Time Series

The analysis of economic data collected periodically through time is one of the functions of statistics and economics. A time series may be defined as *a sequence of repeated measurements of a variable made periodically through time.* The result of such periodic measurements may be shown in the form of a table or a graph. From the time-series data several types of refinements and measures may be developed, as this chapter will show.

Table 12.1

Gross National Product or Income (in Current Dollars), 1950–1964

Year (X)	Product or Income (billions of dollars) (Y)
1950	284.6
1951	329.0
1952	347.0
1953	365.4
1954	363.1
1955	397.5
1956	419.2
1957	442.8
1958	444.5
1959	482.6
1960	502.6
1961	518.7
1962	556.2
1963	583.9
1964	622.3

SOURCE: *Economic Report of the President*, 1965.

Time-series data tend to be deceptively simple. Because of the apparent simplicity of this "one-variable through time" structure, it is easy to overlook some of the most important and fundamental matters relating to the measured variable. Therefore, at the outset of this chapter, it will be well to look carefully at some of the background information essential to understanding time series.

First of all, it will be desirable to show a time series. For this purpose look at Table 12.1, which gives the annual value of Gross National Product or Income for 1950 through 1964.

Few statistical sets of data would appear more simple than Table 12.1. However, the problems which arise when one studies the background of this type of measurement are far from simple. For example, how are the dollar figures gathered? How are the concepts of the component parts of the measure defined? Why are some services included (auto mechanics, for example) and others (do-it-yourself projects, for example) excluded? To explore the background of this series requires a thorough study of national income accounting. Thus, while the series given in Table 12.1 looks quite simple and uncluttered as it is printed, a thorough understanding of the data requires some sophistication in economics.

Since the task of the present chapter is to explore the statistical aspects of time series, it is necessary to examine some of the theoretical foundations of time-series analysis. Only the one-variable or single-classification type of time series will be considered in this book.

Periodic measurement of a single variable through time is a "functional" type of problem. The word "functional" is here used to mean that when two variables are related in such a manner that for every value of one variable, a value exists for the other variable, the relationship may be called *functional*. Now, the question arises, where did the second variable come in when the measurements only concerned one variable? Clearly, one of the two variables is time. The problem of time as a "variable" will be explored more fully in a subsequent paragraph.

In functional analysis, the first variable (call this variable Y) is related to the second variable (call this variable X) in this way: For every value of X there is a definite value of Y. Thus, Y is said to be a function of X. If X is considered to be the "independent" variable, then Y is considered the "dependent" variable. The two variables are graphed in the usual manner—that is, values of X are shown along the horizontal scale (abscissa) and the values of Y are placed along the vertical scale (ordinate).

Now, because time-series data are really only the measurement of one variable and because time is the incidental second variable, time series are rather unique functional types. Let us explore this matter more fully. The X variable is considered to be time measured in years, months, and so on, while the Y data consists of some variable in which the statistician or economist is interested. This Y variable might be sales, prices, income, number of units produced by a production process, and so on. While the value of Y (say gross national income) can be measured at any convenient point in time, the value of Y (income) is hardly *caused* by the value assigned to time. That Y (income) is *related* to time is obvious enough, but causation is quite a different matter. Thus, the value of Y (income) is interesting because the statistician would like to know how Y changes through time, but the statistician does not regard income as a mathematical function of time.

Time-series data and analysis are considered part of descriptive statistics and do not involve statistical inference. The set of repeated measurements which form a time series are not random samples. A knowledge of sampling is useful to the student as background information against which to set time-series analysis, but none of the techniques of sampling is directly applicable because inferences about parameters or confidence intervals are not employed with time-series data.

Since this chapter is concerned with *time series*, it might be well to observe the role played by time in the collection and analysis of the data. The word "time" is not easily defined in precise terms. Time does refer to a period elapsing between two points, acts, or events. In this respect it is possible to speak of a "day," an "hour," a "month," a "year," and so on.[1] If, then, a variable (say income) be measured between two points in time and if this measurement is repeated for the same interval over a longer period of time, a series of quantitative measurements are recorded. Even though these measurements are made through time, time itself is not considered to be a cause of the changes in the variable. Time can thus be thought of as the independent variable. Perhaps this is a bit of a misnomer because time itself is really not variable, since it "elapses" at a constant rate. Be this as it may, it will be convenient to think of time as the "independent variable" and, when graphed, time is placed on the X axis.

Measurements of a variable periodically through time, then, form a time series. The measurements made refer to a variable which ideally can be counted or measured in constant units. This test would be met in the case of many variables, as for example in kilowatt hours, pounds, miles, and so on. However, in the case of many economic variables the test might not be met so neatly. For example, a count of freight cars loaded per month in a given city might actually overlook rather wide variations in the content and even in the size of the cars themselves. The loading of an iron-ore car differs somewhat from a carload of wheat even though each can be considered a "freight-car loading" for some purposes. However, and even though an ideal test of uniformness may not be met, the measurement is still useful for many purposes. Many economic time series are really measurements of variables which are not reported in uniform units, and it is often useful to keep this point in mind when making final judgments and analyses of data.

Since this chapter concerns time *series*, it will be well to look briefly at the word "series." "Series" suggests the notion of a "sequence" together with the idea that something (measurement in this case) occurs repeatedly to form the sequence. A *time series* then is a sequence of repeated measurements of a variable made at evenly spaced periods through time.

---

[1] Certain problems exist here because of calendar variations. For example, some months have more "working" days than others. For the sake of simplicity these calendar variations will be ignored in the remainder of this chapter. However, see Appendix E.

At this point the question may be raised: What are the objectives to be served by the repeated measurement of a variable through time? Perhaps the prime objective is to discover if changes in the magnitude of the variable display any *pattern* or if there are discernible repetitive features through time. If a pattern exists, what forces have produced it? For example, if a firm discovers that its sales are always low in February and high in August, then the firm can make reasonable predictions or forecasts about the future of sales in these months and seek reasons for this pattern of sales.

Table 12.2

Number of Freight Cars Loaded "Piggyback" on Class I Railroads of the United States, 1955–1964

X Year	Y Cars Loaded
1955	168,150
1956	207,783
1957	249,065
1958	278,071
1959	416,508
1960	554,115
1961	591,246
1962	706,441
1963	797,474
1964	890,216

SOURCE: Association of American Railroads, Bureau of Railway Economics, *Railroad Transporation, A Statistical Record, 1921–1964*, p. 22.

A variant of the same objectives of discerning repetitive patterns—if any—in the data is to permit analysis of what has happened to the variable in the past in order to discover if this has any possible bearing on the future. In this respect, the objective is historical analysis. Too, an objective of time-series measurement and analysis may be simply to permit description of the variable to observe how the variable behaves and, if possible, to describe that behavior. If some repetitive pattern exists, reasons may be sought to explain the pattern. If no pattern exists, reasons may be sought to explain this phenomenon.

In a few words, then, the objectives of time-series analysis can be summarized as descriptive, historical, and predictive.

To illustrate time-series data, consider the data on railroad freight cars loaded "piggyback" for the years 1955 through 1964 as reported by the Association of American Railroads. Since this type of freight transportation is a relatively recent but proven type of innovation, it could be expected that the service would find wider application as time passes. It might therefore be expected that the series would exhibit a growth trend. The actual carloadings through the years and a graph of those data are shown in Table 12.2 and Illustration 12.1.

Illustration 12.1   Number of Freight Cars Loaded "Piggyback" on Class I Railroads of the United States, 1955–1965

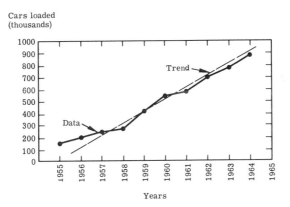

From the table and/or the chart, a perspective relative to the use of this specialized service may be formed. The data show what the past record *has been* and where the variable stands *at present* (the last year for which data are shown). Observing the general direction of change in the variable, it seems logical to surmise that this service will probably continue to grow in the *immediate future*. Of course, in the future the service may grow at a slower rate, a more rapid rate, or continue its present rate. What actually happens will depend upon a host of factors. For example, if the entire economy grows, the demand for this service is likely to grow too. As the service proves out costwise to some shippers, this fact may be brought to the attention of other shippers who will subsequently find the service profitable. As a result, the demand for piggyback service might continue to grow even if the economy should decline temporarily. A look into the future always involves uncertainty and any forecast is necessarily based on assumptions regarding the fundamental factors affecting the course of the variable through time.

Notice that a straight-line trend has been drawn on the chart in such manner as to indicate both the *average direction* and the *magnitude of change* in the carloading data. *Trend* may be defined as the *average direction and magnitude of change in the data through time*. A trend may or may not appear as a straight line. Trends are caused by persistent forces (inflation, for example) acting upon the time series in a manner resulting in growth, decline, or stability of the variable being measured.

Persistent forces generate *trends*, but the data are also influenced by cyclical, seasonal, and random forces. *Cyclical* forces are considered to follow a more or less regular pattern and are generally caused by changes in overall economic conditions. *Seasonal* forces originate in the customs or habits of human behavior or in the changes caused by weather and climate. *Random* forces are those which have no systematic pattern and may be said to "just happen."

The persistent forces which cause trends may be thought of as being either *external* or *internal* with reference to the management unit itself. Forces external to the business or administrative unit are those forces over which the decision-maker has little or no control. These forces would include such factors as general economic conditions involving prosperity, levels of employment, levels of income, changes in tastes, and so on. Internal factors would include production or sales policies, the degree of management effectiveness, application of technology, and similar factors. Generally speaking, management would have a large degree of control over internal factors and could tailor them to the most desired combination.

The student of business and economics will probably, in a quantitative sense, meet more time-series and trend data in his worldly career than almost any other type of statistical information. Indeed, it is difficult to perceive how any administrative unit can operate efficiently without a good knowledge and understanding of appropriate time series. However, one ought to be wary of regarding time series as an informational panacea. For example, it would appear that the administrator of a successfully functioning management unit will have formed a good mental image of past performance without the aid of more refined tools than clear observation, experience, a curious and inquiring mind, and a memory for detail. Indeed, in many management units (particularly small units) it would be an unnecessary expense to collect and maintain more than a bare minimum of sophisticated information. Even if this is the case, some informational concepts will nevertheless have been formed and be available in a limited way through memory—but memory of details frequently turns out to be somewhat unreliable.

As a further illustration of the potential usefulness of a particular type of time series, consider the informational problems of the sales manager of a particular company whose representatives are generally traveling a given geographical area. Would not the alert manager be interested in population data? He would wish to know whether the number of inhabitants has been increasing, remaining constant, or decreasing. There would be some question about changes in the average income of potential customers during, say, the past decade. Other pertinent

information would include trends in styles, changes in customer preferences or in the marketing pattern. The manager might wish to determine
if the sales force has changed in terms of numbers or quality; whether the
average territory served by each salesman has changed and if it is too
large or too small for effective representation. What is likely to be the
demand for the product or service during the coming year? Or during
the next five or ten years? Certainly these are questions which require
answers, either based on accurate and timely information or else arrived
at by default. Time series will not necessarily provide all the pertinent
information, but such data may well be part of the requisite factual
background.

12.4   Use of Time Series and Trends in Forecasting

The problem presented by the sales manager's situation indicates the
need for analysis of the past as well as estimation of the future—that is,
forecasting. A forecast may be an extension or projection of past trend
forces based on the assumption that the underlying forces will (or will not)
remain unchanged. For example, if sales have averaged a 5 per cent
increase per year, it might be expected that next year will also show about
a 5 per cent gain. Thus, forecasting *projects past trends into the future*.
However, forecasts may also be made by assuming some change in the
underlying forces (such as a general increase in personal income or
employment or both) and the projection might thus be more than 5
per cent as suggested in the sales illustration above. Of course, the opposite
situation might be assumed: if personal income falls, sales will not
increase by 5 per cent. On the basis of this forecast, policy decisions
facing the future may be made.

In recent times a good deal of emphasis has been directed to the topic
of forecasting. For example, government agencies and business firms will
wish to have forecasts of the gross national product for tax purposes and
for purposes of supplying market information. Cities and other economic
entities will wish to have forecasts of future population growth in order to
intelligently anticipate the need for city services (education, traffic control,
public utility services, and so on). One of the more readily available
economic forecasts is that published by the Prudential Insurance Company
at the end of each calendar year.[2]

Since appraisals of the future must be made and because the data
on which decisions must be based are always subject to sagacious

---

[2] *Prudential's Economic Forecast* (Year) (New York: Planning and Development Department, The Prudential Insurance Company of America).

interpretation, it may be seen that forecasts are of greater certainty when some of the variables are controllable by the policy-maker. On the other hand, there is always the possibility that something unanticipated—and over which the policy-maker has no direct control—will occur and change the course of events. Thus, and in general, it may be said that the probability of unforeseen occurrences increases as the time span covered by the forecast grows longer. Control of some of the variables may decrease the uncertain element, but this factor of uncertainty cannot be reduced to zero.

Another element, that of human judgment, plays a major part in time-series analysis. This is particularly true in forecasting. Judgment is an intangible factor but is none the less important for that fact. Data must ultimately be judged and acted upon in terms of individual knowledge and experience. In the interpretation of economic data, analysis requires that the individual possess a broad knowledge of the economic world and a specific knowledge of economic theory. Without this background much useful information which would provide guides, clues, and insights will be by-passed and its value lost.

12.5   Origins and Composition of Time-Series Data

There are many sources of business and economic data. The ordinary business firm acquires a great deal of its control information through *internally* generated processes. The accounting department generates much of the financial information while the production divisions generate data relating to quantities of product, and the engineering or quality control departments supply information necessary to make technical decisions concerning the production process. Other internal sources would include data from the shipping department as to numbers and types of units dispatched; the sales force will supply data from its field observations; the purchasing department will furnish data as to prices and quantities of incoming materials and equipment. Periodic inventories —or perhaps a perpetual inventory—will determine the firm's posture with respect to those items. All of these "readings" are generally taken at predetermined periods and are expressed numerically in terms of dollars, units, hours, pounds, and so on. Each set of consistent periodic measurements of a variable will form a time series of informational, analytical, and decision-making value to some part of the administrative unit.

While internally generated information assists in guiding internal operating procedure, *a second source of valuable information originates outside the firm* and is collected and distributed by government agencies, private research firms, colleges and universities, labor organizations, trade associations, and other sources. These sources provide data which, to a firm, would be measurements of external environmental variables. Such measurements would include, for example, money in circulation, bank debits, retail store sales, employment, cost of living, wholesale price indices by industry, sales and inventory positions, housing starts, industrial production indices, agricultural statistics, special survey information such as that provided by a local industrial study, and hundreds more.[3]

Of course all of these are of no avail unless they be clearly analyzed and made available to decision- and policy-makers. Frequently the data—as received—are in an undigested form, and must be reworked to be suited to current need and, perhaps, to mesh present with past data. Much of what this chapter is about—indeed what statistics is about—centers on how and why the raw data are structured into a finished and usable informational product for analysis and decision-making.

12.6   Composition of Time Series

Many business and economic time series can be thought of as the final product of some combination of four distinct forces. These forces or components are generally identified as (a) cyclical forces, (b) secular trend, (c) seasonal patterns, and (d) random fluctuations. It is not implied that all sets of economic data can or should be dissected into this four-fold dichotomy. What we are saying at the moment is that it may be possible to "pull out" one or more of these components—should this be desirable for analytical purposes.

To illustrate the composition of a time series, consider the succession of monthly net profit figures for a business firm. Suppose data are available for several years of operation. The immediate objective will be to isolate the four basic elements of these data—that is, cyclical, trend, seasonal, and random fluctuations.

We might note first of all that since firms do not operate in an economic vacuum, the general ups or downs of the prevailing economic situation would have some effect on profits. These *cyclical* forces would spread themselves over the various stages of the business cycle: prosperity, recession, depression, and revival. Thus, and in general, it can be said that if the environmental economic conditions are prosperous, the particular firm is likely to be operating at a higher level than if economic conditions were characterized by depression. The cyclical factor in a time series *refers to a "rhythmic" swing in the data brought about by regularly*

---

[3] Readily available sources of data include the *Federal Reserve Bulletin, Survey of Current Business, Bulletin of Labor Statistics, Statistical Abstract of the United States,* and many others. The student should consult one or more of these publications in the college library.

Illustration 12.2   Hypothetical Cyclical Change

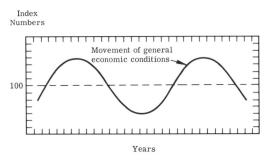

Years

recurring economic conditions. Seen in terms of a chart, the cyclical factor would (in an idealized version) appear as shown in Illustration 12.2.

A second set of economic forces acting on the firm's profit figures would include economic trends. (See Illustration 12.1.) Among the factors responsible for trend are economic growth or decline, long-term inflation or deflation, population changes, and the shifting of consumer demand and tastes. These forces will tend to push (or pull) the firm (and other administrative units) in the direction of the force.[4]

A third set of forces acting on firms and other units originates in *seasonal* changes caused largely by weather conditions and customs, which repeat themselves during a period of a year or less. The monthly profit statement of many firms will be influenced by the financial impact of Christmas, Easter, and other holidays, vacation periods, as well as by the sale of seasonal products such as skis, boating equipment, anti-freeze, fuel oil, lawn and garden equipment, and the like. Sales and profits of many business firms will tend to rise and fall as the seasons repeat their impact year after year. Too, a firm will tend to discover recurring "patterns" in at least some of the variables recorded at periodic intervals during the year. *A seasonal is thus a pattern which tends to repeat itself over the same time period year after year, month after month, week after week, or day after day.* A seasonal pattern is shown in Illustration 12.3.

It should be observed that the term "seasonal" or "seasonal index" may also be used to describe a daily, weekly, or monthly pattern. After all, administrative units find peak loads and slack periods developing at

---

[4] Some administrative units may be pulled in a direction opposite to that of the force itself. For example, college enrollments may rise in a period of deflation and depression. The sale of certain products may run counter to the general trend. For an illustration of this situation it is said that the sale of yard goods and patterns used in home sewing of clothing rises in a deflationary period and falls in inflationary times when unemployment is at a low ebb and incomes are high. However, customs and attitudes change, and what was true of a past period of time may not necessarily be characteristic of a current time period.

Illustration 12.3 Seasonal Index of Grain Shipments from Duluth, Minnesota

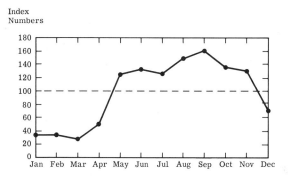

various times during the day, week, or month and these, too, can be described as "seasonals."

Finally, the business firm will be subject to *accidental* or *random* forces. These are unanticipated forces. They "just happen." Examples would include inventions, changing technology, social and cultural changes, legislation, physical damage from hurricanes and floods, strikes, and other events of this "random" nature. It is to be expected that these events would not reoccur, or at least would not reoccur at predictable intervals. Such random events might be catastrophic in nature, or so minor as to scarcely cause a ripple in the firm's operations.

To illustrate how these four factors taken together can affect an economic variable, suppose that the expected (trend) figure for sales of a firm in May is $100,000. In other words, this figure of $100,000 is the expected sales based on the past trend experience of the firm. However, the actual sales will be influenced by the seasonal factor as well as the cyclical and random factors so that the actual May sales are not likely to be exactly $100,000. Suppose that in this line of business a seasonal factor of −10 per cent operates in May while the cyclical factor is +2 per cent and the random forces are equal to +3 per cent. The actual sales figure can be thought of as the *product* of these forces. Thus,

$$\text{sales} = T \times S \times C \times R,$$

where: T = trend factors;
          S = seasonal factors;
          C = cyclical factors;
          R = random factors.

The final value of the variable, sales, is determined by multiplication because it is assumed that the forces can be expressed as percentages of the base. Thus, May sales are generally reduced by about 10 per cent because of the seasonal in this line of business, and the 10 per cent reduction would be expected irrespective of the trend figure to which the percentage is applied. The same reasoning would hold true for the other factors of cyclical and random forces as well.

In this particular case then, the May sales could be computed as:

$$\text{sales} = \$100,000 \times .90 \times 1.02 \times 1.03 = \$94.554.$$

It is not to be expected that May sales will be *exactly* $94,554, since that would be demanding too much accuracy, but it is possible to determine the direction of sales and the approximate amount.

The four elements which may affect time-series data have been briefly discussed. It is quite possible that in a specific firm certain internal factors of the firm could account for some changes in the time-series factors themselves. For example, management policies might account for part of the trend in sales; changes in engineering concepts might cause certain irregularities in production data; while sales and marketing policies could be responsible for other fluctuations in data behavior. Clearly these factors may be important in some circumstances while they may have little or no significance in other situations. We now begin to find ourselves entering an area in which only specific knowledge of the particular series of data can provide full and final answers. However, the techniques of data treatment and analysis developed herein would be invaluable in an analysis of internally or externally generated change.

12.7 Some Cautions and Limitations

It has been indicated that business and economic data can be analyzed in terms of four major categories: cyclical, trend, seasonal, and random fluctuations. However, it is not to be expected that each of these factors in every time series is necessarily weighted equally with the others. Before the statistician goes to a great deal of trouble trying to "break down" a time series, he ought to be reasonably certain that some pattern is contained in the data and that knowledge of this pattern will be important to the problem at hand. Certainly one ought not to jump to the conclusion that all time-series data must necessarily be refined and presented in the most sophisticated manner.

12.8 Some Illustrative Time-Series Examples

In order to provide illustrations for further discussion and to build a general basis for understanding time series and trends, consider the sets of data in Tables 12.3 and 12.4.

Table 12.3

Personal Consumption Expenditures and Industrial Production in the United States, 1951–1964

Year	Personal Consumption (billions of dollars, current prices)	Industrial Production (1957–59 = 100)
1951	209.8	81.3
1952	219.8	84.3
1953	232.6	91.3
1954	238.0	85.8
1955	256.9	96.6
1956	269.9	99.9
1957	285.2	100.7
1958	293.2	93.7
1959	313.5	105.6
1960	328.2	108.7
1961	337.3	109.8
1962	356.8	118.3
1963	375.0	124.3
1964	399.2	131.9

Table 12.4

Sales and Employment Data for the XYZ Corporation, 1963

Month	Gross Sales	Employment
Jan.	$1,380,000	50
Feb.	1,150,000	48
Mar.	1,100,000	48
Apr.	1,130,000	47
May	1,150,000	47
June	1,280,000	49
July	1,290,000	51
Aug.	1,200,000	55
Sept.	1,100,000	53
Oct.	1,120,000	49
Nov.	1,170,000	53
Dec.	1,400,000	57

When the data of Tables 12.3 and 12.4 are graphed, the charts appear as shown in Illustrations 12.4 through 12.7. If we briefly analyze each of the illustrations, the following points may be noted.

Personal Consumption Expenditures (Table 12.3 and Illustration 12.4)

Over the 14-year span shown, it is clear that personal consumption expenditures for the United States as a whole has grown rapidly. Observe that the consumption figure has shown growth in all years, although the growth rate was more rapid in some years than in others. For example,

Illustration 12.4 Personal Consumption Expenditures, United States, 1951–1964

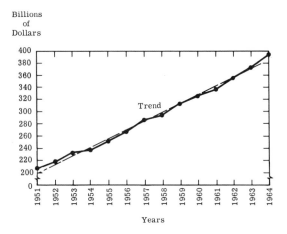

Illustration 12.5 Index of Industrial Production, United States, 1951–1964 (1957–59 = 100)

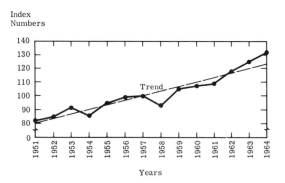

Illustration 12.6 Gross Sales, XYZ Corporation, 1963 (Data from Table 12.4)

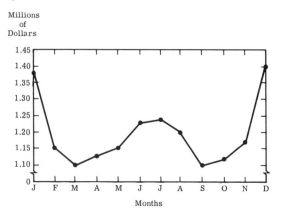

Illustration 12.7 Number of Employees, XYZ Corporation, 1963 (Data from Table 12.4)

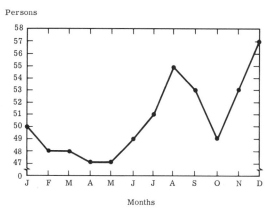

from 1953 to 1954 the rate was slower than in the preceding years, and the rate from 1957 to 1958 was slower than in the several preceding years. The average direction of change is positive and the trend (see the dashed line) progresses at an impressive slope. Of course, the visual impression of slope is a function of the scales selected for the X and Y coordinates of the graph. Nevertheless, the growth pattern is clearly visible in both the data and the graph.

The data do show some variation from the straight-line trend. To explain the deviations, the economic analyst must bring to bear his knowledge of general economic conditions as well as the more specific factors which affect personal consumption expenditures. For example, the slowing in rate of change between 1954 and 1955 might be attributed to an adjustment period following the Korean conflict. The rate change from 1957 to 1958 can be assigned to the recession of 1957–58. However, the most notable feature of the series is the extremely regular growth pattern of the data, which would indicate the vitality of the United States economy in producing goods and services and in distributing income in this period.

Industrial Production (Table 12.3 and Illustration 12.5)

The data for industrial production are in the form of index numbers showing relative changes in the variable rather than absolute amounts of change. The graph clearly shows the two recession periods of 1954 and 1957–58 and, while these represent departures from the general trend (see the dashed line of Illustration 12.5), the trend of the data is clearly positive and the slope is relatively steep, indicating a good rate of production gain in these years. If the trend line is projected into the future, it might be expected that the industrial production index would be at least 126 in 1965. Projection of the trend in this manner assumes that the underlying variables (the forces which act to produce the trend) remain unchanged in the period for which the forecast was made. As a matter of fact, the forecasted values will probably turn out to be incorrect—as point estimates generally are—but within limits the forecast can nevertheless be useful. Incidentally, it is not possible to construct a confidence interval for the forecast because of the absence of a probability distribution applicable to this type of problem.

Gross Sales (Table 12.4 and Illustration 12.6)

Here we have shown the gross sales figures for a particular business firm during one year of operation. The illustration clearly shows the impact of seasonal variation on the firm. Sales are relatively high during the summer months, drop to somewhat lower levels in the fall, and then rise sharply under the influences of Christmas. After the holiday season, sales again tend to drop, and they pick up only slightly until the summer season becomes more pronounced. If this is a typical pattern for the business firm, the manager could program his firm's activities in accordance with the known seasonal factors, thereby hoping to increase the firm's efficiency by such means as smoothing the workload through advance preparations for summer or Christmas and by readiness to meet the demands of customers promptly and fully. It is to be expected that random factors will cause deviations from a typical season pattern. An unusually wet summer might well reduce expected sales by 10 per cent or more. The opening of a new recreation area near the firm might, in a given year, increase sales by, say, 10 per cent or more. Management must be prepared to cope with such changes in fortune as occur in this random or accidental manner.

Employment (Table 12.4 and Illustration 12.7)

Employment data for the firm suggest a correspondence (correlation) between gross sales and employment. On the other hand, the data show that the seasonal factor of employment is less pronounced than gross sales. Apparently management has achieved a smoothing of employment irregularities, but nevertheless finds it necessary to utilize some part-time help in the peak seasons. This, of course, is precisely what might be expected with the seasonal pattern of this business.

A technical problem is presented by the employment data: Did the firm employ exactly 50 persons during the entire month of January and then dismiss two employees on January 31? Or, did the firm dismiss (or accept the resignation of) these two employees at some period prior to the end of January? Obviously, the loss of two (or temporarily of more) employees may have occurred anytime during the month. To provide a basis for the monthly employment figure some type of averaging process appears essential. For example, the number of employees actually on the payroll each day could be noted, the sum could be obtained at the end of the month and then divided by the number of working days in the month. The result would be the average number of employees working during that time period. The average is not likely to result in whole numbers and will require rounding to integers.

A technical explanation of trends will be given in the sections which follow.

Exercise 12.1

1. Define: time series; trend; forecast.

2. In what manner is a good general knowledge of economics valuable to the statistical analyst?

3. What use or uses may be made of time-series data? In other words, why collect such data in the first place?

4. To what extent do you suppose "external" information such as the consumer price index will be a useful time series to an administrative unit? Where does this type of information fit into the more complete administrative decision-making framework?

5. Suppose you are responsible for the administration of a management unit producing films for television. Your specific task is to forecast the demand for such films in Australia. What information would you seek to obtain? How much of this information would be statistical in nature? Would you include time series? If so, what series?

6. If you were advising a client on whether or not to purchase a certain firm's common stock, what time-series data would you study?

7. If you were studying a set of time-series data, say "hourly wages in manufacturing," what qualitative factors as opposed to quantitative information might you be interested in? Might these qualitative factors be equally as important as the statistical information?

8. May time-series data reveal "patterns," "uniformities," and "regularities and irregularities" that are of use in analytical studies? Why or why not?

12.9   Trends: A Brief   View

The following sections examine a number of techniques for determining trend values. These techniques are: (1) freehand trend fitting, (2) the method of dual averages, (3) the method of semi-averages, and (4) the moving average.

The following chapter will examine more complex techniques including the method of least squares as applied to both the straight line and the parabola. The logarithmic straight-line trend is shown in Appendix D.

As the several methods of trend fitting presented in this chapter are examined, it will be important to keep in mind the following general principles.

1. The data should first be plotted on a graph to determine if a trend (and other) elements are actually present in the data. The graph provides a visual inspection, and situations could arise where there is some question as to whether any discernible pattern is present. In this situation one would have to decide whether or not it is worthwhile to go ahead and expend any more time and effort on the data.

2. It will be assumed that the time-series data to be employed have already been accumulated and adjusted for calendar or other variations. One such adjustment was explained in the previous example of the monthly employment data (calculating the average number of employees).

3. Having charted the data, it is now necessary to determine which trend curve and type (freehand, moving average, parabola, and so on) will apparently best fit the data. In other words, what kind of an average is appropriate? This question cannot be fully answered until after a discussion of the various kinds of trends and methods of trend fitting.

12.10   Freehand Trend Fitting

The simplest technique of trend fitting—and for some purposes the most satisfactory—is to draw a graph of the data, then sketch in the trend by use of a ruler or French curve. To use the freehand technique one simply draws a line through the data in such manner as appears to best represent the data. In fitting the trend line the criterion is that the line is to be an *average* and, as such, requires that the distance between the trend

Table 12.5

Illustration of a Set of Data to Which a Freehand Straight-Line Trend Has Been Fitted

(1)	(2)	(3) Trend Values Y_c	(4) Deviations $Y - Y_c = d$
Year	Y Data		
1959	5	6.0	−1.0
1960	7	6.4	+0.6
1961	6	6.8	−0.8
1962	8	7.2	+0.8
1963	7	7.6	−0.6
1964	9	8.0	+1.0
	42	42.0	0.0

line and data should be equal for the positive and negative deviations (see Illustration 12.8).

As an example of the freehand trend, consider the data given in Table 12.5 and graphed as shown in Illustration 12.8. The illustration employed here is purposely made very short to demonstrate the basic principles involved in employing the freehand method. (Note that columns 3 and 4 were derived from the graph of Illustration 12.8.)

Illustration 12.8   Freehand Trend Fitting (Data from Table 12.5)

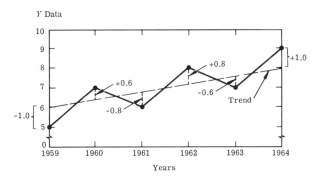

Freehand trend fitting involves a nicety of judgment in order to determine precisely where the center of the data is located. Table 12.5 indicates a method for judging the trend line shown in Illustration 12.8. However, the deviation column (column 4) would not ordinarily be computed; it is shown here only to indicate the arithmetic computations which *could be made* to judge the exactness of the line.

The freehand trend is both easily and quickly fitted. It is, to some extent, inexact. The freehand trend line cannot be said to be as precise as the more sophisticated mathematical techniques of trend fitting. On the other hand, there is an appeal about freehand trend fitting in terms of ease and time saved. Of course, freehand trend fitting assumes that the informational requirement is itself not precise. Like all good tools, freehand trend fitting may be considered appropriate in certain circumstances, but not under all conditions. The statistician must judge each situation on its own merits and then decide what method of analysis is most appropriate.

Exercise 12.2.   *Freehand Trend Fitting.*   At the end of this chapter several series of data are provided. You are to fit freehand trends to the data of Exercise 12.7, problems 1, 2, and 3. First plot the data on ordinary graph paper, then carefully draw in the trend following the rule that $\Sigma\, d = 0$. When the trend has been drawn, consider critically whether or not this method is a desirable one and under what circumstances it might be clearly appropriate.

12.11 The Method of Dual Averages (Straight-Line Trend)

From a knowledge of freehand trend fitting it is a logical step to recognize that one might fit a *straight-line trend* with a good degree of precision if two values located near the ends of the data could be determined rather accurately. Given these two values, it would only be necessary to use a straight edge to complete drawing the trend line.

Table 12.6

Illustration of Trend Fitting by Dual Averages

X	Y
Year	Sales in Millions of Dollars

Year	Sales	
1	185 ⎫	
2	232 ⎬ $\sum_1 = 720;\ \bar{X}_1 = 240$	
3	303 ⎭	
4	313 ⎫	
5	240 ⎬ $\sum_2 = 885;\ \bar{X}_2 = 295$	
6	332 ⎭	

Illustration 12.9 Trend Fitting by Dual-Averages (Data from Table 12.6)

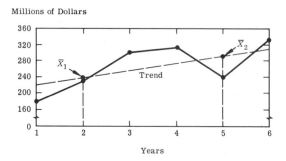

To fit a straight-line trend by the method of dual averages, the time-series data are divided into two equal parts; the average of each part is determined and the respective averages may then be marked on the time centers of the data segments. This method is illustrated in Table 12.6. (Note: Since the actual time periods have no bearing on the mechanics of the problem the *Y* data are simply given consecutively.) The data and the two averages are shown in graphic form in Illustration 12.9.

This method is simplest when the number of time periods is even and the data happen to divide neatly into two equal parts, each possessing an odd number of periods. However, certain difficulties arise when the number of items *in each part* is even. Should the latter be the case, the average of each section may be plotted on the "half-year" and the straight line drawn as before. (The "half-year" is shown in Illustration 12.10.)

If the method of dual averages is applied to data which divide into two "even" parts, the determination of averages and subsequent drawing of the trend line may be illustrated as shown in Table 12.7 and Illustration 12.10.

Table 12.7

Illustration of Trend Fitting by Dual Averages

X Year	Y Sales in Millions of Dollars	
1	80	
2	90	$\sum_1 = 440; \ \bar{X}_1 = 110$
3	130	
4	140	
5	100	
6	120	$\sum_2 = 500; \ \bar{X}_2 = 125$
7	90	
8	190	

Illustration 12.10   Trend Fitting by Dual-Averages (Data from Table 12.7)

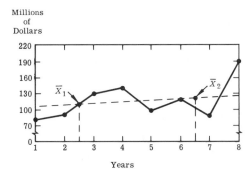

If the total number of time periods is uneven, the time-series data may be broken in two parts as before, but the middle year is omitted from the calculation of the averages. It may be seen immediately that the method of dual averages is only a "rough" measure and is essentially in the category with freehand trend fitting. The method is rapid, but it lacks precision.

Exercise 12.3. *Fitting Trends by Dual Averages.*   Fit straight-line trends to the following sets of data using the method of dual averages. First graph the data, then subsequently draw in the trend. Since the actual time periods have no bearing on the mechanics of the problem, the Y data are simply given in consecutive time periods.

1. Y data: 40, 60, 50, 60, 80, 70.
2. Y data: 35, 45, 34, 40, 42, 47, 55.
3.   When you have graphed these problems, decide if the trend line is a good fit judged by an observation as to whether or not the area above and below the trend line is equal—that is, whether the + and − deviations are equal.

12.12   The Method of Semi-Averages (Straight-Line Trend)

The method of trend fitting by semi-averages is a straight-line method and makes use of a formula to calculate the position of the line. It is therefore desirable to look first at the method of construction for straight lines and understand what the formula means and how it is used before proceeding to the mechanics of the semi-averages method.

The formula for a straight line as used by statisticians is:

$$Y_c = a + bx,$$

where Y_c = a computed Y value,
   a, b = constants,
       x = a unit of time;
and, for semi-averages:

$$a = \bar{Y},$$

$$b = \frac{\sum\limits_{2} - \sum\limits_{1}}{n(N - n)} = \frac{\dfrac{\sum Y_2}{n} - \dfrac{\sum Y_1}{n}}{N - n}.$$

Note: Since a straight line is really a set of points on the X and Y coordinates of a graph, any Y_c value is only one point on that line. Thus, it is necessary to compute at least two Y_c values to be able to draw a straight line on a graph.

The easiest way to explain the formula will be by use of Illustration 12.11. On the graph of Illustration 12.11 note that a is employed as the

Illustration 12.11 Mechanics of a Straight-Line Trend (Time-Centered)

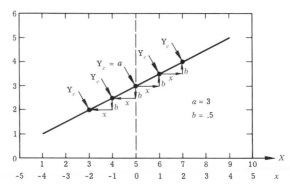

starting point and it occurs in the time center of the graph (as indicated by the x scale). Observe that the other Y_c values are obtained by adding b vertically for each unit change in x. Values of Y_c at the left of the time center of the graph are obtained by subtracting b for each unit of x subtracted. Notice, too, that the set of Y_c points fall on a straight line, and this line could be extended in either or both directions as far as required by the problem.

The method of trend fitting by semi-averages is not mathematically precise (even though a formula is employed) but is more accurate than either the freehand or dual averages previously examined. In trend fitting by the semi-averages method, the data are broken into two halves as in the dual-averages method. If the total number of items (N) is even, the two halves comprise the entire set of data. If, however, the number of items is odd, then the central item may be dropped from the calculations.[5]

The mechanics of the method of semi-averages are as follows. (1) The data are broken into two parts (omit the central item if there is one) and the sum of each part is obtained ($\sum_1$ and $\sum_2$). (2) The value of b is then determined according to the formula:

$$b = \frac{\sum_2 - \sum_1}{n(N-n)},$$

where $\sum_1, \sum_2$ = the sum of the first and second halves of the data,

n = number of items in each half,
N = number of items in the entire set of data,
b = the trend increment per time period.

(3) Using the time-centering method, the value of a is then taken to be the mean of the entire series—that is,

$$a = \frac{\Sigma Y}{N},$$

where a is the value of the trend at the median time period. (4) Once a and b have been calculated, these values are then substituted in the trend equation, $Y_c = a + bx$, and the desired trend values calculated. This is a time-centered method.

---

[5] Alternatively, the central item may be added to each half, or the central item may be divided by two and the result added to both halves. The latter situation calls for utilizing a weighted average in which the end items are weighted twice the "value" of the middle item.

This method may be illustrated as shown in Table 12.8. The trend

Table 12.8

Calculation of *a* and *b* (Semi-Averages Method)

Year X	x	Sales in Millions of Dollars, Y	
1	−3	87⎫	
2	−2	90⎬	$270 = \sum_1$
3	−1	93⎭	
4	0	98	
5	1	97⎫	
6	2	105⎬	$318 = \sum_2$
7	3	116⎭	
		686	

$$b = \frac{318 - 270}{3(7 - 3)} = 4, \qquad a = \frac{686}{7} = 98$$

values will be obtained by solving the straight-line equation $Y_c = a + bx$. When this is done, the resulting Y_c (trend) values are as shown in Illustration 12.12 and Table 12.9. Observe that time is centered on the median year.

Illustration 12.12   Trend as Calculated from Table 12.8

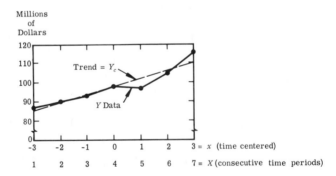

Table 12.9

Trend Values for Data of Table 12.8

X	x	Y_c
1	−3	86
2	−2	90
3	−1	94
4	0	98
5	1	102
6	2	106
7	3	110
		686

Note that ideally the sum of the Y_c values should equal the sum of the Y data. This is true because the trend line is an "average" and one of the characteristics of the arithmetic mean is $N \bar{Y} = \Sigma Y$. However, in approximate methods including the dual and semi-averages method, the ΣY_c may approximate but not necessarily equal ΣY.

The procedure applicable when the number of time periods is even may be illustrated by Tables 12.10 and 12.11. (Observe that the necessary adjustments are made in the method of centering.)

Table 12.10
Hypothetical Sales Data

Year X	Sales in Millions of Dollars, Y	
1	38.5	
2	45.0	127.5 = $\sum_1$
3	44.0	
4	43.0	
5	47.0	141.0 = $\sum_2$
6	51.0	
	268.5	

Table 12.11
Calculation of the Semi-Averages
Trend for the Data of Table 12.10

X	x	Y_c = Trend
1	−2.5	41.0
2	−1.5	42.5
3	−0.5	44.0
4	0.5	45.5
5	1.5	47.0
6	2.5	48.5
		268.5

$$b = \frac{141.0 - 127.5}{9} = 1.5, \qquad a = \frac{268.5}{6} = 44.75$$

The preceding illustrations of straight-line trend fitting by the method of semi-averages indicate that the labor of calculation is held to a minimum, yet trend equation values of a and b may be determined with reasonable accuracy for the calculation of Y_c (trend) values. Too, forecasting by projecting the trend is readily accomplished; that is, additional values of Y_c may be computed. The major limitation of this method is that the resulting trend is not mathematically precise. In other words, the trend is not necessarily a "line of best fit," although it may be considered a "good" fit.

Exercise 12.4. *Fitting a Trend by the Semi-Averages.* Fit straight-line trends to the following sets of data by the method of semi-averages. Construct a graph of the original data and subsequently draw in the trend line. Since the actual time periods have no bearing on the mechanics of the problem, the Y data are given consecutively.

1. Y data: 150, 163, 170, 176, 188.

2. Y data: 200, 230, 260, 271, 260, 290, 302.

3. (a) The following Y data closely approximate the consumer price index for the decade following World War II—that is, 1946 through 1955. Fit a straight-line trend by the method of semi-averages and graph the results.

   (b) What information does the b value convey?
      Y data: 83, 96, 103, 102, 103, 111, 114, 115, 114, 116.
4. (a) The following Y data closely approximate the index of industrial
      production for the decade following World War II. Fit a straight-line
      trend by the method of semi-averages and graph the results.
   (b) Compare the b value of this series with the b value of the consumer
      price index series in problem 3. Did the trend of industrial production
      follow the consumer price index closely? To what extent would it
      seem reasonable to believe that the two indices should move together?
      Y data: 95, 100, 103, 99, 113, 123, 127, 138, 130, 147.

5. (a) The following Y data closely approximate the money supply of the
      United States for the decade following World War II. The "money
      supply" is here defined as currency, demand deposits, time deposits,
      and U.S. Government deposits. Fit a straight-line trend by the method
      of semi-averages and graph the results.
      Y data: 167, 171, 172, 174, 181, 190, 200, 205, 215, 220.

12.13 The Moving Average

   As one of the tools in the statistician's kit, the moving average
deserves a special place because of its flexibility and appropriateness to
many different trend patterns. The moving average is, as the words
themselves suggest, an *average* which *moves* through the data. As an
average, it has the very valuable advantage of "smoothing" the data by
removing most of the impact of irregular or accidental fluctuations.
The moving average has an unfortunate disadvantage in that it will not
provide values to coincide with ending (or beginning) data. Thus, the
moving average has only limited applicability to forecasting.
   The moving average may now be demonstrated by examples:

1. The data given are a time series. They have been collected and made
   available in the best possible form. In other words, the question as to
   whether or not the data were properly collected and presented is not a
   matter of concern. We shall simply take the data as given.

2. A three-year moving average will be illustrated first. This means that we
   shall take years 1, 2, and 3 as the first "set," find the average, record the
   average opposite the median time period (year 2), and move on to take the
   second set of three-year data (years 2, 3, and 4). Finding the average, it is
   recorded at the median year (year 3). We then "move on" to take the
   average of the third set of data, which will comprise years 3, 4, and 5. This
   process is repeated until the entire time series has been completed.

3. Upon completing the calculations, we emerge with a set of three-year
   averages. The values may then be graphed to show the smoothing effect
   of the moving average and to contrast it to the original data.

The three-year moving average as just illustrated clearly *smooths the data* somewhat, but the student will observe the impossibility of deriving either a beginning or ending value for the calculations. Observe also that the longer the time span covered by the moving average the smoother the resulting curve. Too, the student will probably already have noted that

Table 12.12

Computation of a Three-Year Moving Average

(1)	(2)	(3)	(4)
		Sum of Each Consecutive	*Three-Year*
Year	*Y Data*	*Three Years*	*Moving Average*
1	110	..	
2	145	110 + 145 + 135 = 390	390/3 = 130
3	135	145 + 135 + 140 = 420	420/3 = 140
4	140	etc. 402	etc. 134
5	127	378	126
6	111	327	109
7	89	279	93
8	79	243	81
9	75	246	82
10	92	276	92
11	109	342	114
12	141	..	..

Illustration 12.13   Chart of the Three-Year Moving Average from the Data of Table 12.12

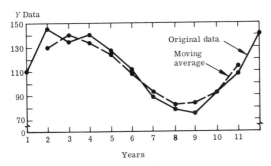

the three-year moving average centers time nicely because there is always a median time period to which the three-year total and average will correspond. As a matter of fact, this desirable situation will occur whenever the period chosen is an uneven number. But now suppose we ask: What about selecting an even time period of say, four years?

Whenever the time period chosen for the moving average is an even number, an additional step is required to center the final moving average to correspond to the proper time period of the data. The problem is solved by running two consecutive moving averages. In this case the method is to first run a four-year moving average, then follow by running a two-year moving average on the four-year averages. Again, this is best illustrated by use of an example. (See Table 12.13.) The student should

Table 12.13

Illustration of the Four-Year Moving Average

(1)	(2)	(3)	(4)	(5)	(6)
Year X	Data Y	Four-Year Total	Four-Year Moving Average	Two-Year Moving Total	Four-Year Centered Moving Average
1	40	..	..		..
2	55	..	..	..	..
3	70	240	60	126	63.0
4	75	264	66	131	65.5
5	64	260	65	124	62.0
6	51	236	59	113	56.5
7	46	216	54	109	54.4
8	55	220	55	116	58.0
9	68	244	61	130	65.0
10	75	276	69	143	71.5
11	78	296	74	..	..
12	73	..	..	..	..

Calculation of the four-year uncentered moving average

Calculation of the two-year moving average to center the data

note that the four-year average is calculated first and set in the proper column. As the second step, the calculations required are performed for the two-year moving average and the numbers set in the proper column. When this final step is completed, a four-year, *centered* moving average has been constructed.

The procedure given in Table 12.13 could have been simplified somewhat by successively combining two of the four-year totals and dividing by 8. To illustrate: The first two moving totals are 240 and 264. These sum to 504, and 504/8 = 63.0, the first two-year centered moving average. In ordinary circumstances it would be preferable to combine the totals rather than going through the additional steps as shown in Table 12.13.

The nature of the moving average derived from Table 12.13 is indicated by Illustration 12.14.

The two distinct possibilities of the moving average have now been illustrated by: (1) using an example where the time period selected was uneven and (2) using an example where the period of years was even. These two combinations cover all moving-average possibilities. From these illustrations it may be surmised that a seven-year moving average will behave exactly as a three-year, except that the data will have been smoothed

Illustration 12.14   Chart of the Four-Year Centered Moving Average from the Data of Table 12.13

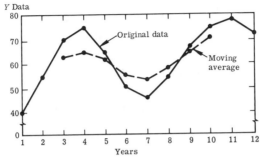

more than in the three-year average and there will be a loss of three years on either end of the moving average. On the other hand, a ten-year moving average will behave exactly as a four-year moving average except for the additional smoothing effect and the loss of five years' data on either end. The ten-year moving average requires centering by use of the two-year moving average.

What are the reasons for choosing the moving average as a means of trend identification? *One* basic objective of a trend is to smooth the data, to iron out the irregular values by averaging and combining them with the more regularly occurring values. A *second* basic objective is to identify the trend, if it exists. A trend as isolated by the moving average from actual data is not likely to be of the straight-line variety. Thus, the moving average is a useful technique for showing other than "regular"- shaped trends. However, the very irregularity of such a trend often minimizes its usefulness in analytical and decision-making contexts. *Third*, the moving average may be used to remove the cyclical component of the data—if cyclical factors are present. To illustrate: If a regular cycle of, say, a seven-year period is discovered in the data, then a seven- year moving average will remove the cycle and leave only the trend. Unfortunately, economic data are not likely to be marked by such simple regularity so that when a moving average is utilized, the result will not likely be a straight-line trend. Some irregularities will remain in the moving average. Too, if the cycle is irregular in terms of both length and amplitude, the resulting moving average will be more difficult to analyze and interpret.

To summarize: The moving average is an excellent technique for smoothing data, subject to the limitations mentioned previously. In general, the isolation of trend by the moving average requires a long time span. Thus, and in general, the moving average, like all "tools," has both advantages and limitations. It must be used carefully and cannot be applied indiscriminately.

12.14   Summary

The primary objective of this chapter has been to provide an introduction to the fundamental principles and theory of time series and trends. Because there is nothing particularly difficult about the arithmetic, the illustrations were reasonably simple and relatively uncluttered. In a pragmatic sense, the only arithmetic problems encountered are normally those concerned with assuring oneself that they were carried through without error.

However, while all this simplicity is to the good, there are far more sophisticated questions to be dealt with in time-series analysis. A basic objective of time series and trends is to provide an accurate but simplified picture of the original set of data. This objective is, itself, not particularly difficult to obtain. When the data have been transformed into a trend or a moving average, there is indeed a picture of change and a knowledge of direction of movement in the series under study. The deeper knowledge and sophistication enters both before and after this "picture" objective has been reached.

Certain questions are always appropriate in time-series analysis. In the first place, what time series are to be the subject of analysis and why? What information is sought? Is this information of real value to the decisions and hypothesis ahead? Is the time-series information, as gathered, reliable? Does it measure what it is purported to measure? How does the time-series information dovetail (if at all) with other existing information?

In the second place, once these questions have been answered satisfactorily, there remains the question of utilizing the information either in terms of further analysis or in the decision-making context. Here again, all the individual's knowledge, experience, intuition, and formal and informal study of economic and business theory must be brought to bear on the problem. The fate of a business enterprise or of a policy may turn on whether these matters are successfully analyzed and decided. Time series and trends, indeed all statistical knowledge, can be brought to bear on the final decision and thus materially increase the probability of "success," but there is no guarantee, no necessary point at which $P(E) = 1.0$.

Key Terms and Concepts of This Chapter

Centered data	Random variations
Cyclical variation	Seasonal variation
Dual averages	Semi-averages
Forecasting	Time series
Freehand trend fitting	Trend
Moving average	$Y_c = a + bx$
Noncentered data	

Exercise 12.5. *The Moving Average.*

1. (a) Run a three-year moving average on the following data. Observe to what degree the irregularities are smoothed.

    (b) Run a six-year moving average and again observe the smoothing effect. Graph the results.

Year	Millions of Kilowatt Hours Produced
1953	15
1954	21
1955	18
1956	27
1957	24
1958	30
1959	36
1960	33
1961	42
1962	48
1963	45
1964	45
1965	45

2. The following data are cyclical in nature. Run an appropriate moving average to remove the cyclical component.

Year	Tons of Fertilizer Sold by the St. Louis County Co., Inc.
1954	1,000
1955	1,500
1956	500
1957	1,200
1958	1,700
1959	700
1960	1,400
1961	1,900
1962	900
1963	1,600
1964	2,100
1965	1,100

Exercise 12.6. The following sets of data are appropriate for trend fitting and moving averages. Students should use these for freehand trend fitting and as extra problems for practice on any of the time-series techniques of this chapter.

1. The following table gives United States Gross National Product for the years 1953 through 1963.

Year	Gross National Product (billions of dollars)
1953	440.1
1954	431.4
1955	464.9
1956	474.7
1957	483.9
1958	476.7
1959	508.4
1960	521.3
1961	531.2
1962	563.6
1963	585.0

SOURCE: *Economic Report of the President.*

2. The following table gives United States business expenditures for new plant and equipment for the years 1953 through 1963.

Year	Expenditure for New Plant and Equipment (billions of dollars)
1953	28.32
1954	26.83
1955	28.70
1956	35.08
1957	36.96
1958	30.53
1959	32.54
1960	35.68
1961	34.37
1962	37.31
1963	39.05

SOURCE: *Economic Report of the President.*

Bibliography

References are given at the end of Chapter 13.

TREND FITTING
AND
SEASONAL INDICES

13.1   Introduction

The preceding chapter dealt with the general subject of time series and explained certain elementary methods of trend fitting. The present chapter continues to discuss time series but will be concerned with the mathematically more precise methods of trend fitting. Methods for removing the trend and seasonal components from time-series data will also be discussed. Since time series and their analysis are so significant and so frequently used in the business and economic world, a brief introduction to the analytical techniques will be in order.

To undertake an empirical study of a problem it is first necessary to identify the areas in which the effort expended is likely to be fruitful and to obtain measurements of the variables believed to be relevant. Sometimes measurements will be made by the person undertaking the research, although for many types of problems data may already exist. At the present time many economic variables are measured and reported periodically. A large quantity of data is published by government agencies, business firms, labor unions, universities, trade associations, and others. The data supplied by these agencies are made available to statisticians, economists, econometricians, business analysts, and others who wish to obtain a perspective on the changes taking place in the business environment.

The uses to which existing data may be put are many. For example, time-series data on consumer expenditures may be used to provide a factual basis for theoretical formulations concerning principles of consumer behavior through time. Other time series might be used in the study of demand for agricultural products, or to test hypotheses. For example, the hypothesis that per capita income has increased in the United States by about 3 per cent per year in the period 1955 to 1965 could be tested by the use of empirical data.

Statistical series can also be employed in basic research which takes as its goal the discovery of new relationships and new laws of behavior without regard to whether or not the discoveries (if any) will have immediate practical application. For example, research might be undertaken to discover if population changes for a geographic area could be predicted with reasonable accuracy. Or, a firm might undertake a study of its inventory problems to discern if some kind of pattern or common thread can be found to provide clues which might suggest improved techniques of inventory control in the future. In this latter case, the discovery of seasonal or cyclical patterns might provide valuable clues for further attention. Or, in another situation, a trade association might study the trend in consumer expenditures for the product or services offered by the member firms.

The foregoing paragraphs should not be taken to imply that all empirical studies involve the study of time series, or that time-series analysis is the principal type of data employed. In studying problems and seeking possible solutions to the problems under study, the statistician employs whatever statistical techniques and economic analysis give promise of yielding results. Nevertheless, time series are often an important part of the essential data in business and economic research.

Another type of situation frequently arises in regard to research of an empirical nature. It is sometimes impossible to design experiments to supply the particular kind of information which the statistician or economist may wish for scientific purposes, and it thus becomes necessary to rely on data collected by one or more of the agencies previously indicated as publishing time series and other types of data. Frequently these data were collected for purposes other than the immediate ones of the researcher. This means that some ingenuity must be exhibited by the researcher to apply the data to his current purposes. Analytical techniques of statistics are often the only tools available to adapt the data to current purposes.

Too, budgetary limitations of empirical research frequently mean that the researcher must take whatever statistics are available, since he frequently cannot afford to develop precise series to fit his particular purposes. Thus, he must take whatever germane statistics are available and adapt them to the research at hand. Sometimes the researcher may be fortunate enough to develop new data or begin a new series, but for the most part he must rely on existing data. This problem often means *the researcher must be ingenious in using statistical techniques to wring the desired information from the data.* Techniques for the analysis of time series (including those presented in this chapter) thus become a matter of major importance in permitting efficient use of the data.

Symbols Employed in This Chapter

The student should keep in mind the following symbols, which are employed frequently in the present chapter.

c = a parameter used in calculating parabolic trends.
T = trend.
S = seasonal.
R = random factors.
C = cyclical factors.

13.2   The Least-Squares Straight-Line Trend

The basic mechanics of calculating the straight-line trend were explained in Section 12.12. To construct a straight-line trend it is necessary to obtain values for a and b which are then substituted in the formula $Y_c = a + bx$. Several methods exist for the calculation of the a and b values, and one of these methods (the method of semi-averages) was explained in Section 12.12. A more precise method of trend fitting known as the *least-squares* method will now be discussed.

The method of least squares fits a trend line to the data in a manner such that the sum of the squared deviations $\Sigma (Y - Y_c)^2$ is a minimum value. This means that no other set of Y_c values could, by this criterion (of least squares), be more closely fitted to the data than the ones derived by the least squares method. On these grounds, the resulting trend line can be characterized as a "line of best fit." When this trend line is shown on a graph, the gain in precision of the least-squares method over the more elementary methods is hardly noticeable, but because the least-squares trend is mathematically accurate, the trend values are appropriate to forecasting and for any additional calculations.

Methodology

The first step in trend fitting is to determine whether a trend actually exists. Consequently, a graph of the data should be constructed to determine by visual inspection whether a trend is present and, if present, the type of curve most appropriate. The present chapter will consider only the straight-line and parabolic trends.

Once it has been determined that a trend, say the straight-line trend, is appropriate, the data are then subjected to the proper arithmetic manipulation, as explained below. It is important to observe that the data are time-centered in exactly the same manner as explained previously for the semi-averages trend.

When the data have been structured (as shown in Table 13.1), the

a and b values for the trend line are determined as

$$a = \frac{\Sigma\, Y}{N}, \tag{13.1}$$

$$b = \frac{\Sigma\, xY}{\Sigma\, x^2}. \tag{13.2}$$

The a and b values are then utilized in the straight-line trend formula:

$$Y_c = a + bx, \tag{13.3}$$

where Y_c = the trend values, x = time-centered values measured from the median time period, and a and b can be considered parameters.

Finally, the a and b values are then substituted in the straight-line equation (13.3) and the necessary Y_c values are calculated.

The steps outlined above are shown in Table 13.1(a).

Table 13.1(a)

Calculation of the Least-Squares Straight-Line Trend (Y Values Are Demonstration Data; Data Centered on the Median Year)

Year	Time Periods X	Data Y	x	xY	x²	Trend Values a + b · x = Y_c
1961	1	105	−2	−210	4	$150 + (20) \cdot (-2) = 110$
1962	2	140	−1	−140	1	$150 + (20) \cdot (-1) = 130$
1963	3	150	0	0	0	$150 + (20) \cdot (\ \ 0) = 150$
1964	4	160	1	160	1	$150 + (20) \cdot (\ \ 1) = 170$
1965	5	195	2	390	4	$150 + (20) \cdot (\ \ 2) = 190$
..	..	750	..	200	10	750

$$a = \frac{\Sigma\, Y}{N} = \frac{750}{5} = 150, \qquad b = \frac{\Sigma\, xY}{x^2} = \frac{200}{10} = 20$$

Under certain circumstances, particularly where calculating machines are readily available, it is sometimes desirable to use a non-time-centered method. This is demonstrated in Table 13.1(b).

Table 13.1(b)

Calculation of the Least-Squares Straight-Line Trend by the Non-Time-Centered Method (Demonstration Data)

Year	Time Periods X	Original Data Y	XY	X²	Trend Values a + b · X = Y_c
1961	1	105	105	1	$90 + (20)(1) = 110$
1962	2	140	280	4	$90 + (20)(2) = 130$
1963	3	150	450	9	$90 + (20)(3) = 150$
1964	4	160	640	16	$90 + (20)(4) = 170$
1965	5	195	975	25	$90 + (20)(5) = 190$
..	15	750	2,450	55	750

The values for a and b are then determined by employing noncentered equations as follows:

$$b = \frac{\Sigma\, XY - \dfrac{\Sigma\, X \Sigma\, Y}{N}}{X^2 - \dfrac{(\Sigma\, X)^2}{N}} = \frac{2{,}450 - \dfrac{(15)(750)}{5}}{55 - \dfrac{(15)^2}{5}} = 20, \qquad (13.4)$$

$$a = \frac{\Sigma\, Y - b\,\Sigma\, X}{N} = \frac{750 - (20)(15)}{5} = 90. \qquad (13.5)$$

When time is not centered, the value of a is determined for the time period $X = 0$, which means that a (centered) does not equal a (noncentered) However, the resulting trend (Y_c) values are identical.

Substituting the known values of a and b in the trend equation $Y_c = a + bX$, the Y_c values of 110, 130, 150, 170, and 190 may be determined. These are identical to the Y_c values as shown in Table 13.1(a).

Returning to the time-centered method of determining least-squares trend values, suppose the number of data items was even, so that the median time period fell precisely in between the middle two years. Table 13.2(a) shows how the necessary values are calculated.

Table 13.2(a)

Calculation of the Least-Squares Straight-Line Trend (Y Values Are Demonstration Data; Time Centered on the Half-Year)

Time	Data Y	x	xy	x^2	Trend Values $a + b \cdot x = Y_c$
1961	61	−2.5	−152.5	6.25	$55 + (-2)(-2.5) = 60$
1962	57	−1.5	−85.5	2.25	$55 + (-2)(-1.5) = 58$
1963	54	−0.5	−27.0	0.25	$55 + (-2)(-0.5) = 56$
1964	56	+0.5	28.0	0.25	$55 + (-2)(+0.5) = 54$
1965	53	+1.5	79.5	2.25	$55 + (-2)(+1.5) = 52$
1966	49	+2.5	122.5	6.25	$55 + (-2)(+2.5) = 50$
..	330	..	−35.0	17.50	330

$$a = \frac{\Sigma\, Y}{N} = \frac{330}{6} = 55, \qquad b = \frac{\Sigma\, xY}{x^2} = \frac{-35}{17.5} = -2$$

Also: $$\Sigma\, Y = \Sigma\, Y_c$$

An alternative method of time-centering on the half-year considers the "half-year" as "units" of time and establishes an integer scale for x. This may best be illustrated by an example shown in Table 13.2(b), which uses the same data as Table 13.2(a).

Table 13.2(b)

Calculation of Least-Squares Straight-Line Trend (Y Values Are Demonstration Data; Time Centered on Half-Year Units)

Year	Data Y	x	xY	x^2	Trend Values
1961	61	−5	−305	25	60
1962	57	−3	−171	9	58
1963	54	−1	−54	1	56
1964	56	1	56	1	54
1965	53	3	159	9	52
1966	49	5	245	25	50
	330		−70	70	330

$$a = \frac{\Sigma Y}{N} = \frac{330}{6} = 55, \qquad b = \frac{\Sigma xY}{\Sigma x^2} = \frac{-70}{70} = -1$$

In Table 13.2(b) observe that b is exactly one-half the value of the same parameter calculated in Table 13.2(a). This is necessary because the method of time-centering used in Table 13.2(b) considers the half-years as "units" and there are twice as many half-years as whole years. Thus the difference in b values. The a values, however, are identical in the two methods.

Substituting the known values of a and b in the trend equation $Y_c = a + bx$, the Y_c values of 60, 58, 56, 54, 52, and 50 may be determined.

13.3 A Word on Forecasting

Business firms must, in a changing environment, continually assess their current economic position and come to some decision about the next steps to be taken. There is no alternative to intelligent decisions made today to guide the business firm tomorrow. If, for example, there is every reason to believe that the gross national product will rise during the next year, a firm's sales policy and strategy can be formulated with this rise in mind. It will also be important to know about how much the gross national product will rise. A large rise may call for a different sales policy than a gentle rise. To obtain some indication of the possible increase, trend projection may be utilized. Thus, if the b value of the gross national product straight-line trend is $15 billion, an administrator may know that his firm can expect approximately a $2 million increase in sales. This kind of information provides a most useful guide for the decision-making process.

Technically, any time series is subject to trend analysis and projection. When a trend has been calculated on the basis of existing (historical) data, that trend can be projected for a number of time periods into the future. Since it is generally assumed that past economic forces will continue to operate at about the same strength in the immediate future as in the immediate past, the trend projection provides an estimate of the variable in the future. However, economic forces are continually changing and the farther in the future a projection of trend is made, the less the reliability of the forecast owing to unknown factors which may enter in the future. Hence, there is a compelling need for continual revision of forecasts.

The business statistician will probably find himself confronted with many problems of forecasting. Among these are the problems of forecasting such variables as gross national product, income, population, industry sales, and trend of the variables most impQrtant to the industry as well as projecting trends of the variables associated with an individual firm. Keeping track of all these variables and relating each variable to the other is a task of considerable magnitude.

The mechanical techniques of trend projection for forecasting purposes are relatively simple. The method is this: Once a and b are known, simply calculate Y_c for as many time periods in the future as are desired by placing the appropriate x values in the trend equation. Suppose, for example, a value is requested for the year 1967 from the data of Table 13.2(a). The equation would be: $55 + (-2)(3.5) = 48$. Since this is a falling trend, the forecast for 1967 will show a value of 48 as compared to the 1966 value of 50. Whether or not the value 48 indicates a desirable situation depends upon the nature of the data. If the Y data measure an index of capital costs for a particular firm, the negative slope of the trend line will doubtless be viewed with considerable satisfaction. On the other hand, should the Y data be a measure of net profits, the negative slope would certainly be viewed with considerable apprehension.

Exercise 13.1. *Fitting the Least-Squares Straight-Line Trend.* Instructions: Fit a least-squares trend line to the following sets of data. Determine a, b, and the Y_c values. Forecast values for each problem for an additional two time periods. Graph each problem by plotting the original data as well as the trend line and its forecasted values.

Problem 1		Problem 2		Problem 3	
Year	*Employment (thousands)*	*Year*	*Sales (thousands)*	*Year*	*Population (thousands)*
1961	32	1961	15	1920	67
1962	56	1962	24	1930	60
1963	58	1963	30	1940	60
1964	68	1964	18	1950	52
1965	46	1965	38	1960	46

Problem 4		Problem 5	
Year	Exports, Smith Mfg. Co. (millions of $)	Year	Cords of Wood Bought, Blank Paper Co. (4 zeros omitted)
1959	27	1960	18
1960	18	1961	27
1961	26	1962	25
1962	30	1963	34
1963	34	1964	39
1964	42	1965	37
1965	33		

6. Suppose the XYZ paper company reported its production of paperboard and paper for the years 1956 through 1965 as follows (round to millions):

Year	Paperboard and Paper (tons)
1956	3,551,407
1957	3,457,642
1958	3,739,961
1959	3,974,129
1960	3,848,373
1961	3,726,766
1962	4,087,308
1963	4,033,754
1964	4,087,181
1965	4,184,144

(a) Draw a graph of the data; (b) fit a straight-line trend by the least-squares method; (c) interpret the meaning of the a and b values; (d) project the trend for 1966 and 1967. (e) From the actual data and trend, how much reliance would you attach to the 1966 and 1967 projections?

7. Using the Y data of Exercise 12.4 (semi-averages), calculate the straight-line trend for problem 3 which utilized cost-of-living indices. Compare the least-squares a and b values with the semi-averages a and b values. What differences, if any, exist? Can you explain why these differences or similarities exist? For this particular problem, which method—semi-averages or least-squares—appears best, all factors considered?

8. Explain the differences between the time-centered and non-time-centered methods of fitting a straight-line trend by the least-squares method. If you were to be assigned a long problem with 25 time periods and in which the Y values were four digits or more, which method would you prefer and why?

9. Obtain a recent copy of the annual report of a large corporation. Examine the statistical data for the time series and trends. What percentage of the statistical information in the report is conveyed in time-series and trend form? Are trends used extensively? Why or why not? Can you find examples in this report where you feel the data presentation could be improved? How?

10. In examining the annual report as suggested by problem 8 above, you probably discovered that very few trends were actually shown—although trends could be derived from the information shown. Do you suppose the company statisticians have constructed the trends and made certain this information went to management? How might the management utilize the trend information?

13.4 The Least-Squares Parabolic Trend

When graphed, time-series data may exhibit the characteristics of a parabolic curve as shown in Illustration 13.1. When the data are increasing

Illustration 13.1 Parabolic Trends (Generalized)

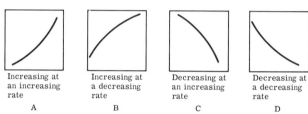

Increasing at an increasing rate	Increasing at a decreasing rate	Decreasing at an increasing rate	Decreasing at a decreasing rate
A	B	C	D

at an increasing or decreasing rate (see A and B), or the data are decreasing at an increasing or decreasing rate (see C and D), then a polynomial type of curve, the parabola, is likely to be appropriate. In the material which follows it is assumed that the parabolic type of trend is correct for the data of the illustrations and exercises.

The least-squares parabola possesses the same general characteristics as the least-squares straight-line trend. Because of its least-squares mathematical properties, it is a line of "best fit" for the type of trend considered. This means that no other set of Y_c values could by this criterion be more closely fitted to the data than those derived by the least-squares method. The trend line is the "average" of the time-series data. The parabolic trend may be used for forecasting purposes in the same manner as explained for the straight-line trend.

The following steps show the mechanical procedure in calculating the least-squares parabolic trend. These will first be stated, then illustrated by an example (Table 13.3).

1. The original data are plotted on graph paper and a determination made as to the type of trend to be used. In this section the appropriate trend is considered to be a parabola.

2. The data are centered with respect to time. The median value is selected as the time center of the data and given an x value of zero.

3. The data are set up in tabular form to derive the necessary totals for the parabolic equations. The proper column headings are shown in Table 13.3.

4. When the necessary sums have been obtained, the following relationships are used:

$$a = \frac{\Sigma\,Y - c\,\Sigma\,x^2}{N},\qquad (13.6)$$

$$b = \frac{\Sigma\,x\,Y}{\Sigma\,x^2},\qquad (13.7)$$

$$c = \frac{N\,\Sigma\,x^2\,Y - \Sigma\,x^2\,\Sigma\,Y}{N\,\Sigma\,x^4 - (\Sigma\,x^2)^2}.\qquad (13.8)$$

5. Having determined the necessary parameters, the parabolic trend formula

$$Y_c = a + bx + cx^2 \qquad (13.9)$$

is used to provide the required trend values.

Table 13.3

Calculation of the Least-Squares Parabolic Trend (Y Values Are Demonstration Data; Data Centered on the Median Year)

Year	Y	x	xY	x^2	x^2Y	x^4	a	$+ bx$	$+ cx^2 =$	Y_c
1961	8	-2	-16	4	32	16	14	$+ (2) \cdot (-2)$	$+ (-1) \cdot (4)$	6
1962	7	-1	-7	1	7	1	14	$+ (2) \cdot (-1)$	$+ (-1) \cdot (1)$	11
1963	14	0	0	0	0	0	14	$+ (2) \cdot (0)$	$+ (-1) \cdot (0)$	14
1964	19	1	19	1	19	1	14	$+ (2) \cdot (1)$	$+ (-1) \cdot (1)$	15
1965	12	2	24	4	48	16	14	$+ (2) \cdot (2)$	$+ (-1) \cdot (4)$	14
..	60	..	20	10	106	34	..	..	..	60

$$b = \frac{\Sigma\,x\,Y}{\Sigma\,x^2},\qquad c = \frac{N\,\Sigma\,x^2\,Y - \Sigma\,x^2\,\Sigma\,Y}{N\,\Sigma\,x^4 - (\Sigma\,x^2)^2},\qquad a = \frac{\Sigma\,Y - c\,\Sigma\,x^2}{N},$$

$$b = \frac{20}{10} = 2.\qquad c = \frac{(5)(106) - (10)(60)}{(5)(34) - (100)},\qquad a = \frac{60 - (-1)(10)}{5},$$

$$c = -1.\qquad\qquad a = 14.$$

To consider the type of parabolic problem in which the data lack a median year, it will be convenient to use the method of centering which employs half-year "units." The next illustration (Table 13.4) indicates the procedure. Observe that the formulae for a, b, and c are the same as those employed for Table 13.3 where the data possessed a median year.

Observe in the calculation of a, b, and c for parabolic problems it is unlikely these values would turn out to be even numbers. Therefore the problem of rounding is encountered, and this introduces some degree of error in the final calculations. This situation is clearly shown in Table 13.5, where the sum of Y_c (346.0058) is slightly in excess of the sum of Y (346). In a practical sense this is one of the problems faced in calculating trends.

Table 13.4

Calculation of the Least-Squares Parabolic Trend (Y Values Are Demonstration Data; Data Centered on the Half-Year)

X	Y	x	xY	x^2	x^2Y	x^4
1	16	−5	−80	25	400	625
2	34	−3	−102	9	306	81
3	56	−1	−56	1	56	1
4	78	1	78	1	78	1
5	80	3	240	9	720	81
6	82	5	410	25	2,050	625
	346		490	70	3,610	1,414

$$b = \frac{490}{70} = 7,$$

$$c = \frac{(6)(3,610) - (70)(346)}{(6)(1,414) - (70)^2} = -.7142,$$

$$a = \frac{346 - (-.7142)(70)}{6} = 66.$$

Table 13.5

Calculation of Trend Values for Data of Table 13.4

a	$+ bx$	$+ cx^2$	$= Y_c$
66	+ (7)(−5)	+ (−.7142)(25)	= 13.1450
66	+ (7)(−3)	+ (−.7142)(9)	= 38.5720
66	+ (7)(−1)	+ (−.7142)(1)	= 58.2858
66	+ (7)(1)	+ (−.7142)(1)	= 72.2858
66	+ (7)(3)	+ (−.7142)(9)	= 80.5722
66	+ (7)(5)	+ (−.7142)(25)	= 83.1450
			346.0058

Exercise 13.2. *Fitting the Least-Squares Parabolic Trend.* Instructions for problems 1 through 5: Fit a least-squares parabolic trend to the following sets of data. Determine a, b, c, and the Y_c values. For each problem, project the data for an additional two years. Graph the original data and the trend as well as the projected values. Round the data to two places.

	Problem 1		Problem 2		Problem 3

	Problem 1		Problem 2		Problem 3
Year	*Sales (millions of $)*		*Transistors Produced by the Able Company*	*Year*	*Demonstration Data*
1959	32	*Year*	*(millions)*	1	100
1960	38			2	50
1961	54	1959	9	3	46
1962	64	1960	5	4	8
1963	84	1961	17	5	16
1964	99	1962	21	6	0
1965	119	1963	41		
		1964	53		
		1965	78		

Problem 4		Problem 5	
Year	*Fishing Licenses Issued (thousands)*	*Year*	*Number of Stockholders in the Baker Corporation (thousands)*
1960	45	1959	220
1961	57	1960	188
1962	53	1961	234
1963	73	1962	228
1964	82	1963	300
1965	100	1964	300
		1965	368

6. The XYZ airline reported its passenger service revenues for the years 1958 through 1964 as follows (round to millions):

Year	Passenger Service Revenues (dollars)
1958	3,351,782
1959	4,933,487
1960	6,137,216
1961	7,372,333
1962	8,702,455
1963	11,388,135
1964	12,660,869

(a) draw a graph of the data; (b) fit a parabolic trend by the least-squares method; (c) project the trend for 1965 and 1966; (d) from the actual data and trend, how much reliance would you attach to the 1965 and 1966 projections? (e) Do you believe the parabolic trend to be more appropriate to these data than, say, a straight-line trend? Why?

7. Is a parabolic trend necessarily appropriate to a time series exhibiting growth? Explain.

8. Examine the annual report of a large corporation. Are any of the trends shown as parabolic trends? Explain why parabolic trends might or might not be shown in an annual report.

13.5 Removal of Trend from Data—Percentage Deviation Method

It is sometimes desirable to present, either in tabular form or as a graph, the changes of a time series from which the influence of trend has been removed. The result will then be a pattern of variation above and below a common reference or zero line. This line of reference is generally designated as the 100 per cent line and the deviations above and below are likewise measured in percentages. Trends are frequently removed from the data to more clearly portray the cyclical factor.

Customary procedure in eliminating the trend utilizes percentage deviation in exactly the same manner as if percentage change were being computed. (1) The original Y data are divided by the corresponding trend values. (2) The quotient is multiplied by 100 and converted to a relative—that is, percentage. (3) Percentage deviation is derived by subtracting 100 per cent from the result. Thus:

$$\left(\frac{Y}{Y_c} \times 100\right) - 100 = \text{per cent deviation.}$$

Example. When the data of the straight-line trend given in Table 13.1 are converted to a percentage deviation from the trend, the calculations are carried out as shown in Table 13.6. Removal of the trend line by the percentage deviation method may be shown graphically by Illustration 13.2.

Table 13.6

Removal of Trend, Percentage Deviation Method

	(1)	(2)	(3)	(4)	(5)	(6)	(7)
Year	Y	Y_c	(Y/Y_c)	$\times\ 100$		$-\ 100$	$=\ \%\ Deviation$
1961	105	110	$(105/110)$	$\times\ 100 =$	95.4	$-\ 100 =$	-4.6
1962	140	130	$(140/130)$	$\times\ 100 =$	107.5	$-\ 100 =$	$+7.5$
1963	150	150	$(150/150)$	$\times\ 100 =$	100.0	$-\ 100 =$	0.0
1964	160	170	$(160/170)$	$\times\ 100 =$	94.3	$-\ 100 =$	-5.7
1965	195	190	$(195/190)$	$\times\ 100 =$	102.5	$-\ 100 =$	$+2.5$

Illustration 13.2   Removal of Trend, Percentage Deviation Method (Data from Table 13.6)

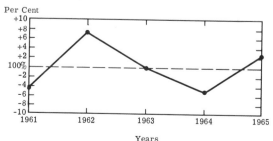

Exercise 13.3

1. Utilizing the Y and Y_c data of problems 1 through 6 of Exercise 13.1, remove the trend from the data by the percentage deviation method. Graph the results. In each case consider how clearly the results of change are shown. What variations now remain in the data?

2. The following data represent the average number of persons employed by a large manufacturing firm by years in the fifteen-year period from 1951 through 1965. Remove the trend by the percentage deviation method. Graph. The Y-data values are as follows: 2,400; 2,100; 4,000; 2,200; 1,400; 1,600; 1,900; 3,200; 2,800; 2,000; 2,100; 4,800; 4,300; 3,400; 4,200.
    (a) Is this firm's employment subject to cyclical variation?
    (b) Does the timing of the cyclical factor, if any, suggest a rhythmic, evenly spaced pattern?
    (c) Do the data suggest that the firm might well consider making a strenuous effort to overcome the cyclical problem? Why? Is more information needed to provide an answer to the question?

13.6   Seasonal Indices

Many business and economic data are subject to systematic variation originating in "seasonal" factors—that is, factors which recur with predictable regularity over short periods of time. A seasonal factor may be described as *a force acting persistently at regular time intervals of one year or less and causing systematic changes in the variable being measured.* An obvious illustration would be the impact of Christmas on retail store sales. However, a "seasonal pattern" may be apparent in the course of a year, a month, a week, or even in a day. The daily pattern exhibited by the number of customers patronizing a certain restaurant may be considered a seasonal pattern. In business and economic data it cannot be expected that the pattern will repeat itself in an exact, identical manner, season after season.

Many techniques exist for deriving a seasonal pattern from time-series data. The purpose here is not to review all these techniques and their various refinements, but rather to concentrate on two basic methods: (1) the percentage method and (2) the ratio-to-moving-average method. As a good deal of time-consuming, routine work is involved in the calculation of a seasonal index, the problems and illustrations will be made as short as possible without sacrificing the basic principles of construction and analysis.

Why should the economic analyst be interested in identifying and studying seasonal variation? Among the answers to this question are the following: (1) To obtain historical knowledge of the past seasonal factor in a particular time series. This may be done simply because the knowledge is interesting in itself, or because the pattern may be expected to repeat itself (to some degree) in the future. (2) In analyzing the time movements of a variable, it may be desirable to identify the seasonal factor in order that it may be removed from the data. When the seasonal is removed, a residual of trend, cyclical, and random factors will remain. (3) The seasonal pattern may be of use in forecasting future values of the time series. Certainly the responsible officials of an administrative unit possess intuitive knowledge of the seasonal ups and downs experienced by the unit, but a more precise calculation may be desirable. Too, while intuitive knowledge is, itself, excellent, the economic analyst will ordinarily wish to make this knowledge more specific and accurate by developing precise values for the seasonal factor based on past performance of the data. (4) Finally, the seasonal factor may be identified as part of the general information furnished by statistical methods to serve as a factual basis for the administrative decision-making function, for analysis, and for comparison.

Data to be subjected to seasonal analysis must be available on a periodic basis. That is, the data must be gathered quarterly, monthly, weekly, daily, or even hourly. In order to construct a seasonal, enough data must be available to supply a reasonable average. Five "years" of data are a minimum; that is, at least five sets of periodic values should be employed. It would be more accurate to have available eight to ten or more "years" of data from which the seasonal may be derived.

To construct a seasonal index by the percentage method, the arithmetic average is used to provide "typical" values. The set of Y data shown in Table 13.7 will illustrate the seasonal index computations.

Table 13.7

Construction of Seasonal Index—Percentage Method. Production of Steel Fence Posts by Firm A (000 omitted)

Year	Y Data by Quarters				Overall Quarterly Average by Year
	First	Second	Third	Fourth	
1960	21.7	21.9	21.4	19.1	21.0
1961	18.6	20.2	19.1	13.0	17.7
1962	18.3	22.8	23.8	12.9	19.4
1963	23.8	24.2	20.2	22.3	22.6
1964	22.5	21.6	19.1	16.8	20.0
1965	22.9	24.4	22.7	23.0	23.3
Totals	127.8	135.1	126.3	107.1	124.0
Average for quarter	21.3	22.5	21.0	17.8	Overall quarterly $\bar{X}$ 20.7
Quarterly seasonal index	102.9	108.7	101.4	87.0	Average of the seasonals 100.0

The method for determining the seasonal index as shown in Table 13.7 utilizes the following steps: (1) Obtain the arithmetic average of the data for each quarter and from this (2) compute the overall yearly average (20.7 in this case), and (3) compare each quarterly average with the overall quarterly average for the entire set of data Thus, for the first quarter (21.3/20.7) × 100 = 102.9; for the second quarter, (22.5/20.7) × 100 = 108.7; for the third quarter, (21.0/20.7) × 100 = 101.4; for the fourth quarter, (17.8/20.7) × 100 = 87.0. Note that under some circumstances the seasonals might not average exactly 100.0 because of rounding, and it might be desirable to adjust the indices to average exactly 100.0. (See the method of adjustment used in Table 13.11.)

The seasonal index itself is basically a percentage—that is, the relationship between the actual periodic data and the value that theoretically would have occurred had there been no seasonal variations. Thus, the seasonal index as shown in Table 13.7 is the percentage relationship that each quarterly average bears to the overall quarterly average.

If the original data are shown graphically, the six-year productive record appears as in Illustration 13.3.

Illustration 13.3   Production of Steel Fence Posts by Firm A (000 omitted)

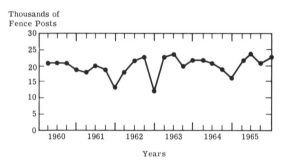

If the four indices obtained from the quarterly data of Table 13.7 be shown graphically, the result shown in Illustration 13.4 is obtained.

Illustration 13.4   Seasonal Index, Production of Fence Posts by Firm A

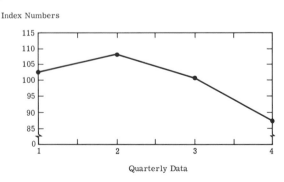

Use of the Seasonal Index in Forecasting

If the seasonal index were to be used in forecasting, several approaches might be employed, depending upon the assumptions made. For example, it may be assumed that underlying economic conditions will not change in the period for which the forecast is to be made. Clearly, many other assumptions could be made, depending upon the analyst's interpretation of the future. Probably the most frequently utilized forecasting technique—and one which assumes no major changes in underlying conditions—is to consider that the first quarter's (refer to Table 13.7) production of steel fence posts for 1966 will be the quarterly average for 1965, multiplied by the seasonal index *in decimal form* for the first quarter. Thus:

$$\frac{\text{Predicted first quarter}}{\text{production for year 7}} = (23.3)(1.029) = 24.0.$$

Predictions for succeeding quarters would be made in the same manner. It is important to notice, however, that this type of prediction makes one very broad assumption, namely, that no changes are expected in the underlying determinants of the system. This assumption may or may not turn out to be correct. On the other hand, the forecast can be considered a reasonable one based on known fact and coincides with known information concerning the seasonal pattern.

Adjustment for Seasonal Variation (Deseasonalizing the Data)

If it should be desired to remove the influence of seasonal factors on the production of fence posts by this firm, the result may be accomplished by dividing each quarterly production figure by the seasonal index *expressed as a decimal value* for that quarter. Thus, in 1960, we have:

$21.7/1.029 = 21.1 =$ adjusted production, first quarter, year 1;

$21.9/1.087 = 20.1 =$ adjusted production, second quarter, year 1;

$21.4/1.014 = 21.1 =$ adjusted production, third quarter, year 1;

$19.1/0.876 = 21.8 =$ adjusted production, fourth quarter, year 1.

If the data for the six years as given are adjusted for seasonal we have the result shown in Table 13.8.

When the data have been adjusted for seasonal variation, the influence of seasonal factors will have been removed. The adjusted data will still contain the cyclical, trend, and random factors. When data are adjusted for seasonal variation a partial smoothing effect takes place as shown by a comparison of Illustrations 13.3 and 13.5. When the seasonal influence has been removed from a time series, one major purpose is to study

Table 13.8

Quarterly Production of Steel Fence Posts Adjusted
for Seasonal Variation

		Quarters		
Year	First	Second	Third	Fourth
1960	21.1	20.1	21.1	21.8
1961	18.1	18.6	18.8	14.9
1962	17.8	21.0	23.4	14.8
1963	23.1	22.3	19.9	25.6
1964	21.9	19.9	18.8	19.3
1965	22.2	˙22.4	22.4	26.8

Illustration 13.5   Production of Steel Fence Posts Adjusted for
Seasonal Variation (Data from Table 13.8)

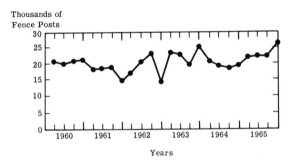

the remaining trend, cyclical, and random factors. A second major
purpose in computing the seasonal index is to study the influence of
seasonal variation on the data series. Thus, a firm might wish to consider
how its production record for this year compares with last year in regard
to the seasonal factor.

Adjustment for seasonal variation can also be illustrated as follows:
Since the time-series data will include the four factors $T \times S \times C \times R$,
then division by S leaves $T \times C \times R$. In the illustration employed here
(which for purposes of simplicity includes only six years) one could hardly
expect the longer swings of the business cycle to be exhibited, but the
trend, some cyclical, and the random factors would remain in the season-
ally adjusted data.

Exercise 13.4

1. *Computation of the quarterly seasonal index.* Given the following set of
    quarterly data representing millions of dollars of new installment loans
    made by a large bank for automobile purchases. Specific years are not
    necessary for the computations.

Y Data by Quarters (6 zeros omitted)

Year	First	Second	Third	Fourth
1	84	103	102	105
2	90	100	98	104
3	92	105	102	110
4	86	98	95	102
5	78	90	84	98
6	95	110	108	115

(a) Graph the data and fit a freehand trend.

(b) Compute the seasonal index and graph the results.

(c) Is the seasonal pattern a definite pattern?

(d) Is the pattern about what you might expect? Why?

(e) Is the trend of the Y data a definite and clear-cut trend?

(f) Do you detect any random factors in the Y data? What causes might account for any random factors you detect?

(g) Does the freehand trend assist you in visualizing the random and seasonal factors present in the Y data? Would a least-squares trend line have provided you with a better "line of reference"? If not, why not? If so, why?

(h) Now, deseasonalize the data. Graph the results.

(i) Do you have a much smoother curve than the one resulting from the original Y data? Is this what you should expect? Why?

(j) What factors remain in the deseasonalized data?

(k) Forecast automobile installment loans for year 7 by the method shown in Section 12.6.

    (1) To what extent would you personally rely on the accuracy of this forecast?

    (2) If you were a loan official of a particular lending company, what would this forecast mean to you? To what degree would you utilize the forecast in decision-making for year 7?

2. *Computation of the quarterly seasonal index.* Given the following set of quarterly data representing the value in millions of dollars of a certain corporation's profits after taxes.

Y Data by Quarters (millions of dollars)

Year	First	Second	Third	Fourth
1956	16.2	19.0	23.7	26.0
1957	21.7	18.8	16.9	17.3
1958	18.1	16.6	16.4	17.6
1959	17.9	18.2	17.5	13.4
1960	15.8	16.3	16.2	17.4
1961	19.7	20.3	21.5	23.0
1962	21.6	21.3	20.4	22.8
1963	22.5	21.2	21.4	19.2
1964	15.7	16.5	18.8	21.9
1965	22.6	25.6	22.6	23.0

(a) Graph the data and fit a freehand trend.

(b) Compute the seasonal index and graph the results.

(c) Do you find a pronounced seasonal pattern?

(d) Adjust the data for the seasonal factor—that is, deseasonalize the data and plot the results. Is the curve smoothed considerably by the effect of adjustment?

(e) Is this about what you should expect?

(f) Forecast corporate profits after taxes for year 1966.

(g) Suppose that by actual fact these profits turned out to be as follows: 23.8, 23.4, 21.3, 22.0. How valuable would the forecast have been?

(h) If you were to forecast corporate profits after taxes, how might the results be stated, given the possibility of recession or inflation?

Computation of Seasonal Index by Ratio-to-Moving-Average Method

A more elaborate method of constructing the seasonal index for monthly data is known as the "ratio-to-moving-average method." The general procedure for this method is as follows (see also Table 13.9):

1. The original monthly data for several years are obtained.

2. A 12-month moving average is computed for these data. Construction of the moving average will cause a loss of 6 months of data at each end of the table. Since the 12-month moving average represents an even number of time periods, subsequent centering by use of the 2-month moving average is required. However, the same result can be readily accomplished by use of a 24-month moving total as shown in column 5 of Table 13.9. In the absence of computers, an adding machine with a tape is very useful since subtotals can be recorded and a new month added, while the earlier month is subtracted on each computation.

3. When the 12-month, centered moving average is obtained, the corresponding original Y value is divided by the moving average to obtain a ratio. Subsequently all ratios are multiplied by 100 for presentation in the usual seasonal form. This, then, is the ratio of the original Y value to the typical value for that month as represented by the moving average. (See column 7 of Table 13.9.)

4. The computed ratios are then arranged in tabular form by month and year as shown in Table 13.10.

5. The seasonal indices are then arrayed by month—that is, ranked from low to high—and the median value selected as the "typical" seasonal value for that particular month. Note: Because these are medians, their average will not necessarily be 100.0 for the 12-month period. Slight adjustments may be required as noted below Table 13.11.

The ratio-to-moving-average method for calculating the seasonal index requires considerable clerical effort. The hand labor in calculating the 12-month moving average may take several hours. When this task is completed, two or three more hours may be required to actually derive the resulting seasonal index. However, if a computer is available, the amount of hand labor is substantially reduced.

In the set of data given in Table 13.9, the monthly figures given represent new loans made by a commercial bank in a medium-sized city. The figures may be thought of as exclusive of automobile and mortgage loans. In other words, the figures given are new short-term loans for that particular month.

Table 13.9

Computation of Seasonal Index by the Ratio-to-Moving-Average Method

(1) Year	(2) Month	(3) Data (millions of $)	(4) 12-Month Moving Total	(5) 24-Month Moving Total (to Center the Data)	(6) (5) ÷ 24 Months = the Moving Average	(7) Ratio of Original Data to Moving Average: (3) ÷ (6)
Year 1	Jan.	32.0				
	Feb.	56.0				
	Mar.	52.0				
	Apr.	80.0				
	May	64.0				
	June	68.0	767.1			
	July	69.6	768.7	1,535.8	64.0	108.8 July
	Aug.	72.0	770.3	1,539.0	64.1	112.3 Aug.
	Sept.	64.0	769.5	1,539.8	64.2	99.7 Sept.
	Oct.	68.0	765.5	1,535.0	64.0	106.3 Oct.
	Nov.	69.0	767.9	1,533.4	63.9	108.0 Nov.
	Dec.	72.5	767.4	1,535.3	64.0	113.2 Dec.
Year 2	Jan.	33.6	765.8	1,533.2	63.9	52.6 Jan.
	Feb.	57.6	763.4	1,529.2	63.7	90.4 Feb.
	Mar.	51.2	761.0	1,524.4	63.5	80.5 Mar.
	Apr.	76.0	757.0	1,518.0	63.2	120.2 Apr.
	May	66.4	756.0	1,513.0	63.0	105.4 May
	June	67.5	756.5	1,512.5	63.0	107.1 June
	July	68.0	756.3	1,512.8	63.0	107.9 July
	Aug.	69.6	756.5	1,502.8	62.6	111.2 Aug.
	Sept.	61.6	758.1	1,514.6	63.1	97.6 Sept.
	Oct.	64.0	766.1	1,524.2	63.5	100.8 Oct.
	Nov.	68.0	767.7	1,533.8	63.9	106.4 Nov.
	Dec.	73.0	770.0	1,537.7	64.0	114.1 Dec.
Year 3	Jan.	34.4	772.0	1,542.0	64.2	53.6 Jan.
	Feb.	57.8	776.1	1,548.1	64.5	89.6 Feb.
	Mar.	52.8	779.3	1,555.4	64.8	81.5 Mar.
	Apr.	84.0	781.7	1,561.0	65.0	129.2 Apr.
	May	68.0	784.0	1,565.7	65.2	104.3 May
	June	69.8	783.7	1,567.7	65.3	106.8 June
	July	70.0	785.2	1,568.9	65.4	107.0 July
	Aug.	73.7	787.5	1,572.7	65.5	112.5 Aug.
	Sept.	64.8	788.3	1,575.8	65.7	98.6 Sept.
	Oct.	66.4	785.3	1,573.6	65.6	101.2 Oct.
	Nov.	70.3	784.5	1,569.8	65.4	107.4 Nov.
	Dec.	72.2	786.7	1,571.2	65.5	110.2 Dec.
Year 4	Jan.	35.9	790.3	1,577.0	65.7	54.6 Jan.
	Feb.	60.1	791.8	1,582.1	65.9	91.2 Feb.
	Mar.	53.6	793.4	1,585.2	66.0	81.2 Mar.
	Apr.	81.0	795.0	1,588.4	66.2	122.4 Apr.
	May	67.2	794.4	1,589.4	66.2	101.5 May
	June	72.0	796.2	1,590.6	66.3	108.6 June
	July	73.6	797.1	1,593.3	66.4	110.8 July
	Aug.	75.2	797.8	1,594.9	66.4	113.3 Aug.
	Sept.	66.4	799.4	1,597.2	66.6	99.7 Sept.

Table 13.9 (*Continued*)

(1) Year	(2) Month	(3) Data (millions of $)	(4) 12-Month Moving Total	(5) 24-Month Moving Total (to Center the Data)	(6) (5) ÷ 24 Months = the Moving Average	(7) Ratio of Original Data to Moving Average: (3) ÷ (6)
	Oct.	68.0		—1,600.2—	—66.7—	—101.9 Oct.
			800.8			
	Nov.	69.7		—1,603.2—	—66.8—	—104.3 Nov.
			802.4			
	Dec.	74.5		—1,605.5—	—66.9—	—111.4 Dec.
			803.1			
Year 5	Jan.	36.8		—1,605.1—	—66.9—	— 55.0 Jan.
			802.0			
	Feb.	60.8		—1,606.2—	—66.9—	— 90.9 Feb.
			804.2			
	Mar.	55.2		—1,609.9—	—67.1—	— 82.3 Mar.
			805.7			
	Apr.	82.4		—1,612.0—	—67.2—	—122.6 Apr.
			806.3			
	May	68.8		—1,612.9—	—67.2—	—102.4 May
			806.6			
	June	72.2		—1,608.7—	—67.0—	—107.8 June
			805.1			
	July	72.5		—1,609.4—	—67.0—	—108.2 July
			804.3			
	Aug.	77.0		—1,607.8—	—67.0—	—114.9 Aug.
			803.5			
	Sept.	67.9		—1,607.8—	—67.0—	—101.3 Sept.
			804.3			
	Oct.	68.6		—1,609.4—	—67.1—	—102.2 Oct.
			805.1			
	Nov.	70.0		—1,607.8—	—67.0—	—104.5 Nov
			802.7			
	Dec.	73.0		—1,607.0—	—67.0—	—109.0 Dec.
			804.3			
Year 6	Jan.	36.0		—1,612.1—	—67.2—	— 53.6 Jan.
			807.8			
	Feb.	60.0		—1,616.2—	—67.3—	— 89.2 Feb.
			808.4			
	Mar.	56.0		—1,616.9—	—67.4—	— 83.1 Mar.
			808.5			
	Apr.	83.2		—1,618.8—	—67.4—	—123.4 Apr.
			810.3			
	May	66.4		—1,622.6—	—67.6—	— 98.2 May
			812.3			
	June	74.3		—1,627.1—	—67.7—	—109.7 June
			814.8			
	July	76.0				
	Aug.	77.6				
	Sept.	68.0				
	Oct.	70.4				
	Nov.	72.0				
	Dec.	75.5				

Table 13.10

Seasonal Indices from Column (7) of Table 13.9

Month	Year 1	Year 2	Year 3	Year 4	Year 5	Year 6
Jan.	..	56.2	53.6	54.6	55.0	53.6
Feb.	..	90.4	89.6	91.2	90.9	89.2
Mar.	..	80.5	81.5	81.2	82.3	83.1
Apr.	..	120.0	129.2	122.4	122.6	123.4
May	..	105.4	104.3	101.5	102.4	98.2
June	..	107.1	106.8	108.6	107.8	109.7
July	108.8	107.9	107.0	110.8	108.2	..
Aug.	112.3	111.2	112.5	113.3	114.9	..
Sept.	99.7	97.6	98.6	99.7	101.3	..
Oct.	106.3	100.8	101.2	101.9	102.2	..
Nov.	108.0	106.4	107.1	104.3	104.5	..
Dec.	113.2	114.1	110.2	111.4	109.0	..

The computed seasonal indices are shown in Table 13.10. Observing these indices, it is clear that a pattern of regularity does exist in the data. Now, to isolate the seasonal factor more specifically, the data should be ranked by month as shown in Table 13.11.

As a first step, the values are ranked and the median is determined for each of the 12 months. Since the number of items is odd, take the third item in each column and place this value in the "Medians(unadjusted)" row.

The next and final step in constructing the seasonal index is to determine whether the sum of the 12 indices is 1,200.0. Theoretically, the 12 seasonal indices should average to 100 (sum to 1,200). However, because the median value (an average of position) is used rather than the mean (an average of calculation), it is unlikely that the 12 indices would total exactly 1,200.0. Adjustment to a total of 1,200.0 is necessary if the index is to be used for seasonal adjustment of data (rather than simply identifying the seasonal); otherwise, extraneous factors are introduced. Use of the median as a measure of central tendency is appropriate because it is here desired to eliminate unusually high or low values from the computation. Unusual values might arise in a period marked by unordinary circumstances such as recession, inflation, strikes, floods, natural disasters, and so on.

In the illustration, the indices total 1,199.4. In order to adjust this total to 1,200.0, each index should (in theory) be multiplied by a factor which in this case looks a bit unrealistic. Thus:

$$\frac{1,200.0}{1,199.4} = 1.0005250125.$$

In the seasonal index row, the "unadjusted" values have been raised slightly to bring the total to 1,200.0. Whether or not this adjustment might be considered picayune depends upon the judgment of the individual concerned. The adjustment does have the advantage of making the seasonal index consistent. In this particular case the highest-valued items were increased by 0.1. Obviously, in another problem the correction might have been negative and one or more values would thus have been adjusted downward. Too, under some circumstances it might have been preferred to carry all computations to two places and then bring the final rounding to one place as the last step of the computations.

If the seasonal index is plotted on an appropriate scale, the graph shown in Illustration 13.6 is obtained.

The monthly pattern will not be as "smooth" as a quarterly index for the same data. Clearly, a monthly seasonal index with 12 values has the opportunity of being characterized by more "peaks and valleys" than a quarterly index consisting of only 4 values. Since the seasonal pattern

Table 13.11

Seasonal Indices of Table 13.10 Ranked by Month

Rank	Jan.	Feb.	Mar.	Apr.	May	June	July	Aug.	Sept.	Oct.	Nov.	Dec.	Total
1	56.2	91.2	83.1	129.2	105.4	109.7	110.8	114.9	101.3	106.3	108.0	114.1	
2	55.0	90.9	82.3	123.4	104.3	108.6	108.8	113.3	99.7	102.2	107.1	113.2	
3	54.6	90.4	81.5	122.6	102.4	107.8	108.2	112.5	99.7	101.9	106.4	111.4	
4	53.6	89.6	81.2	122.4	101.5	107.1	107.9	112.3	98.6	101.2	104.5	110.2	
5	53.6	89.2	80.5	120.0	98.2	106.8	107.0	111.2	97.6	100.8	104.3	109.3	
Medians (unadjusted)	54.6	90.4	81.5	122.6	102.4	107.8	108.2	112.5	99.7	101.9	106.4	111.4	Total 1,199.4
Seasonal Index (as adjusted)	54.6	90.4	81.5	122.7	102.4	107.9	108.3	112.6	99.7	101.9	106.5	111.5	Total 1,200.0

Note: To adjust the total seasonal index (as shown in the last row of the table) to 1,200.0, each of the unadjusted medians should be multiplied by 1,200.0/1,199.4. Observe that this is a very small adjustment, so small in fact that some months are really unaffected because of the necessity to round to one place at the right of the decimal. Thus, January, February, and March are unchanged by the adjustment. However, April and June, for example, are sufficiently affected to raise the index by 0.1. Notice that when the adjustments are completed for the 12 months, the total of the 12 indices is 1,200.0. This means, of course, that the average of the seasonal indices is 100.0 as it should be.

Illustration 13.6   Seasonal Index, Commercial Bank Loans (Data from Table 13.11)

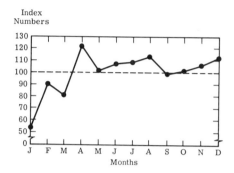

here observed represents the new short-term loans of a small country bank, the pattern might well be expected to show a peak during the income tax period, a peak in the spring when farm demands are in evidence, in July and August when vacations are in prominence, and finally at Christmas when the demand for personal loans is likely to be pronounced.

In constructing, demonstrating, and studying the seasonal index as shown, there is the possibility of overlooking the fact that the pattern is not likely to remain constant through time. The seasonal pattern is determined by averaging past values. Once the seasonal is established by refining past data, it cannot be assumed that the pattern will remain unchanged as time passes. One way to check periodically for change is to recompute the index each year. Clearly, this procedure involves some clerical work, but is necessary to keep the data up to date.

Additional Comments on the Ratio-to-Moving-Average Method

The seasonal index obtained by the ratio-to-moving-average method is logical in that each month's data are compared to an appropriate 12-month centered moving average. This means that each month is divided by the average of the period of which it is the median—that is, the center. In this respect the ratio-to-moving-average method is more accurate than dividing each time period by a single average for the year as shown in Table 13.7 (production of steel fence posts).

The objectives for computing a seasonal index include, as previously noted: (1) isolating and studying the seasonal pattern itself, (2) removing the seasonal factor from the data either (a) to study the remaining forces (T, C, R) or (b) as a preliminary step in removing either the cyclical or trend factor, (3) obtaining knowledge of the seasonal as an aid in forecasting.

Exercise 13.5. *Seasonal Computation Employing the Ratio-to-Moving-Average Method.* The following data closely approximate changes in the durable-goods index of industrial production for six consecutive years.

Year	Jan.	Feb.	Mar.	Apr.	May	June	July	Aug.	Sept.	Oct.	Nov.	Dec.
1	42	49	56	56	52	50	52	53	52	51	46	42
2	41	39	35	34	36	35	34	35	37	39	42	43
3	45	47	48	51	53	55	55	53	57	64	63	61
4	60	61	61	62	57	56	39	55	61	68	66	66
5	64	67	66	63	59	62	50	59	60	59	56	47
6	43	39	38	33	33	39	32	40	46	46	51	52

Note: The values shown are simplified from the original data to reduce the computational effort required for this problem.

Instructions: (a) Draw a graph of the original data. (b) Compute the seasonal index by the ratio-to-moving-average method. (c) Draw a graph of the seasonal index. (d) Since the data given here closely approximate the empirical situation, would you say the seasonality of durable-goods manufacturing is pronounced in the six-year period? (e) Since in the computations you have derived a 12-month moving average, plot this series on the same chart as the original data. (f) How effective is this moving average in smoothing the data? (g) Is a trend present in the data? If so, what type of trend would best describe the data? (h) Would you say that a projection of the trend line would provide a reasonable forecast for the first six months of year 7? (i) In forecasting, would you prefer to use the projection-of-trend method, or would you rather project by use of the seasonal index as explained in Section 13.5? Why? (j) For how many years in the future would the seasonal index constructed from these data be appropriate?

13.7 Summary

The study of time series, trends, and seasonal variations constitute one highly significant segment of business and economic statistics. These measures are widely employed as information-carriers throughout the business and economic world. The accuracy of such statistics depends upon the degree of accuracy achieved in the original measurements of the variable in question and on the assumptions underlying those measurements. While trends and seasonal variations can be used to "forecast" future values, we have observed that many underlying determinants may subsequently change and negate at least part of the value of the forecast.

On the other hand, it is necessary to consider both the past and the future in present calculations, and the statistical measures surveyed in this and Chapter 12 provide a set of techniques for obtaining information on which to base forward-looking decisions.

The basic theory of trends and seasonal variations is simply that the average change of a variable as refined from past measurements will be typical of actual changes which occurred. We have observed some of the statistical methods for isolating and interpreting trend and seasonal factors in order that analysis and decisions may be based on as accurate information as possible.

Key Terms and Concepts of This Chapter

Adjustment for seasonal variation
Cyclical factors
Forecasting
Parabolic trend
Random factor

Removal of trend
  (a) Percentage-deviation method
  (b) Ratio-to-moving-average
      method
Time centering
  (a) Whole years
  (b) Half years

Exercise 13.6.   *Parabolic Trend*

1. *Fitting the parabolic trend to actual data.* Assume the following data closely approximate the growth in total assets of a life insurance company over a seven-year period. (a) Fit a parabolic trend to the data. (b) Draw a graph of the data and trend. (c) Project the trend two years in the future.

Total Assets of a Small Life Insurance Company

Year	Total Assets (millions of $)
1	73
2	78
3	84
4	91
5	98
6	108
7	118

2. From your graph and knowledge of the values of the parameters, answer the following questions:
   (a) If you were asked to predict the firm's total assets in year 8, what would your answer be: (1) on the assumption that no fundamental changes would occur in general economic conditions; (2) on the assumption that a recession of mild proportions, say a 2 per cent drop in gross national product, would occur?
   (b) If you were sitting on the board of directors of this insurance company, what policy or policies would you advocate for year 8 on the basis of a predicted mild recession?
   (c) Again, you are sitting in on a meeting of the board of directors. The company statistician brings the graph and trend line with a two-year projection to the meeting. The company president argues that the projection for year 9 is "probably about right." Would you agree and why?

Exercise 13.7.   A certain manufacturing company has recorded the following quarterly sales totals.

	First Quarter	Second Quarter	Third Quarter	Fourth Quarter
Year 1	72	68	80	70
Year 2	76	70	82	74
Year 3	74	66	84	80
Year 4	76	74	84	78
Year 5	78	74	86	82

1. Construct a seasonal index of sales for this firm by the method illustrated in Table 13.7. Draw a graph of the seasonal index.
    (a) Looking at the original data, would you say the seasonal index you constructed is quite "typical" or "representative" of the data?
    (b) Forecast sales for year 6.
    (c) In making the forecast, what assumption(s) are implicit in the forecast? To what extent might these assumptions turn out to be incorrect? If you were planning the production and sale of this product would you "rely" on the forecast? Explain.

2. Using the original data given above, construct a seasonal index by the ratio-to-moving-average method. (See Tables 13.9, 13.10, and 13.11.)
    (a) If the moving average is not a 12-month moving average, what time period must be used?
    (b) How many average values are lost in the process of constructing the moving average? What bearing, if any, does this fact have on the validity of the seasonal index?
    (c) How does the seasonal index you constructed by the ratio-to-moving-average method compare with the index constructed by the percentage method as illustrated in Table 13.8? In what ways are these two indices different? Similar?
    (d) Are there any criteria by which you could judge one method to be clearly superior to the other? Why or why not?

3. Explain what use might be made of the seasonal-index data of this problem.

4. Deseasonalize the data using the ratio-to-moving-average index.
    (a) How does this process change the data in the original table of sales values? What was the net effect of deseasonalizing the data?
    (b) What factors have remained in the data after they were deseasonalized? What other decomposition techniques might be used on the data after they have been deseasonalized? To what extent might decomposition be desirable from a decision-making point of view?

5. (a) Remove the trend from the deseasonalized data. Draw a graph of the result.
    (b) What factors now remain in the data? What explanation could be given for the variations which do remain?

Exercise 13.8

1. Construct a straight-line trend by the method of dual averages for the following Y data (consecutive years): 310, 300, 269, 270, 246, 240.

2. Now draw a graph of the trend computation and the original data.

3. Construct a straight-line trend by the least-squares method for the data given above.

4. Compare the two graphs. Which do you prefer and why? What reasons can be given to substantiate your choice of methods? If the data of this problem involved several additional years, would this have any bearing on the choice of method?

Bibliography

Bowen, Earl K., *Statistics*, chaps. 9, 10, and 11. Homewood, Ill.: Richard D. Irwin, Inc., 1960.

Croxton, Frederick E., and Dudley J. Cowden, *Practical Business Statistics*, 3rd ed., chaps. 28, 24, 30, and 21. Englewood Cliffs, N.J.: Prentice-Hall, Inc., 1960.

Ekeblad, Frederick A., *The Statistical Method in Business*, chaps. 16, 17, and 18. New York: John Wiley & Sons, Inc., 1962.

Hirsch, Werner Z., *Introduction to Modern Statistics*, chaps. 15 and 16. New York: The Macmillan Company, 1957.

Mills, Frederick C., *Statistical Methods*, 3rd ed., chaps. 10, 11, and 12. New York: Holt, Rinehart & Winston, 1955.

Neiswanger, William Addison, *Elementary Statistical Methods*, rev. ed., chaps. 15, 16, and 17. New York: The Macmillan Company, 1956.

Neter, John, and William Wasserman, *Fundamental Statistics for Business and Economics*, chaps. 15, 16, and 17. Boston: Allyn and Bacon, Inc., 1961.

Moroney, M. J., *Facts from Figures*, rev. ed., chap. 17. Baltimore: Penguin Books, Inc., 1956.

Spurr, William A., Lester S. Kellogg, and John H. Smith, *Business and Economic Statistics*, chaps. 14, 15, and 16. Homewood, Ill.: Richard D. Irwin, Inc., 1954.

Tuttle, Alva M., *Elementary Business and Economic Statistics*, chaps. 15, 16, 17, and 18. New York: McGraw-Hill Book Company, 1957.

14 TWO-VARIABLE LINEAR CORRELATION

14.1 Introduction

The task of this chapter is to consider the subject of two-variable linear correlation. Although correlation techniques and analysis represent a degree of sophistication in data-handling, a good deal of background has already been provided by previous chapters. For example, the concepts involved in fitting a trend line will be useful here. However, rather than employing the term "trend line" it is now desirable to speak of a *regression line*, which may also be termed a *line of conditional means*. A *regression line* is a line of average relationship between two variables known as *paired variables*. The regression line is used mainly for forecasting values of the *Y* variable from the *X* variable. The word *correlation* will be defined to refer to the *degree of association or relationship between two variables*. This association will be positive when the values of the two variables generally increase simultaneously and negative when one of the variables generally increases as the other decreases. Thus it can be said that some mathematical degree of correlation exists between two variables when the increases or decreases are more or less regular or uniform.

Correlation is used to measure the degree of association between two variables. Regression is employed (1) when correlation is high-valued and (2) when it is desired to forecast or predict values of the *Y* variable from specific values of the *X* variable. To grasp these notions, consider a very simple example from the natural sciences. If a gas is placed in a sealed container at a given temperature, the pressure of the gas in the container can be measured. It is commonly known that temperature and pressure are associated under these conditions—that is, if the temperature rises, the pressure will rise and vice versa. This is the idea of correlation. If, however, it is desired to predict the pressure, given the temperature, the problem is one of regression. Clearly, correlation and regression are related concepts. Correlation is a meaningful concept by itself, but if regression is to have any accuracy, a high degree of correlation must be present.

It may also be noted that correlation and regression are really part of inferential statistics. In most practical problems, the data which result from measurements of the paired variables will have been obtained from a sampling process. Thus, incomplete information from samples is employed to draw conclusions about the parameters of the universe. Under these circumstances, the knowledge of probability which has been so useful in studying sampling and statistical inference is equally useful in studying correlation and regression.

Since the concepts of correlation and regression are best grasped through the use of examples, consider a certain problem faced by the manager of a city traction company. Suppose the manager of this company must make some decisions as to the amount of traction equipment to be purchased in the next few years. The manager will require this information to take the best advantage of the capital market by anticipating needs and acquiring new funds at the most appropriate time. But how can the manager make predictions which require knowledge of the number of passengers to be carried in future years? One approach to the problem would be, of course, to construct a graph and a trend line employing the passenger data accumulated over the past several years. Here the manager could employ trend analysis as described in previous chapters.

Now, suppose the manager approaches the problem of passenger estimation by a slightly different route. In considering the problem he formulates the hypothesis that there is a relationship between the number of passenger automobiles registered in the city each year and the number of passengers carried in that year. If some relationship does exist between these two variables, common sense suggests that as the number of automobiles increase, the demand for traction service will decrease. Quite obviously, the problem faced by the manager is not likely to be quite this simple, for other variables such as the growth of city population and the available parking space in the downtown area are among the other factors to be considered. However, at the moment let the problem be confirmed to two variables, namely numbers of autos and number of bus passengers by year.

The manager has at his disposal values of the variables for each of the past ten years. These are arranged as shown in Table 14.1. For each year he will observe the number of autos in the city and the number of bus passengers carried. Thus, for a given year, say 1964, he has a "pair of variables." Casual observation of the ten sets of paired variables (see

Table 14.1) would indicate broad changes through time, but the manager wishes to be more precise. He now decides to employ a graphic technique in which each pair of variables will be plotted as "dots" on the coordinates of a graph. The completed graph is shown in Illustration 14.1(a). Notice that time is not a variable.

Table 14.1

Passenger Autos and Bus Passengers, 1955–1964

Year	Passenger Automobiles Registered, X (hundreds of thousands)	Bus Passengers Carried, Y (millions of persons)
1955	1.1	35.4
1956	1.2	34.1
1957	1.3	33.6
1958	1.5	32.5
1959	1.6	30.2
1960	1.7	29.2
1961	1.9	27.3
1962	2.0	26.8
1963	2.1	26.1
1964	2.3	25.7

Observe Illustration 14.1(a). The construction of the graph is as follows. It is hypothesized that the number of passenger autos is a variable which can be used to predict bus passengers carried. Therefore, the number of autos is plotted on the X axis. The number of bus passengers is thought to be in some way dependent upon the number of passenger autos registered. Bus passengers are therefore plotted on the Y axis. Now take, for example, the year 1955. The number of autos (110,000) is located on the X axis while the corresponding number of bus passengers is located on the Y axis. At the coordinate point of the X and Y values, a dot is placed and labeled "1955." This process is then completed for the

Illustration 14.1(a)   Scattergram for the Data of Table 14.1

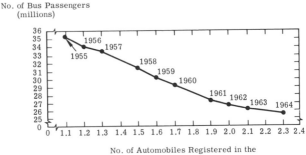

No. of Bus Passengers (millions)

No. of Automobiles Registered in the City (hundred thousands)

remaining pairs of values. The resulting graph is known as a *scattergram* and presents a visual impression of the relationship between the two variables.

From the graph shown in Illustration 14.1(a) the manager notices a fact which might be disturbing, but nevertheless the pattern of dots is convincing evidence that as autos registered in the city increase, passenger service of the traction company declines. The relationship is negative. Too, it is observed that the relationship is very close indeed. This relationship is shown by the fact that the dots, while not indicating a perfect straight-line relationship, do nevertheless fall in a pattern closely approximating a straight line. After studying the scattergram, it could be said that the correlation between the two variables is "high." Too, one could observe that if this relationship is used to predict the number of bus passengers to be carried *given* a definite number of autos, the results might be startingly accurate. For example, suppose it were given that 180,000 autos are registered in the city. About how many passengers could the traction company expect in that year? A glance at the graph of Illustration 14.1(a) indicates that a good guess would be about 28.2 million passengers—give or take a few thousand passengers either way.

A number of observations useful in the remainder of this chapter may now be made. Observe that the X variable (number of passenger autos) is being employed to predict the Y variable (number of bus passengers). Therefore X may be considered the *estimating* variable and Y may be described as the *estimated* variable. It might now be concluded that X is the independent variable and Y the dependent variable or that X is the cause and Y is the effect. However, one must be cautious in assigning cause and effect because in anything as complex as the business and economic world, cause and effect relationships are not likely to be this simple. It is much better to think of the *estimating* and *estimated* variables.

Observe that it is possible to take a ruler and draw in a "trend line" for Illustration 14.1(a). The trend line might be declared a "good fit." However, the straight line which could be drawn as a trend line is not really a trend line at all (although it would do no great harm to think of it as a trend line) but is rather a *regression* line. This means that the line is useful in *predicting* Y values from X values. The regression line is really a *line of conditional means* of the Y variable.[1] By this it is implied that whenever a value is given for X, say 180,000, then the most probable

---

[1] The term "conditional" as used here refers to the conditional probability of Y *given* X. In other words, the conditional probabilities which were described in Section 5.8, may also be applied to correlation analysis.

value of Y at that particular X value would be 28.2 million passengers. (The student should check these figures on the graph.) In a normal distribution, the most probable value is also the mean value. Thus, for each value of X there is a "most probable" value of Y. The set of all points along the regression line will be designated as the *line of conditional means*. These matters will be considered in detail in the remainder of the chapter.

In summary, it may be said that problems involving the relationship between two variables generally require measuring the strength of associa-tion between these variables, and there is also a need to ascertain whether good estimates of one variable could be made *given* knowledge of the other.

Symbols Used in Correlation Analysis

a = value of the regression line at the origin.

r = the coefficient of correlation. r ranges from -1 to $+1$.

r^2 = the coefficient of determination. r^2 ranges from 0 to $+1$.

k^2 = the coefficient of alienation. k^2 ranges from 0 to $+1$.

r_r = the coefficient of rank correlation. r_r ranges from -1 to $+1$.

d = rank difference—that is, $X_{\text{rank}} - Y_{\text{rank}} = d$.

D = the percentage of determination. See Formula (14.18).

$y_u = Y - Y_c$.

$y_c = Y_c - \bar{Y}$.

$y = Y - \bar{Y}$.

$\bar{Y}$ = the arithmetic mean of the Y series.

$\bar{X}$ = the arithmetic mean of the X series.

$x_c = X_c - \bar{X}$.

σ_y = the standard deviation of the Y series, universe values. (S_y for samples.)

σ_x = the standard deviation of the X series, universe values. (S_x for samples.)

σ_{yc} = the standard deviation of the regression (Y_c) values. Note: If sample values are employed, the notation changes to S_{yc}.

S_{yx} = the standard error of estimate. This is the "standard deviation" of the Y data measured around the regression line. See below.

$Y_c = a + bx$ (origin at $x = 0$), or $a + bX$ (origin at $X = 0$).

Basic Formulae Used in Correlation Analysis

A complete listing of correlation formulae used in this chapter is given for reference on page 429. However, it will be well to introduce the following relationships at this point. Additional formulae will be presented as the material of the chapter unfolds.

$$\sigma_y = \sqrt{\frac{\Sigma (Y - \bar{Y})^2}{N}} \qquad \text{(universe values)},$$

$$S_y = \sqrt{\frac{\Sigma (Y - \bar{Y})^2}{n - 1}} \qquad \text{(sample values)}. \qquad (14.14a)$$

The formulae above measure the standard deviation of the Y series of data. In squared form, σ_y^2 would represent the total variation in the Y series. Note: S_{yx} may be used in both cases.

$$S_{yx} = \sqrt{\frac{\Sigma (Y - Y_c)^2}{N}} \qquad \text{(universe values)},$$

$$S_{yx} = \sqrt{\frac{\Sigma (Y - Y_c)^2}{n - 2}} \qquad \text{(sample values)}. \qquad (14.14b)$$

Measures the standard error around the regression line. Also, measures the variation in the Y data not accounted for by variations in X—that is, measures a partial variation.

$$r = \frac{\Sigma\, xy}{\sqrt{\Sigma\, x^2 \cdot \Sigma\, y^2}}. \qquad (14.4)$$

r is the coefficient of correlation.

When the X and Y data are "centered" on their respective means, then

$$a = \bar{Y} \qquad \text{and} \qquad b = \frac{\Sigma\, xy}{\Sigma\, x^2}. \qquad (14.2)(14.3)$$

The accompanying illustration shows the relationship between S_{yx} (the standard error of estimate) and σ_y (the standard deviation of the Y series).

Illustration 14.1(b)   Relationship Between the Regression Line, S_{yx} and σ_y

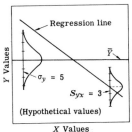

Some Major Features of Correlation Analysis

1. The basic idea of correlation is to discover how two sets of paired values are related, or if they are related at all. If two variables, X and Y, move in a predictable pattern, they are said to be correlated. If Y moves in response to X, then the question correlation analysis seeks to answer is this: How much of the change or variation in Y can be said to be associated with changes in X? If most of the variation in Y is associated with changes in X, the correlation is said to be "high"; if only a small proportion of the changes in Y can be said to be associated with changes in X, the correlation is said to be "low."

2. Correlation analysis seeks (a) to measure what relationship, if any, exists between two pairs of variables, designated as X and Y; (b) to determine if the relationship between the variables can be considered significant as measured by the F table; (c) to determine if any possible cause-and-effect relationship appears to exist. However, cause and effect is not easily determined by statistical methods alone—although statistical methods may be helpful—and logical proof of cause and effect is normally also sought on other than statistical grounds.

3. The basic technique employed in measuring correlation is really quite simple—even though the calculations do not always give that impression. The basic technique is this: The dispersion of the Y items is measured by the variance of Y. Thus σ_y^2 can be thought of as the total dispersion in the problem. Then, how well the regression line fits the data can be described by the variance S_{yx}^2 of the Y data measured around the regression line. Thus, if σ_y^2 be thought of as 100 per cent of the variation in the problem, then S_{yx}^2 can be considered as that part of the total variation in the Y series which is not associated with—or explained by—variations in the X series. Then, $(S_{yx}^2/\sigma_y^2) \times 100 = k^2$, the percentage of variation in Y which is not determined or explained by variations in X. Thus, k^2 represents the percentage of nondetermination, which means the amount of variation in Y not determined by variations in X. Apparently, then, the amount of determination is $r^2 = 100\% - k^2$. The coefficient of determination is r^2 and the coefficient of correlation is r.

4. There is one rather undesirable feature about r. Since r is calculated as the square root of a percentage based on the quotient of two variances, r is an abstract number and thus is not easily grasped. On the other hand, r^2 is a percentage and, as such, is easily understood. Thus, from some points of view, r^2 is a more usable measure than r.

14.2   The Nature of Correlation

Previous chapters have considered problems or experiments involving a single variable. This variable might have been sales, income, number of employees, a price level, the level of industrial production, or whatever. In time-series analysis, time was considered as the independent (estimating) variable. Time, however, is a unique variable in that its rate of change is constant, and in no manner is the rate of change related to fundamental changes in the data. *Time, by itself, is not considered to cause changes in the data.*

The word *correlation* refers to the *degree of association or the degree of relationship between two paired variables.* The test of such a relationship is *how well knowledge of one variable can be used to estimate values of the other.* Consider the problem faced by the manager of a firm when he must form a notion of the value of production for his firm one month in advance of the actual production period. The manager could simply guess the production figure, and on the basis of his experience he might be able to make quite good estimates. The estimating error—the standard deviation of a set of such estimates—is, however, likely to be quite large. Assuming the data to be normally distributed, a logical guess would be the mean production value based on past data. In Table 14.2 the best guess—that is, the most probable value—would be 10, the mean of the Y series.

Table 14.2

Payroll and Value of Finished Product for the ABC Corporation (All Values Simplified)

Month	Total Monthly Payroll X	Production: Total Value of Finished Products Y	Straight-Line Regression (Trend) for the Y Data Y_c	$(Y - Y_c)^2$
January	5	8	8	0
February	6	9	9	0
March	7	9	10	1
April	9	11	12	1
May	8	13	11	4
	35	50	50	6
	$\bar{X} = 7$	$\bar{Y} = 10$	$\bar{Y}_c = 10$	$S_{yx} = \sqrt{6/5}$
		$\sigma_y = 1.79$	$\sigma_{y_c} = 1.41$	$S_{yx} = 1.10$

Suppose, however, the manager casts about for some kind of information which would help him estimate the monthly value of production and which would provide some assurance of an estimate subject to a smaller standard error than would be possible by intelligent guessing alone. In other words, the problem faced by the manager is this: Given no prior information except a knowledge of production values, he must estimate the value of production one month in advance. The manager is well aware that such guesses are subject to a wide standard deviation. He now questions whether this deviation error can be reduced by employing some kind of prior information which will help estimate the value of next month's production. If the manager obtains prior information about, say, payroll, can he use this to reduce the estimating error for the value of production? If he obtains this prior information about payroll, will the estimating error for production be reduced over what it would have been in the absence of prior information?

Here, then, is essentially a problem in probability. A set of estimates made with no prior knowledge is a case of unconditional probability in a given sample space. But a set of estimates based on prior knowledge that a given event (a particular payroll value) has occurred is a case of conditional probability which reduces the sample space, thus raising the probability of the remaining events.

The information given in Table 14.2 is purposely made very small in order to minimize the calculations and to show the essential nature of the correlation problem without unnecessary detail. Too, it is here assumed that the data are the entire universe, thus minimizing the mechanical details involved. It is well, however, to recognize that in practical problems the amount of data is likely to be quite large, perhaps two or three hundred items, and such data would probably be considered to be a sample drawn from a larger universe. In the materials of the following paragraphs remember that simplicity is sought to facilitate the exposition.

The manager is interested to discover whether an observable relationship exists between payroll and production. Further, if a relationship can be said to exist, how close is this relationship? The test of such a relationship would be as follows: *If* payroll knowledge can be used to predict production more accurately than can be accomplished in the absence of such knowledge, *then* a relationship (correlation) is present in the paired sets of payroll and production data.

At this point some notion can be formed of the relationship between payroll and production by observing that if the manager had no knowledge other than the production data, his best guess of monthly production is the mean of Y—that is, 10—a guess which is subject to a standard deviation of 1.79. Thus, assuming a normal distribution of Y (production) values, if he predicted that production for June would be 10 ± 1.79, his probability of being correct would be about .68. Now, suppose that the manager is given prior knowledge as to the payroll for June, let us say 9. In addition, suppose the manager has available the straight-line trend data shown in the Y_c column. Now, he can make a better estimate than formerly by observing that if, say, $X = 9$, the predicted or estimated value of Y_c is 12. (See Table 14.2.) The standard deviation of the Y_c data is 1.41. Thus, the possession of prior knowledge has enabled the manager to reduce the estimating error from 1.79 to 1.41, or to achieve an error reduction of 21 per cent $[(1.79 - 1.41)/1.79] \times 100$. It is clear that a degree of association does exist between the two variables.

Given the data of Table 14.2, the problem faced by the plant manager is to determine how closely production is related to total payroll. Certainly it would be common sense to believe that if the payroll increased, the value of the finished product would also rise, and that a falling payroll would be accompanied by a falling product. It appears logical to formulate the hypothesis that an increase in X (payroll) would be accompanied by an increase in Y (production) and vice versa. The ability to estimate production when payroll is known would be of considerable value in setting sales targets, or perhaps in quoting prices and quantities to prospective customers.

How might the data be structured to discover the relationship (correlation) between these two variables of payroll and product? The first step is to construct a graph (scattergram) of the X and Y data to obtain a general notion of the degree of closeness between the two series. Illustration 14.2 indicates the nature of the scattergram and the visual relationship of the paired variables shown in Table 14.2.

Illustration 14.2 Scattergram for the Payroll and Production of the ABC Corporation (Data from Table 14.2)

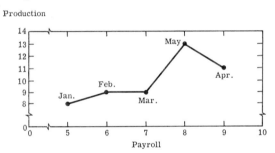

Each dot on the chart represents the (X, Y) coordinates of one pair of values. The dots have been identified by placing the corresponding month nearby. Now, observing the pattern produced by the dots, it may be noted the dots tend to exhibit a positive slope. It is not difficult to visualize a trend (regression) line fitted to the data and, in terms of our previous knowledge of trend/regression lines, the fit would appear to be rather close. However, the dots do not lie on a straight line but rather display some deviation from a linear regression line which might be fitted to the data.

Observing Illustration 14.2 it appears correct to say that, in general, an increase in X (payroll) is associated with an increase in Y (production), although enough deviations from this rule do occur to make the rule only partially true. The deviations $Y - Y_c$ from the regression line may be computed as an ordinary standard deviation and designated S_{yx}, hereafter known as the *standard error of estimate*. If, then, a major purpose of correlation is to measure the degree of association between X and Y for subsequent purposes of estimating Y from X, it might tentatively be concluded that correlation between payroll and production is rather "high" since both series tend to move closely together. Too, a straight-line trend would appear by inspection to fit the data rather well since the dots would lie close to the trend (regression) line.

The above conclusions and reasoning may now be examined more closely. The problem involves discovering *what relationship* (*if any*) *exists* between payroll and production and, if a relationship exists, whether it *permits better predictions* of production than can be made without prior payroll knowledge. Would an "index" of correlation (relationship) show a high or a low value? Viewing the problem in terms of a regression line fitted to the data, would the dots pack closely to the regression line or would the dots be widely scattered about the line? If the dots were closely packed around the regression line, it could be said the correlation was "high" because for each value of X there would be a corresponding Y value at or near the regression line. The standard error of estimate S_{yx} would be relatively small. If the dots were widely scattered about the line, correlation would be low. This, then, is the general nature of correlation. The problem now is to develop an index to provide a numerical value describing the relationship between X and Y. Such an index should be of broad applicability and should be readily understandable.

In order to visualize the problem of measuring and evaluating the degree of correlation some possibilities of the association between two variables are shown in the accompanying Illustrations A through D.

In Illustration A the dots representing various (X, Y) coordinates are widely scattered. It is impossible to discover a satisfactory relationship between X and Y. It may therefore be concluded that correlation is nonexistent.

In Illustration B the dots representing various (X, Y) coordinates are loosely arranged about a linear regression line fitted to the data. Some

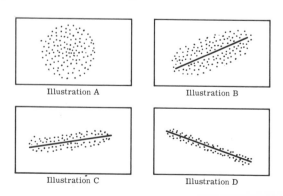

Illustration A

Illustration B

Illustration C

Illustration D

relationship exists between X and Y, but the relationship is not particularly strong. The relationship is positive as measured by the slope of the regression line.

In Illustration C the dots representing the various (X, Y) coordinates are closely packed about the regression line. A fairly high degree of association appears to exist between X and Y. The correlation is positive.

In Illustration D the dots representing various (X, Y) coordinates are closely packed about the regression line. A fairly strong association appears to exist between X and Y. Since the regression line exhibits a negative slope, the correlation is said to be negative.

From Illustrations A through D it may be observed that whenever an increase in the value of Y is associated with an increase in X (whether or not the correlation is high) the variables are said to be positively correlated. When a decrease in the value of Y is associated with an increase in the value of X, the variables are said to be negatively correlated. Observe also that a key to evaluating correlation is found in the "scatter" of the dots about the regression line. This scatter can be measured by (1) the method of rank correlation and (2) the method of least squares.

Exercise 14.1

1. What is the meaning of "paired variables"? Explain.

2. Why is it often difficult in business and economic data to know whether or not two variables are causally related?

3. Look up the words "correlate" and "correlation" in the dictionary. Do the definitions given therein agree closely with the illustrations and examples used in this section?

4. To what extent would you agree (after answering questions 2 and 3) that correlation is a matter of degree rather than a matter of absolutes?

5. Explain why the degree of correlation is stronger in Illustration C than in Illustration B.

6. Distinguish between correlation and regression.

14.3 Rank Correlation

Now that the general nature of correlation has been explored, the concepts can be made more exact and an index of correlation can be developed. Given a problem with several pairs of values for X and Y, and if Y increased whenever X increased, it could be concluded that some degree of positive association (that is, correlation) existed. Suppose these relationships are translated into "ranks" by assigning numbers to each X and each Y value in accordance with the relative magnitude of each X and Y. That is, the X and Y values are ranked from highest to lowest. If, then, each high value of X is associated with a high value for Y, the ranks of the X and Y values ought to correspond closely. By measuring the correspondence between the ranking of X and Y, a numerical value may be assigned to the degree of correlation present in the paired values. The ranking method is shown in Table 14.3, which utilizes the set of data given in Table 14.2. Notice that the X and Y data are ranked from highest to lowest, which means that the highest X (and Y) values are given rank 1, and so on.

Table 14.3

Rank Correlation—An Illustrative Example

Month	Payroll X	Production Y	X Rank (X_r)	Y Rank (Y_r)	Rank Differences $(X_r - Y_r = d)$	d^2
Jan.	5	8	5	5	0	0.00
Feb.	6	9	4	3.5	+.5	.25
Mar.	7	9	3	3.5	−.5	.25
Apr.	9	11	1	2	−1	1.00
May	8	13	2	1	+1	1.00
						2.50

The coefficient of rank correlation (r_r) may be determined as follows:

$$r_r = 1 - \frac{6d^2}{N(N^2 - 1)} = 1 - \frac{(6)(2.5)}{(5)(24)} = 1 - \frac{15}{120} = 0.875 = r_r, \quad (14.1)$$

where r_r = the coefficient of rank correlation,
    N = the number of paired variables.

What has been accomplished by this relatively simple procedure? It is now possible to state the coefficient of rank correlation as a number (.875), thus (1) facilitating comparison between correlations of other sets of data, if these exist, and (2) providing a means of interpreting the *degree* of correlation in the paired variables of payroll and production. Now, how might the value r_r = .875 be interpreted?

It may be seen from the construction of the formula for r_r that if the rankings of X and Y *do not correspond closely*, the differences measured by d will be large, and Σd^2 will be large. Note that d is a crude measure of nonassociation. Therefore, when division by $N(N^2 - 1)$ is performed, a relatively high value will be obtained which, when subtracted from 1.0, leaves r_r close to zero. Observe that the number 1 is really the total possible amount of association. If the ranking of X and Y *corresponded perfectly*, then $6 \Sigma d^2/N(N^2 - 1)$ would yield a value of zero to be subtracted from 1; that is, r_r is 1.0 (perfect association). *Thus, the formula yields values close to zero when little or no correlation is present, and displays values near 1 when the degree of correlation is high.* In other words, the formula provides a correlation range from -1 to $+1$ in which 0 implies no correlation and $+1$ or -1 implies perfect correlation. Values of r_r may be interpreted against this scale. Note: The sign of r is determined from the scattergram.

Now, a note of caution in interpreting r_r against the scale of 0 to $+1$ or -1. The r_r scale is not linear. For example, an r_r of .6 is not 20 per cent better than an r_r of .4. The scale by which to interpret r_r may be considered as if it were approximately logarithmic. This implies that values near the upper end of the scale are more closely packed together (in the manner of a slide rule) and, by analogy, this may be interpreted as meaning that r_r becomes progressively "better" as it approaches $+1$ or -1. Additional information on the interpretation of the coefficient of correlation will be presented later in this chapter.

When the mechanics of rank correlation and the interpretation of r_r have been dealt with, certain methodological questions remain. One question is this: Does the manner of ranking, whether from highest to lowest, or from lowest to highest, affect the value of r_r? As long as both series are ranked in a consistent manner, r_r is not affected. A second question is this: What is implied by the sign of r_r? If X and Y tend to increase simultaneously, the b value in a trend equation would be positive, and r_r is considered positive. If, on the other hand, Y were to decrease as X increased, the regression would be negative and r_r would be preceded by a negative sign.

Another question concerns the mechanics of ranking data. It is simple enough to rank the data if all the values are different, but what should be done when two or more values are identical? The average-rank method will be used. For example, suppose it were necessary to rank, from highest to lowest, the values, 6, 7, 9, 10, 10, 11, 11, 11, 12. The question here is how to treat the two tens and the three elevens. One way out of the dilemma is to *assign each of the tied numbers the average rank.* Thus, the three elevens would each be assigned rank 3 and the two tens would each be assigned the average rank 5.5. Other methods could be used. For example, since the two tens occupy ranks 5 and 6, one of the tens could be assigned rank 5 at random and the other ten then assigned rank 6. If this method is used, it should be used consistently throughout the problem. The problems of Exercise 14.2 should be solved on the basis of the average-rank method.

As a final comment on correlation by the ranking method, it may be seen that this technique is relatively simple and uncluttered; calculations may be performed rapidly, and the resulting coefficients of correlation may be evaluated on a scale of 0 to $+1$ or -1 (with reservations as previously noted). *Rank correlation does not assume the variates are normally distributed.* A major criticism of rank correlation is that the ranking method is not as precise as the least-squares method to be examined in subsequent sections. Too, rank correlation is not particularly useful in making estimates, since the probability concepts associated with a normal curve are not applicable. Too, the method of rank correlation does not allow as refined an analysis of data as does the least-squares method.

Exercise 14.2

1. (a) Draw a scattergram of each of the sets of data given below. Be certain you plot the values of X and Y in units of the original data, not in terms of ranks.
   (b) Compute the coefficient of rank correlation (r_r) for each set of data.
   (c) From the scattergram and the value of r_r, from a notion of the relationship between "scatter" and correlation (r_r) values.

Set A			Set B			Set C		
Week	X	Y	Month	X	Y	Year	X	Y
1	10	4	1	20	20	1	126.7	52.2
2	12	5	2	20	18	2	132.6	57.7
3	8	3	3	22	14	3	141.6	64.2
4	14	7	4	26	12	4	145.7	67.6
5	9	7	5	26	14	5	155.9	70.6
6	16	10	6	30	10	6	160.9	82.6
7	17	10	7	34	11	7	165.1	90.3
8	17	12	8	35	14	8	170.1	93.9
			9	40	12	9	185.2	98.2
			10	40	12	10	191.0	112.0

2. From your graphs of A, B, and C, answer the following questions:
   (a) For graph A: Draw in a freehand straight-line trend. Make an estimate of how well the trend line (known as a regression line in correlation analysis) actually fits the data. If you were to be asked to predict Y ranks from X ranks, how confident would you be of the accuracy of each set of paired X_{rank}, Y_{rank} values?
   (b) For graph B: Instructions are the same as those for graph A, but add the following question: What is the sign of r_r in this problem? Why?
   (c) For graph C: Instructions are the same as those for graph A, but add the following questions: What is the sign of r_r in this problem? Why? Interpret the meaning of a "high" value of r_r whose sign is positive. How would this interpretation differ from an identical r_r where the sign was negative?

3. Explain to your nonstatistics friend what is meant by the term "correlation" and suggest how various values of r_r should be interpreted. Now, explain the theory of rank correlation.

14.4   Least-Squares Linear Correlation

Perhaps the first thing that should be pointed out as we briefly examine the least squares method of correlation is that in the next few pages we will meet a number of formulae. Many others could be developed since "least squares" lends itself to the discovery of numerous "interesting" relationships. However, here only those relationships considered most useful will be presented.

It will be well to begin this section with a restatement of one of the basic objectives of correlation analysis: *If two variables can be said to be related, it is desirable to know if this relationship permits improved estimates of Y given knowledge of X.* For example, in the previous case involving payroll and production (see Table 14.2) it was possible to employ values of X to make predictions of the value of Y. From a knowledge of sampling and inference, it can be seen that if the problem is one of esti-mates, then a mean and a standard error (S_{yx}) can be employed as the basis for making confidence-interval statements about the value of Y *given a value for X.* The confidence-interval statements are based on the normal curve of probability. This assumes that both the X and Y variables *are actually normally distributed*—an assumption which may not always be correct. Too, this method of prediction assumes a conditional probability distribution of the Y values because Y is always predicted on the basis of a given value for X.

Now, the problem of deriving a least-squares measure of correlation may be explored more fully. Suppose we are given a set of paired values for X and Y data. A regression line is to be fitted to these data. This regression line (which is really a line of conditional means) will be employed to yield estimates of Y whenever a value of X is selected. Then, by computing the standard error of estimates of this regression line (S_{yx}) probability statements can be made about Y values associated with partic-ular values of X. For example, using the payroll-production data of Table 14.2, the following statement could be made: Given that the value of the payroll is 6, the estimated value of production is between 6.84 and 11.16 at the 95 per cent confidence level. Observe that the confidence interval is constructed in the usual manner; that is, if $X = 6$, then Y_c, the regression value, is 9. Therefore 9 is the mean of a conditional probability distribution whose standard error of estimate is 1.10. (See Table 14.2.) The interval is constructed as $9 \pm 1.96 \times 1.10 = 6.84$ and 11.16.

In Chapter 13 it was pointed out that a trend line fitted by the method of least squares could, by the least-squares criterion, be considered a line of best fit. By the same reasoning, the line of conditional means (the regression line) may be considered "best" in that the sum of the squared deviations measured around this line is at a minimum. Since the basic concept of correlation involves measuring the degree of scatter of the "dots" about the regression line, it is important that the line be fitted as accurately as possible. Too, since it will be desirable to use the line of conditional means as an estimating line, the line should be located as accurately as possible.

To illustrate the least-squares method of correlation, consider first the least-squares coefficient of correlation r in its squared form, r^2. r^2 is known as the *coefficient of determination*, and may be defined as follows:

$$r^2 = \frac{\Sigma\,(Y_c - \bar{Y})^2}{\Sigma\,(Y - \bar{Y})^2} = \frac{\Sigma\,y_c^2}{\Sigma\,y^2},\qquad (14.12)$$

where r^2 is the coefficient of determination. r^2 ranges between 0 and $+1$.

Y_c is the computed "trend" value of Y paired with a given value of X. The set of computed Y_c values forms the line of conditional means.

$\bar{Y}$ is the mean of Y.

Y values represent the independent or estimated variable.

These relationships are shown graphically in Illustrations 14.3, 14.4, and 14.5.

Least squares correlation breaks the squared deviations into three parts as follows: First, the total deviations $\Sigma\,(Y - \bar{Y})^2$, then the explained deviations $\Sigma\,(Y_c - \bar{Y})^2$ and the residual or unexplained deviations

Illustration 14.3   Visual Example of the Set of Total Squared Deviations in the Correlation Problem of Table 14.4 on Page 409

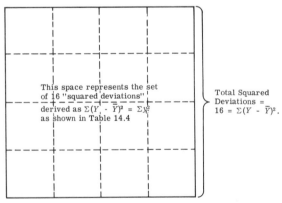

$\Sigma\,(Y - Y_c)^2$. The next three illustrations based on data of table **14.4** show these points. Note that a perfectly correlated series ($r^2 = 1$) would exist only when all the dots fell precisely on the regression line. In this case the standard error of estimate would be zero. If this were the case, then the Y values could be predicted accurately from X values via the regression line. If, however, the dots were scattered about the regression line, then the greater the scatter the smaller would be the ratio between $\Sigma (Y_c - \bar{Y})^2$ and $\Sigma (Y - \bar{Y})^2$. Thus it may be said that r^2 measures the proportion of squared deviations in the problem which are "explained" or accounted for by the regression line. Admittedly it is difficult to think of squared deviations but such a mathematical relationship is useful as a measure of correlation analysis, and perhaps the illustrations will have helped.

Illustration 14.4 Visual Example of the Subset of Squared Deviations "Accounted for" or "Explained by" the Regression Line (Y_c) As It Passes Through the Data of Table 14.4 on Page 409

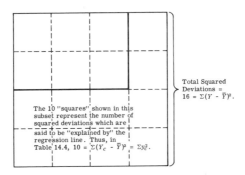

Total Squared Deviations = $16 = \Sigma(Y - \bar{Y})^2$.

The 10 "squares" shown in this subset represent the number of squared deviations which are said to be "explained by" the regression line. Thus, in Table 14.4, $10 = \Sigma(Y_c - \bar{Y})^2 = \Sigma y_c^2$.

Another way of stating the matter is to say that *r^2 measures the reduction in predicting error which occurs in the variance when prior knowledge of the estimating variable is given.*[2] See Formula (14.6). In other words, the conditional probability of Y (production) given a value for X (payroll) increases (or decreases) as r^2 increases (or decreases). The unconditional probability of Y, which means that predictions are made with no prior knowledge of X, may be thought of as representing a certain sample space. When, however, there is prior knowledge of X and this knowledge yields a conditional probability value which is calculated on a smaller sample space than the unconditional probability, there is a degree of correlation which can be measured by r or r^2. The larger the value of r or r^2, the greater the conditional probability that the estimates of Y, given a value for X, are close to the true, parametric (but undetermined) Y values.

Illustration 14.5 shows the "explained" and "unexplained" squared deviations as subsets of the total squared deviations in the problem. By now it may be seen that r^2 is simply a ratio between two sets of squared

---

[2] When D, the percentage of determination, is calculated, as in Formula (14.18), the quantity being measured is the reduction in standard deviation which occurs when S_{yx} is employed in place of σ_y. Thus, r^2 deals with variance, and D with standard deviation.

Table 14.4

Linear Correlation—An Illustrative Example

Month	X	Y	$X - Y$		x^2	xy	Total Squared Deviations	Y_c	Total Explained Deviations		Total Unexplained Deviations	
			x	y			y^2		$Y_c - \bar{Y}$ y_c	y_c^2	$Y - Y_c$ y_u	y_u^2
Jan.	5	8	−2	−2	4	4	4	8	−2	4	0	0
Feb.	6	9	−1	−1	1	1	1	9	−1	1	0	0
Mar.	7	9	0	−1	0	0	1	10	0	0	−1	1
Apr.	9	11	2	1	4	2	1	12	2	4	−1	1
May	8	13	1	3	1	3	9	11	1	1	2	4
	35	50	0	0	10	10	16	50	0	10	0	6

See page 412 for calculations.

Where Σy^2 = the total squared deviations in the problem,
$\quad\Sigma y_c^2$ = the total squared deviations "explained by" the regression line,*
$\quad\Sigma y_u^2$ = the total "unexplained" squared deviations in the problem.

* The term "explained by" means that if the paired variables X and Y vary in a consistent manner, then at least some of the variations in Y are said to be explained by (can be accounted for by or are due to) variations in X. Since the regression line is the average relationship between X and Y, this line can be thought of as explaining some or all of the deviations in Y, depending upon the degree of correlation present in the data. For example, in the bus passenger/passenger automobile registration problem at the beginning of this chapter, some of the change in bus passengers can be explained by the number of automobiles, but other factors such as the weather are also determinants of the number of passengers, and these other factors are not explained or accounted for by variations in X, the number of passenger automobiles. It might be said that the variations in Y are divided or decomposed into two parts: one part (Σy_c^2) is explained by variations in X, while the other part (Σu_c^2) is not explained by variations in X. See the sequence of structuring the squared deviations for Table 14.4 in Illustrations 14.3, 14.4, and 14.5.

Illustration 14.5   Visual Example of the Subset of Squared Deviations Which Are "Not Accounted for" or "Explained by" the
Regression Line (Y_c) as It Passes Through the Data of Table 14.4
on Page 409

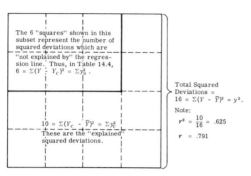

deviations. See Formula 14.12. Now let us observe another point. An
extremely important property is found in the y_c deviations, namely that
they are the basis for measuring the standard deviation of the regression
line (S_{yx}) and thus serve as a measure of the predictive or estimating ability
of the line. S_{yx} is known as the standard error of estimate and calculated
as a standard deviation. [See Formula (14.14).]

The relationships and the methodology of least-squares linear
correlation may be seen by the use of an example, the original data for
which are found in Table 14.4. Note that the data are "centered" on the
mean of X and the mean of Y. Note, too, the Y_c values as viewed in
Table 14.4 do not appear to the eye as a straight line. This is due to the
method of centering, which differs somewhat from the time-series method.
The Y_c values do, however, form points on a straight line when shown on a
graph.

Basic Correlation Formulae and Relationships

In order to keep the presentation as simple as possible for the moment,
let us note that in correlation analysis the most basic formulae are five in
number and they are not particularly complex:

$$a = \bar{Y}, \tag{14.2}$$

$$b = \frac{\Sigma\, xy}{\Sigma\, x^2}, \tag{14.3}$$

$$r = \frac{\Sigma\, xy}{\sqrt{\Sigma\, x^2\, \Sigma\, y^2}}, \tag{14.4}$$

$$S_{yx} = \sqrt{\frac{\Sigma\,(Y - Y_c)^2}{N}}, \tag{14.14}$$

$$Y_c = a + bx, \tag{14.5}$$

where $x = X - \bar{X}$. This is not a "time-centered" regression line but rather is centered on the mean of X.

Now, calculating the values for Table 14.4,

$$a = \bar{Y} = 10,$$

$$b = \frac{\Sigma\, xy}{\Sigma\, x^2} = \frac{10}{10} = 1,$$

$$r = \frac{\Sigma\, xy}{\sqrt{\Sigma\, x^2\, \Sigma\, y^2}} = \frac{10}{12.6} = .791,$$

$$S_{yx} = \sqrt{\frac{\Sigma\,(Y - Y_c)^2}{N}} = \sqrt{\frac{6}{5}} = 1.1.$$

Calculation of the regression-line values (Y_c):

$$Y_c = a\ + (b)(x);$$
$$8 = 10 + (1)(-2),$$
$$9 = 10 + (1)(-1),$$
$$10 = 10 + (1)(0),$$
$$12 = 10 + (1)(2),$$
$$11 = 10 + (1)(1).$$

Additional Correlation Formulae

While the five basic correlation formulae have been shown above, the following relationships are sometimes also useful. Note particularly the alternative formula for r.

$$r^2 = \frac{\Sigma\, y_c^2}{\Sigma\, y^2}. \tag{14.6}$$

Standard deviation of the Y series $= \sigma_y = \sqrt{\dfrac{\Sigma\, y^2}{N}}.$ (14.7)

(For sample values use $n - 1$.)

Standard deviation of the regression line $= S_{yx} = \sqrt{\dfrac{\Sigma\, y_c^2}{N}}.$ (14.8)

(For samples values use $n - 2$.)

$$b = r\frac{\sigma_y}{\sigma_x}, \tag{14.9}$$

$$r = \frac{\sigma_{y_c}}{\sigma_y}, \tag{14.10}$$

$$r = \sqrt{\frac{\Sigma y_c^2}{\Sigma y^2}},$$ (14.11)

$$r^2 = \frac{\Sigma y_c^2}{\Sigma y^2},$$ (14.12)

$$r^2 = \frac{b \, \Sigma \, xy}{\Sigma \, y^2},$$ (14.13)

$$S_{yx} = \sigma_y \sqrt{1 - r^2}.$$ (14.15)

Coefficient of nondetermination $= k^2 = \dfrac{\Sigma y_u^2}{\Sigma y^2}.$ (14.16)

A check on computations may be made from

$$\Sigma y^2 = \Sigma y_c^2 + \Sigma y_u^2.$$ (14.17)

Technical note: When the paired values have been obtained by sampling, then the variance formulae as shown earlier divide by $n - 1$ rather than by N. S would then replace σ. However, in the case of S_{yx} the divisor should be $n - 2$. Too, the "t" distribution should be used with small samples if σ is unknown. It may also be pointed out that the regression line and the standard error of estimate (S_{yx}) are estimates of the corresponding population parameters. This may be recognized as a natural extension of sampling theory to data applied to correlation analysis.

Interpreting r

It may be observed from a glance at one of the formulae for r, say Formula (14.11), that if correlation were perfect, r would equal 1. If no correlation occurred in the data, r would equal 0. Note too, that all the formulae for r yield positive values. *Thus, a negative r occurs when the regression line slopes downward and r should be given the sign of b employed in the regression equation, $Y_c = a + bx$.* However, in the interpretation of r, the sign indicates whether correlation is positive or negative, but does not alter any other consideration. Thus, in summary form, when $r = +1$ or -1, correlation is perfect; all dots lie along the trend line. In actual practice such a result would be highly unlikely. When $r = 0$, correlation is absent. This too is unlikely. Interpreting the extreme values of r is not difficult because either there is no correlation present, or the correlation is so perfect that we may suspect something has gone astray.

Interpreting intermediate values of r is more difficult. From its construction, r is an abstract concept because it is the square root of a complex relationship:

$$r = \sqrt{\frac{\Sigma y_c^2}{\Sigma y^2}}.$$ (14.11)

In order to understand the meaning of r, let us look again at r^2. The meaning of r^2 (the coefficient of determination) can best be viewed in terms of percentage. Thus r^2 is the per cent of total squared deviations in the Y series ($\Sigma\, y^2$) accounted for or "explained" by the regression line. The total squared deviations accounted for by the regression line is given as $\Sigma\, y_c^2$. Consequently r^2 may be thought of in terms of the percentage of total deviation in the problem accounted for by the regression line, or may be thought of as the percentage of deviation in Y accounted for (or explained by) X. Viewed somewhat differently, r^2 *indicates the mathematical ability of the regression line to predict any given Y value from a given X value.* This is precisely the same type of reasoning used in ordinary straight-line trend construction. If r^2 is high-valued, then the standard error will be relatively small—that is, all dots are grouped close to the regression line. Conversely, if r^2 is low-valued, the precision with which Y can be estimated from X is seriously impaired—that is, the dots are widely scattered about the trend line.

Now, how may r be interpreted? For numbers between 0 and 1, the second root is (except for the extremes of 0 and 1) larger than the square. Thus, if r is (say) .707, a value which appears relatively high in a scale ranging from 0 to 1, then r^2 would be 0.5. Thus, if a given r equals .707, it means that only 50 per cent of the variance in the Y series is explained by the variance in X and, consequently, if Y is to be predicted from X the predictions (no matter how good they may look in table form on paper) are not likely to be very accurate. The 50 per cent of total variation not explained by variations in X *must then be found in extraneous variables* which the correlation process fails to take into account. It might, therefore, be concluded that when $r = .707$, the degree of correlation is not particularly high. Since this matter of interpretation is of the

Table 14.5(a)

Relationship of r and r^2

r	r^2	*Per Cent of Squared Deviations in Y Explained by X*
.1	.01	1%
.2	.04	4
.3	.09	9
.4	.16	16
.5	.25	25
.6	.36	36
.7	.49	49
.8	.64	64
.9	.81	81
.95	.9025	90.25
1.0	1.0	100

greatest moment, it will be well to also probe the subject from a slightly different point of view.

To illustrate r and r^2, it will be convenient to construct a table [Table 14.5(a)] showing selected values for r^2 and for r. The table will provide a further means of understanding the manner in which r is interpreted. These relationships are shown in graphic form in Illustration 14.6.

Illustration 14.6 The Relationship Between r and the Per Cent of Squared Deviations in Y Which Are Explained by X

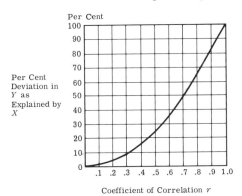

Per Cent

Per Cent
Deviation in
Y as
Explained by
X

Coefficient of Correlation r

Both the table and chart indicate that rather high values of r are required to yield a degree of correlation in which, say, more than 50 per cent of the variation in Y is explained by variations in X. Thus, interpretation, which in the final analysis is up to the judgment of the statistician or decision-maker, must be viewed in the light of the actual problem and its consequences.

Exercise 14.3
1. Using the data of Table 14.4, explain how r^2 has been defined.
2. Using the same data, explain how k^2 has been defined.
3. Explain why r^2 add k^2 must sum to 1. Will r and k for Table 14.4 sum to 1? Why?
4. How is σ_y, the standard deviation of the Y series, defined? Is this definition consistent with previous definitions of σ as given in Chapters 4 and 7?
5. Explain how σ_{yc}, the standard deviation of the regression line, differs from σ_y, the standard deviation of the Y series.
6. Referring to Table 14.4, explain how the X and Y data are centered and explain how this differs from "time centering" as employed in time series analysis.
7. The range of r is from -1 to $+1$. Interpret this statement.
8. If $r = .6$, the percentage of explained deviation is actually _____ . Why?

9. If you were called upon to decide an important issue on the basis of a correlation coefficient, and if your decision could be either your economic fortune or economic ruin, how high would you wish r before you "risk it" and decide "yes"?

14.5   Meaning and Interpretation of Correlation and Regression Analysis

This section will take a critical look at the meaning of correlation and regression analysis. When a correlation experiment has been carried through to the point where the various measures have been calculated, the question naturally arises as to the meaning and interpretation to be placed on the results. Some suggestions of interpretation will be given in this section. The following section will provide a means for interpreting the results of a correlation experiment by use of the F statistic.

The Standard Error of Estimate (S_{yx})

Since both r and r^2 are measures of the degree of "scatter" of the dots around the regression line, it is a logical step to consider that r and r^2 could be related to a standard deviation measured around the regression line. See Illustration 14.8 on page 421 and observe the two "bands" parallel to the trend line. These bands represent the trend line plus and minus one standard error. With the realization that when r or r^2 is high-valued, the dots cluster close to the regression line, previous knowledge indicates that under these circumstances the standard error of the estimate would be small. Conversely, if r or r^2 were low-valued, the cluster of dots about the regression line would be characterized by considerable scatter, and the standard error measuring that scatter would be relatively large.

Since r^2 provides a measure of the ability of X to predict Y, it is clear that the predictive ability of X as measured by r^2 and the "standard error of estimate" (S_{yx}) are closely related. The term "standard error of estimate" is to be interpreted in the same manner as any standard deviation, but it is important to note that the standard error is related to r in a particular manner. This may be shown as follows: S_{yx} is defined as $\sqrt{\Sigma (Y - Y_c)^2/N}$, which indicates S_{yx} is computed as the standard error of the unexplained variance (see Table 14.4 for an illustration). If the standard error of estimate S_{yx} be expressed in its mathematical equivalent, it becomes $S_{yx} = \sigma_y \sqrt{1 - r^2}$. From the latter relationship it is clear that S_{yx} decreases as r^2 increases. And, of course, when S_{yx} diminishes, the predictive ability of X is increased because the error diminishes.

To illustrate the relationship between r^2, σ_y, and S_{yx}, suppose a table similar to Table 14.5(a) is constructed to show the interrelationships and to show clearly how the standard error of estimate S_{yx} shrinks in relation to σ_y as r approaches 1.0.

Table 14.5(b)

Illustrating the Relationship Between r, r^2, and S_{yx} Based on the Formula $S_{yx} = \sigma_y \sqrt{1 - r^2}$ (All Percentages Rounded Slightly)

(1)	(2)	(3)
r	r^2	S_{yx}/σ_y (in Percentage)
.1	.01	99%
.2	.04	98
.3	.09	95
.4	.16	92
.5	.25	87
.6	.36	80
.7	.49	71
.8	.64	60
.9	.81	43
.95	.9025	31
1.0	1.00	00

Column 3 of Table 14.5(b) clearly indicates the relationship between the size of S_{yx} and σ_y. Thus, when r or r^2 is small, the standard error of estimate S_{yx} is almost as large as σ_y. Thus, to use a specific X value to predict Y is of little help in reducing the prediction error. In other words, the conditional probability distribution of Y values—given knowledge of X—is of only slightly more value in reducing predicting errors than is the unconditional probability distribution of Y itself.

Table 14.5(b) has been constructed by substituting values of r^2 in the formula $S_{yx} = \sigma_y \sqrt{1 - r^2}$ and solving for S_{yx}. It is suggested that you compute several such values to determine how the table was constructed. You will discover, of course, that the percentage value of S_{yx}/σ_y is given by $\sqrt{1 - r^2}$, multiplied by 100.

We are now in a position to provide some basis for the interpretation of various values of r^2, the coefficient of determination. From Table 14.5(b) we see that if $r^2 = .36$, then S_{yx} is 80 per cent as large as σ_y. In this case, the improvement which results from predicting Y values from given X values is only a small improvement over what could have been achieved by simply using $\bar{Y}$ as the predicted value. Nor does this predicting error diminish rapidly as r^2 increases. As Table 14.5(b) indicates, even an r^2 of .9025 is subject to a predicting error (S_{yx}) which is 31 per cent of σ_y. Thus, in interpreting r^2 (or r) it is clear that low values of correlation signify little or nothing of value, particularly since forecasts made on the basis of low correlation are subject to wide predicting errors. It must be remembered, too, that *a high value of r proves nothing whatsoever about possible cause-and-effect relationships.* Such proof must be sought on logical grounds backed up by knowledge of the problem itself. However, the cause-effect relationship should not be pushed too far in business and economic data. For example, a pair of variables may exhibit correlation not because of cause-effect but rather because they are resultants of the same set of determining forces. The price of food and of housing may show a high correlation since both are influenced by a set of common economic factors.

The Percentage of Determination D

As previous knowledge of probability suggests, the probability of predicting the correct Y value (actually, the near-correct value of Y) is greater in a correlated series than an uncorrelated series because of the reduction in the predicting error—that is, in S_{yx}. In other words, when prior knowledge of X exists and this prior knowledge reduces the sample space within which the true value of Y can occur, the estimates of Y will have improved. This leads to the thought that a formula might be devised to measure the percentage improvement in the estimate when the value of r (or r^2) is known.

One such measure may be found in the percentage of determination, here labeled D. The term D may be defined *as the percentage reduction in predicting error when a conditional probability distribution is used to predict*

Table 14.5(c)

Illustrating the Relationship Between r, r^2, D, and S_{yx}/σ_y (Percentage Values Rounded Slightly)

(1) r	(2) r^2	(3) S_{yx}/σ_y	(4) D
.1	.01	99%	1%
.2	.04	98	2
.3	.09	95	5
.4	.16	92	8
.5	.25	87	13
.6	.36	80	20
.7	.49	71	29
.8	.64	60	40
.9	.81	43	57
.95	.9025	31	69
1.0	1.0	00	100

Y from X. Thus, *D* is the expected improvement in prediction measured in percentage terms. In formula form,

$$D = 100 - \left[\frac{S_{yx}}{\sigma_y} (100) \right] \qquad (14.18)$$

The reduction in predicting error which results from employing the conditional probability distribution as the basis of prediction can be shown in tabular form as in Table 14.5(c).

Once again, Table 14.5(c) makes it clear that substantial improvement in estimates takes place only at the higher values of *r* or r^2. Too, it would be well to be reminded again that interpretation of correlation values is necessarily a matter of human judgment and will depend, to a large extent, on the nature of the practical problem for which correlation is employed.

A Further Look at the Standard Error of Estimate, S_{yx}

As has been observed, one of the primary reasons for correlation analysis is to determine whether or not the *X* and *Y* variables are related in such manner as to allow prediction. At this point the data of Table 14.2 will be repeated in order to show the paired variables and the regression between them.

Table 14.2 (Abridged)

Month	Payroll X	Production X	Regression Y_c
Jan.	5	8	8
Feb.	6	9	9
Mar.	7	9	10
Apr.	9	11	12
May	8	13	11

The regression line as fitted to the data may be used for purposes of predicting *Y* values from *X* values. For example, if $X = 6.5$, $Y_c = 9.5$. Thus, if the payroll were 6.5, it would be predicted that production would be 9.5. But, the question arises as to how reliable the prediction is likely to be. It has been observed that unless *r* or r^2 is high-valued, the predictive ability of the regression equation (line) is poor. S_{yx} may be utilized to provide confidence intervals in same manner as the standard error was used in sampling distributions to provide a confidence interval for the mean.

If the deviations of the original *Y* data be measured from the regression line, these deviations can be considered as errors of prediction resulting

Illustration 14.7   Use of the Regression Line to Predict Y Values from X Values

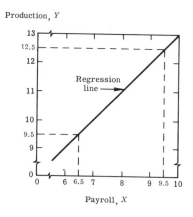

from the fact that the Y data do not completely follow changes in the X data. Considering the regression line as the line of central tendency and measuring the dots from that line, we have approximately the same situation encountered in deviations of the normal curve as measured from the mean. Since the basic formula for S_{yx} is $\sqrt{\Sigma (Y - Y_c)^2/N}$, the resulting value is clearly a standard deviation in which the regression line is the central value and the standard deviations form "bands" around the regression line. Such a band (see Illustration 14.8) may be computed by taking each Y_c value plus and minus $[(S_{yx}(z)]$ and visualizing the result as a normal curve. Thus, the regression line plus and minus S_{yx} would, in a normally distributed variate, include approximately 68 per cent of the data. Each Y_c value plus and minus $[(1.96)(S_{yx})]$ would include approximately 95 per cent of the data, and so on.

How might the standard error of estimate (S_{yx}) be utilized in prediction? Suppose it was desired to predict the value of Y when $X = 6$.

Illustration 14.8   Relationship Between the Regression Line and the Standard Error S_{yx} ($S_{yx} = 1.1$)

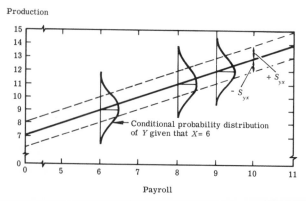

Illustration 14.8 indicates that if the value of X is 6, the predicted value of Y is 9. However, since the degree of correlation is less than perfect, predictive ability is subject to error. Thus, we could say that the probability is .68 that if X is 6, the actual Y value would fall between plus and minus S_{yx}—that is, between the limits of 7.9 and 10.1. Using the 95 per cent confidence level, the predicted value of Y would turn out to be between 6.8 and 11.2 (rounding the values slightly).

It may be seen that every value of X in the range of the variable has a predictable counterpart in Y. Too, for each value of X, a confidence interval exists for Y, its width depending upon S_{yx} and the level of confidence chosen. Regarding all possible values of X as a continuous variable (within the range of the variable) one may visualize a confidence band centered on the regression line and having a surface composed of the contour of a normal curve. Since our interest centers in the base of the curve rather than its height, the maximum ordinate is of no particular importance.

It is clear from the nature of the problem chosen for purposes of illustrating correlation analysis that the prediction of production values from payroll values is far from accurate—the standard error of estimate is too wide. The information supplied is too general to be of much value.

If the objective is a reasonable prediction of Y values from X data, a high value of r (or r^2) is required, which is to say that a relatively small S_{yx} is required. Without these conditions, prediction—which is somewhat tenuous at best—is seriously impaired in accuracy. Too, it should be repeated that caution is called for when reaching the conclusion that *because* there is a high correlation coefficient, there is also a cause-effect relationship between the two variables. For example, a high degree of correlation might be found between the sales of chairs and the consumption of gasoline, but logic and common sense suggest there is no reason to believe that the sales of chairs *cause* gasoline consumption—or vice versa. Actually, many pairs of variables will exhibit some degree of correlation, but this by itself is no reason for concluding the variables are in fact related in any meaningful manner. It is necessary to be extremely wary of drawing conclusions on the basis of correlated data without at the same time being able to substantiate the relationship by general knowledge, by hypothesis, or by experience.

14.6 Significance of the Coefficient of Correlation. The F Statistic

In dealing with correlation problems generally, but particularly when N (or n) is small, the thought arises that the correlation between the pairs of values might have occurred by chance rather than by a mutual relationship between the variables. In other words, it would be desirable to know the probability that r might simply be due to chance factors rather than to a mutual association between the variables. To test the probability of r's having occurred by chance, the statistic F may be used along with prepared tables (see Appendix I) to test the significance of r. The methodology of the F test will now be explained.

The statistic F for two-variable linear correlation may be determined by the following formula:

$$F = \frac{r^2(N - m)}{(1 - r^2)(m - 1)},\tag{14.19}$$

where N = the number of paired variables in the problem,

m = the number of columns in the problem (in two-variable linear correlation, m will always have the value 2),

F = a unique statistic to be used with the F table, as explained below.

Use of the F statistic may be explained as follows: First of all, F is calculated for the problem under consideration by the F formula above. To illustrate the calculation, suppose this is the payroll-production problem of Table 14.2. In that problem, $N = 5$ and $r = .791$. The F value will then be equal to $(.625)(3)/(.375)(1) = 5$. The F value is thus computed to be 5. Now, turn to the prepared table of F in Appendix I; since in two-variable linear correlation m is always equal to 2, only the $m = 2$ column is used. Now, look down the left-hand side of the column to the row in which $N - m = 5 - 2 = 3$ appears, and observe whether the calculated F value exceeds either of the table values shown. For the data of Table 14.2, the values of F shown are 9.55 at the 5 per cent level and 30.82 at the 1 per cent level. It may therefore be concluded that the coefficient of correlation for this problem could have occurred simply by chance since $5 < 9.55 < 30.82$. Thus, considerable doubt is cast over the reliability of correlation for the problem in question. Had the calculated value of F fallen between 9.55 and 30.82, then the interpretation would be that only once in approximately 20 times would as high a correlation coefficient have occurred by chance. Had the value of F exceeded 30.82, then the interpretation would be that only once in approximately 100 times would the coefficient of correlation r have exceeded this value by chance alone.

A Note of Caution on Using the F Statistic

The table of F is based on a normally distributed sampling universe. Therefore the table of F is inappropriate to evaluate the significance of r

if the paired values were drawn from other than normal universes of X and Y. Too, since the normal universe is continuous rather than discrete, the statistic F has to be evaluated in light of the discontinuity associated with the problem under consideration. It is therefore necessary to carefully evaluate the terms of reference in which a particular problem has been set; otherwise, the F table may be used incorrectly.[3]

Exercise 14.4

1. What is S_{xy}, the standard error of estimate?
2. Explain why the standard error of estimate must decrease as r^2 increases.
3. Observe column 3 of Table 14.5(a) and explain what it signifies and how it was derived. If $r^2 = .85$ what would be the corresponding value in column 3? Does the interpretation of the concept of standard error basically differ in correlation from its use in sampling theory? Are these really the same concepts?
4. Table 14.3 shows clearly that unless r is very large, expected predicting errors will be large. Yet, as observed in Chapter 1, predictions (estimates) must be made and issues must be decided. Where would you set r as the minimum value on which to base prediction and make decisions?
5. Why does a high value of r prove nothing about cause-effect? Why must one be careful in trying to isolate cause-effect relationships with economic data?
6. Observe Illustration 14.8. If the payroll value is 7, predict the value of production. How much is the expected predicting error in this situation? How much reliance can be placed on the predicted values of production in this particular problem?
7. Again, observe Illustration 14.8. If the payroll value is 7, the .68 confidence interval is approximately _____. Interpret this statement using the theory of probability and the theory of sampling distributions to do so.
8. What does D refer to? How are D and r^2 related?

14.7 Correlation: A Case Study

To demonstrate the applicability of correlation techniques as well as to indicate the interrelationships between correlation measures, the following problem has been designed as a "case study."

Consider the gross sales of a large department store located in a suburb of a large metropolitan area, called Suburbia. The store has done very well, is popular, and renders satisfactory service to its customers. In its suburban location, population has shifted from time to time and store sales have varied directly with those shifts. Sales and population data are

---

[3] For further information on the use of the F statistic, see George W. Snedecor, *Statistical Methods*, 5th ed., chap. 10 (Ames, Iowa: The Iowa State College Press, 1956).

Table 14.6

Illustrative Example of Population Change in Suburbia Correlated with Gross Sales of a Retail Store in the Community

Year	Population (3 zeros omitted) X	Gross Sales (5 zeros omitted) Y	x	y	xy	x^2	y^2	y_c	$Y_c - \bar{Y}$ y_c	y_c^2	$Y - Y_c$ y_u	y_u^2
1	30	4	-5	-3	15	25	9	5.295	-1.705	2.91	-1.295	1.68
2	28	6	-7	-1	7	49	1	4.613	-2.387	5.70	1.387	1.93
3	32	5	-3	-2	6	9	4	5.977	-1.023	1.05	-0.977	0.96
4	34	7	-1	0	0	1	0	6.659	-0.341	0.12	0.341	0.13
5	32	6	-3	-1	3	9	1	5.977	-1.023	1.05	0.023	0.00
6	36	8	1	1	1	1	1	7.341	0.341	0.12	0.659	0.43
7	37	7	2	0	0	4	0	7.682	0.682	0.46	-0.682	0.47
8	37	8	2	1	2	4	1	7.682	0.682	0.46	0.318	0.10
9	40	9	5	2	10	25	4	8.705	1.705	2.91	0.295	0.09
10	44	10	9	3	27	81	9	10.069	3.069	9.42	-0.069	0.01
Totals	350	70	0	0	71	208	30	70.000	0.000	24.20	0.000	5.80

Computations:

$$a = \bar{Y} = \frac{70}{10} = 7, \qquad b = \frac{\Sigma xy}{\Sigma x^2} = \frac{71}{208} \approx 0.3413,$$

$$S_{yx} = \sqrt{\frac{\Sigma (Y - Y_c)^2}{N}} = \sqrt{\frac{5.80}{10}} = \sqrt{0.58} \approx 0.76,$$

$$r = \frac{\Sigma xy}{\sqrt{\Sigma x^2 \cdot \Sigma y^2}} = \frac{71}{\sqrt{(208)(30)}} = 0.899 \approx 0.9,$$

$$\sigma_y = \sqrt{\frac{y^2}{N}} = \sqrt{\frac{30}{10}} \approx 1.73.$$

Note: In correlated data, b is likely to be a decimal value and therefore subject to slight but necessary rounding. This will cause subsequent calculations to vary slightly from the "true" decimal values. The symbol $\approx$ (approximately equal to) is therefore utilized throughout this problem. Too, if

available. Now, while many factors have determined the success of the department store, the number of persons living in the immediate area is considered a key factor in sales volume. Thus, population data can be regarded as the independent or estimating (X) variable and sales as the dependent or estimated (Y) data. In Table 14.6 these values have been recorded in simplified form as indicated in the column headings.

The store manager has observed the changes both in population and in total volume of sales and believes that in the future the population of Suburbia will grow rapidly. Forecasts of population growth have been

Illustration 14.9   Graph Showing the Relationship Between Population Change and Retail Sales of a Store in Suburbia (Data from Table 14.6)

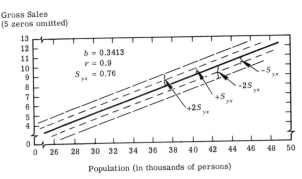

Gross Sales
(5 zeros omitted)

Population (in thousands of persons)

made and are available for the next several years. The store manager wishes to assess present policies and to formulate a forward-looking retail strategy. The manager realizes that population forecasts are subject to error and that correlation data based on past relationships may not necessarily hold true in the future. It is, however, well understood that forward-looking policies must be established even in the face of uncertainty. The manager thus requires specific information, some of which can be made available from correlation analysis.

Table 14.6 shows the arithmetic computations and the organization of the X and Y data.

Among the questions on which information is sought are the following:

1. What is the relationship between population and retail store sales?
2. Assuming no change in the underlying determinants (for example, the competitive situation), what is the expectation of changes in sales for each increase (or decrease) of 1,000 persons residing in Suburbia?
3. Forecast store sales for population values of 45, 46, 47, 48, 49, and 50 thousand people residing in Suburbia.
4. Using the 95 per cent confidence level, show the intervals for the forecasted population values above.

5. Do the data, as correlated, suggest any new or promising avenues of present or future inquiry?

As long as the data are completely worked out and available to us, it will be desirable to note any interrelationships between various formulae and correlation concepts. This we shall attempt to do as the analysis proceeds.

In preparing answers to the questions raised previously, let us first indicate the forecasted values of Y (sales) and the 95 per cent confidence intervals. These are shown in Table 14.7.

Table 14.7

Predicted Sales Values and 95 Per Cent Confidence Intervals for the Data of Table 14.6. [For Actual Dollar Values, Multiply (2) by (3) by 10^5.]

Population X (1)	Predicted Sales Values Y_c (2)	95 Per Cent Confidence Interval $[Y_c \pm (1.96)(\dot{S}_{yx})]$ (3)
45	10.410	9.742 to 11.078
46	10.751	10.083 to 11.419
47	11.092	10.424 to 11.760
48	11.433	10.765 to 12.101
49	11.774	11.106 to 12.442
50	12.115	11.447 to 12.783

We are now in a position to answer the original questions as follows:

1. The coefficient of correlation is .9.
2. For each 1,000 increase in population, store sales increase by $34,130. This is, of course, an average relationship based on past performance and assumes no change in the underlying determinants of store sales.
3. The forecasted sales and the 95 per cent confidence intervals are shown in Table 14.8.
4. The data and the correlation analysis, by themselves, do not indicate any promising new avenues of inquiry. It would be prudent to revise the forecasts each year as new data become available and to meet new problems as they arise. Since the relationship between population and store sales is "high," it may be expected that any changes will cause store sales to follow such changes closely, and policies should be formulated on this basis.

Now, some of the interrelationships among the data and the correlation values may be observed.

1. From Table 14.5(a) it is known that the relationship of S_{yx} to σ_y should be approximately 43 per cent when r equals .9. Does this check out? We see: $S_{yx} = 0.76$, $\sigma_y = 1.73$, and $0.76/1.73 \approx .43$. Check!

2. Calculation of the standard deviation of the regression line is:

$$\sigma_{y_c} = \sqrt{\frac{y_c^2}{N}} = \sqrt{\frac{24.20}{10}} = 1.55.$$

We know r also equals σ_{y_c}/σ_y. Thus, in the example, $1.55/1.73 \approx 0.9$. When r is computed in this manner, it provides a clear understanding of the nature of the elements in the correlation and indicates what is being measured and compared. That is, the standard deviation of the regression line is compared to the standard deviation of the Y series and the relationship expressed as a decimal value.

3. Do the data of this problem yield r^2 by the formula:

$$r^2 = \frac{\Sigma y_c^2}{\Sigma y^2} ?$$

From (2) above it is clear that if the ratio σ_{y_c}/σ_y be squared, then r must also be squared. However, substituting the values of the example, we have $r^2 = 24.20/30 \approx 0.81$. Check!

4. Is S_{yx} equal to $\sigma_y\sqrt{1 - r^2}$? By substitution, $S_{yx} = 1.73\sqrt{1 - 0.81} = 0.76$. Check! The formula indicates that the standard error S_{yx} depends upon the value of r^2 and that the standard error diminishes as r^2 (or r) increases. This is precisely what we should expect from knowledge of correlation theory. In other words, the better our estimates of Y, the narrower the standard error must be. The similarity between correlation and statistical inference may now be seen.

5. Does $k^2 + r^2 = 1.0$? After all, if the problem has been correctly computed, the "explained" plus the "unexplained" variance must sum to unity. Thus,

$$k^2 = \frac{\Sigma y_c^2}{\Sigma y^2} = \frac{5.80}{30} = 0.19;$$

$$r^2 = \frac{\Sigma y_c^2}{\Sigma y^2} = \frac{24.20}{30} = 0.81;$$

$$k^2 + r^2 = 0.19 + 0.91 = 1.0. \qquad \text{Check!}$$

The basic interrelationships in the computation of correlation information have now been surveyed. The student should become thoroughly familiar with the example given above, as it indicates the mechanics of correlation in simple but effective form.

14.8   Summary

This chapter has considered the basic features of simple correlation. Correlation analysis is concerned with the relationship between two variables in paired form. The test of such a relationship is how well knowledge of one variable can be used to estimate values of the other. As applied to the economic world, this relationship is generally not precise but rather is approximate. The coefficient of correlation indicates how closely the variables are related *mathematically*. Unfortunately, the mathematical relationship does not prove that, in the real world, these two variables are linked together in a cause-effect relationship. Knowledge of cause-effect must be proven on other than arithmetic grounds.

Thus, throughout this chapter it has been emphasized that by itself, the existence of a high-valued correlation coefficient *does not prove that a usable association exists between paired variables.* It would be easy to go astray in the use of correlation analysis by claiming too much and jumping to unwarranted conclusions.

It has been assumed that a straight-line relationship existed between the paired variables. This assumption will oversimplify correlation in some instances and, if the data are not linear, straight-line correlation is inappropriate. The scattergram should provide the first clue as to the potential usefulness (if any) of linear correlation. Too, it has been assumed that the standard error (S_{yx}) of the regression line was equal for all values of X. Again, this is a simplifying assumption which makes the problem easier to work with. For some sets of data this assumption of a constant S_{yx} may be inappropriate.

Too, it is desirable not to be led astray by the interesting mathematical relationships which exist in correlation problems. The final test is how well knowledge of one variable allows estimates of unknown values of the other variable. The straight-line regression assumption allows extrapolation of Y_c values for fractional amounts of X, and the regression line permits forecasting values of Y_c for nonexistent X values. But since no data exist for the unknown values, we are really guessing. However, the probability of making reasonably correct guesses is as high as we can make it. Estimating Y_c values can, in some situations, lead to ludicrous results if the correlation relationship is pushed too far. Thus, one must be careful to realize that while the arithmetic may be correct, the real question is whether or not the estimating line actually is appropriate to the data from a realistic, common-sense point of view.

On the other hand, when properly used, correlation does indicate mathematically the strength of association between two variables. The average relationship between variables can be calculated and this knowledge can be used as a means of estimating the value of one variable given the value of the other. The knowledge so obtained can be used in conjunction with knowledge of probability and the normal curve to establish the range of possible error. A knowledge of sampling theory can be used to help understand and interpret correlation results.

Finally, it has been indicated that the mathematics of correlation is not really very complex so that *by itself* correlation analysis is not unusually difficult. In the selection of the data—that is, the relevant variables— to be correlated and in the interpretation of the results we must exercise judgment, and this judgment must be based on both general and specific knowledge of the variables in the problem. When these requirements are met, correlation analysis becomes a valuable tool of research and of understanding.

Key Terms and Concepts of This Chapter

Correlation
  (a) Rank
  (b) Least-squares linear
  (c) Coefficient of

Coefficient of
  (a) Determination
  (b) Alienation
  (c) Association
  (d) Correlation

Standard error of estimate

Variables
  (a) Independent
  (b) Dependent
  (c) Paired

Regression line; Estimating line;
  Scattergram; Line of conditional
  means

Variance
  (a) Total squared variance
  (b) Explained variance
  (c) Unexplained variance

Correlation Formulae

(14.1) $\quad r_r = 1 - \dfrac{6d^2}{N(N^2 - 1)}$

(14.2) $\qquad a = \bar{Y}$

(14.3) $\qquad b = \dfrac{\Sigma xy}{\Sigma x^2}$

(14.4) $\qquad r = \dfrac{\Sigma xy}{\sqrt{\Sigma x^2 \cdot \Sigma y^2}}$

(14.5) $\qquad Y_c = a + bx$

(14.6) $\qquad r^2 = \dfrac{\Sigma y_c^2}{\Sigma y^2}$

See also (14.12)

(14.7) $\qquad \sigma_y = \sqrt{\dfrac{\Sigma y^2}{N}}$

(14.8) $\qquad \sigma_{y_c} = \sqrt{\dfrac{\Sigma y_c^2}{N}}$

(14.9) $\qquad b = r\dfrac{\sigma_y}{\sigma_x}$

(14.10) $\qquad r = \dfrac{\sigma_{y_c}}{\sigma_y}$

(14.11) $\qquad r = \sqrt{\dfrac{\Sigma y_c^2}{\Sigma y^2}}$

(14.12) $\quad r^2 = \dfrac{\Sigma(Y_c - \bar{Y})^2}{\Sigma(Y - \bar{Y})^2} = \dfrac{\Sigma y_c^2}{\Sigma y^2}$

See also (14.6)

(14.13) $\qquad r^2 = \dfrac{b \Sigma xy}{\Sigma y^2}$

$\sigma_y = \sqrt{\dfrac{\Sigma(Y - \bar{Y})^2}{N}}$ (universe values)

(14.14a)

$S_y = \sqrt{\dfrac{\Sigma(Y - \bar{Y})^2}{n - 1}}$ (sample values)

$S_{yx} = \sqrt{\dfrac{\Sigma(Y - Y_c)^2}{N}}$ (universe values)

(14.14b)

$S_{yx} = \sqrt{\dfrac{\Sigma(Y - Y_c)^2}{n - 2}}$ (sample values)

(14.15) $\qquad S_{yx} = \sigma_y\sqrt{1 - r^2}$

(14.16) $\qquad k^2 = \dfrac{\Sigma y_u^2}{\Sigma y^2}$

(14.17) $\qquad \Sigma y^2 = \Sigma y_c^2 + \Sigma y_u^2$

(14.18) $\qquad D = 100 - \left[\dfrac{S_{yx}}{\sigma_y}(100)\right]$

(14.19) $\qquad F = \dfrac{r^2(N - m)}{(1 - r^2)(m - 1)}$

Exercise 14.5

1. Explain or define each of the following:
   (a) $\Sigma(Y_c - \bar{Y})^2$.
   (b) r^2. Explain why r^2 may range from -1 to $+1$.
   (c) $\Sigma(Y - Y_c)^2$.
   (d) $\Sigma y^2 = \Sigma y_c^2 + \Sigma y_u^2$.
   (e) σ_x; σ_y.
   (f) Regression line.
   (g) Paired variables.
   (h) Independent variable; dependent variable.

2. Draw a rough graph for a hypothetical problem in which $r^2 = 1$. What slope did you choose for the regression line? Would the slope affect r^2? Why or why not?

3. In each of the following cases, state what percentage of the total squared deviations in Y were explained by X if $r = .15$; $.25$; $.45$; $.75$; $.85$.

4. Now, using the same values of r given above, show what percentage S_{yx} is of σ_y.

5. Given the following set of paired X and Y values:

Year	Per Capita Consumption of Meat and Poultry	Per Capita Consumption of Eggs
	X	Y
1	143	38
2	170	49
3	182	50
4	196	47
5	186	46
6	173	40

(a) Prepare a scattergram of the data; compute r^2, r, a, b, and S_{yx} (use centered method as shown in Table 14.3).

(b) Does a cause-and-effect relationship exist between the two variables?

(c) In what manner, if any, are the variables related?

(d) Give an evaluation of r. Give an evaluation of r^2 and indicate what percentage of the variation in Y can be said to be explained by X.

(e) Calculate D, the percentage of determination, and relate it specifically to this problem.

(f) Predict Y for each of the following values of X: 150; 160; 170.

(g) State the 95 per cent confidence interval for each value of X given above.

(h) Place the S_{yx} and $[(2)(S_{yx})]$ bands on the scattergram.

(i) Now evaluate the entire problem from the point of view of correlation analysis. Prepare a report of your correlation analysis for this particular set of data.

6. Given the following set of paired X and Y values:

Year	Per Capita Consumption of Meat and Poultry	Per Capita Consumption of Potatoes
	X	Y
1	143	152
2	170	127
3	182	144
4	196	107
5	186	105
6	173	97

(a) Carry out the same instructions as for problem 5.
(b) Explain why r is negative in this problem. In drawing up a report of your correlation analysis, indicate some possible reasons why per capita potato consumption has shown a decline.

7. Given the following set of paired X and Y values:

Year	Acres of Cropland Per Farm	Acres of Grazing Land Per Farm
	X	Y
1	69	37
2	72	53
3	72	66
4	78	89
5	92	111
6	99	121
7	106	125

(a) Carry out the same set of instructions as for problem 5.
(b) Predict the number of acres of grazing land for the following values of cropland: 70, 80, 90, 100, 110.

8. Given the following set of paired X and Y values:

Year	Total Population	Total Number of Households
	X	Y
1	158	43
2	160	45
3	163	46
4	166	46
5	168	47
6	171	48
7	174	49
8	177	50
9	180	51
10	183	53

(a) Carry out the same set of instructions as for problem 5.
(b) Predict the number of households for the following population values: 185, 190.

9. Using the following set of data, work the problem exactly as shown in Table 14.4.

Year	Number of Automobiles Sold	Dollar Value of Automobile Credit Extended
	X	Y
1	4	5
2	8	9
3	13	13
4	12	13
5	13	15
6	14	13
7	15	17
8	17	18

10. A trade association wishes to know if a usable relationship exists between gross national product and new construction activity as reported by the Department of Commerce. It is felt this information would be of value in predicting the amount of building activity from GNP forecasts. Follow the same set of instructions given in problem 5, and predict construction activity when GNP is $610 and $650 billion. (Which variable is X?)

Year	Value of New Construction Activity (billions of $)	Gross National Product (billions of $)
1954	39.2	363.1
1955	44.2	397.5
1956	45.8	419.2
1957	47.8	442.8
1958	48.9	444.5
1959	56.6	502.6
1960	55.6	502.6
1961	57.4	518.2
1962	61.1	554.9
1963	64.7	585.0

Bibliography

Bryant, Edward C., *Statistical Analysis*, 2nd ed., chap. 7. New York: McGraw-Hill Book Company, 1966.

Croxton, Frederick E., and Dudley J. Cowden, *Practical Business Statistics*, 3rd ed., chaps. 25, 26, and 27. Englewood Cliffs, N.J.: Prentice-Hall, Inc., 1960.

Dixon, Wilfred J., and Frank J. Massey, Jr., *Introduction to Statistical Analysis*, chaps. 11 and 12. New York: McGraw-Hill Book Company, 1957.

Ekeblad, Frederick, *The Statistical Method in Business*, chaps. 13 and 14. New York: John Wiley & Sons, Inc., 1962.

Freund, John E., *Modern Elementary Statistics*, chaps. 14 and 15. Englewood Cliffs, N.J.: Prentice-Hall, Inc., 1960.

Greenwald, William I., *Statistics for Economics*, chap. 5. Columbus, Ohio: Charles E. Merrill Books, Inc., 1963.

Mendenhall, William, *Introduction to Statistics*, chap. 10. Belmont, Calif.: Wadsworth Publishing Company, Inc., 1964.

Mills, Frederick C., *Statistical Methods*, 3rd ed. New York: Henry Holt and Company, 1955.

Moroney, M. J., *Facts from Figures*, 3rd ed., chap. 16. Baltimore: Penguin Books, Inc. 1956.

Neiswanger, Willian Addison, *Elementary Statistical Methods as Applied to Business and Economic Data*, chaps 18 and 19. New York: The Macmillan Company, 1956.

Neter, John, and William Wasserman, *Fundamental Statistics for Business and Economics*, 2nd ed., chap. 13. Boston: Allyn and Bacon, Inc., 1961.

O'Toole, A. L., *Elementary Practical Statistics*, chap. 8. New York: The Macmillan Company, 1964.

Wallis, W. Allen, and Harry V. Roberts, *Statistics: A New Approach*, chap. 17. Glencoe, Ill.: The Free Press, 1956.

APPENDIX TO CHAPTER 14: Some Alternative Methods of Calculating the Coefficient of Correlation and Additional Correlation Exercises

Chapter 14 presented a discussion of correlation in the simplest manner possible by utilizing very small sets of data. The objective was to focus understanding on the principles of correlation, and the materials used to illustrate the various principles were selected with the idea of reducing computation to a minimum. Now, however, as a practical matter, problems must be taken as they occur, which means that long, detailed computations might well result—particularly if the x and y deviations turned out to be decimals. Too, the methods of calculation used in Chapter 14 were more suitable to ordinary calculation than to machine treatment. The following methods are generally applicable to machines or to the use of computers where the actual data involve a large N.

14.9 Alternative Methods of Calculation

To eliminate as much of the sheer physical drudgery of calculation as possible, at least two methods are open. One method involves coding the data and using the centering approach. For example, if either the X or Y data (or both) were expressed in decimals, the series might be multiplied through by a constant to clear the decimals, if this appears possible and practical. This process may be termed coding. An example is shown in Table 14.8. Or, in another situation, each X (and/or Y) value perhaps could be divided by a constant to make the values easier to work with. In some cases it might be desirable to multiply one series by a constant and divide the other series by a different constant. The important thing to remember is this: the value of the correlation coefficient r (or r^2) is *independent of the units in which the problem is stated.* Multiplying, dividing, adding, or subtracting a constant merely shifts the position of the "dots" on the coordinate axis, but does not alter the relationship between X and Y. A second method makes use of noncentered data and is illustrated in Table 14.9.

These points may be illustrated with an example. Table 14.8 indicates use of the coded method to simplify calculations. To code the data, the

Table 14.8

Use of Coded Data to Simplify Correlation Calculations

Year	X	Y	Coded X	Coded Y	x	y	x^2	xy	y^2	Y_c in Original Units
1	13,000	1,750	13	175	−6	25	36	−150	625	1,825.74
2	17,000	1,600	17	160	−2	10	4	−20	100	1,608.58
3	18,000	1,650	18	165	−1	15	1	−15	225	1,554.29
4	21,000	1,500	21	150	2	0	4	0	0	1,391.42
5	22,000	1,450	22	145	3	−5	9	−15	25	1,337.13
6	23,000	1,050	23	105	4	−45	16	−180	2,025	1,282.84
	114,000	9,000					70	−380	3,000	9,000.00

original X values were divided by 1,000, and the original Y values were divided by 10.

Calculation of the correlation values:

$$a \text{ (centered)} = \bar{Y} = \frac{9,000}{6} = 1,500.$$

$$b = \frac{\Sigma xy}{\Sigma x^2} = \frac{-380}{70} = -5.429$$

and $(-5.429)(10) = -54.29$ (decoded value).

$$r = \frac{\Sigma xy}{\sqrt{\Sigma x^2 \Sigma y^2}} = \frac{-380}{\sqrt{(70)(3,000)}} = -.830.$$

$$S_{yx} = \sigma_y \sqrt{1 - r^2} = \sqrt{\frac{3,000}{6}} \sqrt{1 - .6889} = 22.4 \sqrt{.3111} = 12.28$$

and $(12.28)(10) = 122.8 = S_{yx}$ (decoded value).

Observe that both b and S_{yx} are expressed in terms of the Y series. Thus, if the original Y series was divided by 10, then b and S_{yx} must be multiplied by 10 to arrive at the decoded values. Since the data are centered, the x column is used in the regression equation $Y_c = a + bx$.

Linear Correlation, Noncentered Method

A second alternative for reducing the amount of computational effort involved in a problem—particularly if N is large—is to utilize the original data in the computations and apply correction factors in the final determination of the desired values of a, b, r, and S_{yx}. This method is particularly suitable to machine calculation. An example is given in Table 14.9.

Table 14.9

Linear Correlation, Noncentered Method

Year	X	Y	X^2	XY	Y^2	Y_c
1	10	17	100	170	289	16.33
2	10	18	100	180	324	16.33
3	9	15	81	135	225	15.66
4	11	18	121	198	324	17.00
5	8	13	64	104	169	14.99
6	7	12	49	84	144	14.31
7	14	25	196	350	625	19.01
8	13	20	169	260	400	18.34
9	12	19	144	228	361	17.67
10	16	13	256	208	169	20.36
	110	170	1,280	1,917	3,030	170.00

The necessary formulas and calculations are as follows:

$$r = \frac{N(\Sigma\, XY) - (\Sigma\, X)(\Sigma\, Y)}{\sqrt{[N(\Sigma\, X^2) - (\Sigma\, X)^2][N(\Sigma\, Y^2) - (\Sigma\, Y)^2]}}$$

$$= \frac{(10)(1,917) - (110)(170)}{[(10)(1,280) - (110)^2][(10)(3,030) - (170)^2]},$$

$$r = .475; \qquad r^2 = .226.$$

$$b = \frac{N(\Sigma\, XY) - (\Sigma\, X)(\Sigma\, Y)}{N(\Sigma\, X^2) - (\Sigma\, X)^2}$$

$$= \frac{(10)(1,917) - (110)(170)}{(10)(1,280) - (110)^2}$$

$$= \frac{470}{700} = .6714.$$

$$a = \bar{Y} - b\bar{X} = 17 - 7.3854 = 9.6146 \qquad \text{(origin as } X = 0\text{)}.$$

$$S_{yx} = \sigma_y \sqrt{1 - r^2}$$

where

$$\sigma_y = \sqrt{\frac{\Sigma\ Y^2}{N} - \left(\frac{\Sigma\ Y}{N}\right)^2} = \sqrt{\frac{3{,}030}{10} - \left(\frac{170}{10}\right)^2} = 3.74;$$

$$S_{yx} = 3.74\ \sqrt{1 - .226} = 3.29.$$

It should also be pointed out that the "centered" summation values may be obtained as follows:

$$\Sigma\ x^2 = \Sigma\ X^2 - \frac{(\Sigma\ X)^2}{N}, \tag{14.23}$$

$$\Sigma\ y^2 = \Sigma\ Y^2 - \frac{(\Sigma\ Y)^2}{N}, \tag{14.24}$$

$$\Sigma\ xy = \Sigma\ XY - \frac{(\Sigma\ X)(\Sigma\ Y)}{N}. \tag{14.25}$$

Use of the centered summations may then be used to check the calculations or may be used directly to calculate r, σ_y, and b. Using the data of Table 14.5, we have

$$\Sigma\ x^2 = 1{,}280 - \frac{(100)^2}{10} = 1{,}280 - 1{,}210 = 70,$$

$$\Sigma\ y^2 = 3{,}030 - \frac{(170)^2}{10} = 3{,}030 - 2{,}890 = 140,$$

$$\Sigma\ xy = 1{,}917 - \frac{(110)(170)}{10} = 1{,}917 - 1{,}870 = 47,$$

and

$$r = \frac{\Sigma\ xy}{\sqrt{(\Sigma\ x^2)(\Sigma\ y^2)}}\ \frac{47}{\sqrt{(70)(140)}} = .475,$$

$$\sigma_y = \sqrt{\frac{\Sigma\ y^2}{N}} = \sqrt{\frac{140}{10}} = 3.73,$$

$$b = \frac{\Sigma\ xy}{\Sigma\ x^2} = \frac{47}{70} = .6714,$$

$$a = \frac{\Sigma\ Y}{N} = \frac{170}{10} = 17 \qquad \text{(when } x = 0\text{).}$$

To reverse the prediction—that is, for X to regress on Y, it is only necessary to reverse the headings for Table 14.9 and use the formulas given above. In other words, the headings and total for Table 14.9 would now appear as in Table 14.10. Coding could be utilized with the non-centered method should this be desirable to simplify the calculations.

Table 14.10

X	Y	X^2	XY	Y^2
170	110	3,030	1,917	1,280

SOURCE: Derived from Table 14.9

At first glance the method shown above may appear formidable. However, the noncentered methods are really quite simple and are particularly well adapted to machine operations. One point to be noticed in Table 14.9 is that a is calculated for the point at which $X = 0$. The remainder of the values derived from the noncentered method are identical in interpretation to the noncentered method previously explained.

Table 14.11

Linear Correlation Involving GNP and Construction Activity for the United States, 1929–1958 (Billions of Dollars; Machine Method of Calculation)

Year	GNP X	Constr. Y	X^2	XY	Y^2	Y_c
1929	104.4	10.8	10,899.36	1,127.52	116.64	6.97
1930	91.1	8.7	8,299.21	792.57	75.69	5.45
1931	76.3	6.4	5,821.69	488.32	40.96	3.72
1932	58.5	3.5	3,422.25	204.75	12.25	1.74
1933	56.0	2.9	3,136.00	162.40	8.41	1.46
1934	65.0	3.7	4,225.00	240.50	13.69	2.49
1935	72.5	4.2	5,256.25	304.50	17.64	3.34
1936	82.7	6.5	6,839.29	537.55	42.25	4.50
1937	90.8	7.0	8,244.64	635.60	49.00	5.42
1938	85.2	7.0	7,259.04	596.40	49.00	4.78
1939	91.1	8.2	8,299.21	747.02	67.24	5.45
1940	100.6	8.7	10,120.36	922.20	75.69	6.48
1941	125.8	12.0	15,825.64	1,509.60	144.00	9.40
1942	159.1	14.1	25,312.81	2,243.31	198.81	13.19
1943	192.5	8.3	37,056.25	1,597.75	68.89	16.98
1944	211.4	5.3	44,689.96	1,204.20	28.09	19.13
1945	213.6	5.8	45,624.96	1,238.80	33.64	19.38
1946	210.7	12.6	44,394.49	2,654.82	158.76	19.05
1947	234.3	17.9	54,896.49	4,193.97	320.41	21.74
1948	259.4	23.2	67,288.36	6,018.80	538.24	24.59
1949	258.1	24.1	66,615.61	6.220.21	580.81	24.44
1950	284.6	29.9	80,997.16	8.509.54	894.01	27.45
1951	329.0	32.7	108,241.00	10,758.30	1,069.29	32.50
1952	347.0	34.7	120,409.00	12,040.90	1,204.09	34.55
1953	365.4	37.0	133,517.16	13,519,80	1,369.00	36.64
1954	363.1	39.4	131,841.61	14,306.14	1,552.36	36.38
1955	397.5	44.0	158,006.25	17,490.00	1,936.00	40.29
1956	419.2	45.8	175,728.64	19,199.36	2,097.64	42.76
1957	442.5	47.8	195,806.25	21,127.60	2,284.84	45.41
1958	441.7	48.9	195,028.90	21,599.13	2,391.21	45.32
	6,229.1	561.1	1,783,172.89	172,191.56	17,438.55	561.00

The preceding table, Table 14.11, indicates the arithmetic computations for a rather large problem, one involving a large number of paired values. For illustrative purposes the problem is solved by both the centered and noncentered methods. If calculating machines are available, the labor involved in problems of this length is reduced substantially. Of course, if a computer is employed, the hand labor is reduced to a minimum.

Calculations:

$$r = \frac{N(\Sigma\,XY) - (\Sigma\,X)(\Sigma\,Y)}{\sqrt{[(N)(\Sigma\,X^2) - (\Sigma\,X)^2][(N)(\Sigma\,Y^2) - (\Sigma\,Y)^2]}}$$

$$= \frac{(30)(172{,}191.56) - (6{,}229.1)(561.1)}{\sqrt{[(30)(1{,}783{,}172.89) - (6{,}229.1)^2][(30)(17{,}438.55) - (561.1)^2]}}$$

$$= .954 \approx .95,$$

$$b = \frac{(N)(\Sigma\,XY) - (\Sigma X)(\Sigma\,Y)}{(N)(\Sigma\,X^2) - (\Sigma\,X)^2}$$

$$= \frac{(30)(172{,}191.56) - (6{,}229.1)(561.1)}{(30)(1{,}783{,}172.89) - (6{,}229.1)^2} = .11369 \approx .114,$$

$$a = \bar{Y} - b\bar{X}$$

$$= \frac{561.1}{30} - \left(.11369 \cdot \frac{6{,}229.1}{30}\right) = -4.903 \qquad \text{(origin at } X = 0\text{),}$$

$$\sigma_y = \sqrt{\frac{\Sigma\,Y^2}{N} - \frac{\Sigma\,Y_c^2}{N}}$$

$$= \sqrt{\frac{17{,}438.55}{30} - \left(\frac{561.1}{30}\right)^2} = 15.22,$$

$$S_{yx} = \sigma_y\sqrt{1 - r^2}$$

$$= (15.22)(.09) = 4.566.$$

$$Yc = a + bX.$$

Example: Yc for 1929

$$Yc_{1929} = -4.903 + (.144 \times 104.4),$$

$$Yc_{1929} = 6.97.$$

If it should be more convenient to use the centered method, the procedure and calculations are as follows.

$$\Sigma x^2 = \Sigma X^2 - \frac{(\Sigma X)^2}{N} = 1{,}783{,}172.89 - \frac{(6{,}229.1)^2}{30} = 489{,}783.4,$$

$$\Sigma y^2 = \Sigma Y^2 - \frac{(\Sigma Y)^2}{N} = 17{,}438.55 - \frac{(561.1)^2}{30} = 6{,}944.11,$$

$$\Sigma xy = \Sigma XY - \frac{(\Sigma XY)(\Sigma Y)}{N} = 172{,}191.56 - \frac{(6{,}229.1)(561.1)}{30}$$

$$= 55{,}686.63,$$

$$r = \frac{\Sigma xy}{\sqrt{(\Sigma x^2)(\Sigma y^2)}} = \frac{55{,}686.83}{\sqrt{(489{,}783.4)(6{,}944.11)}} = .954 \approx .95,$$

$$\sigma_y = \sqrt{\frac{\Sigma y^2}{N}} = \sqrt{\frac{6{,}944.11}{30}} = 15.22,$$

$$S_{yx} = \sigma_y \sqrt{1 - r^2} = (15.22)(.09) = 4.566.$$

$$Yc = a + b\,x. \qquad \text{(note } x = X - \bar{X})$$

Example: Yc for 1929

$$Yc_{1929} = 18.703 + (.11369 \times -103.23),$$

$$Yc_{1929} = 6.97.$$

Exercise 14.6
1. Why is r (or r^2) independent of the units in which X and Y are stated?
2. (a) What is the purpose of "coding" data?
   (b) Explain how coding works with respect to r.
   (c) Explain how a and b are "decoded" to arrive at the proper values.
3. Compare and contrast the methods used with Table 14.8 and 14.9.
4. The formulae applicable to Table 14.9 appear rather long and involved as contrasted to, say, Table 14.4. Explain why this should be the case. Then, consider whether the method used with Table 14.9 is really much longer and more difficult than that used with Table 14.3.
5. What method is used to "reverse the prediction" of Table 14.9?

Exercise 14.7
1. (a) Explain the relationships between the "scatter" of the data on a scatter-gram and the degree of correlation.
   (b) How are r, r^2, and S_{yx} related?
2. Explain the theory of testing the probability of r's having occurred by chance rather than by a mutual association between the variables.

3. What does it mean to say that any given r is "significant at the 5 per cent level"? At the 1 per cent level?

4. Are tests of significance for the coefficient of correlation any different in theory than tests for the significance of the difference between, say, two means?

Exercise 14.8A. Given the following set of data. Draw a scattergram of the data and the regression line. Find r, r^2, and S_{yx} and compute the regression line. Use the noncentered least-squares correlation method.

Year	Population (14 Years of Age and Over; millions)	Labor Force (millions)	Year	Population (14 Years of Age and Over; millions)	Labor Force (millions)
1941	102	58	1953	115	67
1942	103	60	1954	116	68
1943	104	65	1955	117	69
1944	105	66	1956	119	70
1945	106	65	1957	120	71
1946	107	61	1958	122	71
1947	108	62	1959	123	72
1948	109	63	1960	125	72
1949	110	64	1961	128	74
1950	111	65	1962	130	75
1951	112	66	1963	132	76
1952	113	67	1964	134	77

SOURCE: *Economic Report of the President, 1965*, p. 214.

1. Evaluate r and r^2 in the context of the data.

2. (a) What does the value of b imply for these data?
    (b) Does the value of b appear logical? Why?

3. (a) What was the impact of the war years 1942–1945 on the data?
    (b) Would it be logical to remove the war years from this set of data and, if so, on what grounds?
    (c) If this were done, how would the value of r change?
    (d) When the war years were removed, would b then be a better indicator of the relationship between a one million gain in population and the number of persons added to the labor force? Why?

4. Leaving aside the question of the data for the war years, would the degree of correlation exhibited by this problem tend to hold true over a much wider range of population values than those shown?

5. What are some of the relevant variables other than population which would account for some of the variability in the labor-force series? Hint: Custom with regard to years of formal schooling.

6. On the basis of your evaluation of this problem, would you be willing to predict the labor force for various levels of population? Why?

Exercise 14.8B. Given the following set of data. Find r, a, b, and S_{yx} and compute the regression line. Draw a scattergram of the data and regression line. Use the noncentered least-squares correlation method.

Year	Index of Consumer Prices (1957–59 = 100) X	Manufacturing Wages (Weekly; current dollars) Y	Year	Index of Consumer Prices (1957–59 = 100) X	Manufacturing Wages (Weekly; current dollars) Y
1939	48.4	$23.64	1952	92.5	67.16
1940	48.8	24.96	1953	93.2	70.47
1941	51.3	29.48	1954	93.6	70.49
1942	56.8	36.68	1955	93.3	75.70
1943	60.3	43.07	1956	94.7	78.78
1944	61.3	45.70	1957	98.0	81.59
1945	62.7	44.20	1958	100.7	82.71
1946	68.0	43.32	1959	101.5	88.26
1947	77.8	49.17	1960	103.1	89.72
1948	83.8	53.12	1961	104.2	92.34
1949	83.0	53.88	1962	105.4	96.56
1950	83.8	58.32	1963	106.7	99.63
1951	90.5	63.34	1964	108.1	103.38

SOURCE: *Economic Report of the President, 1965*, pp. 224, 244.

1. Evaluate r and r^2 in the context of the data.

2. (a) What does the value of b imply for this data?
   (b) Do the war years 1942–1945 appear to yield extraordinary values of X and Y?
   (c) Would it be logical to remove the war years from this set of data?
   (d) Would r be larger if the war years were removed?

3. From the appearance of the scattergram, would you say that consumer prices and weekly wages in manufacturing are closely related? If so, in what manner are they related?

4. On the basis of your evaluation of this problem, would you be willing to predict weekly wages in manufacturing from consumer prices?

5. What other variables may account for some of the variability of the two series?

6. Is there a cause-and-effect relationship between consumer prices and manufacturing wages? Explain.

APPENDIX A: SOME BASIC NUMERICAL CONSIDERATIONS

The materials in Appendix A are designed to explain briefly (1) the accuracy of numbers, (2) significant figures, (3) rules for rounding numbers, and (4) working with rounded numbers. Exercises are provided following the first three sections. Answers to the exercises may be checked on page 446.

A.1 Accuracy of Numbers

Because few (if any) measurements are exact (that is, most measurements, even those made with precise instruments, involve some margin of error), the quantities expressed as "statistics" will ordinarily be subject to some degree of inaccuracy. The question is: "How much error?"

Illustration: Suppose a dollar-and-cents figure is quoted as, say, $25.32. It is customary to quote prices in whole cents. Any fraction of a cent would be rounded to the nearest cent. If, in the process of pricing, fractions occurred, these would not appear in the quoted price. In the present instance the actual price figure might have been, say, $25.323, which was then rounded to $25.32.

However, to an outside observer who notes the quoted price, $25.32, there is no way of telling whether the figure was rounded up or rounded down, or indeed if it was rounded at all. The observer must then assume that the price as actually computed was somewhere between $25.325 and $25.315. Consequently, it now appears that a variation of plus or minus one-half cent ($.005) has occurred.

We have now discovered that the degree of error in the quoted price is plus or minus one-half cent in a total of 2,532 cents. Our next step is to change this ratio to its more customary form in which the denominator is equal to 1. Thus,

$$\frac{2,532}{0.50} = \frac{5,064}{1}.$$

We may now express the degree of accuracy as "one part in 5,064" or, as is fitting in this case, we may simply say the degree of accuracy is "one part in approximately 5,000."

There is a simpler method of arriving at the accuracy of a number, but unfortunately this method does not indicate the nature of the work being performed. Accuracy may be determined by multiplying the significant digits by 2 and dropping the decimal. Thus, the accuracy of 0.0032 becomes $32 \times 2 = 64$—that is, accuracy to one part in 64.

The *precision* of a measurement refers to the size of the unit employed as a standard (thousandths, hundredths, tenths, and so on). The *accuracy* of a measurement refers to the relative error which measurement units impose on a number.

Exercise A.1.   In the following problems, determine the degree of accuracy.

1. 94.5	2. 78	3. 3,562	4. 32,654
5. 8,000	6. 24,600	7. 92,039	8. 73,220
9. 155,060	10. 356,291	11. 673,500	12. 890,000
13. 9,875,000	14. 32.0	15. 68,502	16. 0.0032
17. 94.5	18. 94.950	19. 0.00320	20. 0.25

A.2   Significant Figures

Significant figures are those digits which show the degree of accuracy of a number. Some general rules of statistical application may be formulated as follows:

1. A number which results from an exact counting or measuring process is said to have as many significant figures as there are digits in the number. Example: A count of the number of employees might indicate 156 persons employed in a given firm. The number of significant digits is therefore three.

2. Large numbers are frequently unwieldy if left in the form which results from an exact counting process. For simplicity such numbers are often rounded to a more convenient figure—that is, zeros are substituted for all but the first few digits. In other cases of measurement it is often clear that the counting process is not precise, and the resulting number is rounded to only those digits which are known or believed to be accurate. For example, if the number 9,682,212 is given as an estimate of the number of nails in a barrel, the number may be considered unwieldy and may also be somewhat inaccurate. The number might be quoted as 9,682,000, or perhaps quoted as "about" 9,700,000.

3. In general, it may be said that zeros are used to place the decimal and are not themselves significant figures, except when the zero (or zeros) fall between other significant digits. By way of illustration: the zero in 306 has significance whereas the zeros in 36,000 are used to place the decimal. Zero is, of course, an even number.

4. Some examples of the preceding general rules are:
    (a) 36 is correct to two significant figures.
    (b) 360 may be correct to either two or three significant figures, depending upon whether or not the number has actually been rounded to a final

zero. If rounded, it is correct to two significant figures. Note: Unless it is known that 360 is exact, we must assume rounding occurred.

(c) 36,020,000 is correct to four significant figures (unless it is known that the final zeros represent an exact amount).

(d) 0.00036 is correct to two significant figures.

(e) 0.0003600 is correct to four significant figures. Zeros which are not necessary for placing the decimal may be assumed to be significant.

Exercise A.2. How many significant figures do each of the following numbers contain?

1. 35	2. 280	3. 965	4. 3,050
5. 2,001	6. 0.00602	7. 74,068	8. 90,602.08
9. 500	10. 0.506000	11. 241.04	12. 9,687,010
13. 0.0202	14. 2.006	15. 200.60	16. 34,000.000
17. 800,040	18. 5,000,002	19. 0.8070	20. 0.06005
21. 1,007,000	22. 64,210	23. 0.0000086	24. 100.0
25. 75,000,300			

A.3 Rules for Rounding Numbers

When it is desirable to round a number, either to make it more convenient or to show the degree of accuracy, the following rules are generally used. (Note: There are no set rules that have been universally accepted. Rounding is, to some extent, a matter of taste. There is a requirement of consistency, however.)

1. When the number to be eliminated is greater than 5, the preceding digit is increased by one. Example: 576 rounds to 580.
2. When the number to be eliminated is less than 5, the preceding digit is not changed. Example: 322 rounds to 320.
3. When the number to be eliminated is exactly 5, the preceding digit is increased by one if that preceding digit is odd. If the preceding digit is even, it is not changed. Examples: 475 rounds to 480. 465 rounds to 460.

Exercise A.3. In the following problems round the numbers to two significant digits.

1. 987	2. 8,450	3. 3,356	4. 975
5. 3,245	6. 8,750	7. 24,320	8. 655
9. 765,003	10. 0.007324	11. .0205	12. 7,949
13. 21.5	14. 6.35	15. 2,154	16. 2,150

Exercise A.4. In the following problems round the numbers to four significant digits.

1. 26,785	2. 381,651	3. 575,050	4. .069715
5. .0050135	6. 20.25	7. 941.54	8. 46.08569
9. 0.0067037	10. 4,692,503	11. 2,000.5	12. 23.355
13. 233.55	14. 6,515.0		

A.4   Working with Rounded Numbers

On occasion it might be necessary to perform arithmetic operations with rounded numbers, and the question then arises as to how accurate one may consider the results. In general, the results of an arithmetic operation with rounded numbers cannot be considered to have more significant figures than the least precise number in the series. For example, in addition we might have a problem as follows:

$$
\begin{array}{r}
10,678.32 \\
106.731 \\
34.6201 \\
\hline
10,819.67
\end{array}
$$

The same general principle would apply in the case of subtraction. Thus, $6,834 - 29.82 = 6,804$. In the case of multiplication, the product cannot be considered to possess more significant figures than the least precise number in the problem. For example:

$$(3.24)(2.6781) = 8.68.$$

The same rule would hold true in division. Thus: $2,961.38 \div 24 = 123$.

Usually the rounding is carried out before the arithmetic operation is performed, in which case the principle explained above has already been accomplished.

Answers

Exercise A.1. (1) 1,890   (2) 156   (3) 7,124   (4) 65,308   (5) 16
(6) 492   (7) 184,078   (8) 14,644   (9) 31,012   (10) 712,582
(11) 13,470   (12) 178   (13) 19,750   (14) 640   (15) 137,004
(16) 64   (17) 1,890   (18) 189,900   (19) 640   (20) 50

Exercise A.2. (1) 2   (2) 2   (3) 3   (4) 3   (5) 4   (6) 3   (7) 5
(8) 7   (9) 1   (10) 6   (11) 5   (12) 6   (13) 3   (14) 4   (15) 5
(16) 2   (17) 5   (18) 7   (19) 4   (20) 4   (21) 4   (22) 4   (23) 2
(24) 4   (25) 6

Exercise A.3. (1) 990   (2) 8,400   (3) 3,400   (4) 980   (5) 3,200
(6) 8,800   (7) 24,000   (8) 660   (9) 770,000   (10) .0073   (11) .02
(12) 7,900   (13) 22   (14) 6.4   (15) 2,200   (16) 2,200

Exercise A.4. (1) 26,780   (2) 381,700   (3) 575,000   (4) 0.06972
(5) 0.005014   (6) 20.25   (7) 941.5   (8) 46.09   (9) 0.006704
(10) 4,693,000   (11) 2,000   (12) 23.36   (13) 233.6   (14) 6,515

APPENDIX B:
A SAMPLING UNIVERSE

Table B.1 is the frequency table of a universe which may be used to illustrate sampling methods. The items may be entered on tags or chips and placed in a box or other container. When the items are randomized, samples of size n may be drawn from the universe and the desired statistics computed. The items for the first 100 samples of $n = 5$ as drawn experimentally by the author are shown in Table B.2.

Table B.1

Distribution of Items in Universe A

X	I	X	I
20	1	50	16
21	1	51	16
23	1	52	15
25	1	53	15
26	1	54	14
27	1	55	14
28	1	56	13
29	2	57	12
30	2	58	11
31	2	59	10
32	3	60	9
33	4	61	8
34	4	62	7
35	5	63	6
36	6	64	6
37	6	65	5
38	7	66	4
39	8	67	4
40	9	68	3
41	10	69	2
42	11	70	2
43	12	71	2
44	13	72	2
45	14	73	1
46	14	74	1
47	15	75	1
48	15	77	1
49	16	79	1
		80	1
			$\overline{386}$

$$N = 386, \quad \Sigma fX = 19{,}386, \quad \bar{X} = 50, \quad \sigma = 10$$

Table B.2

Distribution of Sample Means Drawn from Universe A

Sample	Items Drawn					Σ	x̄	Sample	Items Drawn					Σ	x̄
1	39	46	48	51	55	239	47.8	51	35	57	41	62	53	248	49.6
2	45	51	52	61	65	274	54.8	52	53	60	77	42	42	274	54.8
3	37	39	43	46	52	217	43.4	53	36	60	51	23	46	216	43.2
4	26	27	47	52	66	218	43.6	54	42	52	35	59	59	247	49.4
5	43	48	55	57	61	264	52.8	55	62	47	46	49	36	240	48.0
6	39	51	54	54	55	253	50.6	56	47	48	57	50	43	245	49.0
7	34	46	49	53	54	236	47.2	57	40	33	50	61	54	238	47.6
8	38	47	52	53	54	244	48.8	58	55	55	54	70	49	283	56.6
9	32	42	42	42	59	217	43.4	59	50	57	61	38	51	257	51.4
10	33	51	56	57	77	274	54.8	60	53	56	51	50	53	263	52.6
11	32	38	59	68	69	266	53.2	61	57	45	57	49	43	251	50.2
12	35	40	45	70	71	261	52.2	62	46	49	43	69	65	272	54.4
13	39	45	46	47	52	229	45.8	63	53	55	45	46	44	243	48.1
14	40	43	48	49	52	232	46.4	64	69	59	57	45	47	277	55.4
15	36	38	43	55	67	239	47.8	65	43	47	59	49	55	253	50.6
16	31	47	53	57	67	255	51.0	66	53	44	49	65	41	252	50.4
17	23	28	32	56	71	210	42.0	67	56	40	58	56	63	273	54.6
18	43	45	47	59	66	260	52.0	68	42	41	61	44	45	233	46.6
19	39	44	50	54	70	257	51.4	69	43	49	51	40	35	218	43.6
20	42	45	47	49	62	245	49.0	70	48	45	53	37	53	236	47.2
21	31	36	40	40	47	194	38.8	71	79	47	52	64	56	298	59.6
22	37	44	53	54	61	249	49.8	72	49	54	57	46	48	254	50.8
23	46	49	52	52	64	263	52.6	73	59	45	44	54	55	257	51.4
24	32	41	44	57	61	235	47.0	74	52	75	50	49	33	259	51.8
25	30	39	49	52	61	231	46.2	75	54	36	52	72	34	248	49.6
26	21	43	44	52	59	219	43.8	76	40	58	38	51	43	230	46.0
27	47	49	51	52	80	279	55.8	77	52	53	58	56	55	274	54.8
28	43	48	60	65	79	295	59.0	78	45	62	52	60	41	260	52.0
29	45	47	47	51	53	243	48.6	79	53	39	43	40	53	228	45.6
30	47	49	51	56	60	263	52.6	80	35	38	43	47	48	211	42.2
31	49	66	58	57	51	281	56.2	81	53	36	58	65	47	259	51.8
32	49	58	44	45	43	239	47.8	82	53	41	46	69	42	251	50.2
33	47	48	35	44	64	238	47.6	83	36	47	53	41	47	224	44.8
34	60	36	20	52	51	219	43.8	84	59	47	27	37	55	225	45.0
35	50	52	46	43	59	250	50.0	85	59	48	61	52	48	268	53.6
36	34	52	56	33	65	240	48.0	86	68	65	47	46	60	286	57.2
37	42	57	38	62	65	264	52.8	87	51	39	50	48	64	252	50.4
38	54	46	61	58	53	272	54.4	88	46	47	48	42	39	222	44.4
39	50	50	65	46	38	249	49.8	89	50	57	80	53	32	272	54.4
40	37	54	43	41	50	225	45.0	90	53	54	46	53	44	250	50.0
41	60	52	45	40	57	254	50.8	91	61	36	64	51	33	245	49.0
42	35	50	74	54	52	265	53.0	92	51	43	48	60	46	248	49.6
43	55	44	46	59	49	253	50.6	93	48	31	55	48	57	239	47.8
44	39	21	80	65	55	260	52.0	94	57	47	39	46	69	258	51.6
45	65	49	47	35	49	245	49.0	95	45	40	53	57	40	235	47.0
46	29	50	56	46	51	232	46.4	96	50	43	52	50	57	252	50.4
47	58	46	45	60	45	254	50.8	97	52	39	45	56	47	239	47.8
48	20	69	32	64	47	232	46.4	98	48	57	50	64	51	270	54.0
49	41	71	21	57	54	244	48.8	99	50	55	58	47	54	264	52.8
50	51	45	51	38	68	253	50.6	100	80	45	55	51	32	263	52.6

APPENDIX C:
DETERMINING THE
TOTAL ERROR IN
A FREQUENCY
DISTRIBUTION

One of the questions which may arise in the construction of a frequency distribution from raw data is, "How well do the groupings actually fit the data?" One method by which to provide an objective answer to the question is known as the "rule of least error." The basic principle involved in the method is this: Ideally, the distribution is constructed so that the midpoints of the class intervals are entirely representative of the items in the class. If this were the case, the mean of each class would equal the midpoint of each class. If the midpoints and class means are not equal, then some "error" exists in the distribution. The error is due to grouping the items into classes. Since it is highly unlikely that the data would distribute themselves in such an obliging manner as to achieve equality between class mean and class midpoint, the next best thing is to accept that distribution which has the least total error. In other words, given a choice between two distributions formed from the same data, and if all other things were equal, then that distribution which possessed the least total error would be the preferred distribution.

The general method for determining the total error in a frequency distribution may be illustrated by employing the example found originally in Chapter 2 on the distribution of part-time wages.

Illustration of Error Determination in Frequency Distribution

Class Limits	Midpoint	Class Mean	Difference (d) (Midpoint − Mean)	f	d · f
23–27	25	$25.40	$−0.40	5	$−2.00
28–32	30	29.80	+0.20	10	+2.00
33–37	35	34.70	+0.30	10	+3.00
38–42	40	40.00	.00	12	0.00
43–47	45	45.40	−0.40	10	−4.00
48–52	50	49.75	+0.25	8	+2.00
53–57	55	54.50	+0.50	4	+2.00
58–62	60	60.00	.00	1	.00
				60	+3.00 = total error

Notes: (1) The grouping error per item $= +3.00/60 = .05$, or 5 cents.

(2) If all 60 items of the original data be used to determine the mean, the true mean will be $39.70.

(3) The mean, as calculated from the frequency distribution, is $39.75.

(4) The difference between $37.75 and $39.70 $= 5$ cents, the error per item caused by grouping the items into classes.

(5) To employ the "rule of least error" it is necessary to know the individual values of all the items which have gone into the distribution. If these items are not available, the method described above cannot be employed.

APPENDIX D: LOGARITHMIC STRAIGHT-LINE TREND, LEAST-SQUARES METHOD

For many purposes, certain types of economic data are frequently best portrayed by a logarithmic chart. This is particularly true when the major interest in the series centers about the *relative* growth or decline in the variable.

On the assumption that a logarithmic straight-line trend is appropriate to the data, the methodology will be indicated by use of an example as shown in Table D.1.

Table D.1

Gross Sales of the Exponential Corporation with Calculations
for Logarithmic Straight-Line Trend Equations

Year	X	Y Data	X^2	log Y	X(log Y)
1955	1	293	1	2.46687	2.46687
1956	2	292	4	2.46538	4.90376
1957	3	318	9	2.50243	7.50729
1958	4	341	16	2.53275	10.13028
1959	5	353	25	2.54777	12.73885
1960	6	369	36	2.56703	15.40218
1961	7	363	49	2.55991	17.91937
1962	8	392	64	2.59329	20.74632
1963	9	402	81	2.60423	23.43807
1964	10	407	100	2.60959	26.09590
	55	3,530	385	25.44925	141.37589

To compute the necessary trend equation values, the following formulae are required:

$$\Sigma (\log Y) = Na + b \Sigma X,$$

$$\Sigma (X \cdot \log Y) = a \Sigma X + b \Sigma X^2.$$

For the trend equation we have

$$\log Y_c = a + bX, \qquad \text{where } a \text{ and } b \text{ are expressed as logarithms.}$$

Table D.2

Calculations for Logarithmic Straight-Line Trend;
Original Date Shown in Table

Year	X	a +	(b	· X)	= log Y_c	(Natural Y_c Numbers)
1954	0	2.45126 + 0.01703 ·		0	2.45126	282.6
1955	1	,, +	,,	· 1	2.46829	294.0
1956	2	,, +	,,	· 2	2.48532	305.8
1957	3	,, +	,,	· 3	2.50235	318.0
1958	4	,, +	,,	· 4	2.51938	330.8
1959	5	,, +	,,	· 5	2.53641	344.0
1960	6	,, +	,,	· 6	2.55344	357.7
1961	7	,, +	,,	· 7	2.57047	372.0
1962	8	,, +	,,	· 8	2.58750	386.9
1963	9	,, +	,,	· 9	2.60453	402.3
1964	10	,, +	,,	· 10	2.62156	418.5

Thus, solving for a and b in the problem above we have

(1)
$$25.44925 = 10a + 45b,$$

(2)
$$141.37589 = 55a + 385b.$$

Multiply equation (1) by 5.5; then subtract from equation (2):

$$141.37589 = 55a + 385b$$
$$139.97087 = 55a + 302.5b$$
$$\overline{\quad 1.40502 = \qquad\qquad 82.5b}$$
$$b = .01703,$$
$$a = 2.45126.$$

To calculate the necessary trend values, we may use the procedures shown in Table D.2.

If we now construct a graph of Y_c on semilogarithmic paper, the

Illustration D.1   Y Data of Table 1 Graphed on a Semilogarithmic
Scale with Corresponding Logarithmic Trend Values

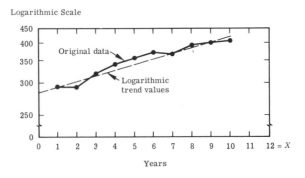

Illustration D.2   *Y* Data of Table D.1 Graphed on an Arithmetic Scale Using the Logarithmic Trend Values from Table D.2

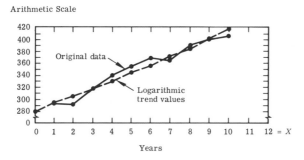

trend values result in a straight-line. See Illustration D.1. If the Y_c values are shown on an arithmetic scale, the trend line will appear as an exponential curve. See Illustration D.2. Incidentally, the percentage rate of growth in the series of data presented in this illustration is the antilog of 0.01703, or 4 per cent (where the antilog of 0.01073 = 1.04), and 1.04 (100) = 104 per cent. Subtracting 100 per cent to obtain the percentage change yields 4 per cent. That is, this series of data displays an average annual compound rate of growth of 4 per cent. We may note that the logarithmic adaptation of the straight-line formula, $Y_c = a + bX$, is log $Y_c = \log a + b \log X$, and the latter is equivalent to the compound interest formula, $S = p(1 + r)^n$. Then, solving for Y_c as we did in the above example yields an exponential function. It should be pointed out that to obtain the compound rate of percentage growth 100 per cent is substracted from the antilog of *b*. Should this subtraction yield a negative value, the percentage rate of growth would then be negative.

The least-squares condition required in the logarithmic straight-line trend is met by computing the values in such a manner that the sum of the squares of the deviations of the logarithmic values from the trend is at a minimum (least-squares) value.

Exercise D.1.   Assume the following set of data represents the total dollar volume (in billions of dollars) of consumer installment credit outstanding during seven years. Years 1 through 7: 23.0; 23.6; 29.0; 31.9; 34.2; 34.0; 39.4. Compute the logarithmic straight-line trend.

1. When the log of *b* is converted to a natural number, what does this number represent?

2. When the original data are plotted on arithmetic paper, does the series appear to be an exponential series? Would a parabolic trend appear to fit the data? What reason or reasons might be advanced for use of the logarithmic straight-line trend versus the parabola?

3. When the original data and logarithmic trend values are plotted on semilogarithmic paper, does the trend line appear to describe the "average

change" of the data? In what visual manner, if any, does the logarithmic trend present a different visual appearance than an ordinary straight-line trend?

4. Predict the volume of consumer installment credit for year 8. How would this logarithmic projection differ from a straight-line trend accurately fitted to the same data?

APPENDIX E:
ADJUSTING DATA FOR
CALENDAR VARIATION

One of the technical problems encountered in certain types of time-series data arises because of irregularities in the calendar from year to year. Easter, for example, may fall anywhere between March 22 and April 25. Some holidays may occur on the weekend in one year and during the regular working days in other years. Consequently when monthly or weekly totals are prepared, these values may not be strictly comparable from one year to the next. Too, some months have 30 days, some 31, while February may have 28 or 29 days. Some businesses may operate on Saturdays, or perhaps Saturday forenoon. During certain parts of the year, some firms may be working overtime. Thus, with these many sources of variation, some type of calendar adjustment may be required to obtain comparable figures.

All of this means that while a month (or week) may ordinarily serve as a unit of operational time, sufficient variations between these time packages will occur which, for informational purposes, preclude comparability. Some technique must, therefore, be employed to arrive at values which may be meaningfully compared, with say, January of one year and January of the next year.

The following are suggestive of techniques which may be used in adjusting data for calendar variation:[1]

1. Some monthly totals may actually not require adjustment if the same holidays reoccur in the same month (as is the general case). However, if Easter should exert an impact on the data, some adjustment for March or April may be necessary. (See item 3 below.)

2. One method of calendar adjustment is to construct a "daily average." That is, the data (sales, mileage, employees, payroll, and so on) obtained for the time period (say a month) are divided by the number of working days in that time period. Thus, if September has 21 working days, the data for that month will be divided by 21 and a "daily average" obtained.

---

[1] For a more detailed description of calendar variation adjustments, see Alva M. Tuttle, *Elementary Business and Economic Statistics* (New York: McGraw-Hill Book Company, 1957), pp. 456–460 and 651–653.

3. A second method of adjustment relies on the analyst's judgment to compensate for irregularities. For example, Easter may be in March or in April. To adjust monthly totals for this event, the analyst would need to allocate—on a logical basis—that part of the upswing in business activity due to Easter which logically could be allocated to each month. Of course, in this type of adjustment an arbitrary element is involved, but if identical techniques are used consistently, the results should be comparable.

4. When weekly figures of original data are involved—that is, values which measure one week's total performance—it may be desirable to attain comparability by converting to a monthly basis, but again, calendar irregularities of the months make it inappropriate to simply multiply the weekly figures by four. Some businesses have solved this "weekly-monthly" problem by adopting a 13-month calendar. However, be all this as it may, the weekly-monthly adjustment can be made by determining the number of weeks properly attributable to each month and adjusting the weekly data in terms of the proper number of days.

5. Price data may be adjusted by either (a) taking the price at a specified date in each month, or (b) constructing an "average daily price." In some cases where prices may be variable through each working day, daily highs and lows may be recorded along with the opening and closing prices. Sometimes these prices will be quoted on a monthly or annual basis by taking the "average" price, and/or indicating the high and low range for that time period. (Note: It is an interesting problem to calculate the average price for a commodity subject to considerable price variation during a trading day.)

APPENDIX F:
TABLES OF SQUARES
AND SQUARE ROOTS[1]

There are a few points to watch in using the table on the following pages. We shall discuss these briefly. First of all, observe that the first column lists all numbers n, from 1.00 through 10.00. Each number in the second column is the square, n^2, of the corresponding number, n, in the first column. For example, $(1.78)^2 = 3.1684$ and $(7.17)^2 = 51.4089$.

The second column can also be used to obtain the squares of other numbers having the same succession of digits as the numbers given in the first column. For example, the square of 17.8 will also have the same succession of digits, 31684, as the square of 1.78. However, the position of the decimal point is not the same and $(17.8)^2 = 316.84$. This can be explained by the fact that we must multiply 1.78 by 10 to get 17.8. When the number is squared, the 10 is also squared $[(17.8)^2 = (10)^2 \cdot (1.78)^2]$. Thus the answer is 100 times 3.1684 or 316.84. Similarly, $(717)^2 = 514{,}089$ because 7.17 must be multiplied by 100 to give 717 and the square of 7.17 is then multiplied by the square of 100, which is 10,000. Note that in each case *the decimal point is moved twice as many places in the square as in the number that is squared.* Consider now the effect of moving the decimal point in the opposite direction. $(.178)^2$ will again contain the digits 31684, but this time the correct answer is .031684. The explanation is that 1.78 must be multiplied by .1 to give .178. The answer is then multiplied by $(.1)^2$ or .01, giving .031684. As another example, $(.0717)^2 = .00514089$. Note that the italicized statement holds regardless of the direction that the decimal point is moved.

The operation of taking the square root is the inverse of the operation of squaring, just as division is the inverse operation of multiplication. The discussion in the preceding paragraph is, therefore, also helpful in understanding the use of the third column of the table. This column gives the square root, $\sqrt{n}$, of the corresponding number, n, in the first column of the table. To further simplify the use of the table for finding square roots, the fourth column, $\sqrt{10n}$, has been added.

[1] From George H. Weinberg, and John A. Schumaker, *Statistics, An Intuitive Approach* (Belmont, Calif.: Wadsworth Publishing Company, Inc., 1963), pp. 309–319. By Permission.

457

Since the first column contains all numbers from 1.00 to 10.00, we know that the third column contains the square roots of all these numbers. For example, $\sqrt{1.78} = 1.33417$ and $\sqrt{7.17} = 2.67769$. The fourth column enables us also to find directly the square roots, $\sqrt{10n}$, of all numbers from 10(1.00) to 10(10.00), that is, from 10.0 to 100.0, where now each number is given only to the nearest tenth. For example, we find from the fourth column opposite 1.78 that $\sqrt{17.8} = 4.21900$ and opposite 7.17 that $\sqrt{71.7} = 8.46759$. Hence from the third and fourth columns we can read directly the square roots of all numbers from 1.00 through 100.0. However, just as we extended the use of the table for squares, so we can extend its use for square roots.

Suppose we want $\sqrt{717}$. From the table we can read both $\sqrt{7.17}$ and $\sqrt{71.7}$. Which should we use? This question is answered when we consider the placement of the decimal point. Remembering that taking the square root is the inverse of squaring, and looking back at the italicized statement earlier in the discussion, we see that *the decimal point is moved half as many places in the square root as in the number.* Now, half of an odd number isn't a whole number and a decimal point can't be moved a fraction of a place. So we must move the decimal point an *even number* of places to begin with when converting a number in order to apply the table and find its square root. Therefore, in our example we want the digits in $\sqrt{7.17}$ that are 267769, and by application of the last italicized statement we have $\sqrt{717} = 26.7769$, since the decimal point is moved two places from 7.17 to 717 and half of two is one. Had the problem been to find $\sqrt{7170}$, we would again have moved the decimal point an *even* number of places in order to obtain a number whose square root we could read directly from the table. In this case we would have the digits in $\sqrt{71.7}$ or 846759. Observing the rule for placement of the decimal point would give us the answer, 84.6759. The problem of finding $\sqrt{.00717}$ leads to the same sequence of digits (moving the decimal point four places), but the answer this time is .0846759. Again, the last italicized statement holds regardless of the direction that the decimal point is moved.

n	n^2	$\sqrt{n}$	$\sqrt{10n}$	n	n^2	$\sqrt{n}$	$\sqrt{10n}$
1.00	1.0000	1.00000	3.16228	1.50	2.2500	1.22474	3.87298
1.01	1.0201	1.00499	3.17805	1.51	2.2801	1.22882	3.88587
1.02	1.0404	1.00995	3.19374	1.52	2.3104	1.23288	3.89872
1.03	1.0609	1.01489	3.20936	1.53	2.3409	1.23693	3.91152
1.04	1.0816	1.01980	3.22490	1.54	2.3716	1.24097	3.92428
1.05	1.1025	1.02470	3.24037	1.55	2.4025	1.24499	3.93700
1.06	1.1236	1.02956	3.25576	1.56	2.4336	1.24900	3.94968
1.07	1.1449	1.03441	3.27109	1.57	2.4649	1.25300	3.96232
1.08	1.1664	1.03923	3.28634	1.58	2.4964	1.25698	3.97492
1.09	1.1881	1.04403	3.30151	1.59	2.5281	1.26095	3.98748
1.10	1.2100	1.04881	3.31662	1.60	2.5600	1.26491	4.00000
1.11	1.2321	1.05357	3.33167	1.61	2.5921	1.26886	4.01248
1.12	1.2544	1.05830	3.34664	1.62	2.6244	1.27279	4.02492
1.13	1.2769	1.06301	3.36155	1.63	2.6569	1.27671	4.03733
1.14	1.2996	1.06771	3.37639	1.64	2.6896	1.28062	4.04969
1.15	1.3225	1.07238	3.39116	1.65	2.7225	1.28452	4.06202
1.16	1.3456	1.07703	3.40588	1.66	2.7556	1.28841	4.07431
1.17	1.3689	1.08167	3.42053	1.67	2.7889	1.29228	4.08656
1.18	1.3924	1.08628	3.43511	1.68	2.8224	1.29615	4.09878
1.19	1.4161	1.09087	3.44964	1.69	2.8561	1.30000	4.11096
1.20	1.4400	1.09545	3.46410	1.70	2.8900	1.30384	4.12311
1.21	1.4641	1.10000	3.47851	1.71	2.9241	1.30767	4.13521
1.22	1.4884	1.10454	3.49285	1.72	2.9584	1.31149	4.14729
1.23	1.5129	1.10905	3.50714	1.73	2.9929	1.31529	4.15933
1.24	1.5376	1.11355	3.52136	1.74	3.0276	1.31909	4.17133
1.25	1.5625	1.11803	3.53553	1.75	3.0625	1.32288	4.18330
1.26	1.5876	1.12250	3.54965	1.76	3.0976	1.32665	4.19524
1.27	1.6129	1.12694	3.56371	1.77	3.1329	1.33041	4.20714
1.28	1.6384	1.13137	3.57771	1.78	3.1684	1.33417	4.21900
1.29	1.6641	1.13578	3.59166	1.79	3.2041	1.33791	4.23084
1.30	1.6900	1.14018	3.60555	1.80	3.2400	1.34164	4.24264
1.31	1.7161	1.14455	3.61939	1.81	3.2761	1.34536	4.25441
1.32	1.7424	1.14891	3.63318	1.82	3.3124	1.34907	4.26615
1.33	1.7689	1.15326	3.64692	1.83	3.3489	1.35277	4.27785
1.34	1.7956	1.15758	3.66060	1.84	3.3856	1.35647	4.28952
1.35	1.8225	1.16190	3.67423	1.85	3.4225	1.36015	4.30116
1.36	1.8496	1.16619	3.68782	1.86	3.4596	1.36382	4.31277
1.37	1.8769	1.17047	3.70135	1.87	3.4969	1.36748	4.32435
1.38	1.9044	1.17473	3.71484	1.88	3.5344	1.37113	4.33590
1.39	1.9321	1.17898	3.72827	1.89	3.5721	1.37477	4.34741
1.40	1.9600	1.18322	3.74166	1.90	3.6100	1.37840	4.35890
1.41	1.9881	1.18743	3.75500	1.91	3.6481	1.38203	4.37035
1.42	2.0164	1.19164	3.76829	1.92	3.6864	1.38564	4.38178
1.43	2.0449	1.19583	3.78153	1.93	3.7249	1.38924	4.39318
1.44	2.0736	1.20000	3.79473	1.94	3.7636	1.39284	4.40454
1.45	2.1025	1.20416	3.80789	1.95	3.8025	1.39642	4.41588
1.46	2.1316	1.20830	3.82099	1.96	3.8416	1.40000	4.42719
1.47	2.1609	1.21244	3.83406	1.97	3.8809	1.40357	4.43847
1.48	2.1904	1.21655	3.84708	1.98	3.9204	1.40712	4.44972
1.49	2.2201	1.22066	3.86005	1.99	3.9601	1.41067	4.46094

n	n^2	$\sqrt{n}$	$\sqrt{10n}$	n	n^2	$\sqrt{n}$	$\sqrt{10n}$
2.00	4.0000	1.41421	4.47214	2.50	6.2500	1.58114	5.00000
2.01	4.0401	1.41774	4.48330	2.51	6.3001	1.58430	5.00999
2.02	4.0804	1.42127	4.49444	2.52	6.3504	1.58745	5.01996
2.03	4.1209	1.42478	4.50555	2.53	6.4009	1.59060	5.02991
2.04	4.1616	1.42829	4.51664	2.54	6.4516	1.59374	5.03984
2.05	4.2025	1.43178	4.52769	2.55	6.5025	1.59687	5.04975
2.06	4.2436	1.43527	4.53872	2.56	6.5536	1.60000	5.05964
2.07	4.2849	1.43875	4.54973	2.57	6.6049	1.60312	5.06952
2.08	4.3264	1.44222	4.56070	2.58	6.6564	1.60624	5.07937
2.09	4.3681	1.44568	4.57165	2.59	6.7081	1.60935	5.08920
2.10	4.4100	1.44914	4.58258	2.60	6.7600	1.61245	5.09902
2.11	4.4521	1.45258	4.59347	2.61	6.8121	1.61555	5.10882
2.12	4.4944	1.45602	4.60435	2.62	6.8644	1.61864	5.11859
2.13	4.5369	1.45945	4.61519	2.63	6.9169	1.62173	5.12835
2.14	4.5796	1.46287	4.62601	2.64	6.9696	1.62481	5.13809
2.15	4.6225	1.46629	4.63681	2.65	7.0225	1.62788	5.14782
2.16	4.6656	1.46969	4.64758	2.66	7.0756	1.63095	5.15752
2.17	4.7089	1.47309	4.65833	2.67	7.1289	1.63401	5.16720
2.18	4.7524	1.47648	4.66905	2.68	7.1824	1.63707	5.17687
2.19	4.7961	1.47986	4.67974	2.69	7.2361	1.64012	5.18652
2.20	4.8400	1.48324	4.69042	2.70	7.2900	1.64317	5.19615
2.21	4.8841	1.48661	4.70106	2.71	7.3441	1.64621	5.20577
2.22	4.9284	1.48997	4.71169	2.72	7.3984	1.64924	5.21536
2.23	4.9729	1.49332	4.72229	2.73	7.4529	1.65227	5.22494
2.24	5.0176	1.49666	4.73286	2.74	7.5076	1.65529	5.23450
2.25	5.0625	1.50000	4.74342	2.75	7.5625	1.65831	5.24404
2.26	5.1076	1.50333	4.75395	2.76	7.6176	1.66132	5.25357
2.27	5.1529	1.50665	4.76445	2.77	7.6729	1.66433	5.26308
2.28	5.1984	1.50997	4.77493	2.78	7.7284	1.66733	5.27257
2.29	5.2441	1.51327	4.78539	2.79	7.7841	1.67033	5.28205
2.30	5.2900	1.51658	4.79583	2.80	7.8400	1.67332	5.29150
2.31	5.3361	1.51987	4.80625	2.81	7.8961	1.67631	5.30094
2.32	5.3824	1.52315	4.81664	2.82	7.9524	1.67929	5.31037
2.33	5.4289	1.52643	4.82701	2.83	8.0089	1.68226	5.31977
2.34	5.4756	1.52971	4.83735	2.84	8.0656	1.68523	5.32917
2.35	5.5225	1.53297	4.84768	2.85	8.1225	1.68819	5.33854
2.36	5.5696	1.53623	4.85798	2.86	8.1796	1.69115	5.34790
2.37	5.6169	1.53948	4.86826	2.87	8.2369	1.69411	5.35724
2.38	5.6644	1.54272	4.87852	2.88	8.2944	1.69706	5.36656
2.39	5.7121	1.54596	4.88876	2.89	8.3521	1.70000	5.37587
2.40	5.7600	1.54919	4.89898	2.90	8.4100	1.70294	5.38516
2.41	5.8081	1.55242	4.90918	2.91	8.4681	1.70587	5.39444
2.42	5.8564	1.55563	4.91935	2.92	8.5264	1.70880	5.40370
2.43	5.9049	1.55885	4.92950	2.93	8.5849	1.71172	5.41295
2.44	5.9536	1.56205	4.93964	2.94	8.6436	1.71464	5.42218
2.45	6.0025	1.56525	4.94975	2.95	8.7025	1.71756	5.43139
2.46	6.0516	1.56844	4.95984	2.96	8.7616	1.72047	5.44059
2.47	6.1009	1.57162	4.96991	2.97	8.8209	1.72337	5.44977
2.48	6.1504	1.57480	4.97996	2.98	8.8804	1.72627	5.45894
2.49	6.2001	1.57797	4.98999	2.99	8.9401	1.72916	5.46809

n	n^2	$\sqrt{n}$	$\sqrt{10n}$	n	n^2	$\sqrt{n}$	$\sqrt{10n}$
3.00	9.0000	1.73205	5.47723	3.50	12.2500	1.87083	5.91608
3.01	9.0601	1.73494	5.48635	3.51	12.3201	1.87350	5.92453
3.02	9.1204	1.73781	5.49545	3.52	12.3904	1.87617	5.93296
3.03	9.1809	1.74069	5.50454	3.53	12.4609	1.87883	5.94138
3.04	9.2416	1.74356	5.51362	3.54	12.5316	1.88149	5.94979
3.05	9.3025	1.74642	5.52268	3.55	12.6025	1.88414	5.95819
3.06	9.3636	1.74929	5.53173	3.56	12.6736	1.88680	5.96657
3.07	9.4249	1.75214	5.54076	3.57	12.7449	1.88944	5.97495
3.08	9.4864	1.75499	5.54977	3.58	12.8164	1.89209	5.98331
3.09	9.5481	1.75784	5.55878	3.59	12.8881	1.89473	5.99166
3.10	9.6100	1.76068	5.56776	3.60	12.9600	1.89737	6.00000
3.11	9.6721	1.76352	5.57674	3.61	13.0321	1.90000	6.00833
3.12	9.7344	1.76635	5.58570	3.62	13.1044	1.90263	6.01664
3.13	9.7969	1.76918	5.59464	3.63	13.1769	1.90526	6.02495
3.14	9.8596	1.77200	5.60357	3.64	13.2496	1.90788	6.03324
3.15	9.9225	1.77482	5.61249	3.65	13.3225	1.91050	6.04152
3.16	9.9856	1.77764	5.62139	3.66	13.3956	1.91311	6.04979
3.17	10.0489	1.78045	5.63028	3.67	13.4689	1.91572	6.05805
3.18	10.1124	1.78326	5.63915	3.68	13.5424	1.91833	6.06630
3.19	10.1761	1.78606	5.64801	3.69	13.6161	1.92094	6.07454
3.20	10.2400	1.78885	5.65685	3.70	13.6900	1.92354	6.08276
3.21	10.3041	1.79165	5.66569	3.71	13.7641	1.92614	6.09098
3.22	10.3684	1.79444	5.67450	3.72	13.8384	1.92873	6.09918
3.23	10.4329	1.79722	5.68331	3.73	13.9129	1.93132	6.10737
3.24	10.4976	1.80000	5.69210	3.74	13.9876	1.93391	6.11555
3.25	10.5625	1.80278	5.70088	3.75	14.0625	1.93649	6.12372
3.26	10.6276	1.80555	5.70964	3.76	14.1376	1.93907	6.13188
3.27	10.6929	1.80831	5.71839	3.77	14.2129	1.94165	6.14003
3.28	10.7584	1.81108	5.72713	3.78	14.2884	1.94422	6.14817
3.29	10.8241	1.81384	5.73585	3.79	14.3641	1.94679	6.15630
3.30	10.8900	1.81659	5.74456	3.80	14.4400	1.94936	6.16441
3.31	10.9561	1.81934	5.75326	3.81	14.5161	1.95192	6.17252
3.32	11.0224	1.82209	5.76194	3.82	14.5924	1.95448	6.18061
3.33	11.0889	1.82483	5.77062	3.83	14.6689	1.95704	6.18870
3.34	11.1556	1.82757	5.77927	3.84	14.7456	1.95959	6.19677
3.35	11.2225	1.83030	5.78792	3.85	14.8225	1.96214	6.20484
3.36	11.2896	1.83303	5.79655	3.86	14.8996	1.96469	6.21289
3.37	11.3569	1.83576	5.80517	3.87	14.9769	1.96723	6.22093
3.38	11.4244	1.83848	5.81378	3.88	15.0544	1.96977	6.22896
3.39	11.4921	1.84120	5.82237	3.89	15.1321	1.97231	6.23699
3.40	11.5600	1.84391	5.83095	3.90	15.2100	1.97484	6.24500
3.41	11.6281	1.84662	5.83952	3.91	15.2881	1.97737	6.25300
3.42	11.6964	1.84932	5.84808	3.92	15.3664	1.97990	6.26099
3.43	11.7649	1.85203	5.85662	3.93	15.4449	1.98242	6.26897
3.44	11.8336	1.85472	5.86515	3.94	15.5236	1.98494	6.27694
3.45	11.9025	1.85742	5.87367	3.95	15.6025	1.98746	6.28490
3.46	11.9716	1.86011	5.88218	3.96	15.6816	1.98997	6.29285
3.47	12.0409	1.86279	5.89067	3.97	15.7609	1.99249	6.30079
3.48	12.1104	1.86548	5.89915	3.98	15.8408	1.99499	6.30872
3.49	12.1801	1.86815	5.90762	3.99	15.9201	1.99750	6.31664

n	n^2	$\sqrt{n}$	$\sqrt{10n}$	n	n^2	$\sqrt{n}$	$\sqrt{10n}$
4.00	16.0000	2.00000	6.32456	4.50	20.2500	2.12132	6.70820
4.01	16.0801	2.00250	6.33246	4.51	20.3401	2.12368	6.71565
4.02	16.1604	2.00499	6.34035	4.52	20.4304	2.12603	6.72309
4.03	16.2409	2.00749	6.34823	4.53	20.5209	2.12838	6.73053
4.04	16.3216	2.00998	6.35610	4.54	20.6116	2.13073	6.73795
4.05	16.4025	2.01246	6.36396	4.55	20.7025	2.13307	6.74537
4.06	16.4836	2.01494	6.37181	4.56	20.7936	2.13542	6.75278
4.07	16.5649	2.01742	6.37966	4.57	20.8849	2.13776	6.76018
4.08	16.6464	2.01990	6.38749	4.58	20.9764	2.14009	6.76757
4.09	16.7281	2.02237	6.39531	4.59	21.0681	2.14243	6.77495
4.10	16.8100	2.02485	6.40312	4.60	21.1600	2.14476	6.78233
4.11	16.8921	2.02731	6.41093	4.61	21.2521	2.14709	6.78970
4.12	16.9744	2.02978	6.41872	4.62	21.3444	2.14942	6.79706
4.13	17.0569	2.03224	6.42651	4.63	21.4369	2.15174	6.80441
4.14	17.1396	2.03470	6.43428	4.64	21.5296	2.15407	6.81175
4.15	17.2225	2.03715	6.44205	4.65	21.6225	2.15639	6.81909
4.16	17.3056	2.03961	6.44981	4.66	21.7156	2.15870	6.82642
4.17	17.3889	2.04206	6.45755	4.67	21.8089	2.16102	6.83374
4.18	17.4724	2.04450	6.46529	4.68	21.9024	2.16333	6.84105
4.19	17.5561	2.04695	6.47302	4.69	21.9961	2.16564	6.84836
4.20	17.6400	2.04939	6.48074	4.70	22.0900	2.16795	6.85565
4.21	17.7241	2.05183	6.48845	4.71	22.1841	2.17025	6.86294
4.22	17.8084	2.05426	6.49615	4.72	22.2784	2.17256	6.87023
4.23	17.8929	2.05670	6.50384	4.73	22.3729	2.17486	6.87750
4.24	17.9776	2.05913	6.51153	4.74	22.4676	2.17715	6.88477
4.25	18.0625	2.06155	6.51920	4.75	22.5625	2.17945	6.89202
4.26	18.1476	2.06398	6.52687	4.76	22.6576	2.18174	6.89928
4.27	18.2329	2.06640	6.53452	4.77	22.7529	2.18403	6.90652
4.28	18.3184	2.06882	6.54217	4.78	22.8484	2.18632	6.91375
4.29	18.4041	2.07123	6.54981	4.79	22.9441	2.18861	6.92098
4.30	18.4900	2.07364	6.55744	4.80	23.0400	2.19089	6.92820
4.31	18.5761	2.07605	6.56506	4.81	23.1361	2.19317	6.93542
4.32	18.6624	2.07846	6.57267	4.82	23.2324	2.19545	6.94262
4.33	18.7489	2.08087	6.58027	4.83	23.3289	2.19773	6.94982
4.34	18.8356	2.08327	6.58787	4.84	23.4256	2.20000	6.95701
4.35	18.9225	2.08567	6.59545	4.85	23.5225	2.20227	6.96419
4.36	19.0096	2.08806	6.60303	4.86	23.6196	2.20454	6.97137
4.37	19.0969	2.09045	6.61060	4.87	23.7169	2.20681	6.97854
4.38	19.1844	2.09284	6.61816	4.88	23.8144	2.20907	6.98570
4.39	19.2721	2.09523	6.62571	4.89	23.9121	2.21133	6.99285
4.40	19.3600	2.09762	6.63325	4.90	24.0100	2.21359	7.00000
4.41	19.4481	2.10000	6.64078	4.91	24.1081	2.21585	7.00714
4.42	19.5364	2.10238	6.64831	4.92	24.2064	2.21811	7.01427
4.43	19.6249	2.10476	6.65582	4.93	24.3049	2.22036	7.02140
4.44	19.7136	2.10713	6.66333	4.94	24.4036	2.22261	7.02851
4.45	19.8025	2.10950	6.67083	4.95	24.5025	2.22486	7.03562
4.46	19.8916	2.11187	6.67832	4.96	24.6016	2.22711	7.04273
4.47	19.9809	2.11424	6.68581	4.97	24.7009	2.22935	7.04982
4.48	20.0704	2.11660	6.69328	4.98	24.8004	2.23159	7.05691
4.49	20.1601	2.11896	6.70075	4.99	24.9001	2.23383	7.06399

n	n	$\sqrt{n}$	$\sqrt{10n}$	n	n^2	$\sqrt{n}$	$\sqrt{10n}$
5.00	25.0000	2.23607	7.07107	5.50	30.2500	2.34521	7.41620
5.01	25.1001	2.23830	7.07814	5.51	30.3601	2.34734	7.42294
5.02	25.2004	2.24054	7.08520	5.52	30.4704	2.34947	7.42967
5.03	25.3009	2.24277	7.09225	5.53	30.5809	2.35160	7.43640
5.04	25.4016	2.24499	7.09930	5.54	30.6916	2.35372	7.44312
5.05	25.5025	2.24722	7.10634	5.55	30.8025	2.35584	7.44983
5.06	25.6036	2.24944	7.11337	5.56	30.9136	2.35797	7.45654
5.07	25.7049	2.25167	7.12039	5.57	31.0249	2.36008	7.46324
5.08	25.8064	2.25389	7.12741	5.58	31.1364	2.36220	7.46994
5.09	25.9081	2.25610	7.13442	5.59	31.2481	2.36432	7.47663
5.10	26.0100	2.25832	7.14143	5.60	31.3600	2.36643	7.48331
5.11	26.1121	2.26053	7.14843	5.61	31.4721	2.36854	7.48999
5.12	26.2144	2.26274	7.15542	5.62	31.5844	2.37065	7.49667
5.13	26.3169	2.26495	7.16240	5.63	31.6969	2.37276	7.50333
5.14	26.4196	2.26716	7.16938	5.64	31.8096	2.37487	7.50999
5.15	26.5225	2.26936	7.17635	5.65	31.9225	2.37697	7.51665
5.16	26.6256	2.27156	7.18331	5.66	32.0356	2.37908	7.52330
5.17	26.7289	2.27376	7.19027	5.67	32.1489	2.38118	7.52994
5.18	26.8324	2.27596	7.19722	5.68	32.2624	2.38328	7.53658
5.19	26.9361	2.27816	7.20417	5.69	32.3761	2.38537	7.54321
5.20	27.0400	2.28035	7.21110	5.70	32.4900	2.38747	7.54983
5.21	27.1441	2.28254	7.21803	5.71	32.6041	2.38956	7.55645
5.22	27.2484	2.28473	7.22496	5.72	32.7184	2.39165	7.56307
5.23	27.3529	2.28692	7.23187	5.73	32.8329	2.39374	7.56968
5.24	27.4576	2.28910	7.23878	5.74	32.9476	2.39583	7.57628
5.25	27.5625	2.29129	7.24569	5.75	33.0625	2.39792	7.58288
5.26	27.6676	2.29347	7.25259	5.76	33.1776	2.40000	7.58947
5.27	27.7729	2.29565	7.25948	5.77	33.2929	2.40208	7.59605
5.28	27.8784	2.29783	7.26636	5.78	33.4084	2.40416	7.60263
5.29	27.9841	2.30000	7.27324	5.79	33.5241	2.40624	7.60920
5.30	28.0900	2.30217	7.28011	5.80	33.6400	2.40832	7.61577
5.31	28.1961	2.30434	7.28697	5.81	33.7561	2.41039	7.62234
5.32	28.3024	2.30651	7.29383	5.82	33.8724	2.41247	7.62889
5.33	28.4089	2.30868	7.30068	5.83	33.9889	2.41454	7.63544
5.34	28.5156	2.31084	7.30753	5.84	34.1056	2.41661	7.64199
5.35	28.6225	2.31301	7.31437	5.85	34.2225	2.41868	7.64853
5.36	28.7296	2.31517	7.32120	5.86	34.3396	2.42074	7.65506
5.37	28.8369	2.31733	7.32803	5.87	34.4569	2.42281	7.66159
5.38	28.9444	2.31948	7.33485	5.88	34.5744	2.42487	7.66812
5.39	29.0521	2.32164	7.34166	5.89	34.6921	2.42693	7.67463
5.40	29.1600	2.32379	7.34847	5.90	34.8100	2.42899	7.68115
5.41	29.2681	2.32594	7.35527	5.91	34.9281	2.43105	7.68765
5.42	29.3764	2.32809	7.36205	5.92	35.0464	2.43311	7.69415
5.43	29.4849	2.33024	7.36885	5.93	35.1649	2.43516	7.70065
5.44	29.5936	2.33238	7.37564	5.94	35.2836	2.43721	7.70714
5.45	29.7025	2.33452	7.38241	5.95	35.4025	2.43926	7.71362
5.46	29.8116	2.33666	7.38918	5.96	35.5216	2.44131	7.72010
5.47	29.9209	2.33880	7.39594	5.97	35.6409	2.44336	7.72658
5.48	30.0304	2.34094	7.40270	5.98	35.7604	2.44540	7.73305
5.49	30.1401	2.34307	7.40945	5.99	35.8801	2.44745	7.73951

n	n^2	$\sqrt{n}$	$\sqrt{10n}$	n	n^2	$\sqrt{n}$	$\sqrt{10n}$
6.00	36.0000	2.44949	7.74597	6.50	42.2500	2.54951	8.06226
6.01	36.1201	2.45153	7.75242	6.51	42.3801	2.55147	8.06846
6.02	36.2404	2.45357	7.75887	6.52	42.5104	2.55343	8.07465
6.03	36.3609	2.45561	7.76531	6.53	42.6409	2.55539	8.08084
6.04	36.4816	2.45764	7.77174	6.54	42.7716	2.55734	8.08703
6.05	36.6025	2.45967	7.77817	6.55	42.9025	2.55930	8.09321
6.06	36.7236	2.46171	7.78460	6.56	43.0336	2.56125	8.09938
6.07	36.8449	2.46374	7.79102	6.57	43.1649	2.56320	8.10555
6.08	36.9664	2.46577	7.79744	6.58	43.2964	2.56515	8.11172
6.09	37.0881	2.46779	7.80385	6.59	43.4281	2.56710	8.11788
6.10	37.2100	2.46982	7.81025	6.60	43.5600	2.56905	8.12404
6.11	37.3321	2.47184	7.81665	6.61	43.6921	2.57099	8.13019
6.12	37.4544	2.47386	7.82304	6.62	43.8244	2.57294	8.13634
6.13	37.5769	2.47588	7.82943	6.63	43.9569	2.57488	8.14248
6.14	37.6996	2.47790	7.83582	6.64	44.0896	2.57682	8.14862
6.15	37.8225	2.47992	7.84219	6.65	44.2225	2.57876	8.15475
6.16	37.9456	2.48193	7.84857	6.66	44.3556	2.58070	8.16088
6.17	38.0689	2.48395	7.85493	6.67	44.4889	2.58263	8.16701
6.18	38.1924	2.48596	7.86130	6.68	44.6224	2.58457	8.17313
6.19	38.3161	2.48797	7.86766	6.69	44.7561	2.58650	8.17924
6.20	38.4400	2.48998	7.87401	6.70	44.8900	2.58844	8.18535
6.21	38.5641	2.49199	7.88036	6.71	45.0241	2.59037	8.19146
6.22	38.6884	2.49399	7.88670	6.72	45.1584	2.59230	8.19756
6.23	38.8129	2.49600	7.89303	6.73	45.2929	2.59422	8.20366
6.24	38.9376	2.49800	7.89937	6.74	45.4276	2.59615	8.20975
6.25	39.0625	2.50000	7.90569	6.75	45.5625	2.59808	8.21584
6.26	39.1876	2.50200	7.91202	6.76	45.6976	2.60000	8.22192
6.27	39.3129	2.50400	7.91833	6.77	45.8329	2.60192	8.22800
6.28	39.4384	2.50599	7.92465	6.78	45.9684	2.60384	8.23408
6.29	39.5641	2.50799	7.93095	6.79	46.1041	2.60576	8.24015
6.30	39.6900	2.50998	7.93725	6.80	46.2400	2.60768	8.24621
6.31	39.8161	2.51197	7.94355	6.81	46.3761	2.60960	8.25227
6.32	39.9424	2.51396	7.94984	6.82	46.5124	2.61151	8.25833
6.33	40.0689	2.51595	7.95613	6.83	46.6489	2.61343	8.26438
6.34	40.1956	2.51794	7.96241	6.84	46.7856	2.61534	8.27043
6.35	40.3225	2.51992	7.96869	6.85	46.9225	2.61725	8.27647
6.36	40.4496	2.52190	7.97496	6.86	47.0596	2.61916	8.28251
6.37	40.5769	2.52389	7.98123	6.87	47.1969	2.62107	8.28855
6.38	40.7044	2.52587	7.98749	6.88	47.3344	2.62298	8.29458
6.39	40.8321	2.52784	7.99375	6.89	47.4721	2.62488	8.30060
6.40	40.9600	2.52982	8.00000	6.90	47.6100	2.62679	8.30662
6.41	41.0881	2.53180	8.00625	6.91	47.7481	2.62869	8.31264
6.42	41.2164	2.53377	8.01249	6.92	47.8864	2.63059	8.31865
6.43	41.3449	2.53574	8.01873	6.93	48.0249	2.63249	8.32466
6.44	41.4736	2.53772	8.02496	6.94	48.1636	2.63439	8.33067
6.45	41.6025	2.53969	8.03119	6.95	48.3025	2.63629	8.33667
6.46	41.7316	2.54165	8.03741	6.96	48.4416	2.63818	8.34266
6.47	41.8609	2.54362	8.04363	6.97	48.5809	2.64008	8.34865
6.48	41.9904	2.54558	8.04984	6.98	48.7204	2.64197	8.35464
6.49	42.1201	2.54755	8.05605	6.99	48.8601	2.64386	8.36062

n	n^2	$\sqrt{n}$	$\sqrt{10n}$	n	n^2	$\sqrt{n}$	$\sqrt{10n}$
7.00	49.0000	2.64575	8.36660	7.50	56.2500	2.73861	8.66025
7.01	49.1401	2.64764	8.37257	7.51	56.4001	2.74044	8.66603
7.02	49.2804	2.64953	8.37854	7.52	56.5504	2.74226	8.67179
7.03	49.4209	2.65141	8.38451	7.53	56.7009	2.74408	8.67756
7.04	49.5616	2.65330	8.39047	7.54	56.8516	2.74591	8.68332
7.05	49.7025	2.65518	8.39643	7.55	57.0025	2.74773	8.68907
7.06	49.8436	2.65707	8.40238	7.56	57.1536	2.74955	8.69483
7.07	49.9849	2.65895	8.40833	7.57	57.3049	2.75136	8.70057
7.08	50.1264	2.66083	8.41427	7.58	57.4564	2.75318	8.70632
7.09	50.2681	2.66271	8.42021	7.59	57.6081	2.75500	8.71206
7.10	50.4100	2.66458	8.42615	7.60	57.7600	2.75681	8.71780
7.11	50.5521	2.66646	8.43208	7.61	57.9121	2.75862	8.72353
7.12	50.6944	2.66833	8.43801	7.62	58.0644	2.76043	8.72926
7.13	50.8369	2.67021	8.44393	7.63	58.2169	2.76225	8.73499
7.14	50.9796	2.67208	8.44985	7.64	58.3696	2.76405	8.74071
7.15	51.1225	2.67395	8.45577	7.65	58.5225	2.76586	8.74643
7.16	51.2656	2.67582	8.46168	7.66	58.6756	2.76767	8.75214
7.17	51.4089	2.67769	8.46759	7.67	58.8289	2.76948	8.75785
7.18	51.5524	2.67955	8.47349	7.68	58.9824	2.77128	8.76356
7.19	51.6961	2.68142	8.47939	7.69	59.1361	2.77308	8.76926
7.20	51.8400	2.68328	8.48528	7.70	59.2900	2.77489	8.77496
7.21	51.9841	2.68514	8.49117	7.71	59.4441	2.77669	8.78066
7.22	52.1284	2.68701	8.49706	7.72	59.5984	2.77849	8.78635
7.23	52.2729	2.68887	8.50294	7.73	59.7529	2.78029	8.79204
7.24	52.4176	2.69072	8.50882	7.74	59.9076	2.78209	8.79773
7.25	52.5625	2.69258	8.51469	7.75	60.0625	2.78388	8.80341
7.26	52.7076	2.69444	8.52056	7.76	60.2176	2.78568	8.80909
7.27	52.8529	2.69629	8.52643	7.77	60.3729	2.78747	8.81476
7.28	52.9984	2.69815	8.53229	7.78	60.5284	2.78927	8.82043
7.29	53.1441	2.70000	8.53815	7.79	60.6841	2.79106	8.82610
7.30	53.2900	2.70185	8.54400	7.80	60.8400	2.79285	8.83176
7.31	53.4361	2.70370	8.54985	7.81	60.9961	2.79464	8.83742
7.32	53.5824	2.70555	8.55570	7.82	61.1524	2.79643	8.84308
7.33	53.7289	2.70740	8.56154	7.83	61.3089	2.79821	8.84873
7.34	53.8756	2.70924	8.56738	7.84	61.4656	2.80000	8.85438
7.35	54.0225	2.71109	8.57321	7.85	61.6225	2.80179	8.86002
7.36	54.1696	2.71293	8.57904	7.86	61.7796	2.80357	8.86566
7.37	54.3169	2.71477	8.58487	7.87	61.9369	2.80535	8.87130
7.38	54.4644	2.71662	8.59069	7.88	62.0944	2.80713	8.87694
7.39	54.6121	2.71846	8.59651	7.89	62.2521	2.80891	8.88257
7.40	54.7600	2.72029	8.60233	7.90	62.4100	2.81069	8.88819
7.41	54.9081	2.72213	8.60814	7.91	62.5681	2.81247	8.89382
7.42	55.0564	2.72397	8.61394	7.92	62.7264	2.81425	8.89944
7.43	55.2049	2.72580	8.61974	7.93	62.8849	2.81603	8.90505
7.44	55.3536	2.72764	8.62554	7.94	63.0436	2.81780	8.91067
7.45	55.5025	2.72947	8.63134	7.95	63.2025	2.81957	8.91628
7.46	55.6516	2.73130	8.63713	7.96	63.3616	2.82135	8.92188
7.47	55.8009	2.73313	8.64292	7.97	63.5209	2.82312	8.92749
7.48	55.9504	2.73496	8.64870	7.98	63.6804	2.82489	8.93308
7.49	56.1001	2.73679	8.65448	7.99	63.8401	2.82666	8.93868

n	n^2	$\sqrt{n}$	$\sqrt{10n}$	n	n^2	$\sqrt{n}$	$\sqrt{10n}$
8.00	64.0000	2.82843	8.94427	8.50	72.2500	2.91548	9.21954
8.01	64.1601	2.83019	8.94986	8.51	72.4201	2.91719	9.22497
8.02	64.3204	2.83196	8.95545	8.52	72.5904	2.91890	9.23038
8.03	64.4809	2.83373	8.96103	8.53	72.7609	2.92062	9.23580
8.04	64.6416	2.83549	8.96660	8.54	72.9316	2.92233	9.24121
8.05	64.8025	2.83725	8.97218	8.55	73.1025	2.92404	9.24662
8.06	64.9636	2.83901	8.97775	8.56	73.2736	2.92575	9.25203
8.07	65.1249	2.84077	8.98332	8.57	73.4449	2.92746	9.25743
8.08	65.2864	2.84253	8.98888	8.58	73.6164	2.92916	9.26283
8.09	65.4481	2.84429	8.99444	8.59	73.7881	2.93087	9.26823
8.10	65.6100	2.84605	9.00000	8.60	73.9600	2.93258	9.27362
8.11	65.7721	2.84781	9.00555	8.61	74.1321	2.93428	9.27901
8.12	65.9344	2.84956	9.01110	8.62	74.3044	2.93598	9.28440
8.13	66.0969	2.85132	9.01665	8.63	74.4769	2.93769	9.28978
8.14	66.2596	2.85307	9.02219	8.64	74.6496	2.93939	9.29516
8.15	66.4225	2.85482	9.02774	8.65	74.8225	2.94109	9.30054
8.16	66.5856	2.85657	9.03327	8.66	74.9956	2.94279	9.30591
8.17	66.7489	2.85832	9.03881	8.67	75.1689	2.94449	9.31128
8.18	66.9124	2.86007	9.04434	8.68	75.3424	2.94618	9.31665
8.19	67.0761	2.86182	9.04986	8.69	75.5161	2.94788	9.32202
8.20	67.2400	2.86356	9.05539	8.70	75.6900	2.94958	9.32738
8.21	67.4041	2.86531	9.06091	8.71	75.8641	2.95127	9.33274
8.22	67.5684	2.86705	9.06642	8.72	76.0384	2.95296	9.33809
8.23	67.7329	2.86880	9.07193	8.73	76.2129	2.95466	9.34345
8.24	67.8976	2.87054	9.07744	8.74	76.3876	2.95635	9.34880
8.25	68.0625	2.87228	9.08295	8.75	76.5625	2.95804	9.35414
8.26	68.2276	2.87402	9.08845	8.76	76.7376	2.95973	9.35949
8.27	68.3929	2.87576	9.09395	8.77	76.9129	2.96142	9.36483
8.28	68.5584	2.87750	9.09945	8.78	77.0884	2.96311	9.37017
8.29	68.7241	2.87924	9.10494	8.79	77.2641	2.96479	9.37550
8.30	68.8900	2.88097	9.11043	8.80	77.4400	2.96648	9.38083
8.31	69.0561	2.88271	9.11592	8.81	77.6161	2.96816	9.38616
8.32	69.2224	2.88444	9.12140	8.82	77.7924	2.96985	9.39149
8.33	69.3889	2.88617	9.12688	8.83	77.9689	2.97153	9.39681
8.34	69.5556	2.88791	9.13236	8.84	78.1456	2.97321	9.40213
8.35	69.7225	2.88964	9.13783	8.85	78.3225	2.97489	9.40744
8.36	69.8896	2.89137	9.14330	8.86	78.4996	2.97658	9.41276
8.37	70.0569	2.89310	9.14877	8.87	78.6769	2.97825	9.41807
8.38	70.2244	2.89482	9.15423	8.88	78.8544	2.97993	9.42338
8.39	70.3921	2.89655	9.15969	8.89	79.0321	2.98161	9.42868
8.40	70.5600	2.89828	9.16515	8.90	79.2100	2.98329	9.43398
8.41	70.7281	2.90000	9.17061	8.91	79.3881	2.98496	9.43928
8.42	70.8964	2.90172	9.17606	8.92	79.5664	2.98664	9.44458
8.43	71.0649	2.90345	9.18150	8.93	79.7449	2.98831	9.44987
8.44	71.2336	2.90517	9.18695	8.94	79.9236	2.98998	9.45516
8.45	71.4025	2.90689	9.19239	8.95	80.1025	2.99166	9.46044
8.46	71.5716	2.90861	9.19783	8.96	80.2816	2.99333	9.46573
8.47	71.7409	2.91033	9.20326	8.97	80.4609	2.99500	9.47101
8.48	71.9104	2.91204	9.20869	8.98	80.6404	2.99666	9.47629
8.49	72.0801	2.91376	9.21412	8.99	80.8201	2.99833	9.48156

n	n^2	$\sqrt{n}$	$\sqrt{10n}$	n	n^2	$\sqrt{n}$	$\sqrt{10n}$
9.00	81.0000	3.00000	9.48683	9.50	90.2500	3.08221	9.74679
9.01	81.1801	3.00167	9.49210	9.51	90.4401	3.08383	9.75192
9.02	81.3604	3.00333	9.49737	9.52	90.6304	3.08545	9.75705
9.03	81.5409	3.00500	9.50263	9.53	90.8209	3.08707	9.76217
9.04	81.7216	3.00666	9.50789	9.54	91.0116	3.08869	9.76729
9.05	81.9025	3.00832	9.51315	9.55	91.2025	3.09031	9.77241
9.06	82.0836	3.00998	9.51840	9.56	91.3936	3.09192	9.77753
9.07	82.2649	3.01164	9.52365	9.57	91.5849	3.09354	9.78264
9.08	82.4464	3.01330	9.52890	9.58	91.7764	3.09516	9.78775
9.09	82.6281	3.01496	9.53415	9.59	91.9681	3.09677	9.79285
9.10	82.8100	3.01662	9.53939	9.60	92.1600	3.09839	9.79796
9.11	82.9921	3.01828	9.54463	9.61	92.3521	3.10000	9.80306
9.12	83.1744	3.01993	9.54987	9.62	92.5444	3.10161	9.80816
9.13	83.3569	3.02159	9.55510	9.63	92.7369	3.10322	9.81326
9.14	83.5396	3.02324	9.56033	9.64	92.9296	3.10483	9.81835
9.15	83.7225	3.02490	9.56556	9.65	93.1225	3.10644	9.82344
9.16	83.9056	3.02655	9.57079	9.66	93.3156	3.10805	9.82853
9.17	84.0889	3.02820	9.57601	9.67	93.5089	3.10966	9.83362
9.18	84.2724	3.02985	9.58123	9.68	93.7024	3.11127	9.83870
9.19	84.4561	3.03150	9.58645	9.69	93.8961	3.11288	9.84378
9.20	84.6400	3.03315	9.59166	9.70	94.0900	3.11448	9.84886
9.21	84.8241	3.03480	9.59687	9.71	94.2841	3.11609	9.85393
9.22	85.0084	3.03645	9.60208	9.72	94.4784	3.11769	9.85901
9.23	85.1929	3.03809	9.60729	9.73	94.6729	3.11929	9.86408
9.24	85.3776	3.03974	9.61249	9.74	94.8676	3.12090	9.86914
9.25	85.5625	3.04138	9.61769	9.75	95.0625	3.12250	9.87421
9.26	85.7476	3.04302	9.62289	9.76	95.2576	3.12410	9.87927
9.27	85.9329	3.04467	9.62808	9.77	95.4529	3.12570	9.88433
9.28	86.1184	3.04631	9.63328	9.78	95.6484	3.12730	9.88939
9.29	86.3041	3.04795	9.63846	9.79	95.8441	3.12890	9.89444
9.30	86.4900	3.04959	9.64365	9.80	96.0400	3.13050	9.89949
9.31	86.6761	3.05123	9.64883	9.81	96.2361	3.13209	9.90454
9.32	86.8624	3.05287	9.65401	9.82	96.4324	3.13369	9.90959
9.33	87.0489	3.05450	9.65919	9.83	96.6289	3.13528	9.91464
9.34	87.2356	3.05614	9.66437	9.84	96.8256	3.13688	9.91968
9.35	87.4225	3.05778	9.66954	9.85	97.0225	3.13847	9.92472
9.36	87.6096	3.05941	9.67471	9.86	97.2196	3.14006	9.92975
9.37	87.7969	3.06105	9.67988	9.87	97.4169	3.14166	9.93479
9.38	87.9844	3.06268	9.68504	9.88	97.6144	3.14325	9.93982
9.39	88.1721	3.06431	9.69020	9.89	97.8121	3.14484	9.94485
9.40	88.3600	3.06594	9.69536	9.90	98.0100	3.14643	9.94987
9.41	88.5481	3.06757	9.70052	9.91	98.2081	3.14802	9.95490
9.42	88.7364	3.06920	9.70567	9.92	98.4064	3.14960	9.95992
9.43	88.9249	3.07083	9.71082	9.93	98.6049	3.15119	9.96494
9.44	89.1136	3.07246	9.71597	9.94	98.8036	3.15278	9.96995
9.45	89.3025	3.07409	9.72111	9.95	99.0025	3.15436	9.97497
9.46	89.4916	3.07571	9.72625	9.96	99.2016	3.15595	9.97998
9.47	89.6809	3.07734	9.73139	9.97	99.4009	3.15753	9.98499
9.48	89.8704	3.07896	9.73653	9.98	99.6004	3.15911	9.98999
9.49	90.0601	3.08058	9.74166	9.99	99.8001	3.16070	9.99500
				10.00	100.000	3.16228	10.0000

APPENDIX G:
TABLE OF AREAS
OF THE NORMAL CURVE[1]

[1] From George H. Weinberg, and John A. Schumaker, *Statistics, An Intuitive Approach* (Belmont, Calif.: Wadsworth Publishing Company, Inc., 1963), p. 321. By permission.

z	.00	.01	.02	.03	.04	.05	.06	.07	.08	.09
0.0	.0000	.0040	.0080	.1200	.0160	.0199	.0239	.0279	.0319	.0359
0.1	.0398	.0438	.0478	.0517	.0557	.0596	.0636	.0675	.0714	.0753
0.2	.0793	.0832	.0871	.0910	.0948	.0987	.1026	.1064	.1103	.1141
0.3	.1179	.1217	.1255	.1293	.1331	.1368	.1406	.1443	.1480	.1517
0.4	.1554	.1591	.1628	.1664	.1700	.1736	.1772	.1808	.1844	.1179
0.5	.1915	.1950	.1985	.2019	.2054	.2088	.2123	.2157	.2190	.2224
0.6	.2257	.2291	.2324	.2357	.2389	.2422	.2454	.2486	.2517	.2549
0.7	.2580	.2611	.2642	.2673	.2704	.2734	.2764	.2794	.2823	.2852
0.8	.2881	.2910	.2939	.2967	.2995	.3023	.3051	.3078	.3106	.3133
0.9	.3159	.3186	.3212	.3238	.3264	.3289	.3315	.3340	.3365	.3389
1.0	.3413	.3438	.3461	.3485	.3508	.3531	.3554	.3577	.3599	.3621
1.1	.3643	.3665	.3686	.3708	.3729	.3749	.3770	.3790	.3810	.3830
1.2	.3849	.3869	.3888	.3907	.3925	.3944	.3962	.3980	.3997	.4015
1.3	.4032	.4049	.4066	.4082	.4099	.4115	.4131	.4147	.4162	.4177
1.4	.4192	.4207	.4222	.4236	.4251	.4265	.4279	.4292	.4306	.4319
1.5	.4332	.4345	.4357	.4370	.4382	.4394	.4406	.4418	.4429	.4441
1.6	.4452	.4463	.4474	.4484	.4495	.4505	.4515	.4525	.4535	.4545
1.7	.4554	.4564	.4573	.4582	.4591	.4599	.4608	.4616	.4625	.4633
1.8	.4641	.4649	.4656	.4664	.4671	.4678	.4686	.4693	.4699	.4706
1.9	.4713	.4719	.4726	.4732	.4738	.4744	.4750	.4756	.4761	.4767
2.0	.4772	.4778	.4783	.4788	.4793	.4798	.4803	.4808	.4812	.4817
2.1	.4821	.4826	.4830	.4834	.4838	.4842	.4846	.4850	.4854	.4857
2.2	.4861	.4864	.4868	.4871	.4875	.4878	.4881	.4884	.4887	.4890
2.3	.4893	.4896	.4898	.4901	.4904	.4906	.4909	.4911	.4913	.4916
2.4	.4918	.4920	.4922	.4925	.4927	.4929	.4931	.4932	.4934	.4936
2.5	.4938	.4940	.4941	.4943	.4945	.4946	.4948	.4949	.4951	.4952
2.6	.4953	.4955	.4956	.4957	.4959	.4960	.4961	.4962	.4963	.4964
2.7	.4965	.4966	.4967	.4968	.4969	.4970	.4971	.4972	.4973	.4974
2.8	.4974	.4975	.4976	.4977	.4977	.4978	.4979	.4979	.4980	.4981
2.9	.4981	.4982	.4982	.4983	.4984	.4984	.4985	.4985	.4986	.4986
3.0	.4987	.4987	.4987	.4988	.4988	.4989	.4989	.4989	.4990	.4990
3.1	.49903									
3.2	.49931									
3.3	.49952									
3.4	.49966									
3.5	.49977									
3.6	.49984									
3.7	.49989									
3.8	.49993									
3.9	.49995									
4.0	.50000									

APPENDIX H:
TABLE OF t

Use of the t distribution is appropriate when S is used as an estimate of σ, which means the t table is substituted for the normal curve in calculating probabilities. However, when $n > 30$ and $S \approx \sigma$, the normal curve is then employed.

The probability values given in the t table refer to the combined area of the two tails of the curve. Thus, when $n = 10$ and $x/\sigma = 2.228$, the combined area of the two tails is .05. For one-tailed values of probability, divide the given P (at the top of the table) by 2.

The table of t has been reproduced from Table IV of R. A. Fisher, *Statistical Methods for Research Workers*, published by Oliver & Boyd, Ltd., Edinburgh, and by permission of the author and publishers.

Table of t

n	$P = .9$	.8	.7	.6	.5	.4	.3	.2	.1	.05	.02	.01
1	.158	.325	.510	.727	1.000	1.376	1.963	3.078	6.314	12.706	31.821	63.657
2	.142	.289	.445	.617	.816	1.061	1.386	1.886	2.920	4.303	6.965	9.925
3	.137	.277	.424	.584	.765	.978	1.250	1.638	2.353	3.182	4.541	5.841
4	.134	.271	.414	.569	.741	.941	1.190	1.533	2.132	2.776	3.747	4.604
5	.132	.267	.408	.559	.727	.920	1.156	1.476	2.015	2.571	3.365	4.032
6	.131	.265	.404	.553	.718	.906	1.134	1.440	1.943	2.447	3.143	3.707
7	.130	.263	.402	.549	.711	.896	1.119	1.415	1.895	2.365	2.998	3.499
8	.130	.262	.399	.546	.706	.889	1.108	1.397	1.860	2.306	2.896	3.355
9	.129	.261	.398	.543	.703	.883	1.100	1.383	1.833	2.262	2.821	3.250
10	.129	.260	.397	.542	.700	.879	1.093	1.372	1.812	2.228	2.764	3.169
11	.129	.260	.396	.540	.697	.876	1.088	1.363	1.796	2.201	2.718	3.106
12	.128	.259	.395	.539	.695	.873	1.083	1.356	1.782	2.179	2.681	3.055
13	.128	.259	.394	.538	.694	.870	1.079	1.350	1.771	2.160	2.650	3.012
14	.128	.258	.393	.537	.692	.868	1.076	1.345	1.761	2.145	2.624	2.977
15	.128	.258	.393	.536	.691	.866	1.074	1.341	1.753	2.131	2.602	2.947
16	.128	.258	.392	.535	.690	.865	1.071	1.337	1.746	2.120	2.583	2.921
17	.128	.257	.392	.534	.689	.863	1.069	1.333	1.740	2.110	2.567	2.898
18	.127	.257	.392	.534	.688	.862	1.067	1.330	1.734	2.101	2.552	2.878
19	.127	.257	.391	.533	.688	.861	1.066	1.328	1.729	2.093	2.539	2.861
20	.127	.257	.391	.533	.687	.860	1.064	1.325	1.725	2.086	2.528	2.845
21	.127	.257	.391	.532	.686	.859	1.063	1.323	1.721	2.080	2.518	2.831
22	.127	.256	.390	.532	.686	.858	1.061	1.321	1.717	2.074	2.508	2.819
23	.127	.256	.390	.532	.685	.858	1.060	1.319	1.714	2.069	2.500	2.807
24	.127	.256	.390	.531	.685	.857	1.059	1.318	1.711	2.064	2.492	2.797
25	.127	.256	.390	.531	.684	.856	1.058	1.316	1.708	2.060	2.485	2.787
26	.127	.256	.390	.531	.684	.856	1.058	1.315	1.706	2.056	2.479	2.779
27	.127	.256	.389	.531	.684	.855	1.057	1.314	1.703	2.052	2.473	2.771
28	.127	.256	.389	.530	.683	.855	1.056	1.313	1.701	2.048	2.467	2.763
29	.127	.256	.389	.530	.683	.854	1.055	1.311	1.699	2.045	2.462	2.756
30	.127	.256	.389	.530	.683	.854	1.055	1.310	1.697	2.042	2.457	2.750
∞	.12566	.25335	.38532	.52440	.67449	.84162	1.03643	1.28155	1.64485	1.95996	2.32634	2.57582

APPENDIX I:
TABLE OF *F*

Use of the *F* table is explained on page 291 and in Section 14.6, p. 421.

5% (Roman Type) and 1% (Bold Face Type) Points for the Distribution of F

f_1 Degrees of Freedom (for Greater Mean Square) — values given as 5% (Roman) / 1% (Bold)

f_2	1	2	3	4	5	6	7	8	9	10	11	12	14	16	20	24	30	40	50	75	100	200	500	∞
1	161 / 4,052	200 / 4,999	216 / 5,403	225 / 5,625	230 / 5,764	234 / 5,859	237 / 5,928	239 / 5,981	241 / 6,022	242 / 6,056	243 / 6,082	244 / 6,106	245 / 6,142	246 / 6,169	248 / 6,208	249 / 6,234	250 / 6,258	251 / 6,286	252 / 6,302	253 / 6,323	253 / 6,334	254 / 6,352	254 / 6,361	254 / 6,366
2	18.51 / 98.49	19.00 / 99.00	19.16 / 99.17	19.25 / 99.25	19.30 / 99.30	19.33 / 99.33	19.36 / 99.34	19.37 / 99.36	19.38 / 99.38	19.39 / 99.40	19.40 / 99.41	19.41 / 99.42	19.42 / 99.43	19.43 / 99.44	19.44 / 9945	19.45 / 99.46	19.46 / 99.47	19.47 / 99.48	19.47 / 99.48	19.48 / 99.49	19.49 / 99.49	19.49 / 99.49	19.50 / 99.50	19.50 / 99.50
3	10.13 / 34.12	9.55 / 30.82	9.28 / 29.46	9.12 / 28.71	9.01 / 28.24	8.94 / 27.91	8.88 / 27.67	8.84 / 27.49	8.81 / 27.34	8.78 / 27.23	8.76 / 27.13	8.74 / 27.05	8.71 / 26.92	8.69 / 26.83	8.66 / 26.69	8.64 / 26.60	8.62 / 26.50	8.60 / 26.41	8.58 / 26.35	8.57 / 26.27	8.56 / 26.23	8.54 / 26.18	8.54 / 26.14	8.53 / 26.12
4	7.71 / 21.20	6.94 / 18.00	6.59 / 16.69	6.39 / 15.98	6.26 / 15.52	6.16 / 15.21	6.09 / 14.98	6.04 / 14.80	6.00 / 14.66	5.96 / 14.54	5.93 / 14.45	5.91 / 14.37	5.87 / 14.24	5.84 / 14.15	5.80 / 14.02	5.77 / 13.93	5.74 / 13.83	5.71 / 13.74	5.70 / 13.69	5.68 / 13.61	5.66 / 13.57	5.65 / 13.52	5.64 / 13.48	5.63 / 13.46
5	6.61 / 16.26	5.79 / 13.27	5.41 / 12.06	5.19 / 11.39	5.05 / 10.97	4.95 / 10.67	4.88 / 10.45	4.82 / 10.27	4.78 / 10.15	4.74 / 10.05	4.70 / 9.96	4.68 / 9.89	4.64 / 9.77	4.60 / 9.68	4.56 / 9.55	4.53 / 9.47	4.50 / 9.38	4.46 / 9.29	4.44 / 9.24	4.42 / 9.17	4.40 / 9.13	4.38 / 9.07	4.37 / 9.04	4.36 / 9.02
6	5.99 / 13.74	5.14 / 10.92	4.76 / 9.78	4.53 / 9.15	4.39 / 8.75	4.28 / 8.47	4.21 / 8.26	4.15 / 8.10	4.10 / 7.98	4.06 / 7.87	4.03 / 7.79	4.00 / 7.72	3.96 / 7.60	3.92 / 7.52	3.87 / 7.39	3.84 / 7.31	3.81 / 7.23	3.77 / 7.14	3.75 / 7.09	3.72 / 7.02	3.71 / 6.99	3.69 / 6.94	3.68 / 6.90	3.67 / 6.88
7	5.59 / 12.25	4.74 / 9.55	4.35 / 8.45	4.12 / 7.85	3.97 / 7.46	3.87 / 7.19	3.79 / 7.00	3.73 / 6.84	3.68 / 6.71	3.63 / 6.62	3.60 / 6.54	3.57 / 6.47	3.52 / 6.35	3.49 / 6.27	3.44 / 6.15	3.41 / 6.07	3.38 / 5.98	3.34 / 5.90	3.32 / 5.85	3.29 / 5.78	3.28 / 5.75	3.25 / 5.70	3.24 / 5.67	3.23 / 5.65
8	5.32 / 11.26	4.46 / 8.65	4.07 / 7.59	3.84 / 7.01	3.69 / 6.63	3.58 / 6.37	3.50 / 6.19	3.44 / 6.03	3.39 / 5.91	3.34 / 5.82	3.31 / 5.74	3.28 / 5.67	3.23 / 5.56	3.20 / 5.48	3.15 / 5.36	3.12 / 5.28	3.08 / 5.20	3.05 / 5.11	3.03 / 5.06	3.00 / 5.00	2.98 / 4.96	2.96 / 4.91	2.94 / 4.88	2.93 / 4.86
9	5.12 / 10.56	4.26 / 8.02	3.86 / 6.99	3.63 / 6.42	3.48 / 6.06	3.37 / 5.80	3.29 / 5.62	3.23 / 5.47	3.18 / 5.35	3.13 / 5.26	3.10 / 5.18	3.07 / 5.11	3.02 / 5.00	2.98 / 4.92	2.93 / 4.80	2.90 / 4.73	2.86 / 4.64	2.82 / 4.56	2.80 / 4.51	2.77 / 4.45	2.76 / 4.41	2.73 / 4.36	2.72 / 4.33	2.71 / 4.31
10	4.96 / 10.04	4.10 / 7.56	3.71 / 6.55	3.48 / 5.99	3.33 / 5.64	3.22 / 5.39	3.14 / 5.21	3.07 / 5.06	3.02 / 4.95	2.97 / 4.85	2.94 / 4.78	2.91 / 4.71	2.86 / 4.60	2.82 / 4.52	2.77 / 4.41	2.74 / 4.33	2.70 / 4.25	2.67 / 4.17	2.64 / 4.12	2.61 / 4.05	2.59 / 4.01	2.56 / 3.96	2.55 / 3.93	2.54 / 3.91
11	4.84 / 9.65	3.98 / 7.20	3.59 / 6.22	3.36 / 5.67	3.20 / 5.32	3.09 / 5.07	3.01 / 4.88	2.95 / 4.74	2.90 / 4.63	2.86 / 4.54	2.82 / 4.46	2.79 / 4.40	2.74 / 4.29	2.70 / 4.21	2.65 / 4.10	2.61 / 4.02	2.57 / 3.94	2.53 / 3.86	2.50 / 3.80	2.47 / 3.74	2.45 / 3.70	2.42 / 3.66	2.41 / 3.62	2.40 / 3.60
12	4.75 / 9.33	3.88 / 6.93	3.49 / 5.95	3.26 / 5.41	3.11 / 5.06	3.00 / 4.82	2.92 / 4.65	2.85 / 4.50	2.80 / 4.39	2.76 / 4.30	2.72 / 4.22	2.69 / 4.16	2.64 / 4.05	2.60 / 3.98	2.54 / 3.86	2.50 / 3.78	2.46 / 3.70	2.42 / 3.61	2.40 / 3.56	2.36 / 3.49	2.35 / 3.46	2.32 / 3.41	2.31 / 3.38	2.30 / 3.36
13	4.67 / 9.07	3.80 / 6.70	3.41 / 5.74	3.18 / 5.20	3.02 / 4.86	2.92 / 4.62	2.84 / 4.44	2.77 / 4.30	2.72 / 4.19	2.67 / 4.10	2.63 / 4.02	2.60 / 3.96	2.55 / 3.85	2.51 / 3.78	2.46 / 3.67	2.42 / 3.59	2.38 / 3.51	2.34 / 3.42	2.32 / 3.37	2.28 / 3.30	2.26 / 3.27	2.24 / 3.21	2.22 / 3.18	2.21 / 3.16

Reproduced by permission from George W. Snedecor, *Statistical Methods* (Fifth Edition, 1956), Table of *F*, Table 10.5.3, copyright the Iowa State University Press, Ames, Iowa.

f_1 Degrees of Freedom (for Greater Mean Square)

f_2	1	2	3	4	5	6	7	8	9	10	11	12	14	16	20	24	30	40	50	75	100	200	500	∞	f_2
14	4.60 / 8.86	3.74 / 6.51	3.34 / 5.56	3.11 / 5.03	2.96 / 4.69	2.85 / 4.46	2.77 / 4.28	2.70 / 4.14	2.65 / 4.03	2.60 / 3.94	2.56 / 3.86	2.53 / 3.80	2.48 / 3.70	2.44 / 3.62	2.39 / 3.51	2.35 / 3.43	2.31 / 3.34	2.27 / 3.26	2.24 / 3.21	2.21 / 3.14	2.19 / 3.11	2.16 / 3.06	2.14 / 3.02	2.13 / 3.00	14
15	4.54 / 8.68	3.68 / 6.36	3.29 / 5.42	3.06 / 4.89	2.90 / 4.56	2.79 / 4.32	2.70 / 4.14	2.64 / 4.00	2.59 / 3.89	2.55 / 3.80	2.51 / 3.73	2.48 / 3.67	2.43 / 3.56	2.39 / 3.48	2.33 / 3.36	2.29 / 3.29	2.25 / 3.20	2.21 / 3.12	2.18 / 3.07	2.15 / 3.00	2.12 / 2.97	2.10 / 2.92	2.08 / 2.89	2.07 / 2.87	15
16	4.49 / 8.53	3.63 / 6.23	3.24 / 5.29	3.01 / 4.77	2.85 / 4.44	2.74 / 4.20	2.66 / 4.03	2.59 / 3.89	2.54 / 3.78	2.49 / 3.69	2.45 / 3.61	2.42 / 3.55	2.37 / 3.45	2.33 / 3.37	2.28 / 3.25	2.24 / 3.18	2.20 / 3.10	2.16 / 3.01	2.13 / 2.96	2.09 / 2.89	2.07 / 2.86	2.04 / 2.80	2.02 / 2.77	2.01 / 2.75	16
17	4.45 / 8.40	3.59 / 6.11	3.20 / 5.18	2.96 / 4.67	2.81 / 4.34	2.70 / 4.10	2.62 / 3.93	2.55 / 3.79	2.50 / 3.68	2.45 / 3.59	2.41 / 3.52	2.38 / 3.45	2.33 / 3.35	2.29 / 3.27	2.23 / 3.16	2.19 / 3.08	2.15 / 3.00	2.11 / 2.92	2.08 / 2.86	2.04 / 2.79	2.02 / 2.76	1.99 / 2.70	1.97 / 2.67	1.96 / 2.65	17
18	4.41 / 8.28	3.55 / 6.01	3.16 / 5.09	2.93 / 4.58	2.77 / 4.25	2.66 / 4.01	2.58 / 3.85	2.51 / 3.71	2.46 / 3.60	2.41 / 3.51	2.37 / 3.44	2.34 / 3.37	2.29 / 3.27	2.25 / 3.19	2.19 / 3.07	2.15 / 3.00	2.11 / 2.91	2.07 / 2.83	2.04 / 2.78	2.00 / 2.71	1.98 / 2.68	1.95 / 2.62	1.93 / 2.59	1.92 / 2.57	18
19	4.38 / 8.18	3.52 / 5.93	3.13 / 5.01	2.90 / 4.50	2.74 / 4.17	2.63 / 3.94	2.55 / 3.77	2.48 / 3.63	2.43 / 3.52	2.38 / 3.43	2.34 / 3.36	2.31 / 3.30	2.26 / 3.19	2.21 / 3.12	2.15 / 3.00	2.11 / 2.92	2.07 / 2.84	2.02 / 2.76	2.00 / 2.70	1.96 / 2.63	1.94 / 2.60	1.91 / 2.54	1.90 / 2.51	1.88 / 2.49	19
20	4.35 / 8.10	3.49 / 5.85	3.10 / 4.94	2.87 / 4.43	2.71 / 4.10	2.60 / 3.87	2.52 / 3.71	2.45 / 3.56	2.40 / 3.45	2.35 / 3.37	2.31 / 3.30	2.28 / 3.23	2.23 / 3.13	2.18 / 3.05	2.12 / 2.94	2.08 / 2.86	2.04 / 2.77	1.99 / 2.69	1.96 / 2.63	1.92 / 2.56	1.90 / 2.53	1.87 / 2.47	1.85 / 2.44	1.84 / 2.42	20
21	4.32 / 8.02	3.47 / 5.78	3.07 / 4.87	2.84 / 4.37	2.68 / 4.04	2.57 / 3.81	2.49 / 3.65	2.42 / 3.51	2.37 / 3.40	2.32 / 3.31	2.28 / 3.24	2.25 / 3.17	2.20 / 3.07	2.15 / 2.99	2.09 / 2.88	2.05 / 2.80	2.00 / 2.72	1.96 / 2.63	1.93 / 2.58	1.89 / 2.51	1.87 / 2.47	1.84 / 2.42	1.82 / 2.38	1.81 / 2.36	21
22	4.30 / 7.94	3.44 / 5.72	3.05 / 4.82	2.82 / 4.31	2.66 / 3.99	2.55 / 3.76	2.47 / 3.59	2.40 / 3.45	2.35 / 3.35	2.30 / 3.26	2.26 / 3.18	2.23 / 3.12	2.18 / 3.02	2.13 / 2.94	2.07 / 2.83	2.03 / 2.75	1.98 / 2.67	1.93 / 2.58	1.91 / 2.53	1.87 / 2.46	1.84 / 2.42	1.81 / 2.37	1.80 / 2.33	1.78 / 2.31	22
23	4.28 / 7.88	3.42 / 5.66	3.03 / 4.76	2.80 / 4.26	2.64 / 3.94	2.53 / 3.71	2.45 / 3.54	2.38 / 3.41	2.32 / 3.30	2.28 / 3.21	2.24 / 3.14	2.20 / 3.07	2.14 / 2.97	2.10 / 2.89	2.04 / 2.78	2.00 / 2.70	1.96 / 2.62	1.91 / 2.53	1.88 / 2.48	1.84 / 2.41	1.82 / 2.37	1.79 / 2.32	1.77 / 2.28	1.76 / 2.26	23
24	4.26 / 7.82	3.40 / 5.61	3.01 / 4.72	2.78 / 4.22	2.62 / 3.90	2.51 / 3.67	2.43 / 3.50	2.36 / 3.36	2.30 / 3.25	2.26 / 3.17	2.22 / 3.09	2.18 / 3.03	2.13 / 2.93	2.09 / 2.85	2.02 / 2.74	1.98 / 2.66	1.94 / 2.58	1.89 / 2.49	1.86 / 2.44	1.82 / 2.36	1.80 / 2.33	1.76 / 2.27	1.74 / 2.23	1.73 / 2.21	24
25	4.24 / 7.77	3.38 / 5.57	2.99 / 4.68	2.76 / 4.18	2.60 / 3.86	2.49 / 3.63	2.41 / 3.46	2.34 / 3.32	2.28 / 3.21	2.24 / 3.13	2.20 / 3.05	2.16 / 2.99	2.11 / 2.89	2.06 / 2.81	2.00 / 2.70	1.96 / 2.62	1.92 / 2.54	1.87 / 2.45	1.84 / 2.40	1.80 / 2.32	1.77 / 2.29	1.74 / 2.23	1.72 / 2.19	1.71 / 2.17	25
26	4.22 / 7.72	3.37 / 5.53	2.98 / 4.64	2.74 / 4.14	2.59 / 3.82	2.47 / 3.59	2.39 / 3.42	2.32 / 3.29	2.27 / 3.17	2.22 / 3.09	2.18 / 3.02	2.15 / 2.96	2.10 / 2.86	2.05 / 2.77	1.99 / 2.66	1.95 / 2.58	1.90 / 2.50	1.85 / 2.41	1.82 / 2.36	1.78 / 2.28	1.76 / 2.25	1.72 / 2.19	1.70 / 2.15	1.69 / 2.13	26

f_1 Degrees of Freedom (for Greater Mean Square)

f_2	1	2	3	4	5	6	7	8	9	10	11	12	14	16	20	24	30	40	50	75	100	200	500	∞
27	4.21 / 7.68	3.35 / 5.49	2.96 / 4.60	2.73 / 4.11	2.57 / 3.79	2.46 / 3.56	2.37 / 3.39	2.30 / 3.26	2.25 / 3.14	2.20 / 3.06	2.16 / 2.98	2.13 / 2.93	2.08 / 2.83	2.03 / 2.74	1.97 / 2.63	1.93 / 2.55	1.88 / 2.47	1.84 / 2.38	1.80 / 2.33	1.76 / 2.25	1.74 / 2.21	1.71 / 2.16	1.68 / 2.12	1.67 / 2.10
28	4.20 / 7.64	3.34 / 5.45	2.95 / 4.57	2.71 / 4.07	2.56 / 3.76	2.44 / 3.53	2.36 / 3.36	2.29 / 3.23	2.24 / 3.11	2.19 / 3.03	2.15 / 2.95	2.12 / 2.90	2.06 / 2.80	2.02 / 2.71	1.96 / 2.60	1.91 / 2.52	1.87 / 2.44	1.81 / 2.35	1.78 / 2.30	1.75 / 2.22	1.72 / 2.18	1.69 / 2.13	1.67 / 2.09	1.65 / 2.06
29	4.18 / 7.60	3.33 / 5.42	2.93 / 4.54	2.70 / 4.04	2.54 / 3.73	2.43 / 3.50	2.35 / 3.33	2.28 / 3.20	2.22 / 3.08	2.18 / 3.00	2.14 / 2.92	2.10 / 2.87	2.05 / 2.77	2.00 / 2.68	1.94 / 2.57	1.90 / 2.49	1.85 / 2.41	1.80 / 2.32	1.77 / 2.27	1.73 / 2.19	1.71 / 2.15	1.68 / 2.10	1.65 / 2.06	1.64 / 2.03
30	4.17 / 7.56	3.32 / 5.39	2.92 / 4.51	2.69 / 4.02	2.53 / 3.70	2.42 / 3.47	2.34 / 3.30	2.27 / 3.17	2.21 / 3.06	2.16 / 2.98	2.12 / 2.90	2.09 / 2.84	2.04 / 2.74	1.99 / 2.66	1.93 / 2.55	1.89 / 2.47	1.84 / 2.38	1.79 / 2.29	1.76 / 2.24	1.72 / 2.16	1.69 / 2.13	1.66 / 2.07	1.64 / 2.03	1.62 / 2.01
32	4.15 / 7.50	3.30 / 5.34	2.90 / 4.46	2.67 / 3.97	2.51 / 3.66	2.40 / 3.42	2.32 / 3.25	2.25 / 3.12	2.19 / 3.01	2.14 / 2.94	2.10 / 2.86	2.07 / 2.80	2.02 / 2.70	1.97 / 2.62	1.91 / 2.51	1.86 / 2.42	1.82 / 2.34	1.76 / 2.25	1.74 / 2.20	1.69 / 2.12	1.67 / 2.08	1.64 / 2.02	1.61 / 1.98	1.59 / 1.96
34	4.13 / 7.44	3.28 / 5.29	2.88 / 4.42	2.65 / 3.93	2.49 / 3.61	2.38 / 3.38	2.30 / 3.21	2.23 / 3.08	2.17 / 2.97	2.12 / 2.89	2.08 / 2.82	2.05 / 2.76	2.00 / 2.66	1.95 / 2.58	1.89 / 2.47	1.84 / 2.38	1.80 / 2.30	1.74 / 2.21	1.71 / 2.15	1.67 / 2.08	1.64 / 2.04	1.61 / 1.98	1.59 / 1.94	1.57 / 1.91
36	4.11 / 7.39	3.26 / 5.25	2.86 / 4.38	2.63 / 3.89	2.48 / 3.58	2.36 / 3.35	2.28 / 3.18	2.21 / 3.04	2.15 / 2.94	2.10 / 2.86	2.06 / 2.78	2.03 / 2.72	1.98 / 2.62	1.93 / 2.54	1.87 / 2.43	1.82 / 2.35	1.78 / 2.26	1.72 / 2.17	1.69 / 2.12	1.65 / 2.04	1.62 / 2.00	1.59 / 1.94	1.56 / 1.90	1.55 / 1.87
38	4.10 / 7.35	3.25 / 5.21	2.85 / 4.34	2.62 / 3.86	2.46 / 3.54	2.35 / 3.32	2.26 / 3.15	2.19 / 3.02	2.14 / 2.91	2.09 / 2.82	2.05 / 2.75	2.02 / 2.69	1.96 / 2.59	1.92 / 2.51	1.85 / 2.40	1.80 / 2.32	1.76 / 2.22	1.71 / 2.14	1.67 / 2.08	1.63 / 2.00	1.60 / 1.97	1.57 / 1.90	1.54 / 1.86	1.53 / 1.84
40	4.08 / 7.31	3.23 / 5.18	2.84 / 4.31	2.61 / 3.83	2.45 / 3.51	2.34 / 3.29	2.25 / 3.12	2.18 / 2.99	2.12 / 2.88	2.07 / 2.80	2.04 / 2.73	2.00 / 2.66	1.95 / 2.56	1.90 / 2.49	1.84 / 2.37	1.79 / 2.29	1.74 / 2.20	1.69 / 2.11	1.66 / 2.05	1.61 / 1.97	1.59 / 1.94	1.55 / 1.88	1.53 / 1.84	1.51 / 1.81
42	4.07 / 7.27	3.22 / 5.15	2.83 / 4.29	2.59 / 3.80	2.44 / 3.49	2.32 / 3.26	2.24 / 3.10	2.17 / 2.96	2.11 / 2.86	2.06 / 2.77	2.02 / 2.70	1.99 / 2.64	1.94 / 2.54	1.89 / 2.46	1.82 / 2.35	1.78 / 2.26	1.73 / 2.17	1.68 / 2.08	1.64 / 2.02	1.60 / 1.94	1.57 / 1.91	1.54 / 1.85	1.51 / 1.80	1.49 / 1.78
44	4.06 / 7.24	3.21 / 5.12	2.82 / 4.26	2.58 / 3.78	2.43 / 3.46	2.31 / 3.24	2.23 / 3.07	2.16 / 2.94	2.10 / 2.84	2.05 / 2.75	2.01 / 2.68	1.98 / 2.62	1.92 / 2.52	1.88 / 2.44	1.81 / 2.32	1.76 / 2.24	1.72 / 2.15	1.66 / 2.06	1.63 / 2.00	1.58 / 1.92	1.56 / 1.88	1.52 / 1.82	1.50 / 1.78	1.48 / 1.75
46	4.05 / 7.21	3.20 / 5.10	2.81 / 4.24	2.57 / 3.76	2.42 / 3.44	2.30 / 3.22	2.22 / 3.05	2.14 / 2.92	2.09 / 2.82	2.04 / 2.73	2.00 / 2.66	1.97 / 2.60	1.91 / 2.50	1.87 / 2.42	1.80 / 2.30	1.75 / 2.22	1.71 / 2.13	1.65 / 2.04	1.62 / 1.98	1.57 / 1.90	1.54 / 1.86	1.51 / 1.80	1.48 / 1.76	1.46 / 1.72
48	4.04 / 7.19	3.19 / 5.08	2.80 / 4.22	2.56 / 3.74	2.41 / 3.42	2.30 / 3.20	2.21 / 3.04	2.14 / 2.90	2.08 / 2.80	2.03 / 2.71	1.99 / 2.64	1.96 / 2.58	1.90 / 2.48	1.86 / 2.40	1.79 / 2.28	1.74 / 2.20	1.70 / 2.11	1.64 / 2.02	1.61 / 1.96	1.56 / 1.88	1.53 / 1.84	1.50 / 1.78	1.47 / 1.73	1.45 / 1.70

f_1 Degrees of Freedom (for Greater Mean Square)

f_2	1	2	3	4	5	6	7	8	9	10	11	12	14	16	20	24	30	40	50	75	100	200	500	∞	f_2
50	4.03 / 7.17	3.18 / 5.06	2.79 / 4.20	2.56 / 3.72	2.40 / 3.41	2.29 / 3.18	2.20 / 3.02	2.13 / 2.88	2.07 / 2.78	2.02 / 2.70	1.98 / 2.62	1.95 / 2.56	1.90 / 2.46	1.85 / 2.39	1.78 / 2.26	1.74 / 2.18	1.69 / 2.10	1.63 / 2.00	1.60 / 1.94	1.55 / 1.86	1.52 / 1.82	1.48 / 1.76	1.46 / 1.71	1.44 / 1.68	50
55	4.02 / 7.12	3.17 / 5.01	2.78 / 4.16	2.54 / 3.68	2.38 / 3.37	2.27 / 3.15	2.18 / 2.98	2.11 / 2.85	2.05 / 2.75	2.00 / 2.66	1.97 / 2.59	1.93 / 2.53	1.88 / 2.43	1.83 / 2.35	1.76 / 2.23	1.72 / 2.15	1.67 / 2.06	1.61 / 1.96	1.58 / 1.90	1.52 / 1.82	1.50 / 1.78	1.46 / 1.71	1.43 / 1.66	1.41 / 1.64	55
60	4.00 / 7.08	3.15 / 4.98	2.76 / 4.13	2.52 / 3.65	2.37 / 3.34	2.25 / 3.12	2.17 / 2.95	2.10 / 2.82	2.04 / 2.72	1.99 / 2.63	1.95 / 2.56	1.92 / 2.50	1.86 / 2.40	1.81 / 2.32	1.75 / 2.20	1.70 / 2.12	1.65 / 2.03	1.59 / 1.93	1.56 / 1.87	1.50 / 1.79	1.48 / 1.74	1.44 / 1.68	1.41 / 1.63	1.39 / 1.60	60
65	3.99 / 7.04	3.14 / 4.95	2.75 / 4.10	2.51 / 3.62	2.36 / 3.31	2.24 / 3.09	2.15 / 2.93	2.08 / 2.79	2.02 / 2.70	1.98 / 2.61	1.94 / 2.54	1.90 / 2.47	1.85 / 2.37	1.80 / 2.30	1.73 / 2.18	1.68 / 2.09	1.63 / 2.00	1.57 / 1.90	1.54 / 1.84	1.49 / 1.76	1.46 / 1.71	1.42 / 1.64	1.39 / 1.60	1.37 / 1.56	65
70	3.98 / 7.01	3.13 / 4.92	2.74 / 4.08	2.50 / 3.60	2.35 / 3.29	2.23 / 3.07	2.14 / 2.91	2.07 / 2.77	2.01 / 2.67	1.97 / 2.59	1.93 / 2.51	1.89 / 2.45	1.84 / 2.35	1.79 / 2.28	1.72 / 2.15	1.67 / 2.07	1.62 / 1.98	1.56 / 1.88	1.53 / 1.82	1.47 / 1.74	1.45 / 1.69	1.40 / 1.62	1.37 / 1.56	1.35 / 1.53	70
80	3.96 / 6.96	3.11 / 4.88	2.72 / 4.04	2.48 / 3.56	2.33 / 3.25	2.21 / 3.04	2.12 / 2.87	2.05 / 2.74	1.99 / 2.64	1.95 / 2.55	1.91 / 2.48	1.88 / 2.41	1.82 / 2.32	1.77 / 2.24	1.70 / 2.11	1.65 / 2.03	1.60 / 1.94	1.54 / 1.84	1.51 / 1.78	1.45 / 1.70	1.42 / 1.65	1.38 / 1.57	1.35 / 1.52	1.32 / 1.49	80
100	3.94 / 6.90	3.09 / 4.82	2.70 / 3.98	2.46 / 3.51	2.30 / 3.20	2.19 / 2.99	2.10 / 2.82	2.03 / 2.69	1.97 / 2.59	1.92 / 2.51	1.88 / 2.43	1.85 / 2.36	1.79 / 2.26	1.75 / 2.19	1.68 / 2.06	1.63 / 1.98	1.57 / 1.89	1.51 / 1.79	1.48 / 1.73	1.42 / 1.64	1.39 / 1.59	1.34 / 1.51	1.30 / 1.46	1.28 / 1.43	100
125	3.92 / 6.84	3.07 / 4.78	2.68 / 3.94	2.44 / 3.47	2.29 / 3.17	2.17 / 2.95	2.08 / 2.79	2.01 / 2.65	1.95 / 2.56	1.90 / 2.47	1.86 / 2.40	1.83 / 2.33	1.77 / 2.23	1.72 / 2.15	1.65 / 2.03	1.60 / 1.94	1.55 / 1.85	1.49 / 1.75	1.45 / 1.68	1.39 / 1.59	1.36 / 1.54	1.31 / 1.46	1.27 / 1.40	1.25 / 1.37	125
150	3.91 / 6.81	3.06 / 4.75	2.67 / 3.91	2.43 / 3.44	2.27 / 3.14	2.16 / 2.92	2.07 / 2.76	2.00 / 2.62	1.94 / 2.53	1.89 / 2.44	1.85 / 2.37	1.82 / 2.30	1.76 / 2.20	1.71 / 2.12	1.64 / 2.00	1.59 / 1.91	1.54 / 1.83	1.47 / 1.72	1.44 / 1.66	1.37 / 1.56	1.34 / 1.51	1.29 / 1.43	1.25 / 1.37	1.22 / 1.33	150
200	3.89 / 6.76	3.04 / 4.71	2.65 / 3.88	2.41 / 3.41	2.26 / 3.11	2.14 / 2.90	2.05 / 2.73	1.98 / 2.60	1.92 / 2.50	1.87 / 2.41	1.83 / 2.34	1.80 / 2.28	1.74 / 2.17	1.69 / 2.09	1.62 / 1.97	1.57 / 1.88	1.52 / 1.79	1.45 / 1.69	1.42 / 1.62	1.35 / 1.53	1.32 / 1.48	1.26 / 1.39	1.22 / 1.33	1.19 / 1.28	200
400	3.86 / 6.70	3.02 / 4.66	2.62 / 3.83	2.39 / 3.36	2.23 / 3.06	2.12 / 2.85	2.03 / 2.69	1.96 / 2.55	1.90 / 2.46	1.85 / 2.37	1.81 / 2.29	1.78 / 2.23	1.72 / 2.12	1.67 / 2.04	1.60 / 1.92	1.54 / 1.84	1.49 / 1.74	1.42 / 1.64	1.38 / 1.57	1.32 / 1.47	1.28 / 1.42	1.22 / 1.32	1.16 / 1.24	1.13 / 1.19	400
1000	3.85 / 6.66	3.00 / 4.62	2.61 / 3.80	2.38 / 3.34	2.22 / 3.04	2.10 / 2.82	2.02 / 2.66	1.95 / 2.53	1.89 / 2.43	1.84 / 2.34	1.80 / 2.26	1.76 / 2.20	1.70 / 2.09	1.65 / 2.01	1.58 / 1.89	1.53 / 1.81	1.47 / 1.71	1.41 / 1.61	1.36 / 1.54	1.30 / 1.44	1.26 / 1.38	1.19 / 1.28	1.13 / 1.19	1.08 / 1.11	1000
∞	3.84 / 6.64	2.99 / 4.60	2.60 / 3.78	2.37 / 3.32	2.21 / 3.02	2.09 / 2.80	2.01 / 2.64	1.94 / 2.51	1.88 / 2.41	1.83 / 2.32	1.79 / 2.24	1.75 / 2.18	1.69 / 2.07	1.64 / 1.99	1.57 / 1.87	1.52 / 1.79	1.46 / 1.69	1.40 / 1.59	1.35 / 1.52	1.28 / 1.41	1.24 / 1.36	1.17 / 1.25	1.11 / 1.15	1.00 / 1.00	∞

APPENDIX J:
TABLE OF CHI-SQUARE[1]

[1] The table of chi-square has been reproduced from Table III of R. A. Fisher, *Statistical Methods for Research Workers*, published by Oliver & Boyd, Ltd., Edinburgh, and by permission of the author and publishers.

n	P = .99	.98	.95	.90	.80	.70	.50	.30	.20	.10	.05	.02	.01
1	.000157	.000628	.00393	.0158	.0642	.148	.455	1.074	1.642	2.706	3.841	5.412	6.635
2	.0201	.0404	.103	.211	.446	.713	1.386	2.408	3.219	4.605	5.991	7.824	9.210
3	.115	.185	.352	.584	1.005	1.424	2.366	3.665	4.642	6.251	7.815	9.837	11.345
4	.297	.429	.711	1.064	1.649	2.195	3.357	4.878	5.989	7.779	9.488	11.668	13.277
5	.554	.752	1.145	1.610	2.343	3.000	4.351	6.064	7.289	9.236	11.070	13.388	15.086
6	.872	1.134	1.635	2.204	3.070	3.828	5.348	7.231	8.558	10.645	12.592	15.033	16.812
7	1.239	1.564	2.167	2.833	3.822	4.671	6.346	8.383	9.803	12.017	14.067	16.622	18.475
8	1.646	2.032	2.733	3.490	4.594	5.527	7.344	9.524	11.030	13.362	15.507	18.168	20.090
9	2.088	2.532	3.325	4.168	5.380	6.393	8.343	10.656	12.242	14.684	16.919	19.679	21.666
10	2.558	3.059	3.940	4.865	6.179	7.267	9.342	11.781	13.442	15.987	18.307	21.161	23.209
11	3.053	3.609	4.575	5.578	6.989	8.148	10.341	12.899	14.631	17.275	19.675	22.618	24.725
12	3.571	4.178	5.226	6.304	7.807	9.034	11.340	14.011	15.812	18.549	21.026	24.054	26.217
13	4.107	4.765	5.892	7.042	8.634	9.926	12.340	15.119	16.985	19.812	22.362	25.472	27.688
14	4.660	5.368	6.571	7.790	9.467	10.821	13.339	16.222	18.151	21.064	23.685	26.873	29.141
15	5.229	5.985	7.261	8.547	10.307	11.721	14.339	17.322	19.311	22.307	24.996	28.259	30.578
16	5.812	6.614	7.962	9.312	11.152	12.624	15.338	18.418	20.465	23.542	26.296	29.633	32.000
17	6.408	7.255	8.672	10.085	12.002	13.531	16.338	19.511	21.615	24.769	27.587	30.995	33.409
18	7.015	7.906	9.390	10.865	12.857	14.440	17.338	20.601	22.760	25.989	28.869	32.346	34.805
19	7.633	8.567	10.117	11.651	13.716	15.352	18.338	21.689	23.900	27.204	30.144	33.687	36.191
20	8.260	9.237	10.851	12.443	14.578	16.266	19.337	22.775	25.038	28.412	31.410	35.020	37.566
21	8.897	9.915	11.591	13.240	15.445	17.182	20.337	23.858	26.171	29.615	32.671	36.343	38.932
22	9.542	10.600	12.338	14.041	16.314	18.101	21.337	24.939	27.301	30.813	33.924	37.659	40.289
23	10.196	11.293	13.091	14.848	17.187	19.021	22.337	26.018	28.429	32.007	35.172	38.968	41.638
24	10.856	11.992	13.848	15.659	18.062	19.943	23.337	27.096	29.553	33.196	36.415	40.270	42.980
25	11.524	12.697	14.611	16.473	18.940	20.867	24.337	28.172	30.675	34.382	37.652	41.566	44.314
26	12.198	13.409	15.379	17.292	19.820	21.792	25.336	29.246	31.795	35.563	38.885	42.856	45.642
27	12.879	14.125	16.151	18.114	20.703	22.719	26.336	30.319	32.912	36.741	40.113	44.140	46.963
28	13.565	14.847	16.928	18.939	21.588	23.647	27.336	31.391	34.027	37.916	41.337	45.419	48.278
29	14.256	15.574	17.708	19.768	22.475	24.577	28.336	32.461	35.139	39.087	42.557	46.693	49.588
30	14.953	16.306	18.493	20.599	23.364	25.508	29.336	33.530	36.250	40.256	43.773	47.962	50.892

For larger values of n, the expression $\sqrt{2\chi^2} - \sqrt{2n - 1}$ may be used as a normal deviate with unit variance.

APPENDIX K:
BINOMIAL PROBABILITY TABLES

Individual Terms, $b(x;\ n,\ p)$

n	x	.01	.05	.10	.20	.30	.40	.50	.60	.70	.80	.90	.95	.99	x
2	0	980	902	810	640	490	360	250	160	090	040	010	002	0+	0
	1	020	095	180	320	420	480	500	480	420	320	180	095	020	1
	2	0+	002	010	040	090	160	250	360	490	640	810	902	980	2
3	0	970	857	729	512	343	216	125	064	027	008	001	0+	0+	0
	1	029	135	243	384	441	432	375	288	189	096	027	007	0+	1
	2	0+	007	027	096	189	288	375	432	441	384	243	135	029	2
	3	0+	0+	001	008	027	064	125	216	343	512	729	857	970	3
4	0	961	815	656	410	240	130	062	026	008	002	0+	0+	0+	0
	1	039	171	292	410	412	346	250	154	076	026	004	0+	0+	1
	2	001	014	049	154	265	346	375	346	265	154	049	014	001	2
	3	0+	0+	004	026	076	154	250	346	412	410	292	171	039	3
	4	0+	0+	0+	002	008	026	062	130	240	410	656	815	961	4
5	0	951	774	590	328	168	078	031	010	002	0+	0+	0+	0+	0
	1	048	204	328	410	360	259	156	077	028	006	0+	0+	0+	1
	2	001	021	073	205	309	346	312	230	132	051	008	001	0+	2
	3	0+	001	008	051	132	230	312	346	309	205	073	021	001	3
	4	0+	0+	0+	006	028	077	156	259	360	410	328	204	048	4
	5	0+	0+	0+	0+	002	010	031	078	168	328	590	774	951	5
6	0	941	735	531	262	118	047	016	004	001	0+	0+	0+	0+	0
	1	057	232	354	393	303	187	094	037	010	002	0+	0+	0+	1
	2	001	031	098	246	324	311	234	138	060	015	001	0+	0+	2
	3	0+	002	015	082	185	276	312	276	185	082	015	002	0+	3
	4	0+	0+	001	015	060	138	234	311	324	246	098	031	001	4
	5	0+	0+	0+	002	010	037	094	187	303	393	354	232	057	5
	6	0+	0+	0+	0+	001	004	016	047	118	262	531	735	941	6
7	0	932	698	478	210	082	028	008	002	0+	0+	0+	0+	0+	0
	1	066	257	372	367	247	131	055	017	004	0+	0+	0+	0+	1
	2	002	041	124	275	318	261	164	077	025	004	0+	0+	0+	2
	3	0+	004	023	115	227	290	273	194	097	029	003	0+	0+	3
	4	0+	0+	003	029	097	194	273	290	227	115	023	004	0+	4
	5	0+	0+	0+	004	025	077	164	261	318	275	124	041	002	5
	6	0+	0+	0+	0+	004	017	055	131	247	367	372	257	066	6
	7	0+	0+	0+	0+	0+	002	008	028	082	210	478	698	932	7
8	0	923	663	430	168	058	017	004	001	0+	0+	0+	0+	0+	0
	1	075	279	383	336	198	090	031	008	001	0+	0+	0+	0+	1
	2	003	051	149	294	296	209	109	041	010	001	0+	0+	0+	2
	3	0+	005	033	147	254	279	219	124	047	009	0+	0+	0+	3
	4	0+	0+	005	046	136	232	273	232	136	046	005	0+	0+	4
	5	0+	0+	0+	009	047	124	219	279	254	147	033	005	0+	5
	6	0+	0+	0+	001	010	041	109	209	296	294	149	051	003	6
	7	0+	0+	0+	0+	001	008	031	090	198	336	383	279	075	7
	8	0+	0+	0+	0+	0+	001	004	017	058	168	430	663	923	8

Individual Terms, $b(x;\ n, p)$

n	x	.01	.05	.10	.20	.30	.40	p .50	.60	.70	.80	.90	.95	.99	x
9	0	914	630	387	134	040	010	002	0+	0+	0+	0+	0+	0+	0
	1	083	299	387	302	156	060	018	004	0+	0+	0+	0+	0+	1
	2	003	063	172	302	267	161	070	021	004	0+	0+	0+	0+	2
	3	0+	008	045	176	267	251	164	074	021	003	0+	0+	0+	3
	4	0+	001	007	066	172	251	246	167	074	017	001	0+	0+	4
	5	0+	0+	001	017	074	167	246	251	172	066	007	001	0+	5
	6	0+	0+	0+	003	021	074	164	251	267	176	045	008	0+	6
	7	0+	0+	0+	0+	004	021	070	161	267	302	172	063	003	7
	8	0+	0+	0+	0+	0+	004	018	060	156	302	387	299	083	8
	9	0+	0+	0+	0+	0+	0+	002	010	040	134	387	630	914	9
10	0	904	599	349	107	028	006	001	0+	0+	0+	0+	0+	0+	0
	1	091	315	387	268	121	040	010	002	0+	0+	0+	0+	0+	1
	2	004	075	194	302	233	121	044	011	001	0+	0+	0+	0+	2
	3	0+	010	057	201	267	215	117	042	009	001	0+	0+	0+	3
	4	0+	001	011	088	200	251	205	111	037	006	0+	0+	0+	4
	5	0+	0+	001	026	103	201	246	201	103	026	001	0+	0+	5
	6	0+	0+	0+	006	037	111	205	251	200	088	011	001	0+	6
	7	0+	0+	0+	001	009	042	117	215	267	201	057	010	0+	7
	8	0+	0+	0+	0+	001	011	044	121	233	302	194	075	004	8
	9	0+	0+	0+	0+	0+	002	010	040	121	268	387	315	091	9
	10	0+	0+	0+	0+	0+	0+	001	006	028	107	349	599	904	10
11	0	895	569	314	086	020	004	0+	0+	0+	0+	0+	0+	0+	0
	1	099	329	384	236	093	027	005	001	0+	0+	0+	0+	0+	1
	2	005	087	213	295	200	089	027	005	001	0+	0+	0+	0+	2
	3	0+	014	071	221	257	177	081	023	004	0+	0+	0+	0+	3
	4	0+	001	016	111	220	236	161	070	017	002	0+	0+	0+	4
	5	0+	0+	002	039	132	221	226	147	057	010	0+	0+	0+	5
	6	0+	0+	0+	010	057	147	226	221	132	039	002	0+	0+	6
	7	0+	0+	0+	002	017	070	161	236	220	111	016	001	0+	7
	8	0+	0+	0+	0+	004	023	081	177	257	221	071	014	0+	8
	9	0+	0+	0+	0+	001	005	027	089	200	295	213	087	005	9
	10	0+	0+	0+	0+	0+	001	005	027	093	236	384	329	099	10
	11	0+	0+	0+	0+	0+	0+	0+	004	020	086	314	569	895	11
12	0	886	540	282	069	014	002	0+	0+	0+	0+	0+	0+	0+	0
	1	107	341	377	206	071	017	003	0+	0+	0+	0+	0+	0+	1
	2	006	099	230	283	168	064	016	002	0+	0+	0+	0+	0+	2
	3	0+	017	085	236	240	142	054	012	001	0+	0+	0+	0+	3
	4	0+	002	021	133	231	213	121	042	008	001	0+	0+	0+	4
	5	0+	0+	004	053	158	227	193	101	029	003	0+	0+	0+	5
	6	0+	0+	0+	016	079	177	226	177	079	016	0+	0+	0+	6
	7	0+	0+	0+	003	029	101	193	227	158	053	004	0+	0+	7
	8	0+	0+	0+	001	008	042	121	213	231	133	021	002	0+	8
	9	0+	0+	0+	0+	001	012	054	142	240	236	085	017	0+	9

Individual Terms, $b(x; n, p)$

n	x	.01	.05	.10	.20	.30	.40	p .50	.60	.70	.80	.90	.95	.99	x
12	10	0+	0+	0+	0+	0+	002	016	064	168	283	230	099	006	10
	11	0+	0+	0+	0+	0+	0+	003	017	071	206	377	341	107	11
	12	0+	0+	0+	0+	0+	0+	0+	002	014	069	282	540	886	12
13	0	878	513	254	055	010	001	0+	0+	0+	0+	0+	0+	0+	0
	1	115	351	367	179	054	011	002	0+	0+	0+	0+	0+	0+	1
	2	007	111	245	268	139	045	010	001	0+	0+	0+	0+	0+	2
	3	0+	021	100	246	218	111	035	006	001	0+	0+	0+	0+	3
	4	0+	003	028	154	234	184	087	024	003	0+	0+	0+	0+	4
	5	0+	0+	006	069	180	221	157	066	014	001	0+	0+	0+	5
	6	0+	0+	001	023	103	197	209	131	044	006	0+	0+	0+	6
	7	0+	0+	0+	006	044	131	209	197	103	023	001	0+	0+	7
	8	0+	0+	0+	001	014	066	157	221	180	069	006	0+	0+	8
	9	0+	0+	0+	0+	003	024	087	184	234	154	028	003	0+	9
	10	0+	0+	0+	0+	001	006	035	111	218	246	100	021	0+	10
	11	0+	0+	0+	0+	0+	001	010	045	139	268	245	111	007	11
	12	0+	0+	0+	0+	0+	0+	002	011	054	179	367	351	115	12
	13	0+	0+	0+	0+	0+	0+	0+	001	010	055	254	513	878	13
14	0	869	488	229	044	007	001	0+	0+	0+	0+	0+	0+	0+	0
	1	123	359	356	154	041	007	001	0+	0+	0+	0+	0+	0+	1
	2	008	123	257	250	113	032	006	001	0+	0+	0+	0+	0+	2
	3	0+	026	114	250	194	085	022	003	0+	0+	0+	0+	0+	3
	4	0+	004	035	172	229	155	061	014	001	0+	0+	0+	0+	4
	5	0+	0+	008	086	196	207	122	041	007	0+	0+	0+	0+	5
	6	0+	0+	001	032	126	207	183	092	023	002	0+	0+	0+	6
	7	0+	0+	0+	009	062	157	209	157	062	009	0+	0+	0+	7
	8	0+	0+	0+	002	023	092	183	207	126	032	001	0+	0+	8
	9	0+	0+	0+	0+	007	041	122	207	196	086	008	0+	0+	9
	10	0+	0+	0+	0+	001	014	061	155	229	172	035	004	0+	10
	11	0+	0+	0+	0+	0+	003	022	085	194	250	114	026	0+	11
	12	0+	0+	0+	0+	0+	001	006	032	113	250	257	123	008	12
	13	0+	0+	0+	0+	0+	0+	001	007	041	154	356	359	123	13
	14	0+	0+	0+	0+	0+	0+	0+	001	007	044	229	488	869	14
15	0	860	463	206	035	005	0+	0+	0+	0+	0+	0+	0+	0+	0
	1	130	366	343	132	031	005	0+	0+	0+	0+	0+	0+	0+	1
	2	009	135	267	231	092	022	003	0+	0+	0+	0+	0+	0+	2
	3	0+	031	129	250	170	063	014	002	0+	0+	0+	0+	0+	3
	4	0+	005	043	188	219	127	042	007	001	0+	0+	0+	0+	4
	5	0+	001	010	103	206	186	092	024	003	0+	0+	0+	0+	5
	6	0+	0+	002	043	147	207	153	061	012	001	0+	0+	0+	6
	7	0+	0+	0+	014	081	177	196	118	035	003	0+	0+	0+	7
	8	0+	0+	0+	003	035	118	196	177	081	014	0+	0+	0+	8
	9	0+	0+	0+	001	012	061	153	207	147	043	002	0+	0+	9

Individual Terms, $b(x;\ n, p)$

n	x	.01	.05	.10	.20	.30	.40	$\overset{p}{.50}$	.60	.70	.80	.90	.95	.99	x
15	10	0+	0+	0+	0+	003	024	092	186	206	103	010	001	0+	10
	11	0+	0+	0+	0+	001	007	042	127	219	188	043	005	0+	11
	12	0+	0+	0+	0+	0+	002	014	063	170	250	129	031	0+	12
	13	0+	0+	0+	0+	0+	0+	003	022	092	231	267	135	009	13
	14	0+	0+	0+	0+	0+	0+	0+	005	031	132	343	366	130	14
	15	0+	0+	0+	0+	0+	0+	0+	0+	005	035	206	463	860	15
16	0	851	440	185	028	003	0+	0+	0+	0+	0+	0+	0+	0+	0
	1	138	371	329	113	023	003	0+	0+	0+	0+	0+	0+	0+	1
	2	010	146	275	211	073	015	002	0+	0+	0+	0+	0+	0+	2
	3	0+	036	142	246	146	047	009	001	0+	0+	0+	0+	0+	3
	4	0+	006	051	200	204	101	028	004	0+	0+	0+	0+	0+	4
	5	0+	001	014	120	210	162	067	014	001	0+	0+	0+	0+	5
	6	0+	0+	003	055	165	198	122	039	006	0+	0+	0+	0+	6
	7	0+	0+	0+	020	101	189	175	084	019	001	0+	0+	0+	7
	8	0+	0+	0+	006	049	142	196	142	049	006	0+	0+	0+	8
	9	0+	0+	0+	001	019	084	175	189	101	020	0+	0+	0+	9
	10	0+	0+	0+	0+	006	039	122	198	165	055	003	0+	0+	10
	11	0+	0+	0+	0+	001	014	067	162	210	120	014	001	0+	11
	12	0+	0+	0+	0+	0+	004	028	101	204	200	051	006	0+	12
	13	0+	0+	0+	0+	0+	001	009	047	146	246	142	036	0+	13
	14	0+	0+	0+	0+	0+	0+	002	015	073	211	275	146	010	14
	15	0+	0+	0+	0+	0+	0+	0+	003	023	113	329	371	138	15
	16	0+	0+	0+	0+	0+	0+	0+	0+	003	028	185	440	851	16
17	0	843	418	167	023	002	0+	0+	0+	0+	0+	0+	0+	0+	0
	1	145	374	315	096	017	002	0+	0+	0+	0+	0+	0+	0+	1
	2	012	158	280	191	058	010	001	0+	0+	0+	0+	0+	0+	2
	3	001	041	156	239	125	034	005	0+	0+	0+	0+	0+	0+	3
	4	0+	008	060	209	187	080	018	002	0+	0+	0+	0+	0+	4
	5	0+	001	017	136	208	138	047	008	001	0+	0+	0+	0+	5
	6	0+	0+	004	068	178	184	094	024	003	0+	0+	0+	0+	6
	7	0+	0+	001	027	120	193	148	057	009	0+	0+	0+	0+	7
	8	0+	0+	0+	008	064	161	185	107	028	002	0+	0+	0+	8
	9	0+	0+	0+	002	028	107	185	161	064	008	0+	0+	0+	9
	10	0+	0+	0+	0+	009	057	148	193	120	027	001	0+	0+	10
	11	0+	0+	0+	0+	003	024	094	184	178	068	004	0+	0+	11
	12	0+	0+	0+	0+	001	008	047	138	208	136	017	001	0+	12
	13	0+	0+	0+	0+	0+	002	018	080	187	209	060	008	0+	13
	14	0+	0+	0+	0+	0+	0+	005	034	125	239	156	041	001	14
	15	0+	0+	0+	0+	0+	0+	001	010	058	191	280	158	012	15
	16	0+	0+	0+	0+	0+	0+	0+	002	017	096	315	374	145	16
	17	0+	0+	0+	0+	0+	0+	0+	0+	002	023	167	418	843	17

Individual Terms, $b(x; n, p)$

n	x	.01	.05	.10	.20	.30	.40	p .50	.60	.70	.80	.90	.95	.99	x
18	0	835	397	150	018	002	0+	0+	0+	0+	0+	0+	0+	0+	0
	1	152	376	300	081	013	001	0+	0+	0+	0+	0+	0+	0+	1
	2	013	168	284	172	046	007	001	0+	0+	0+	0+	0+	0+	2
	3	001	047	168	230	105	025	003	0+	0+	0+	0+	0+	0+	3
	4	0+	009	070	215	168	061	012	001	0+	0+	0+	0+	0+	4
	5	0+	001	022	151	202	115	033	004	0+	0+	0+	0+	0+	5
	6	0+	0+	005	082	187	166	071	015	001	0+	0+	0+	0+	6
	7	0+	0+	001	035	138	189	121	037	005	0+	0+	0+	0+	7
	8	0+	0+	0+	012	081	173	167	077	015	001	0+	0+	0+	8
	9	0+	0+	0+	003	039	128	185	128	039	003	0+	0+	0+	9
	10	0+	0+	0+	001	015	077	167	173	081	012	0+	0+	0+	10
	11	0+	0+	0+	0+	005	037	121	189	138	035	001	0+	0+	11
	12	0+	0+	0+	0+	001	015	071	166	187	082	005	0+	0+	12
	13	0+	0+	0+	0+	0+	004	033	115	202	151	022	001	0+	13
	14	0+	0+	0+	0+	0+	001	012	061	168	215	070	009	0+	14
	15	0+	0+	0+	0+	0+	0+	003	025	105	230	168	047	001	15
	16	0+	0+	0+	0+	0+	0+	001	007	046	172	284	168	013	16
	17	0+	0+	0+	0+	0+	0+	0+	001	013	081	300	376	152	17
	18	0+	0+	0+	0+	0+	0+	0+	0+	002	018	150	397	835	18
19	0	826	377	135	014	001	0+	0+	0+	0+	0+	0+	0+	0+	0
	1	159	377	285	068	009	001	0+	0+	0+	0+	0+	0+	0+	1
	2	014	179	285	154	036	005	0+	0+	0+	0+	0+	0+	0+	2
	3	001	053	180	218	087	017	002	0+	0+	0+	0+	0+	0+	3
	4	0+	011	080	218	149	047	007	001	0+	0+	0+	0+	0+	4
	5	0+	002	027	164	192	093	022	002	0+	0+	0+	0+	0+	5
	6	0+	0+	007	095	192	145	052	008	001	0+	0+	0+	0+	6
	7	0+	0÷	001	044	153	180	096	024	002	0+	0+	0+	0+	7
	8	0+	0+	0+	017	098	180	144	053	008	0+	0+	0+	0+	8
	9	0+	0+	0+	005	051	146	176	098	022	001	0+	0+	0+	9
	10	0+	0+	0+	001	022	098	176	146	051	005	0+	0+	0+	10
	11	0+	0+	0+	0+	008	053	144	180	098	017	0+	0+	0+	11
	12	0+	0+	0+	0+	002	024	096	180	153	044	001	0+	0+	12
	13	0+	0+	0+	0+	001	008	052	145	192	095	007	0+	0+	13
	14	0+	0+	0+	0+	0+	002	022	093	192	164	0z7	002	0+	14
	15	0+	0+	0+	0+	0+	001	007	047	149	218	080	011	0+	15
	16	0+	0+	0+	0+	0+	0+	002	017	087	218	180	053	001	16
	17	0+	0+	0+	0+	0+	0+	0+	005	036	154	285	179	014	17
	18	0+	0+	0+	0+	0+	0+	0+	001	009	068	285	377	159	18
	19	0+	0+	0+	0+	0+	0+	0+	0+	001	014	135	377	826	19
20	0	818	358	122	012	001	0+	0+	0+	0+	0+	0+	0+	0+	0
	1	165	377	270	058	007	0+	0+	0+	0+	0+	0+	0+	0+	1
	2	016	189	285	137	028	003	0+	0+	0+	0+	0+	0+	0+	2
	3	001	060	190	205	072	012	001	0+	0+	0+	0+	0+	0+	3
	4	0+	013	090	218	130	035	005	0+	0+	0+	0+	0+	0+	4

Individual Terms, $b(x;\ n, p)$

n	x	$.01$	$.05$	$.10$	$.20$	$.30$	$.40$	p $.50$	$.60$	$.70$	$.80$	$.90$	$.95$	$.99$	x
20	5	0+	002	032	175	179	075	015	001	0+	0+	0+	0+	0+	5
	6	0+	0+	009	109	192	124	037	005	0+	0+	0+	0+	0+	6
	7	0+	0+	002	055	164	166	074	015	001	0+	0+	0+	0+	7
	8	0+	0+	0+	022	114	180	120	035	004	0+	0+	0+	0+	8
	9	0+	0+	0+	007	065	160	160	071	012	0+	0+	0+	0+	9
	10	0+	0+	0+	002	031	117	176	117	031	002	0+	0+	0+	10
	11	0+	0+	0+	0+	012	071	160	160	065	007	0+	0+	0+	11
	12	0+	0+	0+	0+	004	035	120	180	114	022	0+	0+	0+	12
	13	0+	0+	0+	0+	001	015	074	166	164	055	002	0+	0+	13
	14	0+	0+	0+	0+	0+	005	037	124	192	109	009	0+	0+	14
	15	0+	0+	0+	0+	0+	001	015	075	179	175	032	002	0+	15
	16	0+	0+	0+	0+	0+	0+	005	035	130	218	090	013	0+	16
	17	0+	0+	0+	0+	0+	0+	001	012	072	205	190	060	001	17
	18	0+	0+	0+	0+	0+	0+	0+	003	028	137	285	189	016	18
	19	0+	0+	0+	0+	0+	0+	0+	0+	007	058	270	377	165	19
	20	0+	0+	0+	0+	0+	0+	0+	0+	001	012	122	358	818	20
21	0	810	341	109	009	001	0+	0+	0+	0+	0+	0+	0+	0+	0
	1	172	376	255	048	005	0+	0+	0+	0+	0+	0+	0+	0+	1
	2	017	198	284	121	022	002	0+	0+	0+	0+	0+	0+	0+	2
	3	001	066	200	192	058	009	001	0+	0+	0+	0+	0+	0+	3
	4	0+	016	100	216	113	026	003	0+	0+	0+	0+	0+	0+	4
	5	0+	003	038	183	164	059	010	001	0+	0+	0+	0+	0+	5
	6	0+	0+	011	122	188	105	026	003	0+	0+	0+	0+	0+	6
	7	0+	0+	003	065	172	149	055	009	0+	0+	0+	0+	0+	7
	8	0+	0+	001	029	129	174	097	023	002	0+	0+	0+	0+	8
	9	0+	0+	0+	010	080	168	140	050	006	0+	0+	0+	0+	9
	10	0+	0+	0+	003	041	134	168	089	018	001	0+	0+	0+	10
	11	0+	0+	0+	001	018	089	168	134	041	003	0+	0+	0+	11
	12	0+	0+	0+	0+	006	050	140	168	080	010	0+	0+	0+	12
	13	0+	0+	0+	0+	002	023	097	174	129	029	001	0+	0+	13
	14	0+	0+	0+	0+	0+	009	055	149	172	065	003	0+	0+	14
	15	0+	0+	0+	0+	0+	003	026	105	188	122	011	0+	0+	15
	16	0+	0+	0+	0+	0+	001	010	059	164	183	038	003	0+	16
	17	0+	0+	0+	0+	0+	0+	003	026	113	216	100	016	0+	17
	18	0+	0+	0+	0+	0+	0+	001	009	058	192	200	066	001	18
	19	0+	0+	0+	0+	0+	0+	0+	002	022	121	284	198	017	19
	20	0+	0+	0+	0+	0+	0+	0+	0+	005	048	255	376	172	20
	21	0+	0+	0+	0+	0+	0+	0+	0+	001	009	109	341	810	21
22	0	802	324	098	007	0+	0+	0+	0+	0+	0+	0+	0+	0+	0
	1	178	375	241	041	004	0+	0+	0+	0+	0+	0+	0+	0+	1
	2	019	207	281	107	017	001	0+	0+	0+	0+	0+	0+	0+	2
	3	001	073	208	178	047	006	0+	0+	0+	0+	0+	0+	0+	3
	4	0+	018	110	211	096	019	002	0+	0+	0+	0+	0+	0+	4

Individual Terms, $b(x; \ n, p)$

n	x	.01	.05	.10	.20	.30	.40	p .50	.60	.70	.80	.90	.95	.99	x
22	5	0+	003	044	190	149	046	006	0+	0+	0+	0+	0+	0+	5
	6	0+	001	014	134	181	086	018	001	0+	0+	0+	0+	0+	6
	7	0+	0+	004	077	177	131	041	005	0+	0+	0+	0+	0+	7
	8	0+	0+	001	036	142	164	076	014	001	0+	0+	0+	0+	8
	9	0+	0+	0+	014	095	170	119	034	003	0+	0+	0+	0+	9
	10	0+	0+	0+	005	053	148	154	066	010	0+	0+	0+	0+	10
	11	0+	0+	0+	001	025	107	168	107	025	001	0+	0+	0+	11
	12	0+	0+	0+	0+	010	066	154	148	053	005	0+	0+	0+	12
	13	0+	0+	0+	0+	003	034	119	170	095	014	0+	0+	0+	13
	14	0+	0+	0+	0+	001	014	076	164	142	036	001	0+	0+	14
	15	0+	0+	0+	0+	0+	005	041	131	177	077	004	0+	0+	15
	16	0+	0+	0+	0+	0+	001	018	086	181	134	014	001	0+	16
	17	0+	0+	0+	0+	0+	0+	006	046	149	190	044	003	0+	17
	18	0+	0+	0+	0+	0+	0+	002	019	096	211	110	018	0+	18
	19	0+	0+	0+	0+	0+	0+	0+	006	047	178	208	073	001	19
	20	0+	0+	0+	0+	0+	0+	0+	001	017	107	281	207	019	20
	21	0+	0+	0+	0+	0+	0+	0+	0+	004	041	241	375	178	21
	22	0+	0+	0+	0+	0+	0+	0+	0+	0+	007	098	324	802	22
23	0	794	307	089	006	0+	0+	0+	0+	0+	0+	0+	0+	0+	0
	1	184	372	226	034	003	0+	0+	0+	0+	0+	0+	0+	0+	1
	2	020	215	277	093	013	001	0+	0+	0+	0+	0+	0+	0+	2
	3	001	079	215	163	038	004	0+	0+	0+	0+	0+	0+	0+	3
	4	0+	021	120	204	082	014	001	0+	0+	0+	0+	0+	0+	4
	5	0+	004	051	194	133	035	004	0+	0+	0+	0+	0+	0+	5
	6	0+	001	017	145	171	070	012	001	0+	0+	0+	0+	0+	6
	7	0+	0+	005	088	178	113	029	003	0+	0+	0+	0+	0+	7
	8	0+	0+	001	044	153	151	058	009	0+	0+	0+	0+	0+	8
	9	0+	0+	0+	018	109	168	097	022	002	0+	0+	0+	0+	9
	10	0+	0+	0+	006	065	157	136	046	005	0+	0+	0+	0+	10
	11	0+	0+	0+	002	033	123	161	082	014	0+	0+	0+	0+	11
	12	0+	0+	0+	0+	014	082	161	123	033	002	0+	0+	0+	12
	13	0+	0+	0+	0+	005	046	136	157	065	006	0+	0+	0+	13
	14	0+	0+	0+	0+	002	022	097	168	109	018	0+	0+	0+	14
	15	0+	0+	0+	0+	0+	009	058	151	153	044	001	0+	0+	15
	16	0+	0+	0+	0+	0+	003	029	113	178	088	005	0+	0+	16
	17	0+	0+	0+	0+	0+	001	012	070	171	145	017	011	0+	17
	18	0+	0+	0+	0+	0+	0+	004	035	133	194	051	004	0+	18
	19	0+	0+	0+	0+	0+	0+	001	014	082	204	120	021	0+	19
	20	0+	0+	0+	0+	0+	0+	0+	004	038	163	215	079	001	20
	21	0+	0+	0+	0+	0+	0+	0+	001	013	093	277	215	020	21
	22	0+	0+	0+	0+	0+	0+	0+	0+	003	034	226	372	184	22
	23	0+	0+	0+	0+	0+	0+	0+	0+	0+	006	089	307	794	23

Individual Terms, $b(x; n, p)$

n	x	.01	.05	.10	.20	.30	.40	p .50	.60	.70	.80	.90	.95	.99	x
24	0	786	292	080	005	0+	0+	0+	0+	0+	0+	0+	0+	0+	0
	1	190	369	213	028	002	0+	0+	0+	0+	0+	0+	0+	0+	1
	2	002	223	272	081	010	001	0+	0+	0+	0+	0+	0+	0+	2
	3	002	086	221	149	031	003	0+	0+	0+	0+	0+	0+	0+	3
	4	0+	024	129	196	069	010	001	0+	0+	0+	0+	0+	0+	4
	5	0+	005	057	196	118	027	003	0+	0+	0+	0+	0+	0+	5
	6	0+	001	020	155	160	056	008	0+	0+	0+	0+	0+	0+	6
	7	0+	0+	006	100	176	096	021	002	0+	0+	0+	0+	0+	7
	8	0+	0+	001	053	160	136	044	005	0+	0+	0+	0+	0+	8
	9	0+	0+	0+	024	122	161	078	014	001	0+	0+	0+	0+	9
	10	0+	0+	0+	009	079	161	117	032	003	0+	0+	0+	0+	10
	11	0+	0+	0+	003	043	137	149	061	008	0+	0+	0+	0+	11
	12	0+	0+	0+	001	020	099	161	099	020	001	0+	0+	0+	12
	13	0+	0+	0+	0+	008	061	149	137	043	003	0+	0+	0+	13
	14	0+	0+	0+	0+	003	032	117	161	079	009	0+	0+	0+	14
	15	0+	0+	0+	0+	001	014	078	161	122	024	0+	0+	0+	15
	16	0+	0+	0+	0+	0+	005	044	136	160	053	001	0+	0+	16
	17	0+	0+	0+	0+	0+	002	021	096	176	100	006	0+	0+	17
	18	0+	0+	0+	0+	0+	0+	008	056	160	155	020	001	0+	18
	19	0+	0+	0+	0+	0+	0+	003	027	118	196	057	005	0+	19
	20	0+	0+	0+	0+	0+	0+	001	010	069	196	129	024	0+	20
	21	0+	0+	0+	0+	0+	0+	0+	003	031	149	221	086	002	21
	22	0+	0+	0+	0+	0+	0+	0+	001	010	081	272	223	022	22
	23	0+	0+	0+	0+	0+	0+	0+	0+	002	028	213	369	190	23
	24	0+	0+	0+	0+	0+	0+	0+	0+	0+	005	080	292	786	24
25	0	778	277	072	004	0+	0+	0+	0+	0+	0+	0+	0+	0+	0
	1	196	365	199	024	001	0+	0+	0+	0+	0+	0+	0+	0+	1
	2	024	231	266	071	007	0+	0+	0+	0+	0+	0+	0+	0+	2
	3	002	093	226	136	024	002	0+	0+	0+	0+	0+	0+	0+	3
	4	0+	027	138	187	057	007	0+	0+	0+	0+	0+	0+	0+	4
	5	0+	006	065	196	103	020	002	0+	0+	0+	0+	0+	0+	5
	6	0+	001	024	163	147	044	005	0+	0+	0+	0+	0+	0+	6
	7	0+	0+	007	111	171	080	014	001	0+	0+	0+	0+	0+	7
	8	0+	0+	002	062	165	120	032	003	0+	0+	0+	0+	0+	8
	9	0+	0+	0+	029	134	151	061	009	0+	0+	0+	0+	0+	9
	10	0+	0+	0+	012	092	161	097	021	001	0+	0+	0+	0+	10
	11	0+	0+	0+	004	054	147	133	043	004	0+	0+	0+	0+	11
	12	0+	0+	0+	001	027	114	155	076	011	0+	0+	0+	0+	12
	13	0+	0+	0+	0+	011	076	155	114	027	001	0+	0+	0+	13
	14	0+	0+	0+	0+	004	043	133	147	054	004	0+	0+	0+	14
	15	0+	0+	0+	0+	001	021	097	161	092	012	0+	0+	0+	15
	16	0+	0+	0+	0+	0+	009	061	151	134	029	0+	0+	0+	16
	17	0+	0+	0+	0+	0+	003	032	120	165	062	002	0+	0+	17
	18	0+	0+	0+	0+	0+	001	014	080	171	111	007	0+	0+	18
	19	0+	0+	0+	0+	0+	0+	005	044	147	163	024	001	0+	19

Individual Terms, $b(x; n, p)$

n	x	.01	.05	.10	.20	.30	.40	p .50	.60	.70	.80	.90	.95	.99	x
25	20	0+	0+	0+	0+	0+	0+	002	020	103	196	065	006	0+	20
	21	0+	0+	0+	0+	0+	0+	0+	007	057	187	138	027	0+	21
	22	0+	0+	0+	0+	0+	0+	0+	002	024	136	226	093	002	22
	23	0+	0+	0+	0+	0+	0+	0+	0+	007	071	266	231	024	23
	24	0+	0+	0+	0+	0+	0+	0+	0+	001	024	199	365	196	24
	25	0+	0+	0+	0+	0+	0+	0+	0+	0+	004	072	277	778	25

INDEX

Note: Since most book and author references are given at the ends of the chapters, they are not duplicated in this index. See chapter bibliographies.